PHYSICAL CHEMISTRY OF
PROCESS METALLURGY
Part 2

Conference Committee

C. L. McCabe, *General Chairman*
J. F. Elliott, *Program Chairman*

Pittsburgh Section AIME

J. H. Henderson, *Chairman*
R. S. Crowell, *Vice-Chairman*
Charles Potter, *Treasurer*
J. H. Melvin, *Secretary*

Physical Chemistry of Extractive Metallurgy Committee

G. H. Turner, *Chairman*
W. A. Krivsky, *Past-Chairman*

Physical Chemistry of Steelmaking Committee

C. W. Sherman, *Chairman*
B. R. Queneau, *Past-Chairman*
D. C. Hilty, *Vice-Chairman*
J. C. Fulton, *Secretary*

Melting and Casting Committee

T. E. Leontis, *Chairman*
W. S. Pellini, *Past-Chairman*

Extractive Metallurgy Division

A. E. Lee, Jr., *Chairman*
H. H. Kellogg, *Past-Chairman*
R. Schuhmann, Jr., *Vice-Chairman*
W. R. Opie, *Vice-Chairman*
H. W. St. Clair, *Vice-Chairman*
T. K. Graham, *Vice-Chairman*
T. D. Jones, *Treasurer*
R. W. Shearman, *Secretary*

Iron and Steel Division

Michael Tenenbaum, *Chairman*
K. L. Fetters, *Past-Chairman*
J. J. Golden, *Vice-Chairman*
R. W. Shearman,
 Secretary-Treasurer

Institute of Metals Division

O. T. Marzke, *Chairman*
W. J. Harris, Jr., *Past-Chairman*
T. A. Read, *Vice-Chairman*
J. H. Jackson, *Vice-Chairman*
R. W. Shearman,
 Secretary-Treasurer

The Metallurgical Society of AIME

John Chipman, *President*
W. R. Hibbard, Jr., *Past-President*
C. C. Long, *Vice-President*
T. D. Jones, *Treasurer*
R. W. Shearman, *Secretary*

METALLURGICAL SOCIETY CONFERENCES | VOLUME

8

PHYSICAL CHEMISTRY OF
PROCESS METALLURGY
Part 2

An International Symposium
sponsored by the

Physical Chemistry of Steelmaking Committee
of the **Iron and Steel Division,**

the
Physical Chemistry of Extractive Metallurgy Committee
of the **Extractive Metallurgy Division,**

and the
Melting and Casting Committee
of the **Institute of Metals Division,**

American Institute of Mining,
Metallurgical, and Petroleum Engineers

PITTSBURGH, PENNSYLVANIA, APRIL 27–MAY 1, 1959

Edited by GEORGE R. ST. PIERRE
The Ohio State University

INTERSCIENCE   PUBLISHERS / NEW YORK · LONDON

INTERSCIENCE PUBLISHERS, INC.
250 FIFTH AVENUE, NEW YORK 1, NEW YORK

FOR GREAT BRITAIN AND NORTHERN IRELAND:
INTERSCIENCE PUBLISHERS, LTD.
88/90 CHANCERY LANE, LONDON W.C. 2

PRINTED IN THE UNITED STATES OF AMERICA
BY MACK PRINTING COMPANY, EASTON, PA.

FOREWORD

The Conference has become an essential means for the exchange of information among the scientific and technical people working in a given field. However, like personal visits, personal correspondence, and the publication of papers, they all too often bring together only people who already are in the field and who have a well-established community of interest. It is of great importance to a worker that he be exposed to the results and techniques of other fields, especially those adjacent to his. The value of cross-fertilization of ideas from field to field is sufficiently well-known not to have to be examined in detail here. In spite of the general acceptance of the concept, it becomes increasingly difficult year by year to obtain this vital interaction. The reasons and excuses are numerous and some are valid: The demands for depth and excellence in one's chosen field are sufficient to consume all of one's attention and time. Other areas are highly specialized and one has to spend considerable time and study even to appreciate what is being done. The collateral areas are altogether too numerous. In addition many other reasons can be, and have been, cited.

From time to time there is a need for bringing together people of various interests to obtain these interactions that are so vital for the progress in a field. This can best be done by a General Conference at which many people of diverse, but related, interests are brought together so that they can focus their attention on a central theme. Twice before conferences of this type dealing with Process Metallurgy have been held: one in 1925 under the auspices of the Faraday Society and the second was the Fourth Discussions of the Faraday Society titled "The Physical Chemistry of Process Metallurgy" which was held in London in 1949. In 1957 and 1958 it seemed clear to many working in the field of Process Metallugy that the state of knowledge could profit from another general conference. There had been a considerable broadening of the field since 1949 and much new data had been reported. Also, there were important activities in the related areas that needed to be brought into the realm of the Process

Metallurgist. To summarize in a few brief words the results of considerable planning, it was decided to hold an International Symposium on the Physical Chemistry of Process Metallurgy in Pittsburgh, April 27 through May 1, 1959. The meeting was held under the auspices of The Metallurgical Society of the AIME.

A prime mover in stimulating the development of the Conference was Professor J. Chipman who was then President of the Society. Elsewhere in this volume credit is given to a number of people who worked diligently and patiently to make the Conference a success. Much credit is due to Dr. G. St. Pierre of The Ohio State University who has labored at great length since the Conference to edit these *Proceedings* which contain the contributions and discussions of the meeting.

The Section Chairmen were: *Section I*, C. Law McCabe and John F. Elliott; *Section II*, K. L. Fetters and C. E. A. Shanahan; *Section III*, R. Schuhmann, Jr. and E. R. Morgan; *Section IV*, W. R. Hibbard, Jr. and C. S. Smith; *Section V*, F. D. Richardson and D. W. Murphy; *Section VI*, T. B. King and F. A. Forward; *Section VII*, M. W. Lightner and C. R. Taylor; *Section VIII*, K. R. Van Horn and T. E. Leontis; *Section IX*, H. H. Kellogg and W. G. Courtney; *Section X*, A. M. Samarin and R. D. Hindson; *Sections XI and XII*, J. Lumsden and G. Derge; *Section XIII*, J. H. Richards and C. C. Long.

The success of the Conference was assured by the response to the invitations to submit papers for presentation. These *Proceedings* testify to the breadth of subject matter, the international character of the membership, and the quality of the contributions and the discussions.

In planning the Conference several compromises had to be reached. To provide the desired breadth, a large number of topics had to be treated and a number of papers on each topic were accepted. In spite of·this, certain areas which some may consider important to the field had to be omitted from consideration. The number of contributions required parallel sessions which divided the Conference at times. To spread the value of the Conference, it was open to all who were interested. This resulted in an attendance of 350; not large by many standards, but of sufficient size so that the relatively informal discussion had to be relegated to small groups which collected after each session.

In looking back, several general comments can be made about the Conference which are also pertinent to the present state of the field of Process Metallurgy:

1. Our knowledge of the physical, chemical, and thermodynamic properties of elements and compounds pertinent to process metallurgy, while growing rapidly, is still woefully lacking in many critical areas. To some extent this reflects the lack of interest in inorganic chemistry by the scientific community.

2. Very little is known of the structural charateristics of liquid metals and slags. In this we lag far behind the present knowledge of the effect of structure on the properties of solid metals.

3. We are just beginning to acquire competence to cope with the factors influencing the rate at which a process proceeds. A number of results have been reported, but they are still of a fragmentary nature.

4. Our knowledge is perhaps in the poorest state in that we are unable to assess quantitatively all the factors which control a process, nor are we able from first principles to design a process for producing a product. Our understanding of present processes stems essentially from the description of the process itself. It would appear that we have sufficient knowledge of the properties of materials, the processes of mass transport and chemical reactions, and heat and fluid flow to be able to describe quantitatively, and from a fundamental point of view, the essential characteristics of many of our important processes. Courage, imagination, stamina, and good luck are required if we are to make progress in this direction. Perhaps the next international conference will show progress in this vital area.

5. The provinciality of workers in the field continues. A number attending the Conference came to hear a session or two. However, one can take courage from the fact that a majority came to hear what was said in all sessions.

It can be said without too great a loss of modesty that the Conference was a success. The quality and number of papers, the discussions, and the number in attendance are the usual indices to be considered. On the other hand, the *real success* of the Conference will be known only in five to ten years. It will be judged on whether these *Proceedings* become a real part of the technical literature and whether the contents stimulate many readers to think and experiment more carefully, and to look up and away from their immediate work to see and be influenced by the scientific and technical work going on about them in the near and related fields.

John F. Elliott
Technical Chairman

Cambridge, Massachusetts

C. Law McCabe
Conference Chairman

Pittsburgh, Pennsylvania

CONTRIBUTORS
TO PART 2

C. M. Adams, Massachusetts Institute of Technology, Cambridge, Mass.

John Angus, University of Michigan, Ann Arbor, Mich.

P. M. Audette, The Steel Co. of Canada, Ltd., Hamilton, Ontario, Canada

D. H. Baker, Jr., U. S. Department of the Interior, Boulder City, Nev.

R. F. Blanks, University of Melbourne, Melbourne, Australia

H. H. Brant, Armco Steel Corp., Middletown, Ohio

Chien-Yeh Chien, Carnegie Institute of Technology, Pittsburgh, Pa.

W. G. Courtney, Experiment Inc., Richmond, Va.

T. E. Dancy, Jones & Laughlin Steel Corp., Youngstown, Ohio

D. L. Douglass, Knolls Atomic Power Laboratory, Schenectady, N. Y.

Cuthbert Daniel, New York, N. Y.

A. Decker, Centre National de Recherches Metallurgiques, Liége, Belgium

F. D. Delve, Jones & Laughlin Steel Corp., Pittsburgh, Pa.

S. Eda, Tôhoku University, Sendai, Japan

Merton C. Flemings, Massachusetts Institute of Technology, Cambridge, Mass.

F. A. Forward, University of British Columbia, Vancouver, B. C., Canada

L. M. Foster, Aluminum Co. of America, New Kensington, Pa.

W. B. Frank, Aluminum Co. of America, New Kensington, Pa.

N. A. Gokcen, University of Pennsylvania, Philadelphia, Pa.

Paul Gorsuch, General Electric Research Laboratory, Schenectady, N. Y.

P. Gross, Fulmer Research Institute, Ltd., Stokes Pages, Bucks, England

J. Halapatz, Jones & Laughlin Steel Corp., Youngstown, Ohio

C. Hayman, Fulmer Research Institute, Ltd., Stokes Pages, Bucks, England

John B. Henderson, The Broken Hill Proprietary Co. Ltd., Shortland, N.S.W., Australia

T. A. Henrie, U. S. Department of the Interior, Reno, Nev.

W. G. Hines, The Steel Co. of Canada Ltd., Hamilton, Ontario, Canada

Edward E. Hucke, University of Michigan, Ann Arbor, Mich.

Robert G. Hudson, Carnegie Institute of Technology, Pittsburgh, Pa.

Yukiyoshi Itoh, Fuji Iron Co., Muroran, Japan

Mitsuo Kameda, Tôhoku University, Sendai, Japan

J. S. Kirklady, McMaster University, Hamilton, Ontario, Canada

Tamiya Kishida, Hitachi Metal Co., Shimane, Japan

T. Kurosawa, Tôhoku University, Sendai, Japan

H. N. Lander, Jones & Laughlin Steel Corp., Pittsburgh, Pa.

B. M. Larsen, United States Steel Corp. Research Center, Monroeville, Pa.

D. L. Levi, Fulmer Research Institute, Ltd., Stokes Pages, Bucks, England

K. Li, Jones & Laughlin Steel Corp., Youngstown, Ohio

Gordon F. Lilly, United States Steel Corp., Monroeville, Pa.

J. U. MacEwan, McGill University, Montreal, Quebec, Canada

J. C. McKay, The Steel Co. of Canada, Ltd., Hamilton, Ontario, Canada

W. E. Marshall, Armco Steel Corp., Middletown, Ohio

P. Metz, Centre National de Recherches Metallurgiques, Liége, Belgium

H. W. Meyer, Jones & Laughlin Steel Corp., Pittsburgh, Pa.

Kichizo Niwa, Hokkaido University, Sapporo, Japan

M. Ohtani, University of Pennsylvania, Philadelphia, Pa.

Michel Olette, Institut de Recherches de la Sidérurgie, Saint-Germain-en-Laye, France

David V. Ragone, University of Michigan, Ann Arbor, Mich.

F. D. Richardson, Imperial College, London, England

P. S. Rogers, British Iron and Steel Research Association, London, England

G. R. St. Pierre, The Ohio State University, Columbus, Ohio

N. L. Samways, Jones & Laughlin Steel Corp., Youngstown, Ohio

F. A. Schaufelberger, CIBA Ltd., Basle, Switzerland

Mitsuo Shimoji, Hokkaido University, Sapporo, Japan

J. G. Sibakin, The Steel Co. of Canada, Ltd., Hamilton, Ontario, Canada

L. O. Sordahl, United States Steel Corp. Research Center, Monroeville, Pa.

R. Speiser, The Ohio State University, Columbus, Ohio

S. Takeuchi, Tôhoku University, Sendai, Japan

H. F. Taylor, Massachusetts Institute of Technology, Cambridge, Mass.

M. Tezuka, Tôhoku University, Sendai, Japan

W. A. Tiller, Westinghouse Research Laboratories, Pittsburgh, Pa.

J. W. Tomlinson, Imperial College, London, England

H. Veltman, Sherritt Gordon Mines, Ltd., Vancouver, B. C., Canada

Tsuguyasu Wada, Tôhoku University, Sendai, Japan

J. L. Walker, General Electric Co., Schenectady, N. Y.

G. M. Willis, University of Melbourne, Melbourne, Australia

Ling Yang, Carnegie Institute of Technology, Pittsburgh, Pa.

Akira Yazawa, Tôhoku University, Sendai, Japan

W. V. Youdelis, University of Alberta, Edmonton, Alberta, Canada

John Zotos, Watertown Arsenal, Watertown, Mass.

CONTENTS

IN PART 1

Introductory, Special, and Principal Lectures

Section I: **Physical Chemistry of Metallurgical Phases**
Section II: **Physical Chemistry of Oxide Phases**
Section III: **Thermodynamics of Metals**
Section IV: **The Nature and Structure of Liquid Metals**
Section V: **Transport and Mixing**
Section VI: **Solubility and Phase Equilibria in Metals Systems**

SECTION VII: PROCESS REACTION RATES AND MECHANISMS

. . . .

Rates of Reduction of Some Iron Ores in a Fluidized Bed

H. H. BRANT and W. E. MARSHALL

Armco Steel Corporation, Middletown, Ohio

Abstract

A number of iron ores were reduced in a small laboratory device simulating a fluidized bed.

The results show that the reduction rate for different ores varies widely, particularly in the latter stages of reduction. Also, ores vary in regard to the temperature at which caking occurs.

Therefore, for low temperature direct reduction processes, it is necessary to select ores that reduce rapidly at temperatures below those at which caking begins.

INTRODUCTION

In recent years interest has been greatly accelerated in regard to so-called "direct reduction processes" for producing iron from ore. This has resulted largely from the increasing capital investment required for blast furnace, coke, and agglomeration plant complexes.

Many of the alternative processes, particularly those involving gases for reduction, such as fluidized bed processes, are limited in respect to the maximum temperature at which they can operate. The temperature appears to be limited not so much by the equipment required for heating gases as by the natural characteristics of the ores themselves.

The characteristics of most importance are mainly two; namely, (1) caking (tendency to defluidize), and (2) rate of reduction (removal of oxygen).

CAKING

Experimental experience has shown that most ores after crushing to a particle size suitable for fluidized beds, fluidize without difficulty in air at quite high temperatures. However, when fluidized with reducing gases, caking or defluidization occurs and the temperature at which this happens varies widely for different ores. It also does not occur at any specific degree of reduction. This characteristic has not been studied in wide scope by us and will not be discussed in this paper, but mention of it points out the fact that ores are extremely variable in this characteristic and there is room for much thought, study, and experimental work.

RATES OF REDUCTION

The blast furnace is a wonderful machine because it will make liquid iron out of anything that contains iron, at some price. If it cannot reduce the iron compound fed to it at the relatively low temperatures in the stock column, it will still do it at high temperatures, down in the hearth, with additional heat units, increased coke rate, lower production, and increased cost.

The low temperature reduction processes are unable to reduce some ores fast enough to give economic production rates. Therefore, the use of low temperature processes gravitates to special situations where ores having a high reduction rate are available.

Hence, information pertaining to the reduction rates of different ores should be useful in deciding about the potentialities of reduction processes that do not melt iron in contact with carbon.

DESCRIPTION OF APPARATUS

Although many people have operated small pilot fluidized reactors in the recent past, there have been many mechanical problems to solve that consumed time. Also where the reactors were of considerable size much time had to be given to the preparation of materials.

Reduction rate data of at least a relative nature could be obtained more rapidly on much smaller devices, preferably one that could be set up in an ordinary analytical chemistry laboratory. However, there is a tendency, which many of us have, to believe that doing something on a big scale is more reliable than doing it on a small scale. Therefore, it was with misgivings that the apparatus shown in Figure 1 was set up.

It is, in principle, the same as used by Wood and Barrett of the U. S. Bureau of Mines, by the Ontario Research Foundation, and

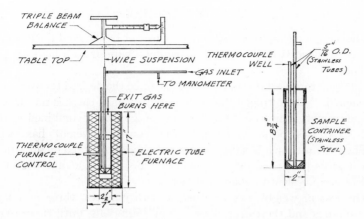

Fig. 1. Apparatus for determining rate of reduction of iron ore.

perhaps by many others. The only difference is that in this case, particle sizes which would fluidize were used.

The sample container is 2 in. in diameter and 9 in. long. It is made of type 304 stainless steel. The tube furnace is 17 in. high and the hole, in which the sample container hangs, is $2^1/_2$ in. in diameter.

Where possible, the particle size was $-20 +100$ mesh. In this case, a loose cap was sufficient to prevent significant carry out of solids at space velocities up to 0.6 fps. When fine concentrates containing large amounts of -325 mesh were tested, it was necessary to close the end of the tube with a porous metallic filter. The filter makes it possible to make tests at higher velocities. The gas was measured with a flow meter and a manometer containing water was attached to the gas line. The manometer served as a fluidization indicator. The water level jiggled steadily when the sample was fluidized. Whenever the water level became inactive, cakes were always found in the sample. No caking was observed during the tests discussed in this paper. Bottled gas was used and arrangements were made to use H_2, CO, N_2 and mixtures of these gases.

The temperature of the bed was automatically controlled from a thermocouple in the ore. An external thermocouple recorded the temperature in the furnace and a powerstat was used to regulate the power input so the furnace temperature varied very little. This resulted in close control of the samples' temperature.

TEST PROCEDURE

The sample of ore, usually 200 g, is placed in the container which is then suspended in the tube furnace, by a wire, from a hook on the balance.

Nitrogen is passed through the sample until the desired temperature is reached. The nitrogen flow is maintained until there is no further loss in weight, indicating that the "loss of ignition" (combined water and CO_2) has been removed. After constant weight has been reached the nitrogen is shut off and reducing gas turned on, at a rate which gives the space velocity desired. For the size tube used 0.2 SCFM is equivalent to about 0.60 fps.

The loss in weight was recorded at two minutes, three minutes, five minutes and thereafter at five minute intervals, until the rate of loss became very slow, after which it was recorded at ten minute intervals.

It was observed, particularly in reduction with hydrogen, that when it was turned on there was a small but very quick rise in temperature. The reason for this is not understood. Since the oxygen content of bottled nitrogen is very small, this heat effect may be related to gas adsorption on the surface of the ore particles.

Within two or three minutes the temperature begins to drop rapidly, apparently due to the endothermic reaction in reducing iron oxide with hydrogen. By use of the powerstat this drop was minimized as much as possible but sometimes it amounted to as much as 60°F. The temperature was rapidly brought back to the level desired, and the greater part of the time it was maintained within limits of about 10°F.

The test was terminated when the loss in weight in five minutes became 0.5 g or less for a few readings.

CALCULATION OF PER CENT REDUCTION

The per cent oxygen in the original ore and the residual oxygen in the reduced material were determined by a method which will not be described here, but which has been found to be reliable. The per cent reduction is defined by the following formula:

$$\% \text{ reduction} = (100\,AS - 100\,BP)/AS$$

where A is the per cent oxygen in the ore, B is the per cent oxygen in the reduced ore, S is the weight of ore sample, and P is the weight of reduced ore.

From the oxygen analyses the final per cent reduction is calculated. The weight losses observed at intervals during the test represent the rate of removal of oxygen and are used to calculate a curve showing the per cent of total oxygen removed as a function of time.

ORES TESTED

The following ores were treated by the described procedure

Name of ore	Figure No.
Northern Labrador	2
Brazilian	3
Venezuelan	4
Marcona	5
Chilean	6
Mexican	7
Rusk Concentrate	8
Rusk Crude	9
Siderite	10
Liberian	11

The analyses of these ores are shown in Table I.

TABLE I
Chemical Analysis of Ores

| Name of ore | Per cent by weight (dry) | | | | |
	Fe	O_2	SiO_2	Al_2O_3	Magnetic, %
Venezuelan	66.5	28.3	0.9	2.4	0.0
Labrador	60.8	25.6	7.9	1.7	0.0
Mexican	64.0	28.1	1.6	1.1	32.3
Siderite	40.5	14.1	10.9	4.2	0.0
Marcona	62.8	26.3	6.7	—	19.8
Rusk Crude	38.8	14.6	15.5	6.5	0.0
Rusk Conc.	42.2	15.4	16.3	7.2	0.0
Brazilian	66.4	28.7	0.6	0.7	1.6
Chilean	64.7	26.4	5.4	1.1	77.8
Liberian	65.1	26.7	3.5	1.2	72.8

RESULTS

Tests on Small Apparatus Described

The results of reduction tests on several ores at 1400°F in hydrogen gas are shown in Figures 2–11, inclusive.   The horizontal axis is time in minutes.   The upper curve shows the per cent reduction, the middle curve shows cumulative weight loss, and the lower curve the rate of loss of oxygen per minute at different times.   These curves represent nothing new in technique.   Similar ones have been used and published by others.

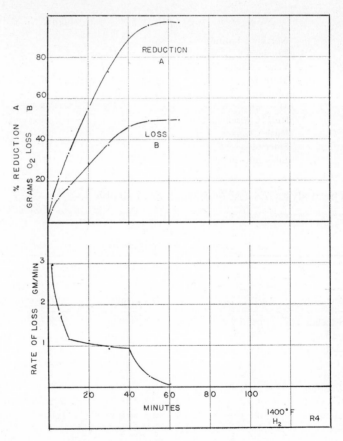

Fig. 2. Reduction rate of Labrador ore.

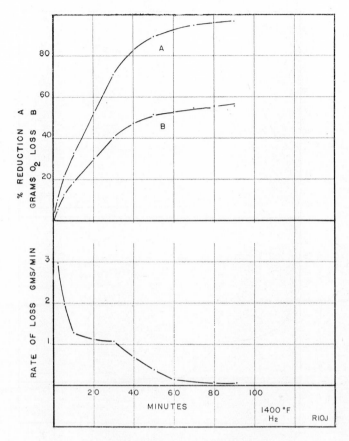

Fig. 3. Reduction rate of Brazilian ore.

These figures show that the time required to reach a given stage of reduction such as 90–95% varies greatly for different ores.

The lower curves for rate of oxygen loss show that the rate starts high and falls rapidly to one that remains at a fairly constant level for a while. Then the curve breaks again and the rate of oxygen removal decreases quite rapidly. For the hematitic ores the first break comes consistently at 33% reduction or where Fe_2O_3 has been converted to FeO. Some of these ores contain magnetite, and in these cases this first break point comes at per cents of reduction less than 33% as might be expected.

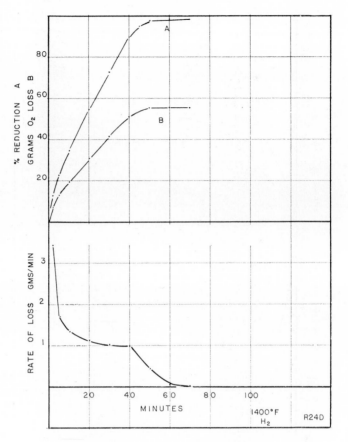

Fig. 4. Reduction rate of Venezuelan ore.

The second break point appears at widely different times and per-cents of reduction and seems to fit no formula. It might be referred to as a rate of reduction cut-off point. The rate is so much slower after this cut-off point that if it occurs before a high per cent of reduction is reached too much time will be required to make a highly reduced product economically.

Table II shows the per cent reduction at which the first and second break in rate occurs for each of these ores.

Table III shows the ores arranged in the order of increasing time required to reach 90 and 95% reduction.

TABLE II
Per Cent Reduction at Which Changes in Rate Occur

Name of ore	Per cent reduction		Magnetite, %
	First break	Second break	
Venezuelan	33	90	0.0
Labrador	33	89	0.0
Mexican	30	85	32.3
Siderite	34	81	0.0
Marcona	33	80	19.8
Rusk Crude	33	79	0.0
Rusk Conc.	33	77	0.0
Brazilian	33	71	1.6
Chilean	25	57	77.8
Liberian	26	45	72.8

TABLE III
Time to Reach 90 and 95% Reduction

Name of ore	Minutes	
	To 90% reduction	To 95% reduction
Siderite	26	34
Rusk Crude	30	40
Rusk Conc.	34	42
Venezuelan	40	46
Labrador	42	48
Mexican	45	64
Brazilian	52	70
Marcona	74	96
Chilean	a	a
Liberian	a	a

a Greater than 140 min.

Since the sample weight treated was constant at 200 g and the per cent oxygen in the ores varies, there is a different weight of oxygen to be removed in each case. For instance, Rusk Concentrate contains 15.4% oxygen and Venezuelan ore 28.3% oxygen. Therefore, a 200-g sample of Rusk ore contains 30.8 g of oxygen while a similar sample of Venezuelan ore contains 56.6 g of oxygen. Table III shows that 95% of the oxygen was removed more quickly from the low grade ores. This is probably largely due to the fact that there was less oxygen in the sample. When the rate is expressed in grams of

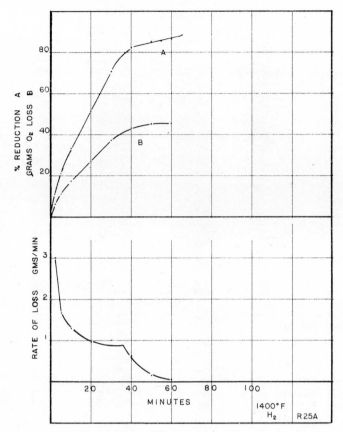

Fig. 5. Reduction rate of Marcona ore.

oxygen removed per minute, the higher grade hematite ores move up in the list. Table IV lists the ores in order of decreasing rate of oxygen removal. This is believed to be the more significant arrangement.

Tests on Reactor of 1 Ft² Cross Section

One of these ores, Labrador, has been tested on a reactor having a circular internal cross section of 1 ft². Some idea of its size can be obtained from Figure 12. It is approximately 24 ft tall and has been

TABLE IV

Rate of O_2 Removal

	Grams O_2 removed/min	
Name of ore	A[a]	B[b]
Venezuelan	1.17	1.28
Labrador	1.02	1.12
Mexican	0.83	1.13
Siderite	0.79	0.96
Brazilian	0.77	1.00
Rusk Crude	0.70	0.87
Rusk Conc.	0.69	0.82
Marcona	0.26	0.32
Chilean	c	c
Liberian	c	c

[a] Averaging grams O_2/min from 0–95% reduction.
[b] Averaging grams O_2/min from 0–90% reduction.
[c] Did not reach 90% reduction.

TABLE V

Effect of % H_2 and Gas Quantity on Rate of Reduction

Batch No.	Time to 90% reduction, min	H_2 in gas, %	Gas quantity, SCFM/lb
1	99	71.7	0.311
2	177	63.7	0.229
3	131	64.8	0.246
4	146	66.5	0.198
5	127	69.6	0.240
6	112	63.1	0.344
7	99	72.3	0.314
8	243	39.0	0.452
9	221	41.0	0.423
10	133	55.0	0.412
11	121	62.0	0.688
12	142	72.0	0.352

operated both as a single bed and a superimposed two-bed reactor. The gas used has consisted principally of H_2 and CO with small percentages of CO_2, CH_4, and H_2O. Batches of approximately 250 lb of ore have been reduced at several gas flow rates.

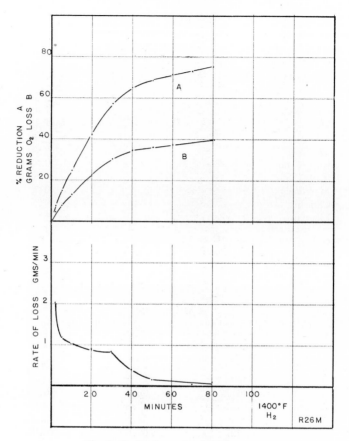

Fig. 6. Reduction rate of Chilean ore.

Table V shows a set of data for twelve batches reduced at 1400°F. The time to reach 90% reduction is tabulated for comparison to the per cent H_2 in the gas and the SCFM per pound of solids in the bed.

By applying a multiple correlation technique to these data Figures 13 and 14 have been obtained. Figure 13 indicates that in the range of data available an increase of 1% H_2 will decrease the time required 4 min when the quantity of gas is 0.3 SCFM/lb of solids. Figure 14 indicates that an increase of 0.10 SCFM/lb solids will decrease the time about 10 min when the gas contains 60% hydrogen.

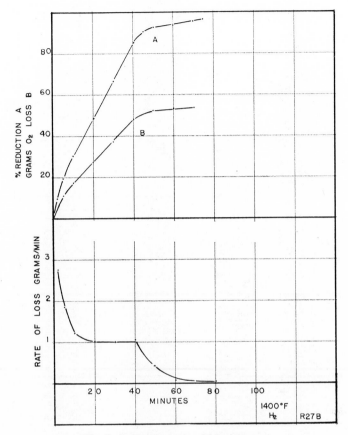

Fig. 7. Reduction rate of Mexican ore.

Since these data from the 1-ft² reactor pertain to one specific ore and were obtained at constant temperature, the effect of variatons in ore characteristics and temperature have been largely eliminated. Under these conditions the quantity of gas and its hydrogen content explain 67% of the variance of time among the batches. The correlation coefficient is 0.82 indicating that there is very little probability that the relations shown can be due to chance. Some of the 33% unexplained variance is likely due to inaccuracies in obtaining the data leaving less than 33% to be explained by unstudied variables.

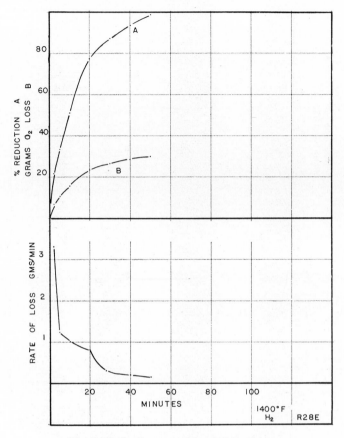

Fig. 8. Reduction rate of washed Rusk ore.

CONCLUSIONS

When iron ores in the form of fine particles are reduced, it would seem that reduction rates should vary much less from ore to ore because the reducing gases do not need to diffuse very far to reach the centers of small particles.

Nevertheless, the data that have been presented here point out strongly the large variation in reduction rate of different ores even when they are processed as small particles. Some of them reduce so

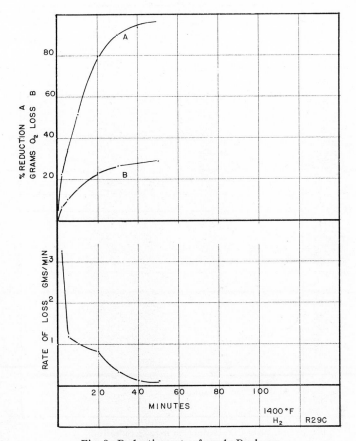

Fig. 9. Reduction rate of crude Rusk ore.

slowly that it is questionable whether experimental work with them should be extended to larger equipment.   These experiments are not nearly as complete as desired, but it is believed they confirm strongly the necessity of selecting ores that reduce rapidly for use in low temperature reduction processes.

The literature has many papers on the reduction of iron ore with gases and in some cases efforts have been made to explain why some ores reduce faster than others.   However, out of these studies there has not developed any really valuable procedure for making a slow

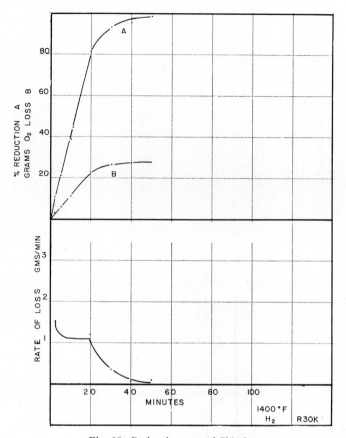

Fig. 10. Reduction rate of Siderite.

reducing ore approach the rate of a naturally fast reducing ore.

The technology and equipment for low temperature reduction have developed so much in recent years that some of the direct reduction processes are on the brink of becoming commercially useful. Further knowledge that would lead to faster reduction of ores would help the progress of these processes. It is hoped that some of our metallurgical scientists, will take a thorough and modern look at this interesting but difficult problem.

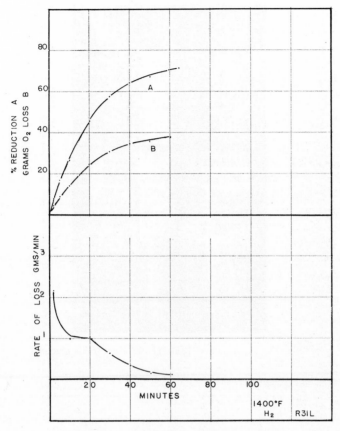

Fig. 11. Reduction rate of Liberian ore.

Discussion

H. U. Ross (*Univ. of Toronto*): In examining any of the so-called "direct reduction processes," I always find myself comparing it with the blast furnace process and wondering whether the direct process can produce iron in quantity and at a rate comparable with the blast furnace. The direct processes in their present state of development cannot compare with the blast furnace because they cannot produce iron at a high enough rate or, at least, in a large enough quantity to be competitive. It is appropriate, therefore, to hear a paper that deals with the rates of reduction of some iron ores because it goes into the most important problem that must be overcome if the direct processes are to succeed; namely, how can the rate of reduction of iron ores be increased?

Fig. 12. Experimental 13 in. ID fluidized solids reactor.

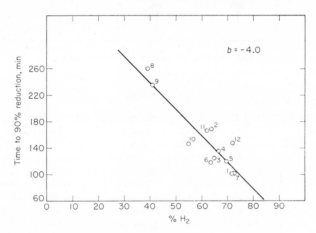

Fig. 13. Effect of % H₂ in gas on rate of reduction (Labrador ore).

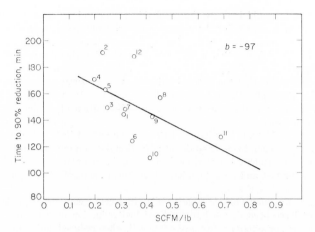

Fig. 14. Effect of gas quantity on rate of reduction (Labrador ore).

An interesting point illustrated in the paper is the so-called "reduction cutoff point." The speed of reduction falls off to a very low rate after this point is reached. All of the ten ores tested exhibited this phenomenon. The authors did not speculate as to why the cutoff point exists, but it is obvious that, if this peculiarity in reduction could be eliminated, the case for the direct reduction process would be greatly improved. This raises two questions: Why do iron ores exhibit this reduction cutoff point, and how can it be eliminated? To find the answer to these two questions would be a worthwhile piece of research. The cutoff point might be eliminated by some kind of ore preparation.

A great deal of work has been carried out in recent years on the preparation of ores for the blast furnace. As a result of suitable ore preparation, furnace capacities have been greatly increased. Likewise, it is conceivable that, with proper preparation, direct reduction processes might be greatly improved also. What constitutes proper ore preparation is worthy of intensive research.

In his discussion, Dr. Squires points out that the direct reduction process could be designed to suit the ore. This would mean that there would be as many designs of process as there would be types of ore. It is my feeling that, if a direct reduction process is to be successful, we should have one process and that we should strive to prepare the ore to suit that process.

H. K. Worner (*Broken Hill Pty. Co., Australia*): So many factors influence the rate at which iron ores are reduced by hydrogen-rich gases, that it is not surprising that the authors have noted wide discrepancies between different ores. Among the factors which my colleagues have found to affect the reduction rates in fluidized systems are: temperature, pressure gas flow rate, gas composition, particle size and shape, particle porosity, and the impurities in the ore.

In the majority of the work described in this paper, the temperature was more or less constant (1400°F) and presumably this was the case with gas composition, pressure, and flow rate. The work to be described by Mr. Henderson in the next paper (p. 671) would indicate that probably a more advantageous temperature could have been chosen for the reduction experiments, particularly if over 90% reduction is desired. The 1400°F (760°C) is in a range where our experience with fine hematites indicates that a rather longer reduction time is required than at about 1000°F (540–550°C).

It is conceivable that the optimal reduction temperature will vary with different ores. Certainly, the other variables I mentioned: namely, particle size; particle porosity; and the nature, size, and distribution of gangue minerals all affect the process.

The work of Messrs. Marshall and Brant is important in that it demonstrates the dangers of generalizing from direct reduction data on one ore under one set of conditions. Considerable experimentation may be necessary to find the optimal conditions for fast and near complete reductions of a particular ore in fluid bed systems.

H. H. Aas (*Union Carbide Metals Co.*): In recent years considerable interest and effort have been devoted to fluidized bed reduction of iron ores. A high grade iron ore, or a high grade concentrate will, when reduced under proper conditions, result in a metallic product which can be utilized directly in the steel furnaces (possibly after briquetting of the powder) and in certain cases for powder metallurgical applications. With low or medium grade ores it is necessary to have an additional processing step to separate the metal from the gangue. I would like to have the authors' opinion on the type of separation processes they think would be most likely. It seems to me that a separation between metal and gangue, in the solid state (i.e., by some ore dressing method) would be very difficult due to the intergrown structure and the fine size of the reduced iron. The lack of coalescence of the fine iron structure into larger particles is largely due to the low temperature one has to use in fluidized bed reduction in order to prevent serious sticking. Conventional melting could be used for separation; however, the cost of such an additional step is considerable.

The authors mention in their paper that there is no really valuable procedure for making a slow reducing ore approach the rate of a naturally fast reducing ore. I would like to make the following comments.

J. O. Edström has clearly shown that hematite crystals reduce faster than magnetite crystals. The difference in the rate of reduction is large when reducing with CO, and also with H_2 as the reducing agent there is a considerable difference. These differences in rates may tend to even out if the ore particles treated are very fine (and porous). It has also been shown that when reducing magnetite with H_2 at temperatures between 700 and 1100°C it is very difficult to remove the last 10–15% of oxygen from the iron. This has been shown on a magnetite concentrate with a particle size of about 50% −200 mesh. The admixture of some CO to the reducing gas will help in obtaining a more complete reduction [*Jernkontorets Ann.*, **138**, No. 4, 177 (1954). *Jernkontorets Ann.*, **140**, No. 2, 116 (1956)].

It therefore seems that the rate of reduction, for certain ores, can be improved.

A. M. Squires (*Hydrocarbon Research*): This paper shows rather wide variations in reduction rate of a number of ores in hydrogen at 1400°F. The Symposium should find it interesting to see similar data obtained by Hydrocarbon

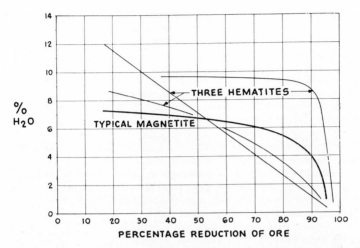

Discussion Fig. 1. Conversion of hydrogen to water achieved in deep fluid beds at
400 psig and 900°F.

Research, Inc. at 900°F.   Discussion Figure 1 shows plots of water content of
gases leaving a bed of iron ore fluidized by hydrogen at 400 psig and 900°F.
Abscissa in the figure is percentage reduction of the ore (i.e., percentage removal
of oxygen chemically bound to iron in the original ore).   The fluid beds were of
practicable bed height, and the hydrogen conversions shown in the figure are
practicable from the standpoint of commercial operation of the "H-iron" process
[A. M. Squires and C. A. Johnson, J. Metals, 9, 586 (1957)], the direct reduction
process newly developed by Hydrocarbon Research, Inc. and Bethlehem Steel
Co.   Results are shown for four typical ores.

1. The curve for magnetite was measured on a Swedish concentrate and is
typical of a number of other magnetites which have been studied.   (Millscale
shows reduction characteristics at 400 psig and 900°F rather similar to magnetites,
except that the curve breaks downward at somewhat higher percentage reduction.)

2. The two steadily declining curves for hematites are typical of a number of
hematites which have been studied.   One of these particular curves was obtained
on Venezuelan Cerro Bolivar ore of low gangue content, while the other was
obtained on a Peruvian Marcona ore of high gangue content (only about 30%
iron).

3. The largely horizontal curve for hematite, which breaks downward at high
percentage reduction, was measured on a Brazilian Itabira ore.   This ore reduced more quickly than Venezuelan, in contrast to Brant and Marshall's results
at 1400°F.

Simple inspection of the figure shows that there is considerable variation in the
times of reduction at 900°F, as Brant and Marshall have shown at 1400°F.

However, in every case it has been possible to achieve 95% reduction in a reasonable length of time, and it is possible to design a commercial H-iron reducer which can handle all of the ores Hydrocarbon Research, Inc. has studied, with relatively small change in reduction capacity as the operator switches from one ore to another. This is seen as the major advantage of low-temperature reduction as practiced in the H-iron process. Because the curves of hydrogen conversion to water break downward at high reduction degree, it is necessary to provide for a degree of countercurrent contacting of hydrogen and ore. Normally three beds are sufficient; and at least three beds are recommended in all cases, since even if a magnetite, for which two beds would be sufficient, is contemplated for initial use, addition of a third bed provides very cheap insurance against the possibility that operation may be switched to a hematite of the Cerro Bolivar variety. With countercurrent contacting, reducer production capacity is set by hydrogen conversion to water at relatively low percentage reduction. Variations from ore to ore in conversion at low percentage reduction can largely be overcome by changes in operating temperature.

This operating flexibility is simply not possible in a direct reduction process operating much above 1000°F, as a large accumulation of data shows. See, for example, J. O. Edström [*J. Iron Steel Inst. (London)*, **175**, 289 (1953)] who showed that magnetite and hematite reduce at widely different rates at 800°C, but at practically identical rates at 450°C.

Hydrocarbon Research, Inc. differs therefore with Brant and Marshall's conclusion that ores must be carefully selected for a low temperature reduction process. If operating temperature is limited to below about 1000°F, only ores of high ferrosilicate or ferrotitanate content appear excluded. At low temperatures no trouble is encountered with ore sticking and defluidization. The H-iron process is seen as having very nearly as general applicability as the blast furnace, subject of course to economic limitations on gangue content of ore.

J. B. Henderson (*Broken Hill Pty. Co., Australia*): In Figures 2 to 11 of the paper under discussion no experimental values of weight loss are reported; hence, in the absence of information on the reproducibility of curve *B* of these figures, the plots of rate of loss against time do not seem to be significant, because small variations in the shape of curve *B* can produce large differences in the rate of loss curves. The authors' interpretation of the "first break point" corresponding to reduction of all Fe_2O_3 to "FeO" is in conflict with the published literature, which indicates that the gaseous reduction of hematite is a topochemical process. The present work has emphasized the large differences in the reduction rates of different ores. This is of fundamental interest, there being strong evidence to suggest that the rate-controlling step of the reduction process is different for different ores. In some cases the process appears to be diffusion controlled and in others adsorption controlled.

W. E. Marshall: We are very much pleased by the interesting discussion in regard to our paper, which is admittedly limited to a very few tests on a very small scale.

We agree with Dr. Ross's comments that much more work needs to be done to find out how to prepare iron ore for fluidized solids reactors. In regard to fluidizing characteristics, iron ores in a reduced state certainly differ from the unreduced ore and also from materials such as oil cracking catalysts.   It requires optimism, at the moment, to believe that all ores can be prepared so that they will be suitable for one process but perhaps research through the years will find a way.   The lower the temperature the better the chance appears for handling a greater variety of ores.   However, lower temperature processes are plagued with pyrophoric products and also require recirculation, which means more capital investment, in order to reduce a ton of iron with an economical amount of gas.

Mr. Warner's comments are also interesting.   We are familiar with experiments in which magnetite reduces faster at lower temperatures than at higher ones, but we have not found this true with the hematites which we have used.   There is still something to be found out along this line also.   Optimum conditions of particle size, porosity, and temperature may be different for various ores.

Mr. Aas has asked about additional processing steps to separate gangue from the reduced metal in cases where the original ore is not pure enough.   At present, magnetic separation or smelting are the only practical choices.   In cases where the gangue is not free and cannot be made free by further grinding, smelting is the only choice.   Where either can be used, local economics must give the answer.

Dr. Squires has made some interesting remarks and it is rather certain that most ores can be reduced and kept fluid at temperatures below 1000°F.   We must repeat, however, that the low temperature processes usually require contacting much more gas per unit of iron reduced.   This requires higher pressures and recirculation for gas economy thus increasing capital investment.

Mr. Henderson has remarked that the gaseous reduction of hematite has been shown in published literature to be a topochemical process and hence the "first break point," we refer to, should not necessarily be associated with conversion of all Fe_2O_3 to FeO.   We are forced to say, however, that all of our work, with small fluidized particles, strongly indicates a step-wise process.   Starting with a non-magnetic hematite, in just a few minutes the product is highly magnetic (Fe_3O_4), a few minutes later it is nonmagnetic again (FeO), and a few minutes later the product becomes again magnetic and increasingly so as complete reduction is approached.   Unfortunately, a detailed study, which could have been made by taking samples at very short time intervals was not made.   Perhaps the difference between our results and those reported in the literature are due to working with small particles as compared to relatively large pieces.

A Study of the Rate and Mechanism of the Hydrogen Reduction of Fine Hematite Ores

JOHN B. HENDERSON

Central Research Laboratories, The Broken Hill Proprietary Company, Ltd., Shortland, N.S.W., Australia

Abstract

The reduction of two high grade Australian hematite ores by hydrogen was studied to ascertain the conditions of maximum reduction rate. Reduction was measured by weighing the water evolved in the reduction reactions.

The occurrence of a rate maximum at about 550°C and the shape of the reduction curves are explained by the difference in permeability to water of the reduced iron above and below this temperature. The mechanism of reduction and factors affecting the rate of reduction are discussed.

INTRODUCTION

Through the years much interest has centered in developing a direct method of iron ore reduction. Some remarkably contradictory statements have appeared regarding the importance to be attached to so-called "direct" processes, but the disagreement is concerned with the lack of a suitable process rather than unsuitable properties of the product. Low temperature gaseous reduction shows especial promise, but confusion persists regarding the factors involved.

A survey of the literature reveals that the equilibrium conditions for the reduction reactions of iron oxides with hydrogen have been well established but that data on the mechanism and rates of reaction are discordant. This paper describes a project designed to define the conditions of maximum rate of reduction in hydrogen of some Australian iron ores and to determine the rate-controlling step of the reduction process.

672   PROCESS METALLURGY

PREVIOUS INVESTIGATIONS
Equilibria

Although the present problem is specifically one of kinetics, a first consideration is the equilibrium of the system, since the reactions to be studied comprise that equilibrium, and their directions and end-points are defined by it. The equilibrium data resulting from research to 1953[1] are depicted in Figure 1, where the oxide phases in equilibrium with different gas mixtures of hydrogen and water are shown.

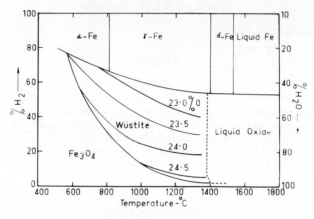

Fig. 1. Iron-oxygen-hydrogen system.

Mechanism

The reduction of iron oxides has often been treated as a gas diffusion problem, especially diffusion through the reduced metal.[2-4] It has long been known[5] that reduction of magnetite at temperatures above about 560°C proceeds by way of the phase wüstite to metallic iron, and penetrates toward the center of the sample, so that concentric layers of the different phases appear. The reduction of hematite is supposed[1] to proceed in a similar manner and concentric layers of magnetite, wüstite, and metallic iron are formed around a hematite core.

Reduction of iron oxides by hydrogen gas goes over an activated adsorption mechanism,[6] the first step of which consists in adsorption of the reducing gas by the oxide surface, the reduction being brought about in the adsorbed state.   It is claimed[7] that reduction is continued because of access of the reducing gas to the oxide surfaces by means of porosities that develop in the solid reduction products.

The specific volumes[1] of the different phases at room temperature are: 0.272 cu cm, Fe_2O_3; 0.270 cu cm, Fe_3O_4; 0.231 cu cm, FeO (23.5% oxygen); and 0.128 cu cm, Fe (per gram of iron); hence, if the external volume of the particles does not decrease, porosities should appear.   Because of swelling, however, porosities as high as 68% have been observed.[8]

Wiberg,[9,10] in the reduction of magnetite, found no porosity in the wüstite phase and assumed that reduction occurs by means of solid state reactions.   Observations of solid state processes have increased[1,11−17] in connection with reduction processes, which may now largely be interpreted in terms of such phenomena.

Besides the gas-oxide reactions and solid state diffusion processes there are reactions in the phase boundaries.   The influence of phase boundary reactions has been pointed out by Stalhane and Malmberg,[18] who found the reduction of magnetite to wüstite to be faster than the reduction of wüstite to iron.   Other workers[19] have found, however, that all iron oxides are reduced at a similar rate.

Factors Influencing Reduction Rate

Among the factors affecting the rate of reduction of iron ores are: temperature, pressure, gas velocity, gas composition, particle size, particle porosity, impurities in the ore, and accessibility of the reducing gas to the ore particles.

It has been claimed[20] that the reduction rate of hematite in hydrogen increases with temperature up to 1000°C, but many other workers[1,3,5,7,21−23] have reported a rate maximum in the vicinity of 600°C. The falling off in rate above this temperature is thought by some[7,21,22] to be due to changes in the micro- and ultra-microporosity of the ore, and by others[3,5] to be due to sintering and recrystallization of the reduced iron, which occurs above 600°C.[24]   Edström[1] reports that the rate minimum at temperatures in excess of 600°C is associated with the formation of a dense wüstite phase.

Schenck[25] observed the velocity of the reducing gas to be a variable in reduction systems, but Leibu[26] claims that flow velocity is of minor importance.   Edström[1] and Trivedi[28] found that a low critical gas velocity exists, above which reaction rate is independent of flow velocity. Gas pressure has been studied[19,27,28] and it is claimed[29] that the mass rate of flow of the gas is the deciding factor, irrespective of gas velocity and gas pressure. The presence of water vapor in the hydrogen stream is known[1] to have a strong retarding effect on reduction, but small amounts of halogens or carbon dioxide have been found[30] to increase the reduction rate.

Particle size of the ore is thought by some[25] to be a variable, but others[20,26] claim it has little effect on reduction rate. Lewis[4] found the time of reduction of iron ore cubes to be directly proportional to their size, but Edström[8] reported no major difference in reduction rate for 0.1 mm grains, 4 mm cubes, or 12 mm diam pellets.

Both the initial porosity and the porosities formed during reduction of the ore can have a pronounced effect on reduction rates,[1,7,8,19,21–23,27] as can the presence of impurities in the ore.[31,32] The question of gas access is of importance since, if the particles of ore do not have complete access to the reducing gas, it is quite possible that characteristics of the experimental system will be measured and not properties of the ore.

PRESENT INVESTIGATION

Materials

The results reported in this paper were obtained on samples of naturally fine hematites obtained respectively from iron ore quarries at Cockatoo Island, Yampi Sound W. A., and the Iron Prince in the Middleback Ranges, South Australia. Chemical analyses of the -200 mesh (B.S.S.) fraction of these ores are shown in Table I.

TABLE I

Analyses of Ore Samples

	Iron Prince, %	Yampi Blue, %
Fe	66.5	69.0
SiO_2	1.0	0.31
Al_2O_3	1.3	0.13
CaO	0.84	0.04
MgO	0.01	0.02
P_2O_5	0.05	0.01
Mn	0.09	0.01
S	0.29	0.01

Cylinders of commercial hydrogen and oxygen free nitrogen were used throughout, the hydrogen being purified by passage over a Deoxo catalytic unit to remove the last traces of oxygen, prior to use.

Apparatus and Experimental Technique

The apparatus used in the majority of the experiments is shown diagrammatically in Figure 2. It consists of a resistance wound, silica tube furnace of 2 in. internal diameter, containing a 22-mm internal diameter, 70 cm long tapered end, Pythagoras combustion tube, with a U-tube containing anhydrous magnesium perchlorate connected to the tapered end. Into the opposite end of the tube is fitted a rubber stopper through which passes a glass gas inlet tube and a silica sheath for the Chromel-Alumel thermocouple. The thermo-

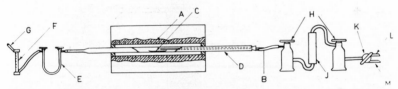

Fig. 2. Diagram of apparatus used in reduction experiments: (A) Nichrome wound silica tube, (B) thermocouple to controller, (C) boat, (D) combustion tube, (E) absorption tube, (F) flow meter, (G) to atmosphere, (C) drying towers, (J) Deoxo, (K) two way clock, (L) to nitrogen cylinder, and (M) to hydrogen cylinder.

couple is connected to a Cambridge indicating controller and the gas inlet tube through a purifying train to a two way cock connecting the gas cylinders.

By adjusting the furnace input voltage with a variable transformer and placing a resistance across the controller contacts, thereby passing only a fraction of the heating current through the controller, gas stream temperatures could be controlled to better than ±5°C, at all temperatures.

The technique consisted of heating a weighed quantity of the ore, spread so as to approximate a single layer on the bottom of an open-ended platinum boat, to the desired temperature in an atmosphere of nitrogen. The flow was then switched from nitrogen to hydrogen for a measured time interval, after which the reaction was stopped by quenching in nitrogen.

The water evolved during the course of the reaction was collected and weighed. By comparison with the weight of water evolved in complete reduction of the sample, the percentage reduction at any time could be calculated. The reproducibility of the results was ±1% and a check of the water collected during complete reduction against the quantity that should be evolved, according to the iron content of the sample, showed the precision to be ±1%.

In order to eliminate the possibility of the results reflecting characteristics of the apparatus and not properties of the particles of ore, some of the results were checked in a completely different type of apparatus shown diagrammatically in Figure 3.

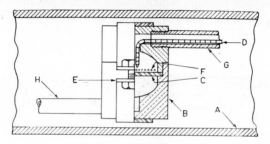

Fig. 3. Apparatus used in confirmatory reduction tests: (*A*) silica tube furnace, (*B*) copper container, (*C*) porous disc, (*D*) thermocouple, (*E*) clamp (*F*) ore sample, (*G*) gas inlet, and (*H*) gas outlet.

A porous disc 20 mm in diameter, of sintered stainless steel, was supported in a two-piece gas-tight copper container, approximately 25 mm in diameter and 30 mm in height. The container was heated in the furnace described previously, the gas passed down through the sample spread to approximate a single layer on the disc, and the water evolved, collected, and weighed as before. Unfortunately, only a few tests were made before the apparatus became unserviceable due to leaks.

RESULTS

The results of experiments designed to test the dependence of reduction rate on temperature are shown in Figures 4 and 5. One-hundred milligram samples of −200 mesh (B.S.S.) ore were reduced in hydrogen at a flow rate of 800 ml/min. In Figures 6 and 7 the data

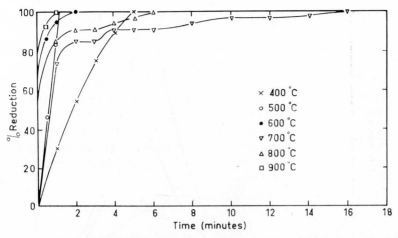

Fig. 4. Effect of temperature on reduction of Yampi Blue ore.

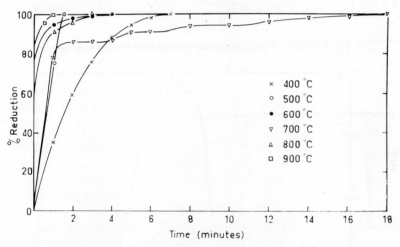

Fig. 5. Effect of temperature on reduction of Iron Prince ore.

are replotted in another way to show the development of a pronounced
rate maximum and minimum as reduction proceeds.

Figure 8 shows the results of confirmatory reduction tests obtained
by reducing 100 mg samples of −200 mesh Yampi Blue ore in hydrogen at a flow rate of 2400 ml/min, using the apparatus described in
Figure 3.

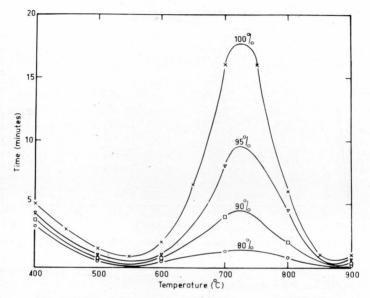

Fig. 6. Effect of temperature on reduction of Yampi Blue ore.

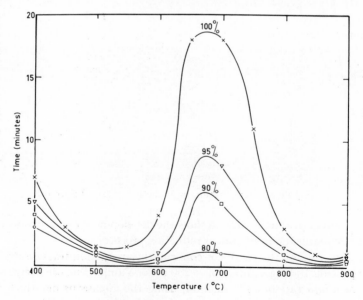

Fig. 7. Effect of temperature on reduction of Iron Prince ore.

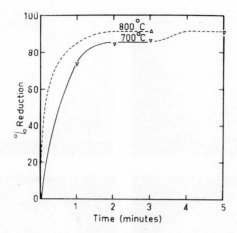

Fig. 8. Confirmatory reduction tests of Yampi Blue ore.

The micrographs of Figure 9 show particles of −200 mesh Yampi Blue ore reduced at various temperatures. The samples for these micrographs were obtained by reducing a few milligrams of −200 mesh Yampi Blue ore on a hot stage microscope in which the temperature could be lowered from 900 to 200°C in 10 sec. The microscope was used because satisfactory cooling rates could not be obtained in either of the types of apparatus described above. The particles were vacuum mounted in a thermosetting plastic and polished.

DISCUSSION

As the results of the confirmatory reduction tests were in all cases within ±1% of those previously obtained, it seems reasonable to suppose that the curves of Figures 4 to 7 reflect properties of the ores and not characteristics of the apparatus. Three features of these curves are noteworthy. First, the initial reduction rate increases from 400 to 550°C, then decreases up to about 725°C and increases again to 900°C. Second, "arrests" and decline in rate are shown by the 700 and 800°C curves which result in a rate maximum at about 550°C. Third, the decline in rate at 700 and 800°C occurs only as reduction approaches completion.

If it is accepted that, as well as the interchange of gas between the oxide-metal reaction surface and the stream of reducing gas, there are

Fig. 9. Single particles −200 mesh Yampi Blue ore reduced in hydrogen, all unetched. (a) particle fully reduced at 400°C, (b) particle fully reduced at 550°C, (c) particle partially reduced at 650°C, (d) particle partially reduced at 725°C, (e) particle partially reduced at 800°C, and (f) particle partially reduced at 900°C.

processes of diffusion in the solid state, then any of the following rates may control the rate of the overall reduction process.

1. Rate of diffusion of hydrogen through the stationary gas layer around the particles and through the layer of reduced iron.

2. Rate of adsorption of hydrogen at the iron–iron oxide interface.

3. Rate of reaction between adsorbed hydrogen and iron oxide.

4. Rate of desorption of water vapor formed during the reaction.

5. Rate of diffusion of water through reduced iron and stationary gas layer.

6. Rate of iron ion or oxygen ion and electronic diffusion across wüstite layer.

7. Rate of diffusion of iron ions or oxygen ions and electrons across a dense magnetite phase.

8. Rate of phase boundary reaction $Fe_3O_4 \rightarrow FeO$ and $Fe_2O_3 \rightarrow Fe_3O_4$.

However, all of these rates could quite reasonably be expected to increase with increasing temperature so that the time-temperature curves of Figures 6 and 7 should have a continuously increasing slope rather than exhibiting a minimum and a maximum. It has been suggested[3,5] that the pronounced "lagging" of the reduction curves at 700 and 800°C is due to sintering and recrystallization of the reduced iron to form an envelope around the unreduced oxide that is pervious to hydrogen but not to water. This means that the water formed would not be able to escape from the reaction zone, hence the reaction would be slowed and result in lagging of the reduction curves.

By reference to Figure 1 it may be seen that if the accumulated water did not escape in some manner it would eventually reach the equilibrium concentration and the overall reaction would stop completely; i.e., complete reduction would not be attained. The trapped water, however, is supposed to build up sufficient pressure to burst the enclosing metal shell, so allowing the metallization reaction to proceed.

The results obtained in the present investigation are compatible with the above theory. Below about 550°C the iron is permeable to the water formed in the reduction reactions, and as the temperature increases from 400 to 550°C both the diffusion speeds of water and hydrogen through the iron and the rate of the hydrogen-iron oxide reaction increase. At 400°C, as reduction proceeds, the diffusion speed of water through the iron is not high enough to remove it from the reaction zone as fast as it is formed; hence, the metallization reaction is retarded and the reduction rate falls off. At 500°C the diffusion speed of water through the iron is higher and the retarding effect of water on the hydrogen-iron oxide reaction less than at 400°C; hence, the initial reduction rate is higher and the falling off in reduction rate, as reduction nears completion, is less. From 500 to about 550°C the diffusion speed of water through the iron further increases, with a corresponding increase in the overall reduction rate. The micrographs of Figures 9a and 9b show the iron formed to be a continuous phase, with what appears to be an extremely fine porosity, which may account for its permeability to water.

Above about 550°C it is thought that some change occurs in the physical properties of the reduced iron, so that it becomes less permeable to water than the iron formed below 550°C, and its permeability decreases with increasing temperature. This means that although the diffusion speed of hydrogen through the iron and the rate of the hydrogen-iron oxide reaction increases with temperature, the diffusion speed of water through the iron decreases. As the temperature is increased above 550°C, then, there are two opposing effects, one tending to increase the reduction rate and the other to decrease it.

At 600°C the diffusion speed of water through the iron is lower than at 550°C and the escape of water from the reaction zone is hindered, leading to a decrease in the initial reduction rate. As reduction proceeds the escape of water from the reaction interface is further hindered, because of the increased diffusion distances involved, and there is a pronounced falling off in the reduction rate.

The initial reduction rate at 700°C is lower than at 600°C, but because of the increased hydrogen diffusion speed, the increased rate of the hydrogen-iron oxide reaction and the decreased retarding effect of water on the hydrogen-iron oxide reaction, water is formed faster at the reaction interface than at 600°C. This trapped water builds up pressure which becomes great enough to crack the envelopes of iron surrounding areas of oxide, so that water formed at the reaction interface must, in order to escape from a particle, diffuse through a layer of iron into a crack and thence to the outside of the particle. Since the cracks contain water, however, water diffusing through a layer of iron must do so against a partial pressure of water, and its diffusion speed is further reduced. Eventually a stage is reached when the diffusion speed of the water through the iron is so low that for a time no water escapes from the particle and the reduction apparently

ceases.   This is shown in Figures 4 and 5 where at 700°C the reduction apparently stops after two minutes.

More water is being formed at the iron-iron oxide interface, however, and the cycle of buildup of pressure, cracking of the iron, and
escape of water is repeated and reduction apparently recommences,
as shown in Figures 4 and 5, after 3 and 4 min, respectively.   From
700°C to about 725°C the decreased diffusion speed of water through
the iron leads to a corresponding decrease in the initial and overall
reduction rates.   The postulate of pressure cracking at temperatures
above 600°C is supported by the micrographs of Figures 9c and 9d,
showing the iron formed at 650°C to be a continuous phase but the
iron formed at 725°C to contain cracks.

Above about 725°C the increased hydrogen diffusion speed through
the iron, the increased rate of the hydrogen-iron oxide reaction, and
the decreased regarding effect of water on this reaction causes the
cycle of entrapment of water, buildup of pressure, cracking of the iron,
and release of water to become sufficiently fast to allow the initial reduction rate to increase.   The diffusion speed of water through the
cracks also increases due to the increased temperature; hence, the
stage when no water escapes from the particle occurs at a higher degree of reduction and is of shorter time duration than at 700°C, as
shown in the 800°C curve of Figure 4.   The increase in the speed of
the iron cracking cycle is shown by the micrograph of Figure 9e,
where the iron formed at 800°C contains more cracks with shorter
distances between cracks, than the iron formed at 725°C.

At 900°C the initial and overall reduction rates are higher than at
800°C because of the increase in the speed of the iron cracking cycle.
This is supported by the micrograph of Figure 9f showing the iron
formed at 900°C to contain a larger number of cracks with shorter
distances between cracks than the iron formed at 800°C.   The falling
off in the overall reduction rate above about 850°C, as shown in Figures 6 and 7, appears to be associated with a phase change in the reduced iron, according to Edström,[1] the reduction of iron oxide to γ-
iron seems to be more retarded than the reduction to α-iron.

In the interests of brevity only those micrographs pertinent to the
argument have been included in this paper.   However, it has been observed, as may be seen in Figure 9f that the cracks in the iron are not
present in the oxide phases and hence are not formed during the transformation of hematite to lower oxides.   Micrographs were also ob-

tained of iron formed at temperatures below 550°C and then heated to 900°C. No cracking was observed in these specimens, hence it may be assumed that the cracking shown in Figures 9d, 9e, and 9f are not due to thermal shock caused by the fast cooling rates from the higher temperatures.

CONCLUSION

For two Australian fine hematites, under conditions of complete reducing gas accessibility, initial reduction rates are high. As reduction proceeds the initial rates fall off at 600, 700, and 800°C so that reduction is complete in approximately the same time at 550 as at 900°C. The rate maximum at about 550°C and the rate minimum at about 700°C are explained by the difference in permeability to water of the iron formed below and above about 550°C.

Below 550°C the iron is permeable to water and the initial and overall reduction rates increase from 400 to about 550°C. Above 550°C the iron is less permeable to water and the permeability decreases with increasing temperature so that the initial and overall reduction rates decrease from 550 to about 700°C. Above about 700°C cracks formed in the iron due to the buildup of water pressure allow the initial and overall reduction rates to increase to 900°C.

Thanks are due to the author's colleagues, and in particular to Mr. G. Brown for his preparation of the specimens for micrographs, to Mr. S. Thompson for the photographs shown in this paper, and to Mr. J. Williams for his assistance in operating the hot-stage microscope used to obtain the samples for micrographs. Appreciation is also expressed to The Broken Hill Proprietary Co. Ltd. for permission to publish this paper.

References

1. Edström, J. O., *J. Iron Steel Inst.* (*London*), **175**, 289 (1953).
2. Woods, S. E., *Discussions Faraday Soc.*, No. 4, 184 (1948).
3. Matoba, S., Y. Otake, and Y. Nagasawa, *Bull. Research Inst. Mineral Dressing and Met.*, **9**, 91 (1953); *Chem. Abstr.*, **49**, 9461b.
4. Lewis, J. R., *Am. Inst. Mining Met. Engrs., Metals Technol., Tech. Publ.*, **14**, 4 (1947).
5. Specht, O. G., and C. A. Zapffe, *Am. Inst. Mining Met. Engrs., Metals Technol. Tech. Publ.*, **13**, 4 (1946).
6. Gel'd, P., and O. Esin, *Bull. acad. sci. U.R.S.S. Classe sci. tech.*, 899 (1946).
7. Chufarov, G. I., and A. P. Lokhvitzkaya, *J. Phys. Chem.* (*U.S.S.R.*), **5**, 1103 (1934); *Chem. Abstr.*, **29**, 3901[6].

8. Edström, J. O., *Jernkontorets Ann.*, **140**, 116 (1956).

9. Wiberg, M., *Jernkontorets Ann.*, **124**, 179 (1940).

10. Wiberg, M., *Discussions Faraday Soc.*, No. 4, 231 (1948).

11. Wagner, C., *J. Metals*, **4**, 214 (1952).

12. Gellner, O. H., and F. D. Richardson, *Nature*, **168**, 23 (1951).

13. Edström, J. O., and G. Bitsianes, *J. Metals*, **7**, 760 (1955).

14. Arkharov, V. I., and V. N. Bogoslovskii, *Fiz. Metal. i Metalloged.*, **2**, 254 (1956).

15. Chaudnon, G., and J. Benard, *Bull. soc. chim. France*, **1949**, D117; *Chem. Abstr.*, **43**, 6901.

16. Lecznar, T. J., *Acta Tech. Acad. Sci. Hung.*, **16**, 383 (1957).

17. Edström, J. O., *Jernkontorets Ann.*, **141**, 809 (1957).

18. Stalhane, B., and T. Malmberg, *Jernkontorets Ann.*, **114**, 609 (1930).

19. Tatievskaya, E. P., G. I. Chufarov, and V. K. Antonov, *Zhur. Fiz. Khim.*, **24**, 385 (1950).

20. Trivedi, H., *Trans. Natl. Inst. Sci. India*, **3**, 211 (1953); *Chem. Abstr.*, **48**, 5046b.

21. Chufarov, G. I., and G. F. Vilesova, *Teoriya i Prakt Met.*, **4**, 10 (1936); *Chem. Abstr.*, **30**, 8115[8].

22. Chufarov, G. I., and B. Avenbukh, *Acta Physiochim. U.R.S.S.*, **4**, 617 (1936).

23. Chufarov, G. I., et al., *Zhur. Fiz. Khim.*, **28**, 490 (1954).

24. Moreau, J., et al., *Rev. met.*, *Memoires*, **8**, 486–494 (1951).

25. Schenck, H., *Stahl u. Eisen*, **75**, 682 (1955).

26. Leibu, H. J., *Schweiz. Arch. Angew. Wiss. u. Tech.*, **14**, 1, 49, 76 (1948); *Chem. Abstr.*, **42**, 4881h.

27. Tenenbaum, M., and T. L. Joseph, *Am. Inst. Mining Met. Engrs.*, *Metals Technol. Tech. Publ.*, **6**, 1 (1939).

28. Trivedi, H., *Science and Culture*, **17**, 423 (1952); *Chem. Abstr.*, **47**, 457d.

29. Marek, L. F., A. Bogrow, and G. W. King, *Trans. Am. Inst. Mining Met. Eng.*, *Metals Technol.*, *Tech. Publ.*, **14**, 4 (1947).

30. Sedlatscheck, K., *Z. anorg. u. allgem. Chem.*, **250**, 23 (1942).

31. Machu, W., and S. Y. Ezz, *Arch. Eisenhüttenw.*, **28**, 367 (1957); *Chem. Abstr.*, **51**, 14499f.

32. Olmer, F., *Rev. met.*, **38**, 129 (1941).

Discussion

H. U. Ross (*Univ. of Toronto*): Mr. Henderson postulates an interesting mechanism for the reduction of hematite ores by hydrogen. He suggests that the reduced iron is more permeable to the diffusion of water at 550°C than at 700°C because, at the lower temperature, the reduced iron ions occupy "positions in a similar relation to each other as those in the oxide lattice." Presumably, at the higher temperature, the ions have sufficient kinetic energy to diffuse to the more stable positions of the alpha- or gamma-iron lattice, which is more compact and less permeable to the diffusion of water. The fact that, at 700°C, the reduction takes place through the wüstite phase must be overlooked of course in this discus-

sion. His postulate appears quite reasonable in view of the experimental evidence
which the author has presented, and I believe that it would be a good thing to
attempt to substantiate his theory by further research. It is suggested that
perhaps x-ray studies on products reduced at various temperatures from relatively
pure iron-oxide materials might throw further light on the manner by which the
structure of the reduced iron permits or retards the diffusion of water. This
study could then be extended to natural iron-bearing materials in order to gain
further knowledge on the various behaviors of different ores during reduction.

H. K. Worner (*Broken Hill Pty. Co., Australia*): In view of the earlier discussion on reduction rates in fluid bed systems, it may be of interest to record
that the fundamental work of Mr. Henderson on our very fine rich hematites has
led us to develop on a small scale a direct reduction process operating at about
1000°F (540°C). Some tests with this unit at other temperatures have provided
at least qualitative confirmation of the rate findings of Mr. Henderson. We note
with considerable interest, and general agreement, that Dr. Squires' group find
optimal reduction rates at much lower temperatures than some others are using
in their direct reduction processes.

A. M. Squires (*Hydrocarbon Research*): I wish to call the Symposium's attention to the technical importance of securing thermodynamic data for active irons
of the type exemplified by Mr. Henderson's low temperature photomicrographs
(Figs. 9*a* and 9*b*). This came to Hydrocarbon Research, Inc.'s attention when
we drew space-velocity curves through our data on conversion of hydrogen to
water in fluid beds of iron ore. Discussion Figure 1 gives a typical chart of conversion versus pounds of iron per unit rate of hydrogen flow. (Abscissa in the
figure may be thought of as representing bed height, if hydrogen flow is fixed.)

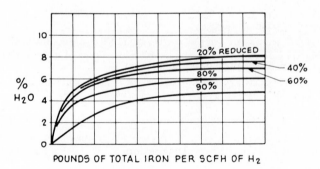

Discussion Fig. 1.   Conversions of hydrogen to water in fluid beds of magnetite
ore at 400 psig and 900°F; abscissa is a reciprocal space velocity and may be
thought of as representing bed height if hydrogen velocity is fixed.

When magnetite ore is 20% reduced, water conversion approaches an asymptotic
value of about 8% at large bed heights, although thermodynamic equilibrium computed for bulk magnetite, bulk iron, hydrogen, and water at 900°F corresponds
to over 16% water. Our data for a number of ores at 900°F make it appear that

a water conversion corresponding to true thermodynamic equilibrium can seldom, if ever, be achieved however deep the ore bed undergoing reduction. M. C. Udy and C. H. Lorig [*Trans. Am. Inst. Mining Met. Engrs.*, **154**, 162(1943)] noticed a similar departure from thermodynamic equilibrium in fixed beds at 700°C and applied the term "quasi-equilibrium" to the water conversion approached in deep beds. The quasi-equilibrium represented by the asymptotic values in the accompanying figure probably represents true thermodynamic equilibrium for hydrogen, water, magnetite, and the active iron present in our fluid beds. If this is the case, we can estimate the free energy of active iron to be about 1.6 kcal/g-mole higher than the free energy of bulk iron. It would be interesting to have confirmation of this free energy estimate from reaction heat data and specific heat data extending close to absolute zero. (Apparently few heat data have been obtained on active solids. Heats of combustion of active carbons range from 3.0 to 5.0 kcal/g-mole higher than graphite. Difference in low temperature specific heats of two natural graphites has been measured by W. De-Sorbo [*J. Am. Chem. Soc.*, **77**, 4713 (1955)] and attributed by him to difference in crystallite size. Marked effect of particle size upon low temperature specific heat of titanium dioxide has been reported by J. S. Dugdale, J. A. Morrison, and D. Patterson [*Proc. Roy. Soc.* (*London*), **A224**, 228 (1954)]; similar effect for magnesium dioxide was reported by W. H. Lien and N. E. Phillips [*J. Chem. Phys.*, **29**, 1415 (1958)].)

The decrease in quasi-equilibrium water conversion at higher percentage reductions is readily understood. At the outset of the reduction process, bulk thermodynamic data for magnetite applies; but as unreduced patches of magnetite remain behind, getting ever smaller as the reduction proceeds, entropy of magnetite must increase, reducing entropy change accompanying the reaction, and reducing quasi-equilibrium water conversion. We have a small amount of data (not conclusive, it must be remarked) which suggests the plausible inference that steam re-oxidation of reduced iron, even of iron reduced by 95%, yields a steam-hydrogen mixture corresponding to the quasi-equilibrium at low percentage reductions (i.e., about 8% water).

J. B. Henderson: It is regretted that the author's statement concerning the initial configuration of the iron ions during reduction is ambiguous and has unfortunately been misunderstood by Mr. Ross. There was meant to be no implication that the ions while "occupying positions in a similar relation to each other as those of the oxide lattice" have any stability or indeed that this structure exists for a finite time, either below or above 550°C. The postulate was made merely to emphasize that the reduced iron does not form a continuous lattice but, for reasons discussed in the paper, a large number of small iron crystals.

The results of some x-ray grain size analyses were presented at the conference but are not included in the paper. It was found that although the particle size of the original ore and the reduced iron was about 10^{-2} cm, the crystals of iron formed at 500°C were about 2×10^{-5} cm in diameter and those formed at 900°C about 10^{-4} cm. In both cases the lattice parameters were those of a-iron. These data conclusively demonstrate that when a particle of fine hematite ore is reduced in hydrogen below 550°C a large number of small crystals of iron are formed and not one large grain. It also shows that the crystals of iron formed above 550°C are larger than those formed below this temperature. Mr. Ross' recommendation for further study of this problem seems well worthwhile, as it is apparent that there is a great deal still to be learned.

The phenomenon of a quasi-equilibrium, observed by Dr. Squires, is of interest since it implies that the retardation of the reaction at the iron-iron oxide interface by water is even greater than would be expected from consideration of the Fe-O-H diagram.

Kinetics of the Carbon-Oxygen Reaction in Liquid Iron

KICHIZO NIWA and MITSUO SHIMOJI

Faculty of Science, Hokkaido University, Sapporo, Japan

TAMIYA KISHIDA

Yasuki Works, Hitachi Metal Company, Shimane, Japan

and

YUKIYOSHI ITOH

Muroran Works, Fuji Iron Company, Muroran, Japan

Abstract

Reaction mechanisms of CO evolution from liquid iron-carbon alloys are investigated, and the rates of carbon oxidation are measured by oxygen blowing into liquid iron. Since the estimated rate of homogeneous reaction is extremely rapid at 2000°K, the rate of C—O reaction may be determined by reactant transports from the uniform bulk to the equilibrium area. Mathematical expressions are given for nucleation, growth, and motion of CO bubbles in liquid iron, and reaction rates in open hearth. Measured rates of $C + 1/_2O_2(g)$ reaction are interpreted on the basis of the present formulation.

REACTION MECHANISM

Homogeneous Chemical Reaction

The theory of absolute reaction rates developed by Eyring et al.[1] provides the estimated rate of a chemical reaction. If the rate of carbon-oxygen reaction in liquid iron were controlled by a "homogeneous process," the rate of the reaction would be approximately

$$-d[c]/dt = RT/N_0h \exp\{-\Delta H^{\ddagger}/RT\}7/1600[C][O] \qquad (1)$$

where [C] and [O] are, respectively, weight per cent of carbon and

689

oxygen in liquid iron, R is the gas constant, T the absolute temperature, N_0 Avogadro's number, h Planck's constant, and $\Delta H^{\pm}$ the
activation energy.   Putting $T \approx 2000°K$ and $\Delta H^{\pm} \approx 28$ kcal,[2] the
estimated $-d[C]/dt \cdot [C][O]$ is found to be roughly $10^7\%$ per hour.
This result is too large compared with observed values.   The same
conclusion has been obtained in Darken's calculation[3] for heterogeneous chemical reaction on the surface of carbon monoxide bubbles.
It is to be noted that the rate of homogeneous reaction is not dependent on the bath size of the liquid metal (or the contents of the
charged metal) as shown in equation (1).   However, in the case of the
heterogeneous reaction the bath size gives an inverse effect on the
rate, in other words, large bath size results in low reaction rate and
vice versa.

Diffusion Film Theory

The rate of CO formation may thus be rapid in terms of chemical
reaction, whether it is homogeneous or heterogeneous.   Now, the
most reasonable process determining CO formation would be trans-
port of the dissolved carbon $(\underline{C})$ and oxygen $(\underline{O})$ to the existing surface
of CO bubbles.   Generally, migration of the materials in liquids is
due to diffusion, stirring, and convection etc., whence a uniform concentration is rapidly established in the liquid state as compared with
the solid state.   However, there is occasionally a concentration
gradient in the liquid near the interface between heterogeneous phases,
as shown in solution process of solid or gas into liquid.   This may be
caused by the viscous effect of the liquid near the boundary surface.
The analogous effect is found in fluid dynamics.   For example, in a
fluid of Reynolds number Re a solid material of dimension r has the
thickness of the boundary layer, influenced by the viscosity of the
liquid Δl given by

$$\Delta l \approx r/\sqrt{Re} \tag{2}$$

Reynolds number Re in the case of CO gas bubbles (assuming a
sphere) in liquid iron is evaluated as follows:

$$Re = \rho v r/\eta \tag{3}$$

where ρ is density of the liquid iron, v the velocity of the bubble,
r the radius and η the viscosity coefficient of liquid iron.   As far as

$v > 1$ cm/sec, which will be described later, and $r \approx 1$ cm, Re in Eq. (3) is roughly 10^3, since $\rho = 7$ and $\eta \approx 10^{-2}$ poise. Consequently, the thickness of the surface layer of a gas sphere with radius of 1 cm will be roughly 0.03 cm. Similar consideration will also be possible in the case of liquid metal, slag interface or air flat interface. The latter case has been observed by Shvartsman et al.[4] in their experiments on the rate of carbon oxidation. In this case the thickness is 0.01 cm. The order of magnitude of this thickness is concordant with the theoretical value. Thus, viscous effect of liquid iron is regarded as an important cause for concentration gradient of C and O near the gas bubbles and slag or solid surfaces. Then, this concentration gradient in the narrow region near the surface of the gas phase (10^{-2} or 10^{-3} cm) may give the respective rate-determining steps of many reactions in liquid iron.

The stationary flows of the dissolved carbon and oxygen through the boundary layer are given by[3,5,6]

$$J_C = D_C(N_0\rho([C] - [C]_\Omega))/1200\Delta l \text{ atoms/cm}^2\text{sec} \qquad (4)$$

$$J_O = D_O(N_0\rho([O] - [O]_\Omega))/1600\Delta l \text{ atom/cm}^2\text{sec}$$

In these equations, D_C and D_O are the diffusion coefficients for C and O, Δl the boundary layer thickness, and $[C]_\Omega$ and $[O]_\Omega$ are, respectively, weight per cent of C and O on the surface. If the distributions of C and O were time dependent so as to be expressed by the Gaussian error integral, one obtains

$$J_C = \{([C] - [C]_\Omega)/1200\} \, \rho N_0\sqrt{D_C/\pi t} \qquad (5)$$

$$J_O = \{([O] - [O]_\Omega)/1600\} \, \rho N_0\sqrt{D_O/\pi t}$$

Of course, an important relation

$$J_C = J_O = J \qquad (6)$$

must always hold in both cases, in order to realize the stoichiometric chemical reaction and to reach chemical equilibrium on gas-metal interface. This relation has also been adopted in their kinetic study of C-O evolution by Parlee et al.[7]

Nucleation of CO Bubbles

The problem of CO bubble formation in liquid iron belongs to a sort of phase transformation. Then, this process can be treated by means of some method such as the Volmer-Becker-Döring theory.[8,9]

In the case of carbon oxidation the following free energy change (per molecule)

$$\Delta G_{CO} = (RT/N_0) \ln P_{CO} K_{CO}/[C][O] \tag{7}$$

must have a negative value. In Eq. (7), K_{CO} is the equilibrium constant for the reaction

$$\underline{C} + \underline{O} \longrightarrow CO(g) \tag{8}$$

and P_{CO} is partial pressure of CO in the bulk gas phase. However, Eq. (7) needs a correction due to surface effect if the size of gas bubble is extremely small. Reaction (8) may be regarded as the following progressive processes:

$$\underline{C} + \underline{O} \longrightarrow CO \tag{9}$$

$$CO + \underline{C} + \underline{O} \longrightarrow (CO)_2$$

$$\cdots$$

$$(CO)_{n-1} + \underline{C} + \underline{O} \longrightarrow (CO)_n$$

where n means the number of CO molecules in the bubble. Hence, the free energy for forming a bubble containing n molecules from the dissolved carbon and oxygen in liquid iron is given by

$$\Delta G_n = n\Delta G_{CO} + \sigma S_n \tag{10}$$

where σ is the surface energy of liquid iron per unit area and S_n is the surface area of the bubble. The first term in Eq. (10) has a negative value, while the second is positive. Then, ΔG_n must pass through a maximum at $n = n^*$. In other words, the growth of submicroscopic bubbles of CO should be permitted to begin when the number of molecules overcomes this critical number n^*. The critical size of the present gas bubble r^* may be evaluated approximately as follows. The relation between the pressure of the bubble and the number of the molecules in the bubble may be described by

$$[P + (2\sigma/r)]\, {}^4/_3\pi r^3 = nRT/N_0 \tag{11}$$

where r is the radius of gas bubble and P is the pressure of the atmosphere plus the ferrostatic pressure. Putting $S_n = 4\pi r^2$, one obtains

$$r^* = [-(2RT/N_0 \Delta G_{CO}) - \,^4/_3]\,\sigma/P \qquad (12)$$

from Eq. (11) and

$$\partial \Delta G_n / \partial r = 0 \qquad (13)$$

Using $[O]_{ce}$, which is defined by

$$[O]_{ce} = K_{CO}/[C] \qquad (14)$$

Eq. (12) can be rewritten as

$$r^* = [2/ln([O]/[O]_{ce}) - \,^4/_3]\,\sigma/P \qquad (15)$$

On the other hand, Vallet[10] derived an important formula from the viewpoint of bubble formation corresponding to "excess oxygen" given by

$$\Delta[O] = [O] - [O]_{ce} \qquad (16)$$

in liquid iron. The radius of this equilibrium bubble is shown by

$$R = 2K_{CO}\sigma/[C]\,\Delta[O] \qquad (17)$$

The methods of the derivations are different between Eqs. (15) and (16), but the conclusion is similar. Namely, when $\Delta[O] \ll [O]_{ce}$, Eq. (10) becomes

$$\lim_{\Delta[O]\to 0} r^* = [(2[O]_{ce}/\Delta[O]) - \,^4/_3]\,\sigma/P \qquad (18)$$
$$\approx (2K_{CO}/[C]\,\Delta[O])\sigma/P$$

Putting P as unit atmospheric pressure, which is assumed in Eq. (17), the present extrapolated equation is in agreement with Vallet's equation. Both equations indicate the tendency of small radius being produced by large increment of $[C]$ and $\Delta[O]$, and vice versa.

The free energy change of critical size of the gas bubble is given by

$$\Delta G^* = 4\pi\sigma r^{*2}\{1 - [(4\sigma/r^*) + 2P]/[(4\sigma/r^*) + 3P]\} \qquad (19)$$

The probability of forming critical size is written by

$$f^* = \exp\{-N_0 \Delta G^*/RT\} \qquad (20)$$

Inserting, $r^* \approx 10^{-3}$ cm and $\sigma \approx 1500$ dynes/cm into Eq. (19) and

(20), one will find that f^* is extremely small. Consequently, the actual origin of bubble formation should exist in another place, where easier processes prevail in terms of energy. These places may be contact surfaces between porous solid and liquid; e.g., the surfaces of furnace bottom, brick wall, limestone, ore materials, and scrap metals, etc.

Growth and Motion of Gaseous Bubbles

As has been discussed by many investigators, the favorable place of origin for bubble formation would be in the hearth-metal interfaces.[6] The holes of the refractory surface may not be entirely filled under the influence of high surface tension of liquid metals, thus creating small gas pockets. These tiny gaseous spaces on the interfaces facilitate continuous bubble formation. If the holes or cavities are assumed to be a cylinder with radius d, the favorable condition for bubble nucleation is that $d > r^*$. This is because of the impossibility of formation of a smaller bubble due to the existence of a large amount of Gibbs free energy change for nucleation of gas bubbles with radius r^* as shown in the above section.

The formation and separation of gas bubbles is analogous to the fall of a liquid drop from a pore or capillary. Then, the equation

$$^4/_3 \pi r^3 \rho' g = 2\pi d\sigma f \tag{21}$$

may be employed for the description of bubble formation.[11] Here, ρ' is the difference of density between liquid metals and gas phase, g is the acceleration of gravity, and f is a dimensionless function determined by the size of capillary. Usually, f is determined experimentally; it varies from 0.59 to 2.0 for gas bubbles. For simplicity, $f \approx 1$ is assumed. Thus, the size of gas bubble separating and rising from the porous cylindrical cavity is given by

$$r = (3d\sigma/2g\rho')^{1/3} \tag{22}$$

from Eq. (21).

On the other hand, the equation of bubble growth could be obtained by

$$dn/dt = 4\pi r^2 J \tag{23}$$

which states that the rate of increase in the number of gaseous molecules in a gas bubble is equal to the current of oxygen (or carbon) from the bulk liquid into the gas-metal interface. Using Eqs. (4) and (11), and integrating Eq. (23), one obtains

$$\Delta t = (1/3JkT)[4\sigma\ln(r/d) + 3P(r - d)] \tag{24}$$

for the time of the bubble radius growing from d to r. Rough estimation of the order of magnitude of Eq. (24) results in $\Delta t \approx 1$ min for the bubble growing from 10^{-3} cm to 1 cm, since $D \approx 10^{-4}$ cm^2/sec, $\Delta 1 \approx 10^{-2}$ cm, $\rho' = 7$, and $T = 2000°K$.

The motion of gas bubbles in liquid iron may be described by the Stokes-Navier equation. If the viscosity of liquid iron denoted by η were large enough (i.e., small Reynolds number), the famous Stokes law

$$F_{RS} = 6\pi\eta rv \tag{25}$$

could be used to express the frictional force of a sphere having radius r and velocity v in liquids. The buoyancy of the gas bubble must be balanced by this frictional force. Thus,

$$v = {}^2/_9(g/\eta)\rho'r^2 \tag{26}$$

is obtained. Using $\rho' \approx 7$, $\eta \approx 2 \times 10^{-2}$ poise, one obtains $v \approx 700$ m/sec for radius of bubble, 1 cm. This figure leads to Re $\approx 10^5$ in Eq. (3). Therefore, Newton's equation should be used in place of Eq. (25). That is, roughly

$$F = \pi r^2 \rho' v^2 \tag{27}$$

Thus, one obtains

$$v = ({}^4/_3 rg)^{1/2} \tag{28}$$

Then, the velocity of the gas bubbles with radius 1 cm is less than 40 cm/sec. This figure in liquid irons is concordant with the discussion in the section entitled "Diffusion Film Theory," in which the large Reynolds number results in formation of the boundary interface layer.

As stressed by Darken[5] and Larsen,[6] the size of the gas bubble in the open hearth is supposed to have the dimension of about 1 cm. Consequently, the present discussion may be a reasonable explanation for the phenomena concerning the gas bubbles in liquid iron.

Rate of Carbon-Oxygen Reaction in the Open Hearth

This problem has been extensively discussed by Darken.[3,4] Here, a modified consideration is presented from a similar point of view. As shown in Eq. (6), the flow of carbon and oxygen from bulk liquid to the surface being in chemical equilibrium must have the same number of respective atoms. Thus, one obtains

$$-\frac{d[C]}{dt} = {}^3/_4 D_O \frac{[O] - [O]_{\Omega e}}{l\Delta l} \frac{S_g}{S_m} \tag{29}$$

$$-\frac{d[C]}{dt} = D_C \frac{[C] - [C]_{\Omega e}}{l\Delta l} \frac{S_g}{S_m} \tag{30}$$

where l is the depth of the liquid metal, S_g is the surface area between gas and metal, and S_m is that between slag and metal. Here, $[O]_{\Omega e}$ and $[C]_{\Omega e}$ satisfy the relation

$$[C]_{\Omega e}[O]_{\Omega e} = K_{CO\Omega} \tag{31}$$

From Eqs. (29) and (30)

$$\frac{[C] - [C]_{\Omega e}}{[O] - [O]_{\Omega e}} = {}^3/_4 \frac{D_O}{D_C} = \frac{1}{\Lambda} \tag{32}$$

is obtained. Substituting Eq. (31) into (32), one has

$$[O]_{\Omega e} = {}^1/_2([O] - \Lambda[C])\left\{1 + [1 + 4K_{CO\Omega}\Lambda/([O] - \Lambda[C])^2]\right\}^{1/2} \tag{33}$$

When $[O] \ll [C]\Lambda$, Eq. (33) can be expanded as

$$[O]_{\Omega e} = K_{CO\Omega}/([C] - [O]/\Lambda) \tag{34}$$

Accordingly,

$$\lim_{[O]\to 0} [O_{\Omega e}] = K_{CO\Omega}/[C] = [O]_{ce} \tag{35}$$

if $K_{CO} = K_{CO\Omega}$. Using limiting value of $[O]_{\Omega e}$ at $[O] \longrightarrow O$, Eq. (29) becomes the same equation as the one given by Darken, that is

$$-\frac{d[C]}{dt} = {}^4/_3 D_O \frac{[O] - [O]_{ce}}{l\Delta l} \frac{S_g}{S_m} \tag{36}$$

which holds in the region of $[C] \gg [O]$. The difference between the present Eq. (29) and Darken's Eq. (36) is shown by the following:

$$[O] - [O]_{\Omega e} \approx ([O] - [O]_{ce}) - (K_{CO}[O]/[C]^2 \Lambda) \qquad (37)$$

The first term on the right-hand side represents the difference of concentration between that in Darken's equation and in the present theory. If $[O]$ is extremely small compared to $[C]$, the second term is unnecessary. However, the second term may be effective with decrease of carbon concentration. In other words, the rate of carbon oxidation $-d[C]/dt$ becomes slower with advancement of the reaction, since $[O] - [O]_{\Omega e} < [O] - [O]_{ce}$. This prediction is in agreement with some observations, showing the slow rate in the high oxygen region.[12] Examining the magnitude of the correction in Eq. (37), one obtains 0.002 $[O]$ for $[C] = 1.0$ and 0.22 $[O]$ for $[C] = 0.1$, etc., since $D_C > D_O$ and $K_{CO} = 0.0022$. Numerical evaluation of Eqs. (29) and (30) can be done by a method similar to that of Darken,[5] which is in agreement with practical observation. The most important point of the present discussion is the fact that the rate of carbon oxidation has a weak tendency to diminish with decrease of carbon concentration. Equation (29) may be applicable to a wider range of $[C]$, though Eq. (36) is limited to the region of high $[C]$.

On the other hand, it is to be noted that there is also a diffusion film between slag and liquid iron; i.e., the abrupt change of oxygen concentration (exactly activity) occurs near this interface according to an earlier explanation of diffusion film theory. The existence of this concentration gradient leads to the steady rate of carbon elimination in an open hearth reaction, because of the constant supply of oxygen into the liquid iron. Ward and Birks[13] have studied this point in detail, especially the systematic variation of the diffusion coefficient, etc. Their equation will also be applicable to the present discussion, with the one exception that oxygen and carbon in an open hearth metal bath are in equilibrium with CO bubbles at a pressure of about 2 atm. As is well known, the average radius of the bubble should be about 1 cm. Then the oxygen and carbon may be regarded as being in nonequilibrium with the bubble, though the radius of nucleation bubble, having the estimated value 10^{-2} or 10^{-3} cm, may correspond to the pressure of 2 atm.

MEASUREMENT OF CARBON OXIDATION IN LIQUID IRON BY MEANS OF OXYGEN BLOWING

Experimental Method

It is interesting to study the rate of carbon-oxygen gas reaction in relation to the above-mentioned mechanism. This procedure has been popular as a subsidiary technique in the open hearth process. The experimental method for this problem is as follows. An alumina Tammann tube was charged with about 40 g of Fe-C alloy (about 4% carbon) and was set in a gas-tight silica tube. When the alloy was molten (induction heating), a mixture ($N_2 + O_2$), which is adjusted according to its molar ratio of nitrogen and oxygen gas, is induced in the depth of 5–8 mm into the liquid alloy through a high alumina blowing pipe (I.D. 6 mm). The amount of gas mixture entering into the liquid alloy is checked by a flow meter. Carbon-oxygen gas generated due to carbon oxidation is measured by being converted into CO_2 through CuO maintained at 350–400°C and by being absorbed in soda-lime by means of the ordinary combustion method.

Experimental Results

The rates of the present reaction measured at various flow rates of the gas mixture whose partial pressure of oxygen is equal to 150 mm Hg are represented in Figure 1, in which carbon dioxide produced by carbon oxidation is plotted against the flow rate of the gas mixture. It is readily seen that the oxygen supplied is completely consumed in the cases of all flow rates. Therefore, it may be emphasized that the rate of the chemical reaction which may occur on the interface between the liquid iron and gas phase is sufficiently rapid to be settled by a supply of reacting species.

The rates against the variations in oxygen pressure are shown in Table I and the degree of decarburization versus oxygen pressure is represented in Figure 2. The unbroken line, the best curve through the points over the range of oxygen pressure less than 300 mm Hg, shows a relation of perfect consumption of oxygen supplied for carbon oxidation, while the dashed line, valid for oxygen pressure higher than 300 mm Hg, represents the constant rate of carbon oxidation independent of oxygen pressure. This is probably due to the fact that the rate-determining factor exists in a sluggishness of transfer of

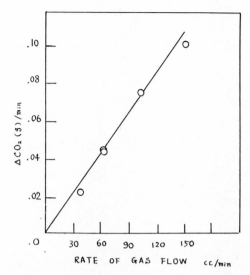

Fig. 1. Yield of carbon dioxide per minute as a function of rate of gas flow at 150 mm Hg of O_2 pressure and 1550°C. Straight line represents the complete consumption of O_2.

TABLE I

The Effect of Partial Pressure of Oxygen Gas on Carbon Oxidation

Partial pressure of O_2, mm Hg	Flow rate, cu cm/min	CO_2 produced per min g/min	Efficiency of C oxidation,[a] %
25	60	0.009	124
50	60	0.018	120
50	150	0.036	98
75	55	0.020	101
150	60	0.045	102
150	60	0.046	104
300	60	0.088	100
300	60	0.086	97
380	60	0.106	97
380	60	0.087	79
450	60	0.097	74
450	60	0.091	69
600	60	0.106	62
600	60	0.106	60
600	60	0.237	48

[a] Efficiency of carbon oxidation is defined as twice moles of carbon monoxide divided by moles of oxygen supplied.

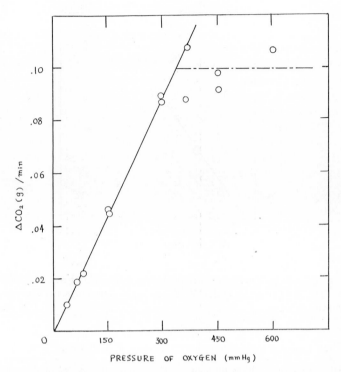

Fig. 2. Yield of CO_2 per minute as a function of partial pressure of O_2, with fixed flow rate, 60 cu cm/min, at 1550°C.

reactants (i.e., carbon) toward the surface where chemical equilibrium may occur.

Interpretation of the Present Data

In view of the above points the following assumptions could reasonably be made to explain the experimental results: (1) Carbon oxidation occurs on the interface between gas phase and liquid iron. (2) Chemical reaction (C + $^1/_2O_2$ = CO) should be fast enough to be regarded as a local equilibrium on the surface. (3) Then what determines the rate of the reaction depends upon rate of diffusion of carbon through liquid iron to the surface of a bubble when oxygen supply is sufficient. (4) The rate of oxygen gas supply determines the rate of the reaction when the amount of oxygen supply is less than that of the corresponding carbon to make CO. (5) It is assumed that diffusion in gas phase is very rapid and that the concentration gradient in liquid iron near the bubble is linear. It is interesting to calculate the case described by assumption (3) on the basis of Eq. (4), while the case of (4) is very simple. For the latter case one has only to use the amount of gas flow itself. For the former case one has the following equation from the discussion of the diffusion film theory:

$$-\frac{d[\mathrm{C}]}{dt} = \frac{D_{\mathrm{C}}S_{gm}}{V} \frac{[\mathrm{C}] - [\mathrm{C}]_\Omega}{\Delta l} \tag{38}$$

where V is the volume of liquid iron, S_{gm} is the surface area of gas bubbles in contact with liquid iron. Integrating Eq. (38) from time t_i to t, one obtains

$$\ln \frac{[\mathrm{C}]_i - [\mathrm{C}]_\Omega}{[\mathrm{C}] - [\mathrm{C}]_\Omega} = \frac{D_{\mathrm{C}} \cdot S_{gm}}{V \Delta l} \tag{39}$$

where $[\mathrm{C}]_i$ is the initial concentration of carbon. Thus, the amount of carbon atoms removed from liquid iron to a single bubble is evaluated by

$$\xi = -\int_{t_i}^{t} \rho V \frac{d[\mathrm{C}]}{dt} dt \times \frac{1}{1200} \tag{40}$$

$$= \frac{\rho V}{1200} ([\mathrm{C}]_i - [\mathrm{C}]_\Omega) \left[1 - \exp \left\{ -\frac{D_{\mathrm{C}}S_{gm}}{V \Delta l} (t - t_i) \right\} \right]$$

where ξ is expressed in terms of the number of gram atoms of carbon. Considering $D_{\mathrm{C}} \approx 1 \times 10^{-4}/\mathrm{cm^2/sec}$, $\Delta l \approx 0.01$ cm and $V \approx 6$ cu cm, Eq. (40) becomes

$$\xi = \frac{\rho D_{\mathrm{C}} S_{gm}}{1200 \Delta l} (t - t_i) \{ [\mathrm{C}]_i - [\mathrm{C}]_\Omega \} \tag{41}$$

as long as $S_{gm}(t - t_i) \ll 10^3$ cm² sec. For a single gas bubble, emerged from the blowing tube, which reacts with carbon in liquid iron, Eq. (41) may be reasonable because the bubble is very short in life and small in surface area due to its shallow depth and its narrow outlet, respectively. The total amount of carbon taken away from liquid iron is

$$\Xi = \sum_n \xi_n$$

$$\approx \frac{\rho_n}{1200} \cdot \frac{D_C S_{gm}(t - t_0)}{\Delta l} \left\{ \frac{[C]_{1t} + [C]_{nt}}{2} - [C]_\Omega \right\} \tag{42}$$

where ξ_n means the amount of carbon for the nth bubble, $[C]_{nt}$ is the initial concentration in the nth bubble. Thus S_{gm} and the life of a single bubble $(t - t_0)$ are assumed to be common to every bubble. Furthermore,

$$\sum_n [C]_n = n([C]_{1i} + [C]_{ni})/2 \tag{43}$$

is assumed. Thus, numerical evaluation of Eq. (42) gives approximately

$$\Xi \approx 1 \times 10^{-2} S_{gm}(t - t_i) \tag{44}$$

in units of mole/min. It is supposed that the order of magnitude of S_{gm} $(t - t_i)$ might be 10^{-1} in the present experiment. This value ($\Xi \approx 1 \times 10^{-3}$) is in rough agreement with observed values in the region of oxygen pressure higher than 380 mm Hg, since $\Xi \approx 3 \times 10^{-3}$ (mole/min) corresponds to yield in Figure 2. The experimental results may be reasonably well explained in a qualitative way by the use of the diffusion film theory.

CONCLUSIONS

The reaction of carbon oxidation in liquid iron,

$$\underline{C} + \underline{O} \longrightarrow CO(g)$$

should be rapid in true terms of homogeneous chemical reaction. This can be confirmed by the fact that

$$\underline{C} + 1/2 O_2(g) \longrightarrow CO(g)$$

is very rapid in the present experiments, as well as by the theoretical reason of the absolute reaction rate theory. The most reasonable view for the rate-determining step of the above reaction may be obtained from the diffusion film theory. Then the thickness of the diffusion layer is briefly discussed in terms of the Reynolds number of liquid iron. The origin and growth of CO gas bubbles are explained from the point of view of the theory of heterogeneous phase transformation and the theory of diffusion film. It is to be noted that the effect of viscosity is limited to the narrow region near the boundary interface but leads to an apparently slow chemical reaction owing to retarding transport of materials.

References

1. Glasstone, S., K. J. Laidler, and H. Eyring, *Theory of Rate Process*, Mc-Graw-Hill, New York, 1941.

2. Fornander, S., *Discussions Faraday Soc.*, No. 4, 296 (1948).

3. Darken, L. S., *Basic Open Hearth Steelmaking*, AIME, 1951, pp. 621–690.

4. Shvartsman, L. A., A. M. Samarin, and M. I. Temkin, *J. Phys. Chem.* (*U.S.S.R.*), **21**, 1027 (1947).

5. Darken, L. S., and R. W. Gurry, *Physical Chemistry of Metals*, McGraw Hill, New York, 1953.

6. Larsen, B. M., see ref. 3, pp. 867–903, and "A New Look at the Nature of the Open-Hearth Process," AIMMPE (1956).

7. Parlee, N. A., S. R. Seagle, and R. Schumann, Jr., *Trans. Met. Soc. AIME*, Feb., 1958, pp. 132–138.

8. Becker, R., and W. Döring, *Ann. Physik.*, **24**, 732 (1935).

9. Garmer, W. E., *Chemistry of the Solid State*, Butterworths, 1955, ch. 6.

10. Vallet, P., *Iron and Steel*, 463 (1955).

11. Bikerman, J. J., *Surface Chemistry*, Academic Press, New York, 1958.

12. Fujii, T., Report of 19th Sectional Committee, Japan, No. 4682, 1957.

13. Ward, R. G., and N. Birks, *National Physical Laboratory Symposium of Physical Chemistry of Metallic Solutions and Intermetallic Compounds*, England, 1958.

The Kinetics and Mechanism of the Conversion of Titanium Oxides to Titanium Nitride*

D. L. DOUGLASS

Knolls Atomic Power Laboratory, Schenectady, New York

G. R. ST. PIERRE and R. SPEISER

Department of Metallurgical Engineering, The Ohio State University, Columbus, Ohio

Abstract

The possible recovery of titanium from ilmenite by the selective formation of TiN was initiated by a study of the conversion of some titanium oxides to titanium nitride.

The nitridization of TiO_2, Ti_2O_3, and TiO with NH_3 followed a parabolic rate law from 900–1070°C and from 0.032 to 1 atm NH_3. The rate constants for the three substances were in the ratio of 9000:3000:1, respectively. Breaks in the plots of weight change vs (time) $^{1/2}$ were observed for TiO_2 at 1010 and 1070°C. Activation energies of 76 and 91 kcal were found for the short and long time sections of the curves, respectively.

Titanium nitride formed adjacent to TiO, the end product of a reduction through the oxides $TiO_{1.95}$, Ti_9O_{17}, Ti_8O_{15}, Ti_7O_{13}, and Ti_2O_3.

Nitride formation appeared to proceed without the appreciable formation of an oxynitride according to x-ray diffraction results. A nitride with $a_0 = 4.238$ A formed over the TiO ($a_0 = 4.178$ A); however, a small weight gain was measured when TiO was used as a starting material in contrast to weight losses from TiO_2 and Ti_2O_3. This phenomenon was ascribed to the solution of nitrogen in vacant oxygen sites over a very thin layer.

Nitride formation occurred by inward diffusion of nitrogen and outward diffusion of oxygen. The pressure dependency of the rate constant was proportional to the 0.75 power of the ammonia pressure at 1010°C. It is suggested that this relationship is related to the pressure dependency of oxygen and nitrogen diffusion.

* This paper is based on a portion of a dissertation submitted by D. L. Douglass to the Department of Metallurgical Engineering, The Ohio State University, in partial fulfillment of the requirements for the degree, Doctor of Philosophy.

705

INTRODUCTION

The conversion of titanium oxides to the nitride has important practical implications in several fields of metallurgical technology. Titanium nitride is a very hard, refractory compound which finds widespread use as the "hard metal" phase in cemented compacts. The nitride is the chief constituent of the hard case of nitrided titanium and offers excellent wear resistance. Nitride formation is also of interest in the high temperature scaling behavior of titanium and its alloys in air. Lastly, the conversion represents the first step in the understanding of the possible selective formation and separation of titanium nitride from ilmenite.

Several methods have been used to prepare the hard metal nitrides. The metal or metal hydride may be reacted with nitrogen or ammonia.[1] Most transition metal nitrides have been produced by reaction of the metal powders with ammonia.[2-9]

The most economical method of preparation involves the reaction of the oxides with either nitrogen or ammonia in the presence of carbon. Unfortunately, the formation of the carbides occurs simultaneously. In the case of titanium, the carbide and nitride are isomorphous, and an impure solid solution of nitride-carbide results. Early work by several investigators showed that titanium nitride could be prepared by reacting TiO_2 with ammonia.[10-12]

The separation of titanium from iron in titaniferous minerals by the formation of titanium nitride is not a new idea. Farup[13] received a patent in 1920 for the preparation of titanium compounds from titaniferous materials by heating the mineral with carbon in an atmosphere of nitrogen. The iron was to be separated from the titanium carbide-nitride product by solution of the iron in acid.

Bichowsky and Harthan[14] obtained a patent in 1922 for forming titanium nitride from ilmenite by reaction with carbon, nitrogen, and sodium carbonate. Andreu and Paquet[15] received a patent in 1924 for virtually the same process.

EXPERIMENTAL PROCEDURE

TiO_2 powder (CP) containing less than 0.02% impurities, was dry-pressed at 5000 psi into bars $1/2 \times 1/4 \times 6$ in. and fired eight hours in air at 1400°C. The density of the sintered compacts was measured by the Archimedes method and varied from 96 to 99% of theoretical (4.26 g/cm³). Samples were cut from the sintered bars on a diamond cut-off wheel. The sample size and shape were varied, depending upon the type of test conducted. Thin rectangular wafers, about 1–2 g, were used for the determination of rate constants; cubes or rectangular prisms were used for topochemical and x-ray diffraction studies.

Rate-Constant Determination

The gravimetric method was used to measure continuously the decrease in weight during nitridization. Samples were suspended by Nichrome wires in a vertical tube furnace, and the total weight change of wire and sample was measured. An unloaded Nichrome wire was run at each temperature and partial pressure of ammonia, and the weight gain of the wire was then subtracted from the cumulative weight change of sample plus wire to give the sample weight change.

Mixtures of argon and ammonia were used to establish various partial pressures of ammonia. Each gas mixture was introduced at the same total pressure (controlled by a blow-off tower through mineral oil) and at some predetermined flow rate.

Topochemical and X-Ray Diffraction Studies

Samples were nitrided for various times under a given set of temperature-pressure conditions and then sectioned for examination of the layers.

X-ray diffraction samples were made for both Debye-Scherrer powder patterns and for the diffractometer. Powder samples were taken from scrapings of the various layers. The powders were crushed and screened through a 325-mesh net and placed in a 0.3-mm glass capillary tube. A 57.3-mm diam camera was used, and the Straumanis, unsymmetrical type of loading was employed. Filtered, $Cu-K\alpha$ radiation was used. Powder patterns were taken at 40 kv and 15 ma for 6 hr. Film shrinkage was less than 0.01 mm. Clear back reflections were obtained for the nitride and monoxide, and lattice parameters were determined by extrapolating a plot of $\sin^2 \theta$ vs a_0 to $180° = 2\theta$.

The diffractometer was used to obtain patterns of the samples at various intervals beneath the surface. The samples were abraded on silicon carbide paper, and patterns were taken at intervals of 0.003

in. below the surface.   Filtered Cu-Kα radiation was used throughout.

The patterns obtained by the diffractometer were not solely from
the surface constituents.   Calculations showed that 0.0016 in. of
titanium nitride was sufficient to reduce the strongest reflection of any
phase to the background level.   Hence, it may be concluded that the
patterns obtained represented the phases present for a depth of
0.0016 in. below the scanned surface.

RESULTS

Nitridization of Rutile—Topochemical and X-Ray Diffraction Studies

Sintered, massive samples of rutile were reacted in ammonia at
1010°C for times ranging from 10 sec to 5000 min.   The samples
were quenched in water immediately after the desired time had
elapsed, and subsequently examined visually, microscopically, and
by x-rays.

The first step in the nitridization was found to be a rapid partial
reduction or dissociation of rutile.   The straw-yellow, fully oxidized
rutile readily lost oxygen as evidenced by a change to a blue-black
color.   The black phase is $TiO_{1.95}$ according to Forland[16] and has the
tetragonal rutile structure.   In fact, it is difficult, if not impossible,
to detect the loss of oxygen by x-ray diffraction.

Samples reacted for less than four minutes consisted of two zones,
an inner core of yellow TiO_2 and an outer layer of black $TiO_{1.95}$.
No nitride formed during this time. X-ray diffraction measurements
of lattice parameters revealed no difference between the two phases,
and the patterns agreed perfectly with the ASTM card index.

After the initial dissociation had been completed, ammonia further
reduced $TiO_{1.95}$ through a sequence of complex oxide structures to
give ultimately the face-centered cubic TiO phase.   The overall
reduction may be represented as

$$TiO_2 + \tfrac{2}{3}NH_3 = TiO + H_2O + \tfrac{1}{3}N_2 \tag{1}$$

Reaction (1) consisted of several steps, each of which represents a
reduction from one oxide to a lower oxide.   The oxides which were
detected by x-ray diffraction of samples which had been abraded
through 0.003 in. intervals from the surface to the center were TiO_2,
Ti_9O_{17}, Ti_8O_{15}, Ti_7O_{13}, Ti_2O_3, and TiO.

The formation of the nitride occurred only as a product of the reaction of TiO with ammonia. Nitride layers were observed only adjacent to TiO layers.

The nature of the nitride was firmly established by x-ray diffraction. Titanium nitride with a lattice parameter of 4.238 A was formed; no evidence of an oxynitride phase was detected. This result was surprising in view of the miscibility of TiO and TiN. Several samples which were run on the spectrometer-goniometer showed both TiO and TiN reflections from the surface layers. If appreciable oxynitride had formed, either of two phenomena would have been observed. First, the identical crystal structures and very nearly identical lattice parameters would give rise to line broadening due to concentration gradients from the pure TiN at the surface to the pure TiO at the other edge of the solid-solution band. Second, if no gradients existed, and a solid solution had formed, a sharp peak for each d spacing would have been observed at values intermediate to pure TiO and to pure TiN. However, only sharp peaks from both phases were present.

The lattice parameters of TiN and TiO were found to be 4.238 and 4.178 A, respectively. These agree very closely with values reported for the pure compounds.

The composition of the TiO from which the nitride formed may be estimated from a plot of the lattice parameter of TiO versus oxygen content.[17] A value of 47 atomic-% oxygen is obtained and indicates that a metal-excess compound exists, which, according to Ehrlich,[18] has approximately only 86% of the oxygen sites occupied. The significance of this statement will be covered subsequently in the discussion of the nitridization of TiO.

Reaction Kinetics—Effect of Temperature

The weight loss as a function of time was measured at 900, 950, 1010, and 1070°C. The corrected weight loss curves versus time are shown in Figure 1. Parabolic-type curves were obtained. A test for the diffusion-controlled parabolic law was made by plotting the weight loss squared against time. A straight line, indicating parabolic behavior, was observed for each temperature. However, a break was present in the curves at 1010 and 1070°C, indicating a possible change in mechanism. The time at which the breaks oc-

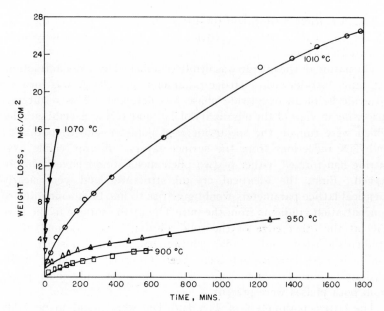

Fig. 1. Comparative weight losses of rutile in 1 atm ammonia at various temperatures.

curred was dependent upon the temperature, decreasing with increasing temperature.

The temperature dependency of the rate constants was determined on an Arrhenius-type plot of log k versus reciprocal temperature in Figure 2. Values of k were plotted for both portions of the weight squared-time curves at 1010 and 1070°C. Two straight-line curves were obtained on the Arrhenius plot, giving values of the activation energy of 76,000 and 91,000 cal for the initial and longer time steps, respectively. The values of k were based on the average of three runs per temperature.

Effect of Pressure

The relative weight losses at NH_3 partial pressures of 0.032 to 1.0 atm and at 1010°C are shown in Figure 3. The pressure dependency of the rate constants showed a nearly linear relationship on a log-log scale, as shown in Figure 4, for k_2, the log time rate constants. A slope of 0.80 was obtained by a least squares analysis. The short time rate constants showed an essentially linear relationship with pressure up to 0.29 atm NH_3 with a slope of 0.75. A continuously decreasing slope was obtained from 0.29 to 1.0 atm NH_3.

Rates of Layer Growth

The thickness of each layer of the sectioned samples was measured in order to obtain data on the relative rates of growth of each zone.

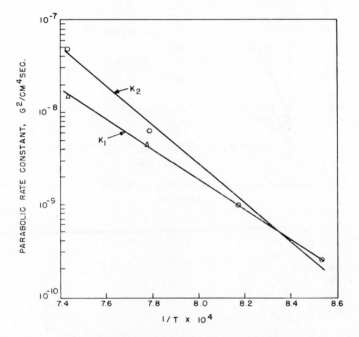

Fig. 2. Temperature dependency of rate constant.

According to Valensi[19] the relative thickness of the various layers is independent of time. Each layer will form according to its individual rate constants, and inasmuch as there are several layers, the overall rate constant is some function of the individual rate constants.

It was possible to obtain data on the rates of layer growth for only TiN, TiO, and Ti_2O_3. The thickness of each layer as a function of time is shown graphically in Figure 5.

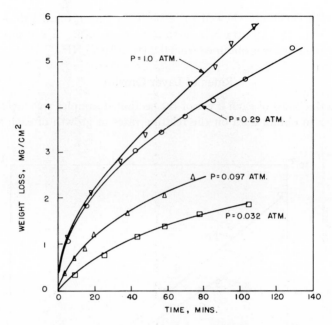

Fig. 3. Comparative weight losses of rutile at 1010°C and various ammonia pressures.

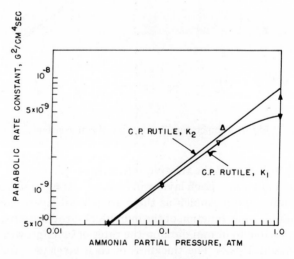

Fig. 4. Pressure dependency of parabolic rate constant at 1010°C.

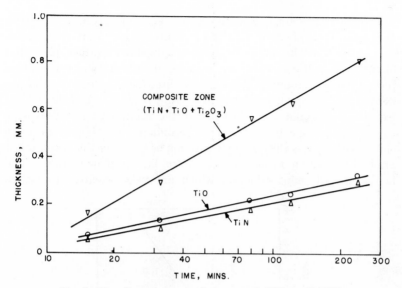

Fig. 5. The effect of time on layer growth TiO_2 at 1010°C.

Nitridization of Ti_2O_3 and TiO

The measurements of the thickness of the various layers on TiO_2 were very uncertain for short reaction times. In addition, the effect of the presence of other oxides undoubtedly influenced the rate of growth of TiN and TiO. It was, therefore, deemed necessary to make similar measurements on pure Ti_2O_3 and on TiO as starting materials. Buttons of these oxides were prepared by triple arc-melting stoichiometric amounts of rutile and metallic titanium. Prisms of TiO were made by the use of a diamond cut-off wheel. However, the Ti_2O_3 was too friable and could not be cut without irregular fractures taking place. It was possible to obtain weight change data on only TiO inasmuch as the area of the regular geometric shapes could be easily measured, whereas, it was not possible to determine the area on Ti_2O_3 samples. Lumps of both oxides were reacted for various times and then sectioned. Measurements of the growth rate of the layers were possible for both starting materials.

The change in weight of TiO was a net gain instead of the previously observed decreases on TiO_2. Parabolic behavior was indicated by a linear relationship between weight gain squared and time. A rate constant of 8.8×10^{-10} was measured.

Growth curves for various layers on Ti_2O_3 are given in Figure 6. It should be emphasized that the measurement of a given thickness was difficult. The highly irregular, nonplanar surface presented obvious difficulties. First, no suitable metallographic preparation procedure was found. Second, the interfaces were not sharply defined due to small irregularities during reaction which may have led to an irregular advancement of the interface and subsequent engulfment of one phase within a second phase. Third, the color change, which was the only real criterion of the layer thickness, was a gradual transition rather than a sharp line of demarcation. The layers are all semiconductors which are very sensitive to lattice

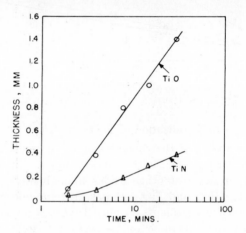

Fig. 6. The effect of time on layer growth Ti_2O_3 at 1010°C.

vacancies, dislocations, and small amounts of impurities insofar as their color is concerned. Johnson and Weyl[20] have shown that small amounts of foreign atoms in solution cause marked changes in color. Even if no solid solubility can be detected by x-ray measurements, small amounts of undetected impurity are quite capable of creating color changes.

It is interesting to compare the difference in thickness between layers on the rutile and on Ti_2O_3 samples. The nitride layer on Ti_2O_3 is about $2^1/_3$ to 3 times thicker than on the rutile sample. A similar comparison of the TiO layers showed that TiO on Ti_2O_3 was about 4 times greater than on rutile. The lesser amount of each layer on rutile implies that some other process in addition to inward diffusion of either nitrogen or hydrogen is influencing the rate.

The layers of nitride which formed on the TiO sample were too thin to be measured at times of less than 195 min. A value of 0.008 mm was obtained by means of a filar eyepiece for a TiO sample nitrided 195 min at 1010°C. This thickness is much less than that observed on Ti_2O_3 for the same time.

DISCUSSION

Dissociation of TiO_2 to $TiO_{1.95}$

The initial step in the nitriding sequence was found to be the rapid partial reduction of rutile to $TiO_{1.95}$. The oxide is a semiconductor of the metal-excess variety and may be visualized as a close-packed array of oxygen ions held together by highly charged Ti^{+4} ions. According to Marshall, Enright, and Weyl[21] the loss of oxygen is accomplished by a reduction of the Ti^{4+} ions and is accompanied by an increase in the number of anion holes.

$$4Ti^{+4} + 2O^{-2} = 4Ti^{+3} + O_2 \qquad (2)$$

The high electrical conductivity associated with the defect structure is due to quasi-free electrons in the vicinity of the vacant oxygen sites. The diffusion of oxygen is favored by the anion vacancies. As oxygen is lost at the surface, a chemical potential gradient is established in the system to drive the diffusion of oxygen from the interior.

Complex Intermediate Oxides

The effect of the Ti_9O_{17}, Ti_8O_{15}, and Ti_7O_{13} phases on the reaction rate and mechanism is unknown. These compounds are very complex, having triclinic, monoclinic, or orthorhombic structures. Since the growth of the nitride layers was more rapid on Ti_2O_3 than TiO_2 specimens, it may be concluded that the intermediate oxides present a barrier. This is not unexpected on the basis of the complex structures and perhaps intricate atom movements required to form the structures.

Formation of TiO

As mentioned previously, nitride formation occurs only by reaction with TiO. Hence, conditions favorable for TiO formation would be favorable for nitride growth. Figures 5 and 6 show the rate of growth of both TiO and TiN on rutile and Ti_2O_3. The ratio of the thickness of TiO and Ti_2O_3 and rutile was about $3^1/_2$ to 1, and the nitride thickness ratio was slightly greater than $2:1$.

The rate at which TiO forms seems to depend upon the outward diffusion of oxygen from Ti_2O_3 or inward migration of titanium ions to the TiO/Ti_2O_3 interface. Both types of migration are possible in TiO according to Wagner,[22] because TiO is stable both as a metal-excess and as a metal-deficient compound.

Although Wagner suggests that either cation or anion migration in TiO is possible, depending upon whether the compound is metal deficient or metal excess, respectively, it is unlikely that in this study, cations will migrate in the metal-excess TiO. The atomic radius of titanium in TiO is 1.48 A, and the atomic radius of oxygen is 0.66 A. Reducing conditions favor anion vacancies, and the migration of titanium is unlikely from size considerations alone.

Nitride Formation from TiO

Titanium nitride growth on TiO as the starting material was shown to be parabolic by the linearity of the weight gain squared versus time relationship. Two possible mechanisms could account for parabolic behavior. First, the reaction may be controlled by diffusion of nitrogen through the nitride to the TiN/TiO interface where further reaction takes place. The second alternative involves the outward diffusion of titanium ions through the nitride layer to the surface, at which point additional reaction ensues.

It was hoped to gain an insight into the relative movements of anions and cations by Kirkendall-type measurements. However, volume changes associated with the reaction were insufficient to draw any conclusions about the relative movement of the TiN/TiO interface. The thickness of the nitride layer on pure TiO was surprisingly small even after 1200 min at 1010°C.

The rather striking similarity between the properties and structure of TiN and TiO permits an analysis similar to that for TiO in the preceding section; namely, the departure of TiN on both sides from the stoichiometric composition would allow both cations and anions to migrate.

But, once again, an analysis of the size relationships between atoms in TiN gives the same argument as was stated for TiO. The titanium atom is much larger than the nitrogen atom, and unless a considerable number of titanium atoms were missing, it is unlikely that titanium could diffuse through the smaller nitrogen sites.

The weight gain–time relation observed in the nitriding of TiO specimens is puzzling.   If the following reaction occurs,

$$TiO + NH_3 = TiN + H_2O + {}^1/_2H_2 \tag{3}$$

the formation of TiN from TiO would involve a simple exchange of nitrogen for oxygen.   The net result upon substitution of an atom of atomic weight 14 for an atom of atomic weight 16 would be a decrease in weight and not the observed increase.   The anomalous weight increase could result then only by the formation of an oxynitride in which case the solution of nitrogen in TiO would take place.   As stated previously, however, the presence of an oxynitride could be detected by line broadening of x-ray patterns or by a lattice parameter change.

A logical conclusion is that some nitrogen dissolved in the TiO lattice, occupying vacant oxygen sites and that no change in lattice parameter occurred which could be detected by x-ray diffraction. It therefore appears that a small amount of oxynitride formed and that the formation of TiN took place by reaction of ammonia with the oxynitride at the gas-solid interface.

Comparison of Nitride Growth on Various Starting Materials

The rate constants for layer growth on Ti_2O_3, TiO_2, and TiO were in the ratio of $9000:3000:1$.   In every case, examination of the layers showed that TiN was always adjacent to a layer of TiO and formed from the TiO.   A layer of Ti_2O_3 was adjacent to the TiO in both the TiO_2 and the Ti_2O_3 starting materials.

The nitridization of TiO_2 in ammonia is apparently controlled by the reduction of the oxide to Ti_2O_3; however, some uncertainty exists because the defect nature of the Ti_2O_3 formed on TiO_2 may be quite different from that of the specially prepared Ti_2O_3.   The slow rate of growth of TiN on TiO specimens compared with Ti_2O_3 and TiO_2 specimens is also difficult to interpret.   Again the defect nature of the TiO may be quite different in each case.   In the absence of electrical conductivity or diffusion data it is impossible to explain the observations with any degree of certainty.

Effect of Temperature

A change in slope was observed in the test for parabolic behavior at 1010 and 1070°C. The rate constants for both portions of the curve were plotted on the Arrhenius-type diagram, giving two straight lines. The calculated activation energies were 76,000 and 91,000 cal for the initial and final rate constants, respectively. The change in slope may be caused by a change in mechanism or different reactions coming into play at different times, although, as will be shown subsequently, this is not necessarily true.

The first rate constant, k_1, probably represents the formation of TiN in view of the fact that the nitride was formed within 6 min at 1010°C. The second rate constant, k_2, probably represents the cumulative nitriding and reduction reactions. The rate constants are composite quantities representing the product of both diffusion and concentration differences. The concentration gradient across any given field is dictated to a certain extent by the equilibrium requirements of the interfaces and to the composition of the gaseous components. In addition, several simultaneous reactions are taking place, each of which has its own individual rate constant.

The activation energies for both k_1 and k_2 do not agree with that of nitrogen diffusion in TiN. In fact, the overall complexity of the system makes it surprising that linear relations were observed at all on the Arrhenius plot, much less that the activation energies should agree. Valensi[19] showed that no simple linear relation between log k and reciprocal temperature should be expected when conjugate layers form, and that this does not necessarily imply a change in the reaction mechanism.

The calculated diffusivity of nitrogen in TiN from the rate constant for the growth of TiN on Ti_2O_3 gives $D = 10^{-8}$, compared to $D = 10^{-10}$ given by Wasilewski and Kehl.[23] The value of D calculated from the growth rate of TiN on TiO gives a value of $D = 6 \times 10^{-11}$. The failure of either to agree with the measured data of Wasilewski and Kehl indicates that nitrogen diffusion is not rate determining.

Effect of Pressure

The discussion of the pressure dependency is largely speculative as the system is very complex. Diffusion is important, as indicated by the parabolic behavior, but it should be pointed out that oxygen must also diffuse outward in addition to the inward diffusion of nitrogen. Undoubtedly, the diffusivity of the rate-controlling specie is affected by the concentration of the specie which is diffusing countercurrently. The diffusivities of both species should be pressure-sensitive. No concise explanation can be offered on the basis of the available data.

SUMMARY AND CONCLUSIONS

The rates of nitride formation on TiO_2, Ti_2O_3, and TiO were studied in the temperature range of 900 to 1070°C. Parabolic behavior was observed for each substance; however, the parabolic rate constants were considerably different, being in the ratio of

$$K_{Ti_2O_3}:K_{TiO_2}:K_{TiO} = 9000:3000:1$$

The initial step was a rapid partial dissociation of TiO_2 to $TiO_{1.95}$ and was attributed to the inherent instability of fully oxidized rutile. The $TiO_{1.95}$ was then reduced through a series of complex intermediate oxides to TiO. Nitride formation was observed only when TiO was present and adjacent to the nitride.

The plots of the test for parabolic rate behavior showed breaks at both 1010 and 1070°C, indicating either a change in mechanism or a complex system associated with conjugate layers. The activation energies were 76 and 91 kcal for the short and long time curves, respectively. Both of these values were greater than the value reported for the diffusion of nitrogen in the nitride.

The pressure dependency was investigated at 1010°C for rutile between 0.032 and 1.0 atm partial pressure of ammonia. The relationship of the rate constant to pressure is of the form

$$k = A p^{0.75}$$

References

1. Agte, C., and K. Moers, Z. anorg. u. allgem. Chem., **198**, 233 (1931).
2. Ehrlich, P., Z. anorg. Chem., **259**, 1 (1949).
3. Chiotti, P., J. Am. Ceram. Soc., **35**, 123 (1952).
4. Duwez, P., and F. Odell, J. Electrochem. Soc., **97**, 299 (1950).
5. Hahn, H., Z. anorg. Chem., **258**, 58 (1949).
6. Brauer, G., Z. Elektrochem., **46**, 397 (1940).
7. Friederich, E., and L. Sittig, Z. anorg. u. allgem. Chem., **143**, 293 (1925).
8. Blix, R., Z. physik. Chem. (Leipzig), **B3**, 229 (1929).

9. Rundle, R. E., N. C. Baenziger, A. S. Wilson, and R. A. McDonald, *J. Am. Chem. Soc.*, **70,** 99 (1948).

10. Friedel, C., and J. Guerin, *Compt. rend.*, **82,** 972 (1876).

11. Montemartini, C., and L. Losana, *Giorn. chim. ind. ed appl.*, **1,** 323 (1924).

12. Ruff, O., and F. Eisner, *Ber. deut. chem. Ges.*, **41,** 2250 (1908).

13. Farup, P., U. S. Pat. 1,343,441 (1920).

14. Bichowsky, F., and J. Harthan, U. S. Pat. 1,408,661 (1922).

15. Andreu, P., and R. Paquet, U. S. Pat. 1,487,521 (1924).

16. Forland, T. S., *International Symposium on the Reactivity of Solids*, Gothenburg, 1952, p. 291.

17. Rostoker, W., *Trans. Am. Inst. Mining Met. Engrs.*, **194,** 981 (1952).

18. Ehrlich, P., *Z. anorg. u. allgem. Chem.*, **247,** 53 (1941).

19. Valensi, G., *International Conference on Surface Reactions*, Pittsburgh, 1948.

20. Johnson, G., and W. A. Weyl, *J. Am. Ceram. Soc.*, **32,** 398 (1949).

21. Marshall, P. A., D. P. Enright, and W. A. Weyl, *International Symposium on the Reactivity of Solids*, Gothenburg, 1952, p. 723.

22. Wagner, C., *Seminar on Atom Movements*, Am. Soc. for Metals, Cleveland, Ohio, 1951, p. 151.

23. Wasilewski, R. J., and G. L. Kehl, *J. Inst. Metals*, **83,** 94 (1954).

A Theory on the Reduction of Titanium Chlorides by Metallic Sodium

T. A. HENRIE* and D. H. BAKER, JR.

Bureau of Mines, U. S. Department of the Interior, Boulder City, Nevada

Abstract

The sodium reduction of titanium chlorides in fused sodium chloride has been studied by the Bureau of Mines. Researchers found two phases present: the α-phase which consisted of dissolved sodium in sodium chloride and the β-phase which was titanium subchlorides dissolved in sodium chloride. It is proposed that the mechanism of the principal reaction between the heterogeneous phases is electrochemical in nature. The model proposed is a galvanic-type reaction at the interfacial region. Sodium metal is ionized at an anodic site on a metal surface in the α-phase. The electrons produced by this reaction are conducted across the interfacial region through the metal to the β-phase where the titanium species are reduced by a cathodic reaction to produce titanium metal.

INTRODUCTION AND EXPERIMENTAL PROCEDURE

A mixture of titanium subchlorides and sodium chloride can be prepared by reacting sodium metal with titanium tetrachloride. If the ratio of two moles of sodium per mole of titanium tetrachloride is carefully reacted at a controlled temperature range of 600–800°C under an inert atmosphere in an iron reactor, a dark green product which contains approximately 18–19% soluble titanium is obtained. The soluble titanium in this fused salt product occurs as a mixture of titanium di- and trichlorides. The relative quantities of each valence species are designated by the term "average effective valence of the titanium" (AEV).[1] Under the above operating conditions, titanium dichloride predominates as the range of the AEV is from 2.05–2.2. There is also a small amount of titanium metal produced which ad-

---

*Present address: Reno Metallurgy Research Center, Bureau of Mines, U. S. Department of the Interior, Reno, Nevada.

heres to the reactor walls. The amount of soluble titanium, titanium metal, and AEV is dependent on the success of the reduction which is a measure of the extent that the following reaction reaches equilibrium:

$$\text{Ti} + 2\text{TiCl}_3 \overset{\text{NaCl}}{\rightleftharpoons} 3\text{TiCl}_2 \tag{1}$$

Because of the chemical affinity of titanium and oxygen, the free titanium metal produced scavenges the salt bath of impurities such as oxygen and as a result small amounts of oxygen from the bath if adsorbed on the titanium metal surface would greatly reduce the apparent activity of titanium in Eq. (1) and shift the equilibrium to the left.

The overall reaction of sodium reduction of titanium tetrachloride is:

$$4\text{Na}(g) + \text{TiCl}_4(g) \longrightarrow \text{Ti}(c) + 4\text{NaCl}(l) \tag{2}$$

This reaction is very exothermic and when carried out by simultaneously adding stoichiometric quantities of sodium and titanium tetrachloride to a reactor, local temperatures of about 1000°C are obtained.

The free energy change of reaction (2) is -135.4 kcal[2] at 1000°C which amounts to the following K_P value:

$$K_P = P_{\text{Ti}} P^4{}_{\text{NaCl}}/P^4{}_{\text{Na}}P_{\text{TiCl}_4} = 10^{+23} \tag{I}$$

Since the activities of Ti and sodium chloride are close to unity in the condensed phase, their partial pressures can be neglected and the equation reduces to

$$P^4{}_{\text{Na}} P_{\text{TiCl}_4} = 10^{-23} \tag{II}$$

At equilibrium the concentration of sodium and titanium tetrachloride is so small that the reduction of titanium tetrachloride with sodium in a commercial reactor must be a series of steady state reactions rather than one of equilibrium.

One can speculate the following *elementary* reactions could be involved in such a process.

$$\text{Na} + \text{TiCl}_4 \longrightarrow \text{TiCl}_3 + \text{NaCl} \tag{3}$$

$$\text{Na} + \text{TiCl}_3 \longrightarrow \text{TiCl}_2 + \text{NaCl} \tag{4}$$

$$2\text{TiCl}_2 \longrightarrow \text{Ti} + \text{TiCl}_4 \tag{5}$$

$$2\text{TiCl}_3 \longrightarrow \text{TiCl}_2 + \text{TiCl}_4 \tag{6}$$

$$2\text{Na} + \text{TiCl}_2 \longrightarrow \text{Ti} + 2\text{NaCl} \tag{7}$$

$$3TiCl_2 \longrightarrow Ti + 2TiCl_3 \tag{8}$$

$$2Na + TiCl_4 \longrightarrow TiCl_2 + 2NaCl \tag{9}$$

$$4TiCl_3 \longrightarrow Ti + 3TiCl_4 \tag{10}$$

$$3Na + TiCl_3 \longrightarrow Ti + 3NaCl \tag{11}$$

Reactions (3) to (6) are bimolecular, (7) to (9) are trimolecular, and (10) and (11) are tetramolecular. From chemical kinetics it is known that the molecularity of an elementary reaction must be a whole number and that unimolecular and bimolecular reactions take place readily where trimolecular reactions rarely take place and more complex reactions are practically nonexistent. From this it can be assumed that reactions (7) to (11) are not paramount in the step-wise reduction of titanium tetrachloride with sodium.

The sublimation points of $TiCl_3$[3] and $TiCl_2$[2] at atmospheric pressures are about 820 to 1280°C, respectively. The boiling point of NaCl is 1465°C. Since the subchlorides of titanium are soluble in fused sodium chloride at the operating temperatures, the dichloride would be dissolved by the condensed phase and the trichloride would establish an equilibrium between the vapor and condensed phase. The elementary reactions which would be paramount by reacting 2 moles of sodium per mole of titanium tetrachloride by feeding them stoichiometrically into a reactor would be:

$$Na(l,v) + TiCl_4(v) \longrightarrow TiCl_3(v) + NaCl(l) \tag{12}$$

$$Na(v) + TiCl_3(v) \longrightarrow TiCl_2(s) + NaCl(l) \tag{13}$$

$$TiCl_3(v) \rightleftharpoons TiCl_3(s) \tag{14}$$

where l, s, and v denote liquid, solvated, and vapor, respectively. The subchlorides of titanium and sodium chloride formed by the above reactions condense to form a homogeneous liquid phase—any excess sodium which is fed into the reactor and sodium that is left over due to trichloride formation reacts with this condensed phase to produce titanium metal.

Notwithstanding the fact that there is considerable discussion whether the electrochemical deposition of titanium at a cathode is a primary or secondary reaction, it is postulated here that the mechanism of the reaction of sodium with titanium subchlorides in fused sodium chloride is of an electrochemical nature (galvanic) between the heterogeneous phases of solvated sodium metal and solvated subchlorides of titanium.

In order to define terms, the postulated reaction can be considered the same as that involved in the well-known Daniel cell, or the same model as proposed for galvanic corrosion of iron in an acidic solution containing oxygen as represented by Figure 1. In the Daniel cell, of course, the electrons pass through an external circuit and can be passed through a potentiometer and measured; however, in the galvanic corrosion of iron the electrons produced by the anodic reaction travel through the iron only from the anodic to cathodic site where the cathodic reaction takes place. The requirements for an electrolytic reaction of this type are: (1) that there is an active metal site for an anodic reaction, (2) that there is a metallic conductor to transport the electrons from the anodic to cathodic site, (3) an electrolyte which is capable of ionic transport, and (4) an ionic or polarizable molecular species which can be reduced at the cathode.

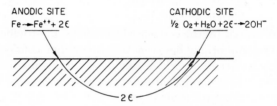

Fig. 1. Galvanic corrosion of iron.

For the condensed phase reaction between sodium metal and titanium subchlorides in solution, the following reactions are proposed:

$$2Na°(s) \longrightarrow 2Na^+(s) + 2\epsilon \text{ (anode)} \qquad (15)$$

$$Ti^+(s) + 2\epsilon \longrightarrow Ti(c) \qquad \text{(cathode)} \qquad (16)$$

(where c denotes the crystal). The anodic reaction takes place at a metal surface (reactor walls or growing titanium crystals) where there is sodium metal, fused sodium chloride, and chloride ions available for the solvation of the sodium ions produced. The cathodic reaction takes place at a metal site where there is available soluble titanium in a fused salt and chloride ions are released to complete the anodic reaction. The electrons would be transmitted between the anode and cathode through a metallic conductor either the mild steel reactor and/or the growing titanium metal crystals. The ionic transport in the fused salt would be by diffusion and migration of the sodium, chloride, or titanium ions depending upon their relative transport numbers.

A similar reaction can be demonstrated by adding Cu_2Cl_2 to a fused-salt bath of alkali or alkaline earth chlorides which are contained in an iron crucible. The iron goes into solution to form ferrous ions as the anodic reaction. Copper ions plate on the surface of the iron and metallic copper grows rapidly as fine filamentary crystals into the bath. This is a heterogeneous reaction where iron is a separate phase from the electrolyte, and it will be demonstrated that the reaction between sodium dissolved in sodium chloride and titanium chlorides

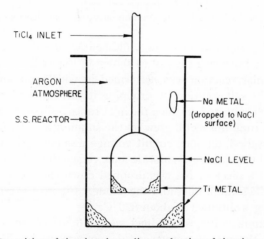

Fig. 2. Deposition of titanium by sodium reduction of titanium chlorides.

dissolved in sodium chloride is a heterogeneous reaction between two separate salt phases.

Some evidences which led to this initial concept of the mechanism are:

1. In the large reactors of the Union Carbide Metals Co., the sponge growth in the condensed phase is considerably below the surface of the liquid level of the salt. The growth appeared to be from the sides and bottom of the reactor walls and in contact with any metal article in the salt such as thermocouple wells, etc.

2. In small experimental reactors in which the reactants titanium tetrachloride and sodium were brought together beneath a submerged

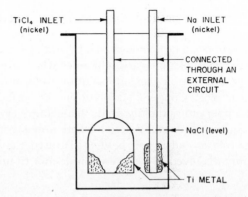

Fig. 3. Deposition of titanium on submerged electrodes.

metal barrier, the titanium grew as filamentary needles in contact with the metal and beneath the salt as shown in Figure 2.

3. A similar reaction was performed in which sodium metal was added to the salt solution by dropping it through a nickel tube. A copper wire connected between the inlet tubes completed the electrical circuit and titanium metal grew on the submerged electrodes.

4. In Figure 3, an open circuit voltage was measured between the sodium and titanium tetrachloride inlet versus time. The initial time being when a piece of Na was dropped down the nickel tube which served as the sodium inlet and the anode. Figure 4 is representative of the voltages obtained at about 820°C.

The maxima voltages obtained were 1.3 to 1.7 for a number of tests. The theoretical voltage at this temperature is 1.5[4] for the galvanic reduction of $TiCl_3$ and 1.4[4] for $TiCl_2$ provided the activity of the

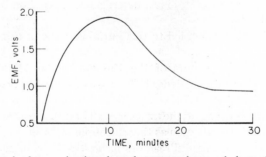

Fig. 4. Graph of open circuit voltage between submerged electrodes vs time.

reacting species are unity. The activities of various species would not be unity under these circumstances, therefore, measured voltages different from theoretical were not entirely unexpected. Similar results were obtained by using a solid magnesium metal anode and operating at lower temperatures. A closed circuit current of 200 ma was measured between these electrodes. Production of an electrical potential and current by these cells, shows that true electrochemical reactions are possible in the metallic reduction of titanium subchlorides in fused salts.

5. In reactions where complete reduction was forced to take place in the gas phase (molecular rather than electrochemical reduction), the titanium produced was a very fine unsintered powdery product rather than spongy filamentary crystals. It is reasonable that the metal produced by a gas phase reaction of this type would be fine powders. This postulate is supported by the gas phase reduction of thorium tetrachloride.[5]

6. On the other hand, the entire titanium metal produced in a normal sodium reduction of titanium chlorides in fused salt is sintered together as evidenced by practically no electrical resistance between any part of the titanium mass and the reactor walls. It does not seem probable that if the titanium species were reduced by molecular-type reactions with free sodium that the fine particles which would be produced could orient themselves and sinter together at temperatures of about one-half the melting point of titanium to form relatively large crystals as observed.

With this preliminary evidence several different methods of bringing together the reactants sodium and titanium subchlorides were tried in order to develop a model of the mechanism of the reaction.

For the most part, the reductions were carried out in stainless steel and mild steel reactors 12 and 14 in. in diameter.

The total charge varied somewhat depending upon the specific technique used but was generally about 100 lb. The apparatus was arranged so that complete control of the rate of addition and amount of reactants charged could be carefully controlled and followed.

A thermocouple well was placed in the reactor so that a thermocouple could be positioned to follow and record the temperatures at various locations on a center line of the reactor. After the reaction was complete the product was removed from the reactor and the location and the crystal form of the titanium metal, as well as the degree of reduction and location of the partially reduced material, was noted.

Reductions were carried out in which stoichiometric amounts of sodium and "master mix" (fused sodium chloride which contained 17–20% soluble titanium mainly as $TiCl_2$ with some $TiCl_3$) were added (1) simultaneously to the top surface of a fused sodium chloride bath, (2) on either side of a vertical baffle which was submerged into the bath, (3) by adding the full charge of master mix, then slowly adding the sodium to the top surface directly or around a baffle which was located just below the surface, and (4) by programed feeding in which the titanium concentration was kept in excess and the reactants simultaneously fed at different rates.

In all the above cases it was noted that the titanium growth started where the reactants first came together, and complete reduction was observed to take place at the entry point of the sodium and extended outward from this location. The titanium near the initial reduction was a fine foil-like deposit, and extending away from the sodium source the crystalline deposit varied from a sponge-like fine acicular intergrowth to larger filamentary deposits which extended into the partially reduced green salt. Under some conditions the filamentary deposits terminated in blocky and plate crystals which had well-defined crystal faces. These different types of crystals are shown in Figures 5 to 7.

Figure 8 is typical of the results obtained by the partial reduction of the master mix by adding sodium to the surface of the salt and slowly heating the entire charge to above 800°C.

The crystal growth from the bottom and sides of the reactor in the dark green salt is illustrated in Figure 9. This growth from the bottom and sides was much more blocky and the filaments were shorter than those crystals which grow near the top of the charge. These crystals were found to be of high purity as determined by the hardness. The Brinell hardness number for this material was from 55 to 65.

A series of experiments were made to determine the effect of using a sodium-sodium chloride mixture as the reducing agent for the master mix. One-half of fused titanium subchloride mix was charged to the reactor; it was then allowed to freeze and a full charge of sodium was added. The reaction mass was heated to about 850°C to allow the reaction to take place. The reaction mass was then frozen and the balance of the master mix charged to the surface of the salt. The objective for the first step of the reduction was to bring about complete reduction of the titanium salts and leave a mixture of sodium chloride

Fig. 5. Photograph of a selected sample of titanium needles(2×). (This material had a Bhn of 80.)

Fig. 6. Filamentary titanium crystals (2×).

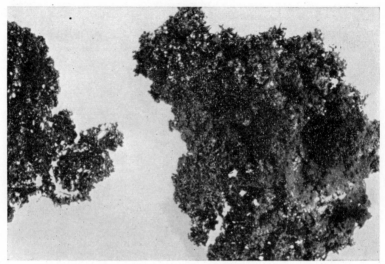

Fig. 7. Fine titanium sponge near the sodium interface (2×).

saturated with free sodium metal to reduce the second portion of the charge by reacting up through the balance of the mix.

After the total charge was added, the reacting mass was maintained at a temperature of 825–850°C overnight. Even after this length of reaction time, it was found that upon cooling and examining the charge there were large areas of unreacted subchlorides adjacent to

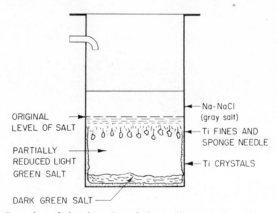

ORIGINAL LEVEL OF SALT

Na-NaCl (gray salt)

Ti FINES AND SPONGE NEEDLE

PARTIALLY REDUCED LIGHT GREEN SALT

Ti CRYSTALS

DARK GREEN SALT

Fig. 8. Location of titanium deposit by sodium reaction of master mix.

an area which contained sodium metal dissolved in sodium chloride. Figure 10 shows the proximity of these two phases to each other. The results of chemical analysis of one area indicated that the gray salt phase (sodium-sodium chloride) contained 4.5 to 4.8 wt-% of sodium metal, while the green salt contained 6.14 wt-% soluble titanium as subchlorides. Close examination of different areas showed that these two phases were always separated by a transparent salt layer which varied in thickness from about 1 mm to over 2 cm. Titanium metal as a crystalline deposit was also found to exist in this transparent

Fig. 9. Blocky crystals showing hexagonal crystal habit (2×). (A sample of this material had a Bhn of 55–59.)

layer. In the thin transparent layers the titanium was present as a thin film adjacent and parallel to the green phase, and when the layer was thicker than about one millimeter the titanium was found to grow across the transparent layer from the sodium-sodium chloride into the titanium subchloride–sodium chloride phase. A simple spot test, which consisted of placing the transparent layer under a microscope and dropping a single drop of water over the area, showed that hydrogen was evolved by the gray and green regions due to sodium and divalent titanium but that hydrogen was not observed to be evolved from the transparent layer.

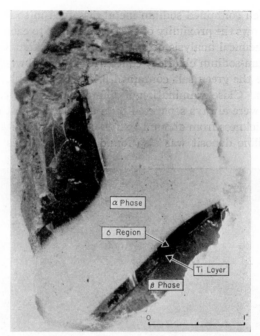

Fig. 10. Unreacted salt showing proximity of the two phases.

These results led to the conclusion that the sodium reduction of titanium subchlorides in fused salt is a heterogeneous reaction between two distinct liquid phases. These phases being sodium in sodium chloride and titanium subchlorides in sodium chloride.

Mechanism of Sodium Reduction of Titanium Chlorides

The mechanism of the reduction of titanium tetrachloride with alkali and alkaline earth metals has been previously considered and studied. For magnesium reduction, the Bureau of Mines[6] has postulated the direct reduction of titanium tetrachloride with magnesium. The magnesium wets the titanium metal and by capillary attraction creeps up the titanium metal surface where the contact is made with titanium tetrachloride and the reduction takes place. A molecular complex mechanism is postulated in a recent Japanese patent.[7] This mechanism can be illustrated by the following reactions.

$$TiCl_4 + Mg \longrightarrow TiMgCl_4 \qquad (17)$$

$$TiMgCl_4 + Mg \longrightarrow 2MgCl_2 + Ti \qquad (18)$$

Keller and others[8] postulate an electrolytic mechanism similar to the one proposed in this discussion in which the sodium reduction of titanium subchlorides in fused sodium chloride occurs by sodium ionizing at a metal surface where sodium is at high concentration and the electrons produced can be carried by the metal to a region of low sodium concentration where either titanium is deposited or sodium metal produced which then would reduce titanium species to produce the metal. Another mechanism proposed by Keller is that Na wets the metal surfaces and subsequently migrates along the metal to a region of low sodium concentration or high titanium chloride concentration where the reduction to titanium takes place.

Dean and his associates[9] have proposed that the condensed phase reduction of titanium chlorides in the electrorefining of titanium is a homogeneous reaction and since it is proposed in this report that sodium reduction is an electrochemical reaction, the mechanism should be similar to electrorefining and the possibility of a homogeneous reaction considered. According to this theory sodium, sodium chloride, and titanium subchlorides form a single-phase homogeneous liquid and the reduction is a direct reaction between free sodium in the melt and the titanium chlorides. To describe the situation involved in the formation of titanium in a homogeneous phase, Dean proposed that free sodium is dissolved by sodium chloride and titanium subchlorides and for the equilibrium condition of

$$Na + TiCl_3 \;\rightleftharpoons\; NaCl + TiCl_2 \qquad (19)$$

the sodium concentration increases with increasing titanium trichloride as well as increasing soluble titanium concentration. This phenomenon is explained by the activity of sodium being a "negative exponential function of its concentration."

The concentration of free sodium, claimed by Gullett,[10] an associate of Dean, in a fused mixture of sodium chloride and titanium subchlorides, ranges from 0.1 to 2.0% for soluble titanium concentrations of 0.25 to 5.0%.

Thermodynamic Considerations

Thermodynamic calculations of the equilibria of the chemical reactions involved show that sodium metal (free sodium) of any appreciable concentration can not exist in fused sodium chloride which contains of the order of 0.25% titanium subchlorides or greater. The accepted physical chemical definition of a *phase* is any homogeneous and physically distinct part of a system which is separated from other parts of the system by definite bounding surfaces. If a system is homogeneous, it must be uniform throughout not only physically but also in chemical composition.

In a system containing sodium, titanium subchlorides, and sodium chloride the following chemical reactions are involved:

$$Na(s) + TiCl_3(s) \rightleftharpoons NaCl(s) + TiCl_2(s) \tag{20}$$

$$2Na(s) + TiCl_2(s) \rightleftharpoons Ti(c) + 2NaCl(s) \tag{21}$$

$$3Na(s) + TiCl_3(s) \rightleftharpoons Ti(c) + 3NaCl(s) \tag{22}$$

where s and c denote solution and crystal, respectively. Reaction (22) is the sum of reactions (20) and (21); hence, it is not necessary to consider reaction (22) separately. By using standard free energy of formation values of the compounds, it is possible to obtain the ratio of the activities of these components in equilibrium at temperature T for the above reactions. The temperature most frequently used in electrolytic work and most often cited is 850°C. Therefore, this temperature will be used for the following thermodynamic calculations. At 850°C (1123°K), the following free energy of formation values[2] were used.

$TiCl_2$	−84,700 cal
$TiCl_3$	−114,500 cal
NaCl	−74,000 cal

For the reaction

$$TiCl_2(s) + NaCl(s) \longrightarrow TiCl_3(s) + Na°(s) \tag{23}$$

$$\Delta F° (1123) = 44,200 \text{ cal}$$

and

$$K_a = a_{TiCl_3} a_{Na}/a_{TiCl_2} a_{NaCl} = 2.5 \times 10^{-9} \tag{III}$$

Here, K_a is the equilibrium constant obtained from $\Delta F°$ and a denotes the activity of each component.

This value for the equilibrium constant indicates that the equilibrium of the above reaction is to the left. Since complexing or solvation effect of sodium chloride on either the species $TiCl_2$ or $TiCl_3$ would be essentially the same and since the activity of sodium chloride would be essentially unity under these conditions, the activity of sodium times the ratio of the $a_{TiCl_3}/a_{TiCl_2} \approx 2.5 \times 10^{-9}$. This means that in any homogeneous phase which contains titanium trichloride, sodium metal is practically nonexistent.

From the above free energy data for the reaction

$$Ti(c) + 2NaCl(s) \longrightarrow 2Na(s) + TiCl_2(s) \qquad (24)$$

$$\Delta F^{\circ} = 63,000 \text{ cal}$$

$$K_a = a^2_{Na}\, a_{TiCl_2}/a_{Ti}\, a^2_{NaCl} = 10^{-12.43} = 3.72 \times 10^{-13} \qquad (IV)$$

Since neither the salt mixture nor sodium is soluble in titanium, the activity of titanium is unity and under these conditions the activity of sodium chloride is near one. Therefore, the equation reduces to

$$K_a \approx a^2_{Na} \times a_{TiCl_2} \approx 3.72 \times 10^{-13}$$

From this calculation it can be seen that for a homogeneous phase which contains any appreciable $TiCl_2$ the activity of sodium is very small.

By knowing the activity equilibrium constant and having means of determining the activity coefficients the concentration of the various species can be calculated. For a schematic reaction

$$aA + bB \rightleftharpoons cC + dD$$

$$K_a = a_C^c a_D^d / a_A^a a_B^b = \gamma_C^c \gamma_D^d / \gamma_A^a \gamma_B^b\, x_C^c x_D^d / x_A^a x_B^b = K_\gamma K_x \qquad (V)$$

where γ is the activity coefficient and x is the mole fraction of the given species.

In order to determine theoretically the mole fraction (concentration) of sodium that would be in equilibrium with titanium dichloride in reaction (24) for the two concentrations of 0.25 and 5.0% titanium dichloride, the following calculations and assumptions are made. For a 0.25% concentration of soluble titanium as a titanium sub-chloride ($TiCl_2$) in NaCl, the mole fraction of $TiCl_2$ is 2.9×10^{-3} and for 5.0 % the mole fraction of $TiCl_2$ is 6.5×10^{-2}. The mole fractions of sodium chloride in these two examples are 0.997 and 0.935, respectively.

From thermodynamic considerations (Raoult's law), as the composition in nonideal solutions approaches that of the pure solvent (in this case NaCl) the deviations from nonideality becomes less and less, therefore, as

$$\chi_{NaCl} \longrightarrow 1 \quad \gamma_{NaCl} \longrightarrow 1 \text{ and hence } a_{NaCl} \longrightarrow 1$$

This holds true also for the case of the solute ($TiCl_2$ or Na), as a solution is progressively diluted the solute tends to obey Henry's law, and the activity coefficient tends to approach a constant thus, as

$$\chi_{solute} \longrightarrow 0 \quad \gamma_{solute} \longrightarrow k \text{ and } a_{solute} \longrightarrow k_H \chi_{solute}$$

Since $TiCl_2$ would tend to complex with sodium chloride in dilute solutions, the deviation from ideality would be negative. Therefore, for the solute $TiCl_2$, the constant k_H is less than unity.

There are no quantitative data on the activity coefficients for $TiCl_2$ in a dilute solution of NaCl. However, Walker[11] and others have measured the activity coefficients for $NiCl_2$ in fused alkali chloride salts for similar concentration ranges. Calculated values, obtained from Walker by private communication, for the activity coefficients of $NiCl_2$ in a LiCl-KCl mixture at 850°C at mole fraction concentrations of $NiCl_2$ of 6.5×10^{-2} and 2.9×10^{-3} are 0.36 ± 0.01 and 0.18 ± 0.04, respectively. The value of the activity coefficient of $TiCl_2$ in NaCl determined from the qualitative plot of activity versus concentration by Komarek and Herasymenko[12] yields a value for about 0.2 for these concentrations. The reason for the values for $NiCl_2$ being less than unity is accounted for by the complex formation of K_2NiCl_4. By assuming that the behavior of $TiCl_2$ would be similar, which would be a good approximation, these values can be used in the calculations to determine the mole fractions of the species of the above reactions.

The activity coefficients of sodium in dilute solutions of sodium chloride have not been determined, but from phase diagram[13] considerations it would be expected that there is positive deviation from ideality since sodium forms a partially immiscible phase with sodium chloride above the melting point of sodium chloride. By definition the activity of Ti equals one and from earlier considerations one can assume that the activity coefficient and activity of sodium chloride approaches unity.

Therefore, Eq. (V) can be rearranged and reduced to

$$\gamma_{Na}^2 \chi_{Na}^2 = K_a / \gamma_{TiCl_2} \chi_{TiCl_2}$$

For the case 0.25% soluble titanium as subchlorides if we assume that γ is 0.18 from the relation of $TiCl_2$ and $NiCl_2$ then

$$\gamma^2_{Na}\chi^2_{Na} = 3.72 \times 10^{-13}/(2.9 \times 10^{-3} \times 0.18) = 7.14 \times 10^{-10} \quad \text{(VII)}$$

For the system with 5% soluble titanium γ-TiCl$_2$ is 0.36

$$\gamma^2_{Na}\chi^2_{Na} = 3.72 \times 10^{-13}/(6.5 \times 10^{-2} \times 0.36) = 1.59 \times 10^{-11} \quad \text{(VIII)}$$

By assuming that the activity coefficient of sodium is unity, which in all probability is the minimum value, then the mole fraction of sodium can be calculated and hence the weight percentage of free sodium that would be in equilibrium with titanium subchlorides in fused sodium chloride determined. The mole fraction values obtained for the above cases are 2.44×10^{-5} and 3.81×10^{-6}, respectively. The corresponding values of free sodium in weight percentage are $9.59 \times 10^{-4}\%$ and $1.41 \times 10^{-4}\%$.

It is obvious from these calculations that it is impossible to have a homogeneous liquid phase consisting of an appreciable concentration of titanium as subchlorides and measurable concentrations of sodium. These calculations which are based on the mass action law show also that for increasing concentration of soluble titanium the concentration of the free sodium decreases.

Mechanism Model

It is possible to have a system in a metastable state which is composed of two phases provided they are separated by an interfacial region. Each of these two homogeneous bulk phases could be internally uniform, physically identified, and separated.

Guggenheim[14] worked out the thermodynamics of surfaces between two phases using this concept. In his treatment, two mathematical surfaces are drawn AA' and BB' parallel to the surface of the phases (see Fig. 11). It seems reasonable to place these surfaces so that there is no appreciable inhomogeneity in the properties of the bulk

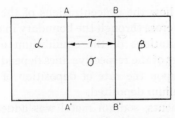

Fig. 11. Definition of surface interfacial region.

phase α up to the surface AA' and in those of the phase β up to the surface BB'. Within the interfacial region σ having thickness τ the properties of the system vary continuously from pure α at AA' to pure β at BB'. This physically inhomogeneous transition "pseudo-phase" is a definite region of matter having its own thermodynamic properties.

In a system of fused sodium chloride which contains titanium sub-chlorides and sodium in excess of that defined by the equilibrium constant,

$$K_a = a^2_{\text{Na}} a_{\text{TiCl}_2} / a^2_{\text{NaCl}} a_{\text{Ti}} = 3.72 \times 10^{-13}$$

this heterogeneous two-phase system can be applied. By designating the α- phase as a solution of sodium-sodium chloride and the β-phase as a solution of $TiCl_2$-NaCl, one can explain the mechanism of sodium reduction of titanium chlorides in sodium chloride. From the K_a above, it can be seen that only titanium metal and sodium chloride can exist in the interfacial region in any quantity. The concentration of sodium metal and of $TiCl_2$ across this interface can be depicted as shown in Figure 12. At the interface BB', the concentration of sodium would be about the same as calculated from the previous thermodynamic argument.

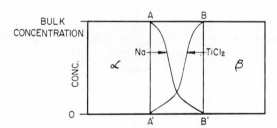

Fig. 12. Concentration gradient of Na and $TiCl_2$ in the interfacial region.

These lines show how the concentrations of the species $TiCl_2$ and sodium drop as they cross through the boundary in order to satisfy the thermodynamic limitations of the equilibrium constant K_a. The thickness τ and slopes of the respective lines depend upon the diffusion of the species and upon the rate of deposition of titanium and the structure of the titanium deposited.

In actual experiments, sodium metal was added to a mixture of sodium chloride and titanium subchloride (17–18 wt-% soluble titanium) and reacted from temperatures just below 800°C to above 900°C. After heating (up to several hours) above 800°C, the reactor was cooled and opened, the mass of material broken up in lumps, and three distinct regions were observed as described in the previous sketches. The α-phase contained free sodium and was gray in color. The β-phase was a greenish-blue color due to the presence of titanium subchlorides in sodium chloride. These two phases were separated by a "boundary phase" of sodium chloride which was colorless and contained varying amounts of titanium in various crystal shapes and structures. The thickness of this colorless layer varied from less than 1 mm to over 5 cm. Figure 12 is a photograph showing these phases. This photograph shows areas of unreacted materials in close contact. Adjacent to the β-phase there was a compact layer of very fine titanium metal crystals. These crystals of titanium are so closely packed that the extent of transport of reacting materials between the α- and β-phases was, no doubt, inhibited. These layers of titanium metal could be the cause of walling off of the reactants and thus account for the observed inhomogeneities and the necessity of maintaining the reactor at temperatures above 800°C for extended periods in order to complete the reduction. In several instances, there were titanium crystals in a fibrous structure extending across the colorless phase into the β-phase.

In several cases, chemical analyses were made of these three regions. In the gray salt or α- phase the sodium was determined by hydrogen evolution in a dilute hydrochloric acid solution and correcting for evolution from any soluble titanium present. Soluble titanium was determined volumetrically by titration of reduced titanium with a standard ferric salt solution. For the colorless salt in the interfacial or σ-region, the soluble titanium was determined as above and assumed to be in the divalent state. The composition of the various regions are given in weight percentages in Table I. The material in both sets of data was heated to above 825°C for several hours before the reactor was cooled. The samples of the first set of data came from a region where the clear salt of the interfacial region was of the order of a centimeter in thickness, whereas the material of the second set was from a region where the clear salt was about 1 mm in thickness.

Since the interfacial bands were so narrow, especially in the material represented by the last set of data, it was difficult to obtain a sample

TABLE I

		Gray salt α-phase	Colorless salt interfacial region Two samples, same electrolyte		Green salt β-phase
1st set	Sol. Ti	Negligible	0.006	0.018	6.38
	Insol. Ti	0.018	13.76	16.80	8.7
	Na (free)	13.13	0.005	0.013	Negligible
2nd set	Sol. Ti	—	0.017		6.14
	Na (free)	4.5–4.8	0.7		

without getting sodium or soluble titanium from the adjacent areas. These values of sodium and soluble titanium are, therefore, probably high. Since both sodium and titanium dichloride are strong reducing agents, in aqueous systems analytical procedures to distinguish between these two are not as precise as would be desired. Figure 13 is a photograph taken of a polished surface of the particular area and shows the distinct phases outlined in the schematic sketch. The colorless region of this sample was between 0.8 and 1 mm in thickness. Figure 14 is a magnification of the same area and shows the sharpness of the α-σ boundary line. Figure 15 which is also a magnification of

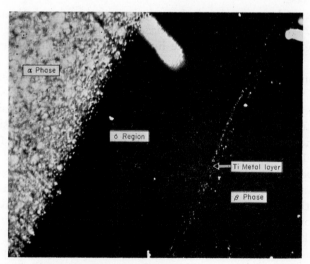

Fig. 13. Interfacial region between the two unreacted phases (17×).

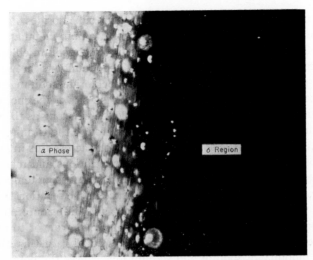

Fig. 14. The α-σ boundary (70×).

the area of the β-σ boundary and shows the dense layer of titanium metal with very fine titanium dendrites just starting to grow from this layer into the green salt region.

The system as described is established when sodium metal comes

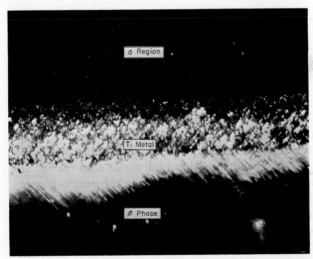

Fig. 15. The β-σ boundary (70×).

into contact with the solution of titanium subchlorides in sodium chloride by the immediate precipitation of titanium metal at the surfaces. This titanium metal and the by-product sodium chloride become the pseudo-phase and serve as the boundary between the sodium-sodium chloride and titanium subchloride–sodium chloride. This pseudo-phase can be identified and has its own thermodynamic properties. The system is in a metastable state as long as the boundary is fused and the material can diffuse through the titanium metal sponge. Control of the steady state reactions across this interface is then possible only by controlling the concentrations and movements of the reactants in the bulk phase. This is done by using temperature, gravity, and concentration gradients. Since in the reaction there is a step in which there is diffusion of sodium and diffusion of titanium subchlorides, the boundary region will appear to grow or to move in one direction unless the diffusion rates are equal. In this case, the greater mobility of sodium and sodium ions causes the boundary, as shown in Figure 13, to migrate from top right to left bottom.

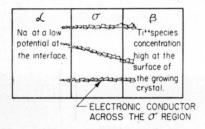

Fig. 16. Conditions for deposition of titanium crystals.

There are only two main conditions in which the metastable state will be stabilized. The more important condition occurs when the initial reaction results in an impermeable mass of titanium metal. The diffusion of the ions is thus inhibited and the rate reaction decreased. The second condition that would stop the reactions would be the solidification of sodium chloride in the pseudo-phase. This can be simply corrected by introducing enough heat to fuse the sodium chloride. Thus, the type of product produced will be determined by the conditions imposed on the system. In Figure 16 the conditions of the system that are necessary for crystal growth are shown. The sequence of the steady state reactions occurring across the system can be represented as molecular diffusion, ionization, conduction, ionic reduction, and ionic diffusion.

After the establishment of the metastable system, the concentration gradient of sodium causes the diffusion of sodium toward the boundary layer $A-A'$. As the sodium moves toward this layer, an environment is encountered where ionization of the sodium takes place on the surface of a metallic conductor. This conductor can be the precipitated metallic titanium, the metal vessel walls, or any conducting object that can reach across the boundary phase.

The increase of the electronic charge in the metal systems makes the metal cathodic with respect to the titanium subchloride–sodium chloride phase. This potential attracts the soluble titanium ions or titanium-bearing species to the most cathodic site where it is adsorbed, desolvated of chloride ions, and reduced. The chloride ions thus released, and the sodium ions must then diffuse toward each other into the intermediate region in order to complete the reaction by balancing the ionic charges in the system.

The mechanism may seem simple; however, there are several factors that should not be overlooked. There are a number of steps as outlined above, and each one will have a particular energy condition that must be met. Since diffusion is important, the geometry of the system used is important in determining the location of the metal deposits and the type of deposits. If the system is stirred, the slow step in the series of reactions is either the ionization of sodium, the desolvation, adsorption, or the final migration of the titanium atoms to a final site on the growing crystal. This indicates that any process that results in the deposition of a solid metal should be conducted so as to make a diffusion step the slow step in order to allow the crystals to grow.

. CONCLUSIONS

From theoretical and experimental evidence presented in this report, it can be concluded that sodium reduction of titanium tetrachloride occurs by step-wise reactions. The overall reaction can in theory and practice be broken down into two main stages. The first stage consists of a reduction of titanic chloride to titanium dichloride and trichloride in the free volume of the reactor in which local temperatures of 800 to 1000°C are obtained. These products are condensed into a fused chloride bath, with the by-product sodium chloride.

The second stage of the reaction consists of the reaction of the titanium subchlorides in the salt bath (master mix) with free sodium which is dissolved in sodium chloride. Indications are that this reaction is of a primary electrolytic reaction between two separate phases.

Much of the data and theory presented in this paper were generated by Dr. Henrie while employed at the Metals Research Laboratories of the Union Carbide Metals Company and the authors wish to express sincere thanks to this company for allowing publication and its cooperation with the Bureau of Mines during this time. Thanks are especially due to A. E. Hultquist at the Metals Research Laboratories for his timely suggestions, criticisms, and assistance in carrying out some of the experiments.

References

1. Cattoir, F. R., J. R. Nettle, and D. H. Baker, *U. S. Bur. Mines, Rept. Invest.* No. **5372,** 1957.

2. Kelley, K. K., and A. O. Mah, *U. S. Bur. Mines, Rept. Invest.*, No. **5490,** 1959.

3. Sanderson, B. S., and G. E. MacWood, *J. Phys. Chem.*, **60,** 314 (1956).

4. Hamer, W. J., M. S. Malmberg, and B. Kubin, *J. Electrochem. Soc.*, **103,** 8 (1956).

5. Reid, R. C., et al., *Chem. Eng. Progr.*, **54,** No. 4, 76 (1958).

6. Wartman, F. S., D. H. Baker, Jr., J. R. Nettle, and V. F. Homme, *J. Electrochem. Soc.*, **101,** 507 (1954).

7. Tokuyama Soda Company, Ltd., Japanese Pat. 2,007/57 (1957).

8. Keller, W. H., et al., U. S. Pat. 2,848,319 (Aug. 19, 1958).

9. Dean, R. S., "Electrolytic Titanium," Chicago Development Corp., Riverdale, Md., 1957; R. S. Dean, W. W. Gullett, and F. X. McCawley, "Electrorefining of Titanium, Zirconium, Hafnium, Vanadium, Chromium, and Molybdenum," presented at the Electrochem. Soc. Meeting, Ottawa, Canada, Abstract No. a76, Oct., 1958.

10. Gullett, W. W., U. S. Pat. 2,817,631 (Dec. 24, 1957).

11. Walker, R. P., et al. "Activities of $NiCl_2$ from EMF Measurements in Molten LiCl-KCl," paper presented to the Electrochem. Soc. Meeting, N. Y., Apr., 1958, Abstract No. 150, Theoretical Division Enlarged Abstract, pp. 65, Apr. 27–May 1, 1958.

12. Komarek, K., and P. Herasymenko, *J. Electrochem. Soc.*, **105,** 218 (1958).

13. Bredig, M. A., J. W. Johnson, and Wm. T. Smith, Jr., *J. Am. Chem. Soc.*, **77,** 307 (1955).

14. Adam, V. K., *The Physics and Chemistry of Surfaces*, 3rd ed., Oxford Univ. Press, New York, 1941, pp. 404.

A New Development in the Production of Titanium by Reaction in the Gaseous Phase

S. TAKEUCHI, M. TEZUKA, T. KUROSAWA, and S. EDA

The Research Institute for Iron, Steel and Other Metals, Tôhoku University, Sendai, Japan

Abstract

A new type of Ti production by the gaseous phase reaction between $TiCl_4$ and Mg vapors was studied. Large massive Ti in crystalline form was deposited with high efficiencies of 98% in $TiCl_4$ and 80% in Mg. The produced Ti was free from $MgCl_2$ and Mg and was of high purity similar to iodide Ti. The hardness of the crystalline Ti was in a range of 85–100 in Vhn, and it was found to have mechanical properties of 30 kg/mm² in tensile strength and 32 m-kg/mm² in Charpy impact value.

1. INTRODUCTION

As is well known, in Kroll's process the reduction of $TiCl_4$ by liquid magnesium produces spongy products of Ti containing much unreacted Mg and $MgCl_2$ as by-product of the reaction, so that secondary processes such as evaporation *in vacuo* at high temperature are required for eliminating impurities and refining the sponge. The spongy state of Ti has the defect of being apt to allow contamination by air. To improve Kroll's process, methods for continuous operation on the reduction and melting have been proposed by Maddex[1] and Powell,[2] but these methods may be considered impractical because they include much difficulty in operation. Recently, studies on the production of Ti by the gaseous reaction between $TiCl_4$ and Mg have been performed by Levy[3] and Denning[4]; the produced Ti, however, was of powder or spongy form of small size containing much $MgCl_2$ and Mg.

To eliminate these disadvantages as far as possible, the produced Ti should be of large crystalline form or dense massive form, and the

745

by-product $MgCl_2$ should be separated out of the products spontaneously during the reaction taking place. From such a standpoint it is desirable to cause $TiCl_4$ and Mg to react in the gaseous phase in order to separate off the by-product as vapor from the reaction system, and it is necessary to find a method producing Ti in massive solid form if it is possible.

We have been successful in the experiments on producing Ti in large and massive crystalline form free from $MgCl_2$ and Mg by using a sort of wall reaction for the reduction of $TiCl_4$ by Mg; that is, by making the mixed gases of $TiCl_4$ and Mg impinge and react on the wall surfaces which consisted of ribbons or cuttings of Ti.

2. THERMODYNAMICAL DISCUSSION AND PRELIMINARY EXPERIMENTS

To produce free titanium from the by-product through the reaction between $TiCl_4$ and Mg, $MgCl_2$ should be separated out of the reaction system spontaneously during the reaction and therefore $MgCl_2$ as well as $TiCl_4$ and Mg are required to be in gaseous state in the course of the reaction. So the question whether such a desired reaction can actively take place has been studied thermodynamically.

The reaction under Kroll's process is considered apparently to take place according to the following reaction:

$$TiCl_4(g) + 2Mg(l) = Ti(s) + 2MgCl_2(l)$$

but the reaction types required include the following:

$$TiCl_4(g) + 2Mg(g) = Ti(g) + 2MgCl_2(g) \qquad (1)$$

$$TiCl_4(g) + 2Mg(g) = Ti(s) + 2MgCl_2(g) \qquad (2)$$

In case (1) the change in free energy ΔG calculated shows a negative temperature gradient and its value ranges between 8 kcal/mole and -3 kcal/mole in the vicinity of 1000°C due to some differences in measured data for the formation energy of $TiCl_4$ or the vapor pressure of Ti by measurers,[5-9] so it is considered that in approximation, $\Delta G \approx 0$ at 1000°C. Therefore, for reaction (1) a very high temperature is required and the process does not proceed readily even at too high temperature. But in this case if the produced Ti becomes highly oversaturated over its equilibrium vapor pressure, it is possibly solidified and then the reaction may be expected to progress. In the case of reaction (2), as shown in Figure 1, ΔG is in the

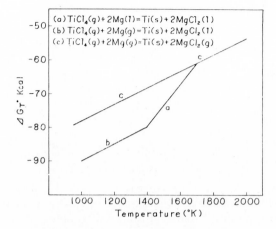

Fig. 1. Temperature dependence of free energy charge ΔG for reduction of TiCl$_4$ by Mg.

order of -70 kcal/mole in the vicinity of 1000°C and its temperature gradient is positive, so that the reaction is expected to progress with adequate activity at about 900–1000°C.

From the above thermodynamical discussions deposition of Ti in solid phase is required in order to make such gaseous reactions as type (2) take place effectively. Thus we need the mixed gas of TiCl$_4$ and Mg to impinge and to react on a wall surface. This lead us to devise means to enlarge the target surface as far as possible and to minimize the factors hampering the escape of by-product of the reaction.

Based on such considerations, an apparatus was constructed for preliminary experiments to study the gaseous reaction. The main parts of this apparatus are as follows: The reaction chamber consists of a cylinder of molybdenum, 15 cm in diameter and 50 cm in length, and inside the chamber thin Ti ribbons of 2–3 mm in breadth were stretched in a network to serve as the wall surface to be impinged by the mixed gas. This reaction tube was inserted into a quartz tube of 1.5 m in length and 20 cm in diameter and was kept *in vacuo* of 10^{-3} mm Hg. After heating the reaction chamber at about 900–950°C, TiCl$_4$ and Mg vapors were injected into the chamber through the pipes of 18–8 stainless steel from the outside of reaction tower of quartz. The reaction took place effectively on

the surface of Ti ribbons, and the by-product $MgCl_2$ and the unreacted Mg vapors were spontaneously separated out of the reaction
zone and condensed in the cooling part of the quartz tube.   The
experiment with this apparatus resulted in markedly effective deposition of Ti, large beautiful crystals of Ti being grown on the surface
of Ti ribbons.   The efficiency of $TiCl_4$ in this experiment was about
95%.

Upon reviewing these preliminary experiments we arrived at the
following conclusions:

1.   Ti may be effectively deposited in crystalline form by making a
mixed jet of $TiCl_4$ and Mg vapor to impinge on a surface of heated
metal.

2.   The efficiency of the reaction may be enhanced by causing the
vapor mixture to flow rapidly in a fixed direction.

3. EXPERIMENTS IN A LARGE-SIZED
REACTION FURNACE

On the basis of the above preliminary experiments a large-sized
reaction furnace was constructed, and a series of experiments for
production of Ti under gaseous phase process was carried out.

The general view of the reaction furnace is shown in Figures 2 and 3.
The reaction tower consists of an inner cylinder of 18-8 stainless
steel, 30 cm in inner diameter and 195 cm in height, and of an external
cylinder of mild steel, 80 cm in diameter and 185 cm in height.   An
electric furnace for heating the inner reaction chamber was placed
between the inner and external cylinder and evacuated to a low pressure of about 10^{-1} mm Hg for preventing deformation and oxidation
of inner reaction cylinder by atmospheric pressure.   Liquid $TiCl_4$ was
dripped into the boiler heated by a water bath kept at 100°C from
its reservoir while regulating its flow rate with a spindle.   Then
vaporized $TiCl_4$ is led into the nozzles set at the top of the reaction
chamber through a leading pipe.   Magnesium is melted in a melting
crucible and flowed into a boiler kept at about 660°C at a given flow
rate regulated with a spindle.   The Mg vapor is sent into a leading
pipe of stainless steel kept at about 700°C and injected into the
reaction chamber at about 950°C through the nozzles at the top of
the reaction tower.   A gas specially devised valve is inserted halfway
in the Mg leading pipe, for facilitating regulation, starting and

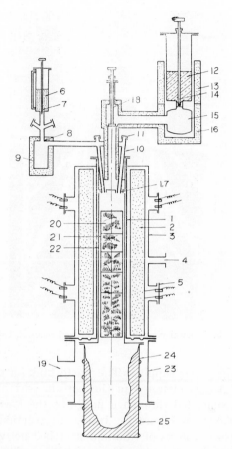

Fig. 2. Sectional view of the large-sized reaction tower. (1) reaction chamber, (2) electric resistance furnace, (3) external cylinder, (4) vacuum opening, (5) terminal board, (6) TiCl₄ reservoir, (7) regulating valve, (8) TiCl₄ boiler, (9) heating furnace for TiCl₄ boiler, (10) injection tube of TiCl₄ vapor, (11) peep hole, (12) molten Mg crucible, (13) heating furnace for Mg crucible, (14) regulating valve, (15) Mg boiler, (16) heating furnace for Mg boiler, (17) nozzle for Mg vapor, (18) valve for Mg vapor, (19) vacuum opening, (20) cuttings of ribbons of Ti stretched netwise, (21) net frame, (22) cylinder, (23) external cylinder, (24) condensing chamber, (25) water cooling pipe.

Fig. 3. General view of the large-sized reaction tower.

stoppage of Mg vapor supply. The waste tank for condensing the
by-product $MgCl_2$ is mounted in the bottom part of the reaction
chamber and connected through a flange at the lowest end of the
chamber, as shown in Figure 2. Inside the reaction chamber are
placed cuttings or ribbons of titanium stretched net-wise on a mild
steel or titanium frame, and a sleeve of mild steel or titanium was
used for holding these frames in place. Before the reaction takes
place, the whole system including the boilers of $TiCl_4$ and Mg, the
reaction chamber and the boilers are heated to the respective pre-
scribed temperatures. The spindles or the gas valves of the two
systems being opened, the $TiCl_4$ and Mg vapors are injected into the
reaction chamber through the nozzles. The jets of Mg and $TiCl_4$
vapors are mixed in the space of the upper part of the chamber.
These mixed vapors flow down to the direction of the cooling zone
of the condensing tank at a considerable velocity and impinge the
surface of the titanium cuttings or ribbons in the reaction chamber
where the reaction occurs very effectively. Titanium is deposited

on the surface of the cuttings or ribbons and grows crystal-wise against the direction of the flowing vapors, while the by product $MgCl_2$ vapor or the unreacted Mg vapor is rapidly condensed in the waste tank, being ejected out of the reaction system spontaneously.

After completing an experiment, argon gas or air is introduced into the reaction system to break the vacuum, then the flange of the waste tank is removed, and the frame with the product is separated from the sleeve supporting it without difficulty. If a method can be devised for replacing the frame, holding sleeve, and waste tank without breaking, vacuum, the operation can be made continuous, without cooling the furnace. An apparatus which can be operated continuously is under construction.

Regulation of the Flow of Mg and TiCl₄

It is of importance for maintaining the efficiency of the reaction process and the yield of Ti to feed the required amounts of Mg and $TiCl_4$ vapors to the reaction tower at a constant rate, so the regulation of vapor flow becomes a grave problem in the gaseous phase reaction.

The amount of flow of Mg vapor from the boiler into the reaction chamber is determined by the rate of evaporation of Mg from the given surface of molten metal in the boiler. Factors influencing the rate of evaporation are the wattage of the electric power used in heating the boiler and the resistance of the leading pipe for the Mg vapor, that is, the cross section and the length of the pipe. For obtaining data on these factors, a series of Mg evaporation tests was carried out. It was found that the rate of evaporation is linearly dependent on the wattage of heating the boiler. If a size of leading pipe is somewhat changed in its cross section or its length, the temperature of molten metal in the boiler is changed, but the rate of evaporation is not influenced. In practice, a simple method for obtaining a measure to show the rate of evaporation is required. Thus, some experiments on the evaporation of Mg were carried out by such an apparatus as shown in Figure 4. Six thermocouples were inserted at equal intervals into the boiler for measuring a temperature distribution between the surface and the bottom of the molten Mg accompanied by evaporation under a constant wattage. If the absorption of evaporation heat is in balance with the heat supplied electrically, temperatures shown by the thermocouples immersed in the melt are constant. But with the progress of evaporation the surface level of melt falls and the thermocouples are exposed above the surface of the melt successively. Once separated out of the melt, its temperature reading jumped up abruptly as shown in Figure 5. By measuring the time period between the abrupt change of temperature as indicated by two adjacent thermo-

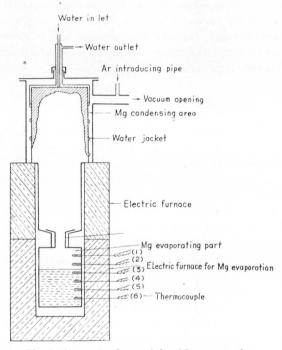

Fig. 4. Apparatus for studying Mg evaporation.

couples, the actual rate of evaporation can be estimated. Thus, the evaporation rate of Mg can be regulated to the desired level by controlling the wattage of the heating electric power.

The flow controlling of TiCl$_4$ had at first taken place by feeding the required amount of the liquid from its storage tank into the boiler through a spindle, while keeping the temperature of the boiler at 300°C by heating from the outside with an electric furnace. But upon measuring the temperature at the bottom of the boiler, we found it violently fluctuating. This is probably attributable to nearly instantaneous evaporation upon dripping down of TiCl₄, and might result in lack of smoothness in the feeding of TiCl₄ into the reaction tower. To prevent such a fluctuation, the TiCl₄ boiler was sunk in a water bath kept at a continuous boiling point, and an orifice gage was inserted in the leading pipe to the reaction chamber in order to measure changes in the flow rate. The results showed that fluctuation in temperature in the boiler and the violent change in the differential pressure at the orifice gauge had ceased, indicating that a smooth TiCl₄ flow was attained.

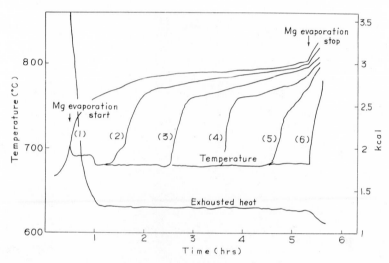

Fig. 5. Variation of temperature and heat liberated by evaporation of Mg.

4. RESULTS AND DISCUSSIONS

A number of series of experiments were carried out using the above described apparatus, and it was found that the method of producing Ti under gas phase reaction between TiCl₄ and Mg is of a very high efficiency in the yields of TiCl₄ and Mg compared with that of Kroll's process. While Kroll's method involved complicated processes of refining *in vacuo*, etc., after the reduction process, by a single process and in a relatively short reaction period, this apparatus produced large crystalline Ti of high purity free from MgCl₂ or Mg.

Figure 6 shows a frame stretched with Ti ribbons to be inserted in the reaction chamber before an experiment. Figure 7 shows the resulting reaction and it can be seen how the Ti crystals are deposited on it. Figure 8 shows characteristics of the crystalline Ti grown on the upper part of the frame. Generally, the crystals deposited on the uppermost part of the frame are particularly large, and the lower the position is the smaller the breadth and the length are; but in any case, all the produced Ti are of high purity free from $MgCl_2$ and Mg, forming beautiful large crystals safe from the danger of absorbing moisture or of oxidation in air.

Fig. 6. A view of a frame stretched with ribbons of Ti, before experiment.

Experimental Studies and Discussions of Factors Influencing the Yield of Ti

The yield of Ti and the efficiencies of $TiCl_4$ and Mg are all influenced by the relative flow rates of the vapors of these raw materials and the precision in regulating the flows, as well as by the manner of stretching of the Ti ribbons forming the wall surface on which the reaction takes place. These factors influencing the yield of produced Ti were examined and discussed.

Fig. 7. The same as Fig. 6, after experiment.

1. When the ribbons or cuttings of Ti for providing wall surfaces for the reaction to take place upon are stretched at uniform and moderately close intervals in all parts of the frame, the deposition of crystals will be dense and abundant only in the upper part of the frame nearer to the jet nozzles of TiCl₄ and Mg vapors, but they will be much poorer in the middle and the lower parts. These facts suggest that the gas phase reaction occurs very efficiently. To assure uniform deposition, therefore, we adopted a method of distrib-

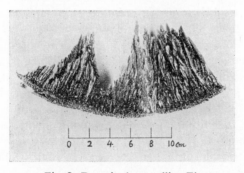

Fig. 8. Deposited crystalline Ti.

uting the ribbons loosely in the upper part to prevent dense deposition in such part only, but the ribbons were densely distributed in the lower part particularly to minimize the quantity of $TiCl_4$ escaping out of the reaction system as far as possible.

2. In such gas phase reaction, the surface area of the Ti ribbons forming the wall surfaces of the reaction is small at the earliest stage of the reaction, but with the progress of the reaction the deposited titanium gradually increases and the effective area of the reaction surface should rapidly increase. So the efficiency of $TiCl_4$ or the yield of Ti is small in a short period of the earliest stage of reaction, but it should rapidly increase with the progress of reaction, that is, the increase of total flow of $TiCl_4$. The relation between the total flow of $TiCl_4$ and the efficiency of $TiCl_4$ was examined experimentally against the different flow rates of Mg, under similar conditions concerning the form of the frames and the mode of stretching the ribbons. It was shown that the efficiency is scarcely affected by the total flow, being nearly constant whether the total flow is large or small.   No remarkable change in the efficiency of $TiCl_4$ was found, even in the exceptional case of re-using the frame with ribbons covered by about 10 kg of crystalline Ti which had been deposited in a previous experiment.   In this case the wall surface of reaction was incomparably larger than that of a frame stretched by new Ti ribbons.   These results show that Ti can be produced with sufficiently high efficiency without using an unessentially large quantity of Ti ribbons for preparing the reaction surface.   In the extreme case of no Ti ribbons being used at all, however, Ti in a powder form, including a large quantity of subchlorides ($TiCl_3$ and $TiCl_2$), is formed due to incomplete reduction.   Thus, it may be considered that only a small quantity of the ribbons of Ti can be necessary and sufficient for the reaction in gaseous phase as the roll of the wall surface on which the reaction takes place.   In our large-sized experimental furnace about 100 g of Ti ribbons of 3 mm in breadth and 0.2–0.4 mm in thickness were necessary and sufficient for obtaining high yield of Ti.

3. From the industrial point of view, the required length of the reaction zone will be another important problem.   But as described above in the case of frames with relatively dense and uniformly stretched ribbons of Ti, it was found that a heavy and dense deposit was obtained in the upper part of the frame only while it was thin in the lower part, and therefore it may be considered that the reac-

tion zone need not be very long. When the frame is extremely short, the yield of Ti may be decreased, but it seems that the frame does not have to be excessively long, a reaction zone of only 50–60 cm in length being adequate for obtaining a high efficiency of 95% for TiCl$_4$. In the vicinity of the jet nozzles of TiCl$_4$ and Mg vapors or in the region of which the mixing of the vapors is not yet thoroughly effected, the corrosion of the once deposited Ti can occur by the locally excessive vapor of TiCl$_4$. Thus, it seems necessary to allow for a mixing zone of adequate length between the jet nozzles and the upper part of Ti ribbons in the frame according to the flow rates and mole ratio of TiCl$_4$ and Mg. In our experiments we have obtained a high efficiency by use of a frame of 100 cm in total length beneath a mixing zone of about 60 cm in the flow rate of 80–90% of that of Mg in mole ratio. At such dimension in our experimental apparatus, the limit of one operation for obtaining sufficiently dense deposition without obstructing the passage for the flow of TiCl$_4$ and Mg by deposited Ti is about 25 kg of deposition; that is, mean density of deposition of 0.45 g/cm^3 over the total volume of the frame.

4. The efficiency of Mg is also an important factor in estimating the industrial value of the method presented, and therefore, it is desired that the flow rate of TiCl$_4$ be controlled to the rate chemically equivalent against the flow rate of Mg in order to obtain a higher efficiency of Mg. But in our experiments, the flow of TiCl$_4$ could not be precisely controlled to the rate chemically equivalent against the flow rate of Mg without reducing the yield of Ti for the following reasons:

(a) Feeding of TiCl$_4$ from its storage tank into the boiler was hand-worked and not performed automatically, and (b) at the outset of operation the rate of supplying TiCl$_4$ from its storage tank through a spindle into the boiler was usually increased gradually and arose to the projected flow rate while the flow rate of Mg was kept at a constant value from the beginning of operation.

Under these circumstances, three series of experiments with different methods of controlling the flow rates were carried out to examine relations between the yield of Ti and the flow rates of TiCl$_4$ and Mg. The results are shown in Figure 9.

5. In the first series of experiments shown by curve I in Figure 9, the TiCl$_4$ boiler was heated directly with an electric furnace, a procedure adopted in the early experiments which was subject to violent

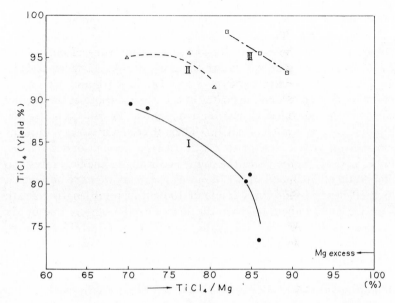

Fig. 9. Relationship between the yield of TiCl₄ and the ratio TiCl₄/Mg in gas mixture flow.

fluctuation of the flow rate of $TiCl_4$ when the frame was 136 cm long and the mixing zone between the upper part of Ti ribbons in the frame and the jet nozzles was too short, as mentioned above. In these cases the efficiency of $TiCl_4$ fell sharply when the projected flow of $TiCl_4$ approached the rate chemically equivalent to the flow rate of Mg. In the second series (II) of experiments, the boiler of $TiCl_4$ was again heated directly with an electric furnace, but the frame was shortened to the length of 100 cm and the mixing zone was enlarged. In this case, too, the efficiency of $TiCl_4$ tended to drop as the flow rate of $TiCl_4$ drew near the equivalent to that of Mg, but the total efficiency was higher than in the first series of experiments.

If the flow of $TiCl_4$ is in excess of that of Mg, temporarily or locally, the deposited Ti is eroded and chlorinated into the subchloride, perceptibly reducing the yield of Ti. In both series of experiments mentioned above, in which the method of directly heating the boiler was adopted and in which the flow rate of $TiCl_4$ was subject to violent fluctuation, the excess cases of $TiCl_4$ will be naturally produced when the projected flow of $TiCl_4$ comes up to the rate equivalent against the flow rate of Mg. These facts probably account for the rapid decrease in the yield of Ti as seen in curves I and II of Figure 9. In the third series (III) of experiments, the method of indirectly heating by a hot-water bath was adopted for obtaining the smooth flow rate of $TiCl_4$, and the frame was shortened to 100 cm to allow a sufficient mixing space between the jet nozzles and the upper part of the frame. In this case the high yield of 98% was realized. Even when the projected flow rate of $TiCl_4$ was brought up to 90% of the rate equivalent to the flow rate of Mg, the yield of Ti was as high as 93%.

In Table I the operation results of two of the representative experiments are shown.

TABLE I
Operation Results for Two Examples of Experiments

		No. 1	No. 3
Produced Ti, kg		17.25	16.91
Reaction time, min		300	309
$TiCl_4$	Yield, %	98.0	95.5
	Total flow, L	40.5	40.8
	Flow rate, cc/min	135	132
	Yield, %	80.0	81.7
Mg	Total flow, kg	21.9	21.0
	Flow rate, g/min	73.0	68.0
Ti ribbons, g		100	110

From these experiments the following conclusions were obtained:

1. The high efficiencies of 98% and 80% for $TiCl_4$ and Mg, respectively, were obtained. If a method of automatic regulation for feeding of $TiCl_4$ and Mg can be introduced for further precision in the control of the flow rates, a fall in the efficiency upon a closer approach of the $TiCl_4$ flow to the rate equivalent against the flow rate of Mg may be prevented, so that the efficiency of Mg may be expected to rise further.

2. It was found that a mixing zone of an appropriate length must be allowed for between the jet nozzles of $TiCl_4$ and Mg vapors and the frame provided with ribbons or cuttings of Ti inserted in the reaction chamber.

3. The quantity of the Ti ribbons or cuttings required for providing adequate wall surfaces for the reaction was found to be only about 0.5% of the deposited quantity of Ti, so that it is meaningless to use ribbons or cuttings in excessive quantity. In a plant of the dimensions used in our experiments, 100 g of such materials are quite sufficient. The ribbons or cuttings should be stretched across the frame at larger intervals in its upper part and at closer intervals in its lower part to ensure effective utilization of the reaction area and uniformly dense distribution of the Ti deposits.

4. It was proved that a period required for completing the reaction in our method is relatively smaller than the reduction period in Kroll's method, in which further processes after reduction are required before producing pure Ti, while in our method we have only one process to finish the whole course of production.

5. The Ti produced by our method was found to consist of crystalline solid masses of high purity free from Mg, MgCl$_2$, and similar impurities.

5. PURITY OF CRYSTALLINE TITANIUM

In Table II the chemical compositions of TiCl$_4$ and Mg used in our experiments are tabulated. The raw material No. 1 of TiCl$_4$ was seemingly rather heavily hydrated, owing to unsuitable preservation in iron containers, being tainted with colloidal precipitates and scums and colored in reddish brown. In Table II the analysis

TABLE II
Chemical Compositions of Impurities Contained in Raw Materials

Element, wt-%	TiCl$_4$ No. 2	TiCl$_4$ No. 1	Element, wt-%	Mg High-purity grade
Si	0.0048	0.001	Si	0.003–0.006
Fe	0.0017	0.0023	Mn	0.002
V	0.001	<0.0025	Al	0.003
Mn		<0.008	Fe	0.001
O$_2$		0.021	Cu	0.007
Cl$_2$(free)		0.029	N$_2$	0.003–0.008
N$_2$		<0.001		

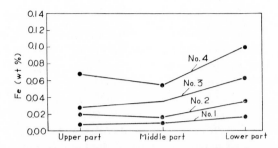

Fig. 10. Iron content in deposited crystalline Ti.

value of oxygen includes only oxygen produced by hydration and that of nitrogen only nitrogen in compounds, free oxygen and nitrogen being excluded in either case. The raw material No. 2 was of high purity specially purified. These raw materials of different purities were used in our experiments, but the different grades of the materials caused no difference in the purity of the product. The reducing material Mg was a product refined by Pidgeon's process.

For closer inquiry into the grade of the crystalline Ti produced, several samples of representative experiments were selected and the iron content in the deposits on the upper, middle, and lower parts of the frame were measured, as illustrated in Figure 10.

The vicinity of the jet nozzles of $TiCl_4$ is in the high temperature range of 800–850°C. If the nozzles consist of stainless steel, they will be heavily corroded by the vapor stream of $TiCl_4$, and the products will be contaminated by a considerable quantity of iron. To prevent this corrosion and contamination, graphite tubes were inserted into the inside of the nozzle, because carbon is a very high anti-corrosion material against $TiCl_4$ in high temperatures also.

The admixture of iron in the products as shown in Figure 10 may be considered as coming mainly from the frame itself and the sleeve supporting it, too, because they are made of mild steel. In experiment No. 4 an iron frame and sleeve were used after acid washing and paper polishing. In experiment No. 3, only the sleeve coated thinly with Ti in the course of the reaction of a previous experiment was used again. In experiment No. 1, both the sleeve and frame coated with Ti in previous experiments were used again and only the ribbons of Ti were renewed. By such measures, the iron content in the deposited Ti decreased step by step in experiments No. 4,

No. 3, and No. 1 as seen in Figure 10.   That is to say, the less frequent the occasion for the TiCl$_4$ gas to come into direct contact with
iron, the less iron content in the produced Ti.   For comparison, in
experiment No. 2, the frame was made of welded titanium bars and
the sleeve of thin titanium plates, but the result was similar or
rather slightly less satisfactory than that of experiment No. 1, in
which Ti-coated iron frame and sleeve were used.   Such a result
suggests that for assuring higher purity, it is not at all necessary to
go to the trouble of making titanium frames and titanium sleeves for
supporting them.

   If the inner wall of the reaction chamber consisting of stainless
steel is not so completely protected by the sleeve, it is possible that
in cases using titanium frame, as well as the titanium sleeve, that
TiCl$_4$ in excess corrodes the inner wall of the reaction chamber,
producing a source of iron content in the product.   Therefore, the
purity of the deposited Ti is also influenced by the accuracy in the
regulation of the flow rate of TiCl$_4$ and Mg during the operation.   As
mentioned above, under the method of using an electric furnace for
direct heating of the boiler of TiCl$_4$ it has been indicated that the
flow rate of TiCl$_4$ is subject to violent fluctuation, so that in such
cases, the occasions for the flow rate of TiCl$_4$ to exceed the rate equivalent to that of Mg are naturally rather frequent.   If so, the fall
of the efficiency due to such a temporary excess of TiCl$_4$ must be
accompanied by an increase of contamination of iron in the product
owing to the corrosion of the inner wall of the reaction chamber.
All experiments illustrated above, except No. 1, were carried out
under such a direct heating method accompanied by fluctuation of
the flow rate of TiCl$_4$.   In experiment No. 1 only, the indirect
heating by the hot water-bath was adopted to control the flow rate
of TiCl$_4$ for high smoothness of feed.   Therefore, the somewhat
larger iron content in the products obtained in No. 2 than in those
produced in No. 1 can account for the less smooth control of the flow
rate of TiCl$_4$ in experiment No. 2.

   The measured contents of Mg, Cl$_2$, C, H$_2$, and N$_2$ are not so distinctly different by experiments.

Hardness Test

   For comparison with Figure 10 above, the relation between the
hardness of the Ti crystals and the position on the frame is given in

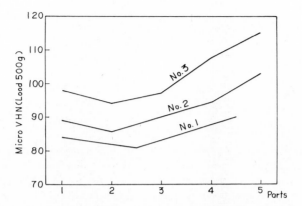

Fig. 11. Micro-Vickers hardness of deposited Ti.

Figure 11.   Figure 12 similarly shows the relation between the hardness of these crystals melted and cast into ingots of 200 g and the position the crystals were sampled from.   As seen from these figures, the micro-Vickers hardness of the Ti crystals and the Brinell hardness of the ingots show a similar tendency to that apparent in Figure 10; namely, somewhat higher hardness was found in the samples taken at experiments resulting in high iron content and in the samples taken from lower sections where the iron content was higher.

In consideration of the chemical analysis and hardness test results, it may be stated that if the jet nozzles are thoroughly protected from corrosion with graphite, the flow rates of TiCl$_4$ and Mg are evenly controlled to assure constant and slight excess of Mg and if

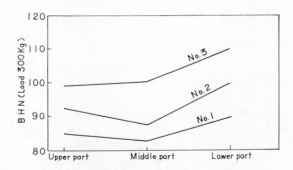

Fig. 12. Brinell hardness of Ti ingot as-cast.

TABLE III
Chemical Compositions of Ti Produced by Different Methods

Element		Fe	N_2	H_2	C	Mg	Cl_2	Bhn	Vhn
U. S. sponge		0.15	0.03	0.005	0.05	0.05	0.10	130	
Japanese sponge Ti	A	0.03	0.02	0.008	0.01			113	
	B	0.02	0.006		0.02	0.02	0.04	100	
Iodide Ti	A	0.02	0.002		0.03		0.03		105
	B	0.0025–0.0035	0.004–0.008	0.009		0.0015–0.002	0.013–0.015		83.4
Crystal Ti		0.01–0.04	0.005–0.008	0.001–0.002	0.01–0.03	0.002–0.01	0.001–0.005	82–97	85–100

the frames and the sleeves are coated by Ti, crystalline Ti of very low content of iron can be produced.

The grades of the Ti specimens produced by gaseous phase reaction operated with attention to these precautions are summarized in Table III. For comparison, the results of analysis of spongy Ti[10] by Kroll's process and iodide Ti[11,12] are shown in the same table. As clearly shown in the table, Ti by the gaseous phase reaction has lesser content of all the impurities. It is compared with the iodide Ti. The contents of Mg and Cl_2 are much lower than those of spongy Ti, so that no volatile matter comes out at melting and the fusibility is excellent. The large crystalline mass of the product and the absence of Mg and $MgCl_2$ in it prevent its absorption of moisture and oxidation in the open atmosphere and imparts excellent preservability in air to the product. Since the process of reaction is effected *in vacuo*, the content of hydrogen in the product is very low, so that the results of Charpy impact tests showed very satisfactory higher valves, as described below.

6. MECHANICAL PROPERTIES

Several specimens of crystalline Ti were sampled from the products at different experiments and were subjected to tensile strength tests and Charpy impact tests. All the test specimens were prepared separately as follows: About 200–1000 g of the crystalline deposit of Ti were arc-melted in a water-cooled copper crucible with a tungsten electrode under argon atmosphere, and then forged at 800°C in air into 15 mm round bars and 12 × 12 mm square bars, from which the test specimens for the tensile strength tests as shown in Figure 13, and specimens with V and U notches for Charpy impact tests were prepared. These specimens were annealed at 800°C for 1 hr *in vacuo* before the tests.

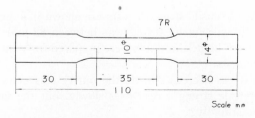

Fig. 13. Dimensions of specimens for the tensile strength test.

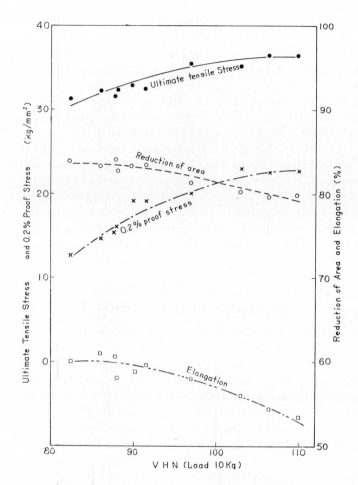

Fig. 14. Correlations between mechanical properties and hardness crystalline Ti.

The results of tensile strength tests are shown in Figure 14. The hardness of the specimens tested was between 82 and 110 in Vhn. The specimens of higher hardness were prepared from the products of earlier experiments.

As the hardness decreases or as the purity of specimens becomes higher, the tensile strength decreases slowly, but the yield strength decreases more rapidly.

The results of impact tests are shown in Figure 15. The specimens

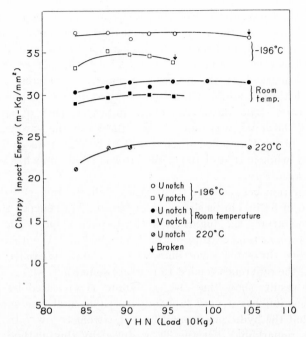

Fig. 15. Effects of hardness on V-notched and U-notched Charpy impact values of crystalline Ti at −190°C room temperature and 220°C.

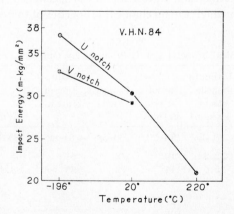

Fig. 16. Effect of temperature on V-notched and U-notched Charpy impact values

used for the Charpy tests were of 84–105 in Vhn. The experiments were carried out on the V- and U-notched specimens at −195°C and room temperature, and on the U-notched specimens only at 200°C. All specimens were unbroken by the Charpy impact except those especially marked in the figure. Specimens of different hardness showed little perceptible difference in their impact values at any temperature. The thickness of the unbroken part of specimens impacted, however, was found larger, the lower the hardness. For example, in the U-notched specimens of 84 in Vhn it was 5–7 mm in thickness, while in that of 100 in Vhn, it was 1.5–2 mm when tested at room temperature.

The relation between the temperature and the impact value of a specimen of 84 in Vhn is shown in Figure 16. In general, the lower the temperature, the higher was the impact value. The impact values at room temperature of the U-notched and V-notched specimens from the same ingot showed very small difference, but at −195°C the difference tended to increase somewhat.

These results show that the crystalline Ti produced by gaseous phase reaction has a very high impact value, and this superiority shows that the hydrogen content in it is extremely low. In particular, it is remarkable that the Ti produced by this method has the merit of showing high excellence in ductility—in elongation, reduction area, and impact value—in spite of its similar tensile strength in comparison with that of the first grade of sponge Ti.

The results of mechanical tests of all the specimens are summarized in Table IV, in which the mechanical properties obtained with sponge

TABLE IV
Mechanical Properties of Ti Produced by Different Processes

Properties		Ultimate tensile stress, kg/mm^2	0.2% proof stress, kg/mm^2	Elonga- tion, %	Reduc- tion of area, %	Vhn	Bhn as-cast
Crystal Ti		30–35	14–20	60–58	84–82	85–100	82–97
Iodide Ti	A	32.2	19	40	61	105	
	B	25.6	14	72	86	83.4	
Japanese							
spongy	A	37	27.1	33			113
Ti	B	41.2	27.5	35			130

Ti[10] and iodide[11,12] Ti are indicated in collation. This table clearly shows that the mechanical properties of the crystalline Ti are very similar to that of the iodide Ti and are much superior to that of the sponge Ti.

7. CONCLUSIONS

1. The possibility of producing Ti in a massive solid form by the gas phase reaction between Mg and $TiCl_4$ was studied from the viewpoint of thermodynamics.

2. By a preliminary experiment it was found that deposition of Ti in crystalline form occurs only on a wall surface by the gaseous reaction, and the by-product $MgCl_2$ and unreacted Mg can be spontaneously separated out of the reaction system during the reaction.

3. Experiments with a large-sized reaction apparatus were performed from industrial standpoints and titanium was produced in crystalline massive form, as expected, with high efficiencies in the yields of Ti, $TiCl_4$, and Mg.

4. It was shown that the crystalline Ti produced by the above apparatus was of higher grade in purity and in mechanical properties than sponge Ti.

References

1. Maddex, P. J., and L. W. Eastwood, *J. Metals*, **188**, 634 (1950).

2. Powell, R. L., *Chem. Eng. Progr.*, **50**, 50 (1954).

3. Levy, J., *Metal Ind.*, **86**, 415 (1955).

4. Denning, C., *Metal Ind.*, **86**, 395 (1955).

5. Kellogg, H. H., *AIME Trans.*, **188**, 862 (1950).

6. Kubaschewski, O., and E. L. Evans, *Metallurgical Thermochemistry*, Pergamon, London, 1951.

7. Blocher, J. M., and E. E. Campbell, *J. Am. Chem. Soc.*, **71**, 4040 (1949).

8. Carpenter, L. G., and W. N. Mair, *Proc. Phys. Soc. (London)*, **B64**, 57 (1951).

9. Edward, J. W., H. L. Johnston, and W. E. Ditmars, *J. Am. Chem. Soc.*, **75**, 2467 (1953).

10. Takeuchi, K., *Light Metals (Japan)*, No. 19, 90 (1956).

11. Jaffee, R. I., H. R. Ogden, and D. J. Maykuth, *AIME Trans.*, **188**, 1261 (1950).

12. Holden, F. C., H. R. Ogden, and R. I. Jaffee, *AIME Trans.*, **197**, 238 (1953).

Reduction of Iron Halide Salts to Filamentary Metals

PAUL D. GORSUCH

General Electric Research Laboratory, Schenectady, New York

Abstract

The growth of iron whiskers by the hydrogen reduction of iron halide salts was found to be a complex chemical process requiring the presence of specific impurities in the halide salt and/or hydrogen. The quantity of whiskers produced as well as their size, shape, orientation, and surface perfection could be related qualitatively to the amount of impurity present. In addition, the growth behavior was found to be discontinuous at the melting point of the halide salt. For the large diameter whiskers at least, growth took place from the base during reduction at low temperatures where the halide salt was solid and growth occurred at the tip at high temperatures where the salt was liquid.

INTRODUCTION

The conditions under which many crystalline solids have been observed to grow in the form of fine filaments and the various models that have been proposed to explain this growth have recently been reviewed by Hardy,[1] Buckley,[2] and Nabarro and Jackson.[3] Although crystals in this form have been observed for many years, marked interest has developed recently because of the high elastic strengths which have been measured for the very small diameter crystals (less than 10 μ)[4-11] and the apparent confirmation of the dislocation mechanism of growth at low supersaturations.[12-14] From a study of the growth kinetics of mercury whiskers, it has been inferred that the small diameter whiskers have only a single axial screw dislocation and their elastic strength properties should approach the theoretical values calculated for perfect crystals.[12]

Gatti and Fullman,[15] Brenner,[9,16] and Cochardt and Weidersich[7] have shown that quantities of iron whiskers for experimental study can be produced by the hydrogen reduction of halide salts. However, much of the detailed information concerning the conditions under which the small diameter elastically strong whiskers were grown was not reported. This paper summarizes the results of a systematic study of the effect of such variables as temperature of reduction, type of halide salt used, influence of impurity additions, etc., on the quantity and type of iron filaments produced. The investigation is one part of a study of the relation between the size, shape, and degree of surface perfection of pure iron whiskers and their crystal structure and mechanical properties.

PREVIOUS EXPERIMENTAL OBSERVATIONS

Gatti and Fullman[15] grew iron whiskers by the hydrogen reduction of mixed aluminum and ferric hydroxide precipitates in the temperature range from 600 to 800°C. The hydroxides were prepared by co-precipitation from an aqueous solution of aluminum and ferric chlorides through the use of ammonium hydroxide, vacuum filtering and drying at 100°C. These filaments, which were predominantly single crystals, were less than 20 to 25 μ in diameter and up to several centimeters in length and could be bent elastically to strains in excess of 1.4%.[3] The whiskers were reported to have a [100] growth direction and to be bounded by four (100) planes. A more detailed study of the nature of the filtrate established: (1) that adsorbed ammonium chloride was probably the active ingredient since whiskers did not grow when a washed precipitate was reduced, (2) that aluminum hydroxide did not contribute to the growth process, and (3) that sodium hydroxide could not be substituted for ammonium hydroxide as the precipitating agent. In addition, it was found that whiskers could be grown by reduction of a wet mixture of ammonium chloride and iron powder.

Brenner[16] reported that iron whiskers could be grown by the hydrogen reduction of ferrous chloride at 730°C and of ferrous bromide at 760°C. The latter required a low hydrogen flow rate. He has subsequently measured the tensile strengths of some of these whiskers and reports a maximum strength of 1340 kg/mm² for a 1.6-μ diameter whisker with a [111] fiber axis.[9] Although he states that iron whiskers were found with axes parallel to the [100] and [110] principal directions as well as the [111], only the fiber axis of the strongest whisker is reported in the compilation of the results.

Cochardt and Weidersich[7] report that iron whiskers can be grown by the hydrogen reduction of sublimated anhydrous ferrous chloride in the temperature range of 500 to 650°C. These whiskers, up to 2 in. in length, also had a [100] fiber axis and were bounded by four (100) planes. Some of the crystals could be bent to elastic strains in excess of 1.5% before kinking.

EXPERIMENTAL

Two methods were used for heating the boats containing the halide salts to the reduction temperature. One was a cylindrical furnace-quartz tube arrangement similar to that used by Brenner.[16] In the other method, the boats were inserted into an iron retort which was open at one end. One of the closed sides had a small inlet pipe through which hydrogen of known purity could be introduced from outside the furnace. The open end of the retort was partially sealed with iron foil so that the excess hydrogen and gaseous reaction products could escape but gases from the furnace atmosphere could not enter. The whole assembly was heated in a large conventional molybdenum-wound hydrogen furnace. This hydrogen retort method was useful for studies involving large quantities of halide salts or salts which readily sublime such as ammonium chloride. The highly volatile compounds had a tendency to condense in the exit tube of the laboratory furnace arrangement and created a dangerous experimental condition. It was possible, for either method, to vary the time required for heating to the reduction temperature over a range from approximately 3 to 30 min or longer.

For visual observation a very simple arrangement was used. A 3-in.-diam quartz tube was wound with a number of turns of Nichrome wire. This tube was placed in slots which were cut in Silocel bricks. The Silocel bricks furnished insulation on all sides except the top. A smaller quartz tube containing the boat of halide was appropriately placed inside the large tube and the progress of whisker growth could be observed as the reduction process proceeded.

The various halides and halide mixtures were reduced at temperatures ranging from 400 to 900°C. Most of the reductions were made with hydrogen which had a −60°F dew point. Other tests were made with hydrogen in which the water vapor content varied from very low (−100°F dew point) to very high (180°F dew point). In some tests various amounts of other gases such as ammonia, argon, carbon monoxide, helium, hydrogen sulfide, and hydrogen chloride were added to the hydrogen during the reduction process.

The influence of both the rate of hydrogen flow and the flow velocity for a given rate of flow was studied. The latter was accomplished by using retorts of various sizes. Hydrogen flow meters were used as required to establish the rate of flow. The optimum combination of hydrogen flow rate and quantity of halide salt reduced had to be experimentally determined as very little information was available concerning the kinetics of the reduction process. The low carbon iron sheet metal boats containing the halide salts were heated to the reduction temperature in flowing hydrogen and also cooled to room temperature under flowing hydrogen.

The raw materials were standard reagent grade chemicals and only a few attempts were made to further purify them. The properties of the materials and many of the chemical reactions which take place during the reduction process are summarized in Appendix A.

Attempts were made to follow the chemical changes that occur during the reduction process. For the halide salts, this was accomplished directly by x-ray methods or was inferred through the use of the colorimetric potassium ferri- and ferro-cyanide tests. The kinetics of the reduction of iron oxide, which was usually present as a purposely added impurity, was also determined by x-ray methods or was inferred from weight change, magnetic characteristics, etc.

The whiskers and the substrate from which they grew were examined by light microscope techniques at magnifications up to 2000 X both after reduction and, in a few cases, at various stages during the reduction process. A number of back-reflection Laue and rotating crystal patterns were taken on straight, smoothly bounded whiskers over a range of sizes and shapes to establish their crystal structure and orientation.

A sufficient number of bend and tensile tests were made on these whiskers to establish that those with small diameters (less than 10 μ) were many times stronger than bulk iron single crystals. Although none has been found as strong as the one example reported by Brenner,[9] the variation of strength with size was similar and the overall level of mechanical properties was considered similar. The results of the study will be summarized in a future paper, and hence no further reference to mechanical properties will be made.

RESULTS

Crystal Structure

All of the samples were found to be single crystals with a body-centered cubic iron structure. The lattice parametersfor two whiskers were 2.8663 and 2.8666 A, respectively, which compared favorably with the 2.8664 A for high purity iron.[17] No attempt was made to determine the crystal structure of whiskers which were kinked, had overgrowths or impinged and welded together during the growth process.

The results of 16 orientation determinations indicated that there is an exact correlation between the external shape of the more perfectly formed whiskers and their fiber axis. The whiskers which are hexagonal or near hexagonal in cross section have a [111] fiber axis and are bounded by six (110) planes. Those which are square have a [100] fiber axis and are bounded by four (100) planes. This correlation was very convenient for determining the relative number of whiskers of each of the two crystal orientations that were present in any given boat. The relation may not be valid for the 200–500-μ-diam whiskers because many of their shapes are poorly defined, and it is not easy to apply for the 1–2-μ-diam whiskers because of the difficulty in determining the crystal shape without destroying the sample.

Hydrogen Reduction of Iron Halide Salts

The most important experimental observations are summarized in Table I and are discussed in the next section of this paper. The detailed results are presented in Appendix B.

SUMMARY OF RESULTS AND DISCUSSION

Interpretation of the results obtained in this study are simplified to some extent by the fact that similar conditions are required for the growth of iron whiskers by the hydrogen reduction of either $FeBr_2$ or $FeCl_2$. The other processes; namely, the ferrous hydroxide and Fe–NH_4Cl are only special examples of growth from $FeCl_2$. The latter processes were important because they demonstrated that iron crystals could be grown in the form of small diameter filaments and indicated the conditions under which the halide salts could be reduced directly to produce equivalent results.

TABLE I

Growth Characteristics of Iron Whiskers Grown from Some of the Halide Samples under Various Reducing Conditions

Material	Additive and/or impurity	Sample preparation	Range of reduction temp, °C	Estimated H dew point during reduction, °F	Condition of halide	No. of whiskers	Max whisker length, mm	Range of whisker diam, μ	Whisker orientation	Whisker growth rate, μ/sec
1.[a] a Fe(OH)₃	None	Washed precipitate	650	−60° or lower	Solid	None				
b Fe(OH)₃	None	Washed precipitate	700–850	−60° or lower	Liquid	None				
2. a Fe(OH)₃	NH₄Cl	Unwashed precipitate dried 100°C	650	120	Solid	Many	1–3	<25	[100]	>3
b Fe(OH)₃	NH₄Cl	Unwashed precipitate dried 100°C	700–850	120	Liquid	Many	10–20	<25	[100]	>25
3. a Fe(OH)₃	NH₄Cl + FeCl₂	Mechanically mixed	650	−10 or lower	Solid	Many	1–3	<25	[100]	>3
b Fe(OH)₃	NH₄Cl + FeCl₂	Mechanically mixed	700–850	−10 or lower	Liquid	Many	10–20	100–500	[111]	>25
4. a Fe Powder	NH₄Cl	Water slurry	600–650	−10 or lower	Solid	Many	1–3	<25	[100]	>3
b Fe Powder	NH₄Cl	Water slurry	700–800	−10 or lower	Liquid	Many	10–20	50–500	[111]	>25

5. a FeCl₂	None	Purified	600–650	−60	or lower	Solid	None				
b FeCl₂	None	Purified	700–900	−60	or lower	Liquid	None				
6. a FeCl₂· 4H₂O	Misc. impurity	Commercial tetrahydrate	600–650	80	or lower	Solid	Few	1–3	<25	[100]	>3
b FeCl₂· 4H₂O	Misc. impurity	Commercial tetrahydrate	700–850	80	or lower	Liquid	Many	10–20	100–500	[111]	>25
7. a FeCl₂	α-Fe₂O₃	Fused 650°C nonreducing atmosphere	400–650	−10	or lower	Solid	Many	10–30	<25	[100]	>3
b FeCl₂	α-Fe₂O₃	Mechanically mixed	700–900	120		Liquid	Many	10–20	<25	[100]	>25
8. a FeBr₂	None	Purified	600–650	−60	or lower	Solid	None				
b FeBr₂	None	Purified	700–900	−60	or lower	Liquid	None				
9. a FeBr₂	BFeO.OH α-Fe₂O₃	Fused at 700°C in nonreducing atm	500–650	−10	or lower	Solid	Few	1–3	<25	[100]	>3
b FeBr₂	BFeO.OH α-Fe₂O₃	Mechanically mixed or already present as impurity	700–900	120		Liquid	Many	10–20	<25	[100]	>25

ᵃ This result first obtained by Gatti and Fullman[16] and subsequently confirmed in this study.

Certain generalities concerning the growth of iron whiskers by the hydrogen reduction of metal halide salts can be deduced from this study. A summary of these observations is not only helpful in planning an experimental program based on the use of whiskers but also has been used in an attempt to assess whether they are consistent with any of the whisker growth mechanisms which have been proposed.[18,19]

It can be postulated that impurities are somehow responsible for whisker growth since small irregular shaped iron particles, rather than whiskers, were produced when high purity iron halide salts were reduced in dry hydrogen ($-60°$F dew point or lower). The conditions necessary for the growth of [100] fiber axis whiskers as compared to those necessary for [111] type growth suggests that the impurities exert an influence on both the nucleation and growth processes.

Whiskers with a [111] fiber axis were produced when the commercially available halides were reduced in a hydrogen atmosphere (estimated to correspond to a dew point of $80°$F or lower). Most of the oxides of iron, whether present in the raw material or purposely added, had been reduced to α-Fe, and it appears reasonable to infer that the whiskers may have been nucleated on these particles. This type of whisker tended to be tapered, poorly formed as to shape, readily kinked and distorted during the growth process and to range in size from about 10 to 500 μ. The average whisker diameter but not the quantity of whiskers was radically increased by increasing the amount of halide reduced in a given boat. The [111] type whiskers were rarely observed for growth from the solid halide salt. Whiskers with a [100] fiber axis were grown when iron oxide particles were present in the liquid halide salt or the solid halide crystals. These results suggest that a different orientation results when the whiskers are nucleated on iron oxide particles (probably FeO) rather than iron particles. It seems reasonable to propose that the iron oxide particles serve the same function for growth from both the liquid and solid halide salts despite the fact that the whiskers grow from the base at a rate of approximately 3 μ/sec for reduction of the solid halide and from the tip at a rate in excess of 25–30 μ/sec for growth from the liquid. The diameter of this whisker type does not appear to be related to the quantity of material reduced and they are usually less than 20–25 μ in diameter. In boats which contain mixtures of [100] and [111] type whiskers, it is believed that the former types grow in the early stages of reduction when oxide particles are present and that the latter types are formed toward the end of the reduction cycle when the impurity oxide particles have been reduced to α-Fe.

The growth characteristics of the [111] type whiskers by the reduction of liquid halide salts and of [100] type whiskers by the reduction of solid halide salts are not significantly altered by the addition of impurities, within reasonable limits, other than iron oxide to either the halide salt or hydrogen. Figure 1, however, schematically indicates the manner in which the average whisker diameters for the [100] type whiskers grown by the reduction of the liquid halides are decreased with increasing impurity content. The effectiveness of a specific impurity in promoting this trend is apparently related to its

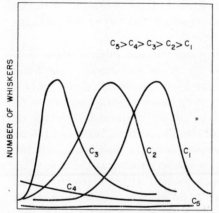

Fig. 1. Schematic variation in range of [100] type whisker diameters with impurity content.

reactivity with iron, and the most effective impurities such as water vapor and hydrogen sulfide cause whisker growth to cease at some critical concentration. Whether growth is inhibited due to poisoning of the nucleation site or due to modification of the reduction kinetics could not be determined. In addition, it was difficult to separate the influence of the iron oxide in the halide salt on growth characteristics from that due to water vapor in the hydrogen since it was necessary to introduce a significant quantity of water vapor into the hydrogen to prevent too rapid reduction of the small oxide particles.

The liquid layer which covers the surfaces of the growing whisker during the reduction of the liquid halide salts apparently serves a useful purpose. The surfaces of the whiskers grown from the liquid are usually quite smooth whereas those grown from the solid are covered with a wide variety of defects which bear a close relation to the geometry of the whisker. Paparteou[20] has observed a similar phenomenon in the growth of dendrites from a liquid. The secondary branches on the large dendrites are frequently found to redissolve and the driving force for the process is the difference in free energy between the small and large dendrite arms. Thus, it is suggested that fluctuations during the growth cycle produce either small surface projections or depressions in the surface of a whisker. These projections or depressions can be eliminated during growth from the liquid by diffusion through the liquid layer on the whisker surface, whereas during growth from the solid they would tend to remain on the whisker surface because of the absence of a halide layer of significant thickness either during or after growth.

The direction of growth was inferred from visual studies of the movement of defects on the surfaces of the whiskers during growth. There are other indications, however, which confirm the directions of growth that have been assumed for growth from the liquid and solid halide salts. Many of the whiskers intersected during growth and the observation of straight sections between growth site and interfering crystal, for growth from the liquid, can only be accounted for by tip growth. The whiskers growing at the base would not be expected to uniformly cease growth after intersection, and the differential growth between the two whiskers would cause an arc to be formed between the whisker base and the interfering crystal. Many such growth patterns are observed for growth from the solid halide salt. It is important to note that growth from the liquid does not cease when the tip of the whisker intersects with another whisker. In fact, there is very little evidence that the intersection modifies the growth of either whisker in any way.

Hydrogen reduction of halide salts is a very inefficient process as far as the conversion of iron into small diameter filaments is concerned. The bulk of the halide is reduced to iron in the bottom and on the sides of the boat. This iron is in the form of either interconnected iron particles or a continuous iron skin depending upon the reduction conditions and the type of halide reduced.

Although the long whiskers were usually observed to grow from clumps of iron particles (which might have been oxide particles at the time of the initiation of growth), the density of these particles could not be related to the tendency for whisker growth. The distribution and density of particles were frequently the same whether whisker growth was or was not observed. The upper surfaces of the particles were frequently smooth and their shape was the same as that of the whiskers. For example, most of the particles were square in regions where [100] type whiskers grew and hexagonal for [111] type whisker growth.

The boat geometry required for whisker growth from the liquid halide indicates that a concentration gradient of H_2O and/or HCl

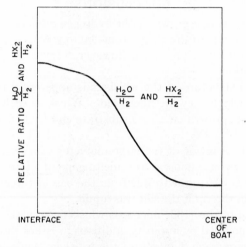

Fig. 2. Probable change in HCl and H_2O content as a function of distance from the hydrogen-halide interface.

(or HBr) in the gas phase is required. Figure 2 shows schematically the estimated variation in concentration of these materials as a function of distance from the hydrogen-halide interface on the sides or bottom of the boat. The decrease in HCl concentration suggests that the whisker grows into a region of continually increasing supersaturation. Growth of whiskers from the solid halide, however, was independent of boat design.

The kinetics of the reduction process varied greatly with temperature. It proceeded very rapidly at high temperatures and the reduction was complete in a few minutes in the range from 800–900°C. At temperatures of 400–500°C, the reduction was extremely slow and it was practically impossible to remove all vestiges of unreduced halide as indicated by the rate of corrosion of the samples upon exposure to air.

The hydrogen flow rate or flow velocity above certain values had little influence on the tendency for whisker growth. The whiskers, however, were badly kinked and distorted for high flow velocities. High flow velocities increased the rate of evaporation or sublimation of the halide salts and the rate of reduction of the oxide particles. Both trends tended to limit the quantity of whiskers produced.

CONCLUSIONS

Iron whiskers can be grown by the hydrogen reduction of iron halide salts over the temperature range from 400 to 900°C. The characteristics of the whiskers produced, however, vary markedly with the growth conditions.

The crystal structure of the whiskers is apparently related to the substrate on which they are nucleated. Whiskers with a [100] fiber axis result from growth on a FeO substrate and [111] from growth on small crystals of α-Fe.

The growth behavior of the large diameter whiskers, at least, appears to be discontinuous at the melting point of the halide salts. It was observed that growth was from the base if the halide salt was solid and from the tip if the salt was liquid.

The growth of the [100] fiber axis whiskers from the liquid halide salt may be modified by impurity additions to either the halide or hydrogen. The average diameter of the whiskers tends to decrease as the impurity content is increased, and the rate of decrease appears to be related to the reactivity of the impurity with iron.

The author wishes to acknowledge helpful discussions with W. R. Hibbard, Jr., J. R. Low, Jr., and D. Turnbull during this investigation and also wishes to thank them for their numerous suggestions and criticisms of this manuscript. In addition, D. H. Wilkins was very helpful in rationalizing the possible chemical reactions which might occur during the reduction process, and R. E. Cech cooperated in making some of the studies evaluating the influence of impurities on whisker growth characteristics.

APPENDIX A.   DESCRIPTION OF MATERIALS

A knowledge of the properties of the chemicals used in this study is essential to an understanding of the nature of the reduction process

For this reason the materials are briefly described and the chemical reactions involved are listed.

Ferrous chloride, $FeCl_2$, has a density of 2.98 g/cu cm and melts at 670–674°C.[21] Figure 3 shows its variation in vapor pressure with temperature. It is usually formed by the action of hydrogen chloride on iron at red heat or by the action of hydrochloric acid on iron out of contact with air.[24] However, it can also be formed by heating iron filings with an excess of NH_4Cl or by the hydrogen reduction of $FeCl_3$.[25] No thermal dissociation at temperatures up to 1000°C has been noted, but there is evidence that some $FeCl_3$ may be formed by partial decomposition.[25] It is known to form many complex salts particularly with ammonia.[24] It reacts with oxygen and water vapor in the temperature range of interest to form various types of iron oxides such as α-Fe_2O_3 and Fe_3O_4.[25] There is some evidence of reaction of $FeCl_2$ with dry hydrogen at temperatures as low as 300°C.[25]

The $FeCl_2$ is commercially available as the tetrahydrate $FeCl_2 \cdot 4H_2O$. Upon melting, this material forms anhydrous $FeCl_2$ and some

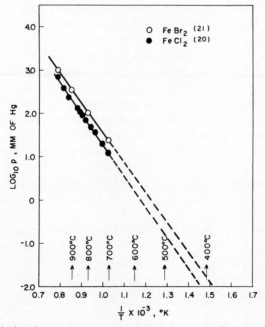

Fig. 3. Variation in vapor pressure of $FeBr_2$ and $FeCl_2$ with temperature.

ferrous oxychloride.[25] Relatively high purity material can be obtained by sublimation of anhydrous $FeCl_2$ in an HCl atmosphere or by hydrogen reduction of high purity $FeCl_3$.[25]

Ferrous bromide, $FeBr_2$, has a density of 4.636 g/cu cm,[21] melts at 684°C[24] and Figure 3 also shows its variation in vapor pressure with temperature. The method of preparation and purification is similar to that of $FeCl_2$.[24] Heating in air at temperatures up to approximately 310°C[24,26] or in an atmosphere containing significant quantities of water vapor at 500°C or higher[25] results in the decomposition of $FeBr_2$ to $\alpha\text{-}Fe_2O_3$.

Ferric chloride, $FeCl_3$, melts at approximately 300°C and boils at approximately 310°C.[24] It is formed by the action of chlorine vapor on red hot iron and by reacting hydrogen chloride with $\alpha\text{-}Fe_2O_3$.[24] It can also be formed by oxidizing $FeCl_2$ or passing NH_4Cl vapor over $\alpha\text{-}Fe_2O_3$ above 350°C.[25] The $FeCl_3$ vapor which exists as the dimer, Fe_2Cl_6, at low temperatures is rapidly reduced to $FeCl_2$ in hydrogen at temperatures of 350°C and above.[27] Thus, as indicated previously, hydrogen reduction of the commercially available anhydrous, purified $FeCl_3$ can be used for obtaining quantities of high purity $FeCl_2$.

The slow hydrolysis of $FeCl_3$ yields a yellow hydrous precipitate which contains an amount of chloride that varies with the conditions of formation.[28] This material, referred to as $\beta\text{-}FeO\cdot OH$, dehydrates to $\alpha\text{-}Fe_2O_3$ at 170°C and higher.[29] Data obtained in this study suggest that a similar hydrolysis occurs in the case of the commercially available $FeBr_2$. The $FeBr_2$ is presumed to oxidize slowly to $\alpha\text{-}Fe_2O_3$ in the presence of air and adsorbed water at room temperature[24] and is converted subsequently to $\beta\text{-}FeO\cdot OH$.

Ammonium chloride, NH_4Cl, is a salt which melts at 520°C but has a sublimation pressure of 1 atm at 337.80°C.[30] The material is important in this study because it reacts with small iron particles above 500°C to form $FeCl_2$ and with $\alpha\text{-}Fe_2O_3$ at temperatures above 350°C to form $FeCl_3$.

Ferric hydroxide, $Fe(OH)_3$, is a reddish-brown amorphous powder which loses water at 500°C to form $\alpha\text{-}Fe_2O_3$.[24] It is normally obtained as a gelatinous precipitate or hydrogel when an alkali is added to a solution of ferric ion. Because of its colloidal nature with high surface area, it has a marked propensity for adsorbing certain types of impurities.

Ferric oxide, $\alpha\text{-}Fe_2O_3$, is reduced rapidly in hydrogen at 500°C and above to Fe_3O_4, FeO, and finally to α-Fe.[24] During reduction the oxygen ions are maintained with a close-packed structure but the iron ions are rearranged in various ways so that a different crystal structure results for each oxide. The α-Fe_2O_3 has an ilmenite structure, Fe_3O_4 a spinel structure, and FeO a NaCl-type structure.[31] These types of structures become important in determining whether oxide particles are providing a substrate on which the whiskers are being nucleated.

The volume ratio of hydrogen chloride gas to hydrogen gas at equilibrium for the reaction of hydrogen with $FeCl_2$ has been measured over a wide range of temperatures.[25,32] These data are used in another paper to measure the distance of the chemical reactions from equilibrium during whisker growth.[33]

APPENDIX B. EXPERIMENTAL STUDIES

In the initial studies, ferric hydroxide and iron powder plus NH_4Cl mixtures, similar to those used by Gatti and Fullman,[15] were hydrogen reduced and evaluated as to whisker producing tendencies. Later the characteristics of the iron crystals grown by the reduction of high purity $FeBr_2$ and $FeCl_2$ with and without additives such as α-Fe_2O_2 and MgO were studied. The results of each group of tests were sufficiently different that it is appropriate to summarize them separately.

The Ferric Hydroxide Process

An example of the results obtained through the use of this process. by Gatti and Fullman[15] is shown in Figure 4. Although these specific whiskers have been distorted by oxidation and/or corrosion, many features of the growth process are still evident. Most of the whiskers grew from the inner surfaces of the iron boat at a point near but definitely separated from the reduced precipitate in the bottom of the boat A few grew on the reduced precipitate which is represented by the irregular shaped clumps of iron particles in the background of the picture. Essentially all of the whiskers are square in cross section and presumably have a [100] fiber axis.

A detailed study of this process revealed that only with certain specified procedures could reproducible results be obtained. In particular, the method of preparation of the precipitate and the rate of heating to the reduction temperature were found to be extremely important.

The $Fe(OH)_3$ precipitate was prepared by reacting NH_4OH with $FeCl_3$ in aqueous solution and vacuum filtering the resulting solution. It was found that the tendency for the hydroxide to collect on filter paper by conventional techniques and to adsorb NH_4Cl from the solution was related to both the temperature of the solution and the molar ratio of NH_4OH to $FeCl_3$. Essentially all of the $Fe(OH)_3$ could be collected on the filter paper for molar ratios greater than 1 and with solution temperatures of 150–180°F or higher, but the maximum in tendency to adsorb NH_4Cl was reached only when the molar ratio was 3 to 4 or higher. The maximum amount adsorbed was

Fig. 4. Iron whiskers grown by the ferric hydroxide process by Gatti and Fullman.[15]   10×.

approximately 70% of that produced in the chemical reaction. Precipitates obtained from solutions at temperatures less than 100°F and with molar ratios less than 1 or 2 were difficult to filter and contained very little NH_4Cl. None of the precipitates was found to contain any $FeCl_2$ or $FeCl_3$ prior to heating in hydrogen to the reduction temperature.

The quantity of whiskers produced by the reduction of a given amount of $Fe(OH)_3$ increased directly with its NH_4Cl content. In addition, the tendency for whisker growth could be further increased by drying the precipitate for 24 hr at 100°C. Since the precipitate contained much adsorbed water, the drying process decreased the volume and hence increased the weight of $Fe(OH)_3$ and NH_4Cl in a given volume of material. This, in turn, increased the amount of $FeCl_2$ produced during the reduction cycle. Higher drying temperatures were detrimental as much of the NH_4Cl was sublimed from the filter cake during the drying process.

It was not possible to follow the reduction of the ferric hydroxide material visually since the sublimed NH_4Cl quickly clouded the observation window. However, the boats were examined at various stages in the reduction process and the growth procedure was inferred from these studies.

The following briefly summarizes the changes which occurred in the precipitate during heating to and holding at 700°C. The time required for heating to temperature was approximately 15 min. In the temperature range from 100 to 300°C, all of the adsorbed water was vaporized from the $Fe(OH)_3$ and a small fraction of the NH_4Cl was sublimed. From 300 to 600°C, small $FeCl_2$ crystals grew first on the inner surfaces of the boat and later on the surface of the bulk precipitate. During this period, the $Fe(OH)_3$ was reduced to α-Fe_2O_3 and a small amount of α-Fe, FeO, and Fe_3O_4. The resulting water vapor appeared to lower the rate of sublimation and vaporization of the NH_4Cl markedly compared to the rate observed in the absence of water vapor. The small quantity of remaining NH_4Cl was vaporized in the temperature range from 600 to 700°C and much of the α-Fe_2O_3 was reduced to α-Fe, FeO, or Fe_3O_4 depending upon its position in the boat. After a 2- to 3-min. incubation period at temperature, whiskers were observed to grow from the regions where the $FeCl_2$ crystals had been located. Whisker growth ceased after approximately 15 min. at temperature, but it was necessary to hold for an additional 15 to 30 min. in very dry hydrogen ($-60°F$ dew point or better) to remove all evidence of adsorbed halide salts as indicated by the rate at which the whiskers corrode upon exposure to air.

The above results suggest that two different steps are involved in the formation of the $FeCl_2$ crystals. At low temperatures (less than 500°C), the NH_4Cl reacts with α-Fe_2O_3 to produce $FeCl_3$ which immediately vaporizes. In the vapor state the $FeCl_3$ is reduced to $FeCl_2$ and condenses along the sides of the boat. At high temperatures (greater than 500°C) the NH_4Cl vapors react with the α-Fe particles [formed by the reduction of the $Fe(OH)_2$ on the surface of bulk precipitate] to form $FeCl_2$ crystals.

Further tests showed that the whisker growing tendency of the ferric hydroxide material was extremely dependent upon the rate of heating. If the time required for heating to the reduction temperature was less than 3–5 min or greater than 20 to 30 min, very limited whisker growth was observed. For the short heating times the NH_4Cl was sublimed from the system before many $FeCl_2$ crystals were formed, and for the longer heating times the $FeCl_2$ crystals were formed but were reduced to iron in the absence of water vapor because most of the $Fe(OH)_3$ was reduced to iron during the heating cycle. Under these latter circumstances small irregular-shaped iron particles, rather than whiskers, were produced.

Fig. 5. Iron whiskers grown from dried ferric hydroxide filtrate at 700°C. 20×.

Figure 5 shows the results obtained when a large sample of dried ferric hydroxide material was reduced by the hydrogen retort method at 700°C with a hydrogen flow rate of 5 ft³/hr. Whiskers were also grown at flow rates as low as 2 and as high as 20 ft³/hr. However, the halide salts were incompletely reduced except for extended holding times with the low flow rates and the high flow rates caused the whiskers to be badly kinked and distorted.

Whiskers were grown by hydrogen reduction over the temperature range from about 650 to 850°C with the optimum at approximately 700°C. Good results could be obtained at the very high temperatures only if the heating rate above 600°C was rapid to maximize the

Fig. 6. Iron whiskers grown from dried ferric hydroxide at 650°C. 6×.

amount of iron oxide reduced at the same time as the $FeCl_2$. The maximum length of the whiskers and their growth rate was much greater for growth at 700°C or higher than for growth at or below 650°C. Many of the former whiskers were up to 2 cm in length and grew at a rate estimated to be at least 25 μ/sec or faster. The latter whiskers, shown in Figure 6, were usually only 1 or 3 mm in length

Fig. 7. Iron whiskers grown at 700°C from an equal weight mixture of $FeCl_2$ and ferric hydroxide. 3.5×.

Fig. 8. Iron whiskers grown from ferric hydroxide at 700°C to which a small amount of FeCl$_2$ had been added. 3.5×.

and grew at a rate of approximately 3 μ/sec. All of the whiskers were square in cross section with a [100] fiber axis and less than 25 μ in diameter.

The addition of such materials as NH$_4$Cl, FeCl$_2$, or FeCl$_3$ to the precipitate greatly increased the quantity of whiskers produced, particularly at slow heating rates but radically changed the size, shape, and degree of perfection of their crystal surfaces. Figure 7 shows an example of the results obtained when a mixture containing equal weights of FeCl$_2$ and the ferric hydroxide material was reduced at 670°C or higher. The whiskers are 100 μ or larger in diameter, hexagonal in shape, and apparently have a [111] fiber axis. The addition of intermediate quantities of these materials produced a mixture of the small diameter [100] type whiskers and the more gross [111] type. Examples of this are shown in Figure 8. These results suggest that a properly prepared precipitate produces the optimum quantity and distribution of FeCl$_2$ for the subsequent growth of small diameter whiskers.

The Fe-NH$_4$Cl Process

The conditions under which small diameter whiskers could be produced by this process and the general growth features were not sig-

nificantly different from that for the ferric hydroxide process.   The
range of crystal sizes and shapes observed, however, was much greater
and a few of the more interesting results are summarized.

Two groups of samples were made in which the weight ratio of car-
bonyl iron powder to NH_4Cl was varied from approximately $2:1$ to
$1:6$.   In one group the two materials were mixed directly and in the
other a wet slurry was made.   For the latter group of samples, the
combined presence of NH_4Cl and water caused the iron powder to be
rapidly corroded to a hydrated iron oxide.   The resulting solid mass
was reground to powder prior to reduction.   Samples of each group

Fig. 9. Iron whiskers grown at inlet end of retort from mixture of iron powder and
NH_4Cl. $3.5\times$.

of materials were reduced by the hydrogen retort method at temperatures ranging from 600 to 800°C.   The quantity of whiskers produced
with the wet mixture increased continuously as the ratio of NH_4Cl to
iron powder was increased.   However, no whisker growth occurred
with the dry mixture at temperatures below 670°C, and the results
were very inferior at the higher temperatures.   This difference in behavior resulted from the greater quantity of $FeCl_2$ indirectly produced
by the reaction of the NH_4Cl with α-Fe_2O_3 as compared to that
directly produced by reaction with iron.

As in the ferric hydroxide process, the nature of the whiskers which

grew above and below the melting point of $FeCl_2$ was radically different. In the temperature range from 600 to 650°C, the whiskers were
1 to 3 mm long and grew in great profusion from the sides of the boat
and from the clump of iron and reduced iron oxide. They were
apparently square in cross section indicating a [100] fiber axis and less
than 25 μ in diameter. The whiskers grown in the temperature range
from 700 to 800°C were many times longer but their appearance was
markedly dependent upon the specific growth conditions. Figures
9 and 10 show the difference in appearance of the whiskers at opposite
ends of an 8-in. long boat for reduction at 700°C. The whiskers at

Fig. 10. Iron whiskers grown at exit end of retort from mixture of iron powder and
NH_4Cl. 3.5×.

the hydrogen inlet end are profuse, large in diameter, covered with
all kinds of growth defects and poorly formed as to shape. The
whiskers at the opposite end of the retort are fewer in number, small
in diameter, and relatively free from overgrowths. Most of the whiskers at the inlet end are hexagonal in cross section indicating [111]
fiber axes and those at the exit end are square with presumably [100]
fiber axes. In general, the minimum whisker diameter for growth at
700°C and above for slow heating rates was approximately 50 to 100
μ and this rapidly increased to approximately 500 μ as the quantity of
material per boat was increased. Most of the very large diameter
whiskers appeared to be single crystals with a [111] fiber axis but

Fig. 11. Iron whiskers grown at 700°C from mixture of iron powder and NH₄Cl. 3.5×.

Fig. 12. Iron whiskers grown at 700°C from mixture of iron powder and NH₄Cl. 20.5×.

would not be expected to be elastically strong. Figures 11 and 12 show typical examples of the remarkably complex growth patterns which were observed.

The Ferrous Chloride Process

Initial tests showed that there was almost no tendency for whiskers to grow during the reduction of relatively pure $FeCl_2$ with hydrogen which had a dew point of −60°F or lower.   The pure $FeCl_2$ was obtained both by the hydrogen reduction of the commercially available anhydrous triple sublimed $FeCl_3$ and by the sublimation of $FeCl_2$ in an equilibrium $HCl-H_2$ atmosphere.   For reductions above the melting point of $FeCl_2$ much of the material vaporized from the system without reduction.   The small amount which was reduced formed large iron particles in the bottom of the boat.   At temperatures below 670°C, reduction of the ferrous chloride crystals produced a fibrous appearing network of iron particles as shown in Figure 13.   Thus, most of the work was directed toward determining the type and quantity of impurities which must be added to either the $FeCl_2$ or to the hydrogen gas to make whisker growth take place.

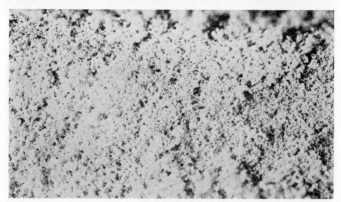

Fig. 13. Fibrous network of iron particles produced by reducing $FeCl_2$ crystals at temperatures below 670°C.   4×.

Figure 14 shows the type of whiskers which can be grown when large quantities of the tetrahydrate are hydrogen reduced above 670°C.   The whiskers range in size from 100 to 500 μ, are markedly tapered, poorly formed both as to straightness and shape and covered with various types of overgrowths.   It can be inferred from both shape and a nominal number of x-ray tests that most have a [111] fiber axis.   The commercial tetrahydrate was found to contain small quantities of β-FeO·OH and additional iron oxides were probably formed by the reaction of ferrous chloride with water vapor during the heating part of the reduction cycle.   The kinetics of the reduction of $FeCl_2 \cdot 4H_2O$ to $FeCl_2$ were such that at least the early stages of whisker growth occurred in an atmosphere which contained a few per cent of water vapor. The moisture content of the hydrogen was estimated to correspond to a dew point at 80°F or lower.

Only a few short small diameter whiskers were obtained if the tetrahydrate was reduced below 670°C, and the appearance of the bulk of the reduced material was similar to that shown in Figure 13. The general features of growth from the liquid as contrasted with growth from the solid halide salts suggested that a sharp discontinuity in the growth procedure occurred at the melting point. Further work confirmed this indication, and the remainder of this summary considers each process separately.

Fig. 14. Iron whiskers grown from the commercial tetrahydrate of FeCl₂ at 700°C. 3.5×.

Many features of the growth of the large diameter crystals produced by the hydrogen reduction of the tetrahydrate at 670°C and higher were determined by visually following the changes in the halide salt during the reduction cycle. Except for the formation of some FeCl₂ crystals during the melting of the tetrahydrate at 310°C, very little change was noted until the FeCl₂ melted at approximately 670°C. The liquid had a tendency to creep up the sides of the boat and the height to which it crept increased as the water vapor content of the atmosphere was increased. After an incubation period of 2 to 5 min, whiskers started growing from the side of the boat near the limit of rise of the liquid. Other whiskers grew from the surface of the liquid apparently supported by surface tension. Those which were firmly attached to the side of the boat continued to grow while those growing in the liquid eventually became sufficiently heavy to sink to the bottom of the boat. Figure 15 shows the nature of the whisker growth at the sides and at the bottom of the boat during the early stages. In general, the final appearance of the boat suggests that whiskers grow only from the sides of the boat.

A study of the movement of defects on a specific whisker during growth indicated that growth was occurring from the tip. The time

Fig. 15. Early stages of whisker growth during the reduction of the commercial tetrahydrate of FeCl$_2$ at 700°C. 18×.

required for the 100- to 200-μ whiskers to grow 1 cm in length varied from approximately 5 to 10 min. The difference may have been related to variations in the whisker size, but this was not established. The marked taper observed on most of the whiskers was apparently related to some feature of the growth process since there was essentially no further increase in the diameter of a whisker after growth to maximum length although it still was in contact with liquid halide salts and/or vapors.

Comparison of these results with those of the previous two processes suggested that the absence of small diameter whiskers in growth from

Fig. 16. Effect of supersaturation on tendency for whisker growth during reduction of the commercial tetrahydrate of $FeCl_2$ at $700°C$. The estimated average per cent HCl by volume is (reading down) 8, 12, 18, and 22. .75×.

Fig. 17. Effect of variation in the NH_3 content of the atmosphere during reduction of the commercial tetrahydrate of $FeCl_2$ at $700°C$. The per cent NH_3 by volume is (reading down) 5, 10, 15, and 20. .75×.

Fig. 18. Iron whiskers grown by the hydrogen reduction of an $FeCl_2-\alpha$-Fe_2O_3 mixture at 700°C. 3.5×.

Fig. 19. Iron whiskers grown by the hydrogen reduction of an $FeCl_2-\alpha$-Fe_2O_2 mixture at 700°C. 18×.

the liquid halide salt might be due to differences in supersaturation and/or presence of ammonia. Figure 16 shows the influence of average supersaturation on the tendency for growth. Although the quantity of whiskers produced was decreased as the supersaturation was decreased, there was no apparent change in the whisker characteristics. A similar trend, Figure 17, was noted for ammonia additions. Ammonia forms complexes with $FeCl_2$ but the interaction had little apparent effect on the nature of the growth of the individual whisker.

Fig. 20. Iron whiskers grown by the hydrogen reduction of an $FeCl_2$-α-Fe_2O_3 mixture at 700°C on a high water vapor content atmosphere. 6.5×.

Although the addition of various amounts of Fe_3O_4, MgO, Al_2O_3, NiO, etc., exerted some influence on the growth characteristics from the liquid, the greatest change was produced by the addition of α-Fe_2O_3. Samples in which 10 to 50% by weight of α-Fe_2O_3 had been added to the tetrahydrate were found to produce many small diameter [100] type whiskers. The best results were obtained when the samples were heated to temperature in 10 min or less with a hydrogen flow of about 3 liters/hr for each gram of mixture. Examples of the results are shown in Figures 18 and 19.

Increasing the dew point of the hydrogen up to 180°F had a marked effect on both the nature of the reduction process and, under some cir-

Fig. 21. Iron whiskers grown by the hydrogen reduction of $FeCl_2$ at 650°C in a high water vapor content atmosphere.   4×.

Fig. 22. Iron whiskers grown from fused mixture of $FeCl_2$ and α-Fe_2O_3 at 500°C.
7×.

cumstances, the character of the whiskers produced.   The increase in moisture content was found to progressively reduce both the rate of evaporation (as measured by weight loss) and the rate of reduction of the halide salt (as indicated by the amounts of unreduced halide after specific reduction periods).   For dew points approaching 180° F, very little halide was evaporated from the boat and very little was reduced during a standard reduction cycle.   The average diameter of the [100] type whiskers grown from the mixture of α-Fe_2O_3 and $FeCl_2$ was found to decrease as the dew point of the hydrogen was increased. Although the total number of whiskers grown with dew points approaching 150°F had significantly decreased, the average diameter of those that grew was less than 10 μ.   An example of these results is shown in Figure 20.

Reduction of the tetrahydrate in hydrogen with a high dew point (greater than 100°F) caused some minor changes in the growth features of the large diameter [111] type whiskers but, in general, no [100] type were produced.   These results established that the growth of the small diameter [100] type whiskers from $FeCl_2$ requires both the presence of iron oxide particles in the halide as well as a significant amount of water vapor in the hydrogen.

Whiskers were grown at temperatures as high as 900°C provided very rapid heating rates were used.   However, the whiskers tended to be larger in diameter and with more marked tapers as the reduction temperature was increased.

Figure 21 shows the type of whiskers which are formed when high purity crystals of $FeCl_2$ are reduced in hydrogen (dew point estimated to be 100°F or higher) at temperatures below 670°C.   Comparison with Figure 14 shows that there has been a significant increase in the quantity of the whiskers produced but the results are poor relative to that reported by Cochardt and Weidersich.[7]   Subsequent studies showed that no significant increase in quantity of whiskers produced could be achieved by mechanically mixing the halide salt with iron oxide as was so successful for growth from the liquid.

In an attempt to get the proper dispersion of oxide particles in the solid halide salt, α-Fe_2O_3 and $FeCl_2$ were heated in a closed system containing H_2 and H_2O at temperatures below 670°C for times up to 4 hr.   This procedure produced a fused mixture which could then be reduced at temperatures as low as 400°C with profuse whisker growths as indicated in Figures 22 and 23.   The precise chemical nature of the

fused mass could not be determined by x-ray techniques.   Lines corresponding to FeO, Fe_3O_4, α-Fe_2O_3, and $FeCl_2$ could be identified in the
x-ray patterns, but many other lines were present which could not be
identified.   It is believed that the whiskers produced by this method
have a [100] fiber axis.   They are not significantly tapered, grow at
the rate of about 1 cm/hr ($\sim$ 3 μ/sec) and most are less than 25 μ in
diameter.   Visual observation of the growth process indicates that
they grow from the base.

Frequently, $FeCl_2$ crystals are observed to grow on the free surfaces
of the iron boat during the early stages of holding an α-Fe_2O_3 and $FeCl_2$

Fig. 23. Iron whiskers grown from fused mixture of $FeCl_2$ and α-Fe_2O_3 at 600°C.
4.2$\times$.

mixture in a nonreducing hydrogen atmosphere in the temperature
range from 600–650°C.   These crystals could later be reduced at
temperatures below 670°C in the proper hydrogen atmosphere to produce the type of whisker growth shown in Figure 24.   This picture
shows a very small fraction of the whiskers which are present because
only those small diameter whiskers which are properly positioned to
reflect light to the camera can be seen.   Growth of this nature is very
difficult to reproduce since it requires a very delicate balance between
hydrogen flow rate, quantity of $FeCl_2$ to be reduced, and moisture content of the hydrogen atmosphere.

The Ferrous Bromide Process

Many of the results obtained with $FeBr_2$ were identical to those for $FeCl_2$. No whisker growth was observed for the reduction of high purity sublimed salt in dry hydrogen ($-60°F$ dew point or less). The whisker growing tendency could be radically increased by the addition of $\alpha\text{-}Fe_2O_3$, and the average whisker diameter of the [100] type whiskers decreased as the dew point of the hydrogen was increased. In addition, the whisker growth characteristics changed discontinuously at the melting point of the halide salt. Except for a special situation as noted later almost no tendency for growth from solid $FeBr_2$ was observed.

Fig. 24. Iron whiskers growing on the surfaces of the iron boats. .75×.

Some of the samples of the commercially available material produced extremely good results and others gave poor results. This was later correlated with the $\beta\text{-}FeO\cdot OH$ content of the samples which was found to vary from approximately 7 to 28 wt-%. The amount present in any sample appeared to be related to the period of time which had elapsed since manufacture. It is presumed that the $\beta\text{-}FeO\cdot OH$ was formed by slow hydrolysis of the $FeBr_2$.

Since $FeBr_2$ can be readily decomposed to $\alpha\text{-}Fe_2O_3$ by heating in air, it was very easy to demonstrate the tremendous influence of iron oxide on the tendency for whisker growth. A boat containing relatively high purity material was heated for 5 min in a temperature gradient in an oxidizing atmosphere with one end of the boat at approximately

100°C and the other at 400°C. Figure 25 shows the nature of the whisker growth in the boat upon subsequent reduction in hydrogen at 720°C. Whisker growth occurred only in the region where the bromide was heated to 300°C or higher and was partially decomposed to α-Fe_2O_3.

In some tests the α-Fe_2O_3 was hydrogen reduced to iron powder prior to mixing with the $FeBr_2$. Subsequent reduction in the proper atmosphere produced only limited tendency for growth. If the mixture, however, were heated to temperature under conditions which reoxidized the iron powder prior to reduction, profuse whisker growth was subsequently observed. It appears reasonably conclusive, therefore, that some form of iron oxide, and not some other impurity

Fig. 25. Iron whisker growth in a boat of $FeBr_2$ heated in an oxygen atmosphere in a temperature gradient prior to reduction at 720°C. 1.5×.

in the $FeBr_2$ or α-Fe_2O_3, is responsible for the nucleation and/or growth of the iron whiskers.

Thus, for $FeBr_2$, satisfactory results can be obtained by either adding α-Fe_2O_3 directly, heating for finite times in an oxidizing atmosphere or allowing the commercial material to decompose over a period of time. The last method appears to be the best, but good results can be obtained from each method if the heating rates are rapid and the hydrogen has a dew point of approximately 80 to 120°F.

Figures 26 and 27 represent typical examples of the quality and quantity of whiskers which can be produced. In general, a bromide-oxide mixture containing 10 to 30 wt-% of α-Fe_2O_3 heated to the reduction temperature in 5 min or less will produce good results. The hydrogen flow rate should approximate 3–5 liters/hr/g of mixture. The design of the boat is extremely important as shown in Figure 28.

Fig. 26. Iron whiskers grown from mixture of $FeBr_2$ and α-Fe_2O_3 reduced at 720°C. 6×.

The whiskers have very little tendency to grow where the hydrogen impinges directly on the growth site. High linear velocities of hydrogen, even for proper boat design, produce badly kinked and distorted whiskers. For this reason it is desirable to have as large a diameter reaction chamber as possible.

Fig. 27. Iron whiskers grown from mixture of $FeBr_2$ and α-Fe_2O_3 reduced at 720°C. 18×.

The $FeBr_2$ has a much higher vapor pressure at a given temperature than $FeCl_2$ and hence one important purpose of water vapor in the hydrogen is to reduce the rate of evaporation. For the reduction of the purified material with dry hydrogen (dew point $-60°F$ or lower) only a few weight-% of the material was actually reduced in the boat. The presence of water vapor also appears to catalyze the reaction of $FeBr_2$ with hydrogen and to increase the tendency for the liquid halide salt to wet the surface of the iron boat. This latter effect is inferred from the increased height to which the liquid halide salt creeps on the

Fig. 28. Influence of boat design on quantity of whiskers produced by the hydrogen reduction of a $FeBr_2$-α-Fe_2O_3 mixture at 720°C. .7×.

sides of the boats as the water vapor content of the atmosphere is increased.

Whiskers were grown for reduction temperatures as high as 900°C provided very rapid heating rates were used. For low temperature reductions (700–720°C), the whiskers were straight, small diameter and exhibited little overgrowth. As the temperature was increased, the amount of taper was radically increased, the whiskers were frequently kinked and distorted and a much greater percentage was hexagonal in shape indicating a [111] fiber axis. For the highest reduction temperature, a significant increase in the quantity of added oxide was required for the production of an equivalent number of whiskers.

Visual observation of the reduction cycle for a α-Fe_2O_3–$FeBr_2$ mixture indicated that heating at temperatures up to 720°C produced few apparent changes except for the growth of some $FeBr_2$ crystals along the inner surface of the boat. After 2–3 min at temperature, the mass in the bottom of the boat fused together and some tendency for the liquid to creep up the side of the boat was observed. This was followed by an incubation period of 2–5 min before the growth of the first whisker. Although many were observed to grow at any given time in the boat, only one at a time appeared to grow from any given position. Whisker growth ceased after 15 to 20 min, but it was necessary to hold an additional period of time in pure dry hydrogen to eliminate all traces of halide salts as indicated by the rate at which the whisker surfaces corroded upon exposure to air. Although it was not measured directly, the minimum growth rate was higher than 25 μ/sec.

A detailed study of the boats at various stages in the reduction cycle indicated that growth ceased when the liquid level dropped below the base of the growing whisker and that the whisker surfaces were apparently covered with a liquid layer during growth. Figure 29 shows an example, after cooling to room temperature, of the deposit which exists on the surfaces of the growing whiskers. This can be contrasted with the bright, shiny surfaces after growth is completed as indicated in Figures 26 and 27.

The oxide phases present at each step in the reduction process were identified by x-ray means. The α-Fe_2O_3 was reduced to Fe_3O_4 upon heating to the reduction temperature, the Fe_3O_4 was reduced to FeO after holding approximately 5 min at temperature and all the FeO was reduced to α-Fe after 20–25 min at temperature. The micron size oxide particles were apparently too small to build up the oxide layer structure usually observed during the reduction of the bulk oxide. The fact that the oxide-bromide mixture fuses when the composition of the oxide corresponds to FeO suggests that $FeBr_2$ preferentially wets FeO or that FeO has a high solubility in $FeBr_2$. There was no indication in the x-ray studies that any intermediate compound was formed.

The influence of various amounts of impurities on the growth of the small diameter whiskers was investigated by reducing an oxide-bromide mixture under conditions which gave good as well as reproducible results. Other materials such as zinc sulfate and phosphate, ferrous sulfide, sulfate and phosphide were added to the bromide-oxide mixture and the hydrogen was modified by the addition of argon, helium, hydrogen sulfide, carbon monoxide, and nitrogen. Except for the inert gases, argon and helium, which had little effect, the average diameter of the whiskers in the boats decreased as the quantity of impurity was increased. At some point, however, the more effective impurities would cause whisker growth to cease. The effect of a given percentage of any of the materials appeared to be related in some manner to their reactivity with iron. For example, about 5% hydrogen sulfide by volume had the same influence as 20% carbon monoxide and 50% nitrogen. Dilution of the hydrogen with the gases such as argon, helium, or nitrogen had no major effects except that it was necessary to adjust the amount of material reduced to correspond to the decreased availability of hydrogen. Frequently, however, the required linear flow velocity was so high that the whiskers were badly distorted.

Growth of whiskers by the reduction of solid $FeBr_2$ could be accomplished only if a mixture of the oxide and bromide was heated for a period of time above the melting point of the bromide in a non-reducing hydrogen atmosphere. Subsequent heating of this fused mass at temperatures below 685°C produced whisker growth, but the results were not as spectacular as those with ferrous chloride. The slow growth rates from the solid allowed most of the ferrous bromide, because of its high vapor pressure, to sublime from the boat.

Whisker growth by reduction of the liquid halide salt was presumed to be from the tip but certain indications suggest that the [100] type whiskers, in particular, might grow from the base. Figure 30 shows the growth appearance when the temperature of the reduction chamber is reduced from 720 to 600°C and reheated to 720°C within a five-minute period during whisker growth. Clumps of iron particles can be seen at various heights on the whisker which might have been pushed from the substrate by growth from the base. Also, many long whiskers extending the full width of the boat are elastically bent.

The nature of the whisker tip and the junction between two whiskers which welded together during growth were studied in great detail. The condition at the tip was found to vary radically. Most were tapered but many had crystalline growths of fantastic degrees of complexity. In general, the segments of the whisker between the growth

Fig. 29. Character of the deposit which exists upon the surfaces of growing whiskers after cooling to room temperature from 720°C. 4.2×.

site and the interfering crystal were straight if grown from liquid halide salt and many were curved for growth from the solid. This observation tends to confirm tip growth for the first and base growth for the latter. There was rarely any evidence that the intersection had any apparent influence on the growth of either crystal in growth

Fig. 30. Character of whisker growth which results when hydrogen reduction at 720°C is interrupted. 3.5×.

from the liquid. The angle of intersection varied from a minimum of about 10° to a maximum of about 170.°

References

1. Hardy, H. K., *Progress in Metal Physics*, Vol. VI, Pergamon Press, New York, 1956, p. 45.
2. Buckley, H. E., *Crystal Growth*, Wiley, New York, 1951.
3. Nabarro, F. R. N., and P. S. Jackson, *Growth and Perfection of Crystals*, Wiley, New York, 1958, p. 11.
4. Sears, G. W., A. Gatti, and R. L. Fullman, *Acta Met.*, **2**, 727 (1954).
5. Herring, C., and J. K. Galt, *Phys. Rev.*, **85**, 1060 (1952).
6. Coleman, R. V., and G. W. Sears, *Acta Met.*, **5**, 31 (1957).
7. Cochardt, A. W., and H. Weidersich, *Naturwissenschaften*, **42**, 342 (1955).
8. Eisner, R. L., *Acta Met.*, **3**, 414 (1955).
9. Brenner, S. S., *J. Appl. Phys.*, **27**, 1484 (1956).
10. Gyulai, Z., *Z. Physik.*, **138**, 317 (1954).
11. Brenner, S. S., *Growth and Perfection of Crystals*, Wiley, New York, 1958, p. 157.
12. Sears, G. W., *Acta Met.*, **1**, 453 (1953).
13. Sears, G. W., *Acta Met.*, **3**, 367 (1955).
14. Sears, G. W., *Acta Met.*, **3**, 361 (1955).
15. Gatti, A., and R. L. Fullman, private communication.
16. Brenner, S. S., *Acta Met.*, **4**, 62 (1956).
17. Barrett, C. S., *Structure of Metals*, McGraw-Hill, New York, 1952, p. 647.
18. Gorsuch, P. D., "Supersaturation Ratios for Iron Whisker Growth," *J. Chem. Phys.*, to be published.
19. Gorsuch, P. D., "On the Theories of Iron Whisker Growth," *J. Appl. Phys.*, to be published.
20. Paparteou, A., *Z. Krist.*, **92**, 89 (1935).
21. *Handbook of Chemistry and Physics*, Chemical Rubber Publishing Co., 36th ed., 1954–55, pp. 526–29, 2426–27.
22. Maier, G. G., *U. S. Bur. Mines Tech. Paper*, No. 360 (1925).
23. Macharen, R. O., and N. W. Gregory, *J. Phys. Chem.*, **59**, 184 (1955).
24. *Encyclopedia of Chemical Technology*, Interscience Encyclopedia, **8**, pp. 58–62.
25. Mellor, J. W., *A Comprehensive Treatise of Inorganic and Theoretical Chemistry*, Vol. XIV, Longman's Green, New York; Fe (Pt. 3), Co, 1935, pp. 9, 40, 117.
26. Sedgwick, N. J., *Chemical Elements and Their Compounds*, Oxford Univ. Press, New York, 1950, p. 1332.
27. Kangro, W., and E. Petersen, *Z. anorg. u. allgem. Chem.*, **261**, 157 (1950).
28. Weiser, H. B., W. O. Milligan, and E. L. Cook, in W. C. Fernelius, ed., *Inorganic Synthesis*, *II*, 1946, p. 215.
29. Weiser, H. B., and O. B. Milligan, *J. Am. Chem. Soc.*, **57**, 238 (1935).
30. Smithells, C. J., *Metals Reference Book*, Vol. II, Interscience, New York-London, 1949, pp. 597, 599, 615.

31. Wells, A. F., *Structural Inorganic Chemistry*, Oxford Univ. Press, New York, 1950, p. 413.

32. Sano, K., *J. Chem. Soc., Japan*, **59**, 1069 (1938).

33. P. D. Gorsuch, "Supersaturation Ratios for Iron Whisker Growth," *J. Chem. Phys.*, to be published.

Discussion

E. Sterling (*M. W. Kellogg Co.*): Your last picture showed some branched filaments. Since the formations you studied are best accounted for by a basal growth mechanism how can one explain such branching? Would you perhaps attribute this effect to some entrained material that was attached to the growing filaments and happened to be capable of nucleating independent filaments?

P. D. Gorsuch: The very complex growth forms and branching shown in Figure 30 are usually found at points along the whiskers where the growth process is interrupted. In this particular instance, the interruption was accomplished by first lowering the temperature of the reduction chamber to stop or retard whisker growth and then reheating back to the previous reduction temperature to continue the growth process. The results may be interpreted as indicating basal growth, but it is believed that growth is from the tip. This makes it difficult, therefore, to attribute the branching to entrained material attached to the growing whiskers.

At present, it is believed that the complex growth patterns and branching result from contamination of the whisker tip with impurity atoms or molecules during the interruption of the growth process. If the concentration of these impurity molecules is sufficiently great, the surface free energy of many lattice planes may be lowered to a point where coherent two-dimensional nucleation can occur in many directions on the tip at one time. After some finite amount of growth, the surface area of the tip increases to a point where the average concentration of impurity atoms drops to a low value and growth is again restricted to the plane or planes with either the correct surface free energy or the proper dislocation geometry for growth at the supersaturation level of the reduction chamber.

SECTION VIII: SOLIDIFI-
CATION OF METALS

. . . .

The Degeneration of Freezing Plane Interfaces in a Controlled Solidification System*

EDWARD E. HUCKE

University of Michigan, Ann Arbor, Michigan

and

MERTON C. FLEMINGS, C. M. ADAMS, and H. F. TAYLOR

Massachusetts Institute of Technology, Cambridge, Massachusetts

Abstract

An apparatus capable of independent control and variation of temperature gradients and solidification velocity is used to freeze highly agitated alloy melts. Liquid agitation is achieved by low frequency, inductive stirring.

Conditions required for interface stability, and the resulting structures and segregation, are investigated for Al-Zn, Al-Cu, and Al-Fe alloys over a range of freezing rates and compositions. Alloy contents range from 2 to 50, 0.5 to 10, and 0.04 to 0.2 wt-% for Al-Zn, Al-Cu, and Al-Fe, respectively.

Conditions necessary for plane front solidification are found to be consistent with those required by the relation:

$$G_L/U = [m(1 - k_0)]/Dk_0 \, C_s$$

By changing the growth conditions away from those of interface stability, the structure changes from columnar to equiaxed grains. The size of the equiaxed grains decreases as the alloy content increases.

Considerable macrosegregation is observed in the plane front heats as well as heats which solidify with degenerate interfaces. The segregation results, as well as those for stability, indicate the expected effect of maintaining bulk liquid agitation.

* This paper is based on portions of theses submitted by Edward E. Hucke and Merton C. Flemings in partial fulfillment of the requirements for the degree of Doctor of Science, Metallurgy Department, Massachusetts Institute of Technology, February, 1954.

INTRODUCTION

The mechanical, physical, and chemical properties of a given cast alloy are functions of the amount, distribution, and compositions of the various phases which comprise the microstructure. These variables can be influenced to a marked degree by the conditions prevailing during solidification. While it has been appreciated that major changes in structure could be brought about by the variation of superheat, cooling rate, alloy additions, mechanical agitation, and nucleating agents it has been only recently that enough information has been gathered in controlled systems so that the interplay of these factors can be understood.

The variables which determine structure and segregation have been classified as (1) those affecting thermal gradients, (2) those affecting concentration gradients in the liquid adjacent a solidifying interface, and (3) crystallographic factors.[1] Unfortunately, it is not possible to isolate the effects of the above parameters in ordinary sand or chill-mold castings; any change in solidification conditions usually affects more than one parameter. For example, increasing the rate of heat removal from an ordinary casting increases thermal gradients but also increases rate of solidification; hence, concentration gradients in the liquid may also be changed.

In order to quantitatively study the importance of individual solidification parameters, it is necessary to utilize a special apparatus by which they can be controlled independently. One such apparatus has been described by Tiller and Rutter[1] in which freezing rate is independent of thermal gradients at the freezing interface. This is accomplished by maintaining near-steady-state heat flow conditions. Experimental results have clearly shown the presence of a boundary layer which contains an excess of solute atoms at the interface. This layer results from the fact that, even at very slow rates of advance, the diffusion of solute away from the interface is not fast enough to equal the rate of solute rejection by the interface until a substantial concentration gradient is established in the liquid. The shape of the concentration profile ahead of the interface has been treated mathematically for several simple conditions of bulk liquid flow; namely, (1) without convection by Chalmers et al.,[2] (2) with natural convection by Wagner,[3] and (3) with forced convection by Burton et al.[4]

The concentration profile at a plane interface advancing at a rate U into a binary liquid of bulb composition C_0, is shown schematically in Figure 1.   The case shown is for a system where addition of a solute decreases the freezing temperature of the melt.   An analogous argument can be given for the reverse case.   It can be shown that a steady state is reached where the amount of solute rejected by the solid at the interface just equals that diffusing away from the interface.   The composition of the interface rises to a value C_i which is greater than C_0.   The solute concentration C_s rises with C_i.   Assum-

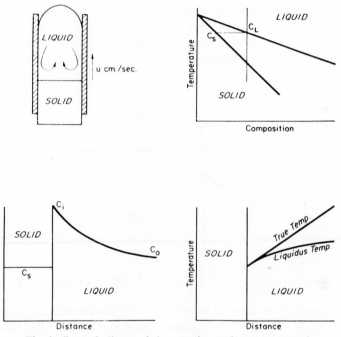

Fig. 1. General scheme of the experimental apparatus used.

ing partition equilibrium

$$C_s = k_0 C_i \tag{1}$$

where k_0 is given by the equilibrium diagram and is assumed independent of composition.   When no stirring exists in the liquid it has been shown[2] that, except for transient zones at the beginning and end of freezing, C_i rises to a value such that C_s equals C_0 and no segregation takes place.   When the liquid is stirred, C_s is less than C_0, but the resulting segregation is by no means that predicted by the equilibrium diagram. It is convenient to define k according to

$$C_s = kC_0 \qquad (2)$$

where k is a function of k_0, D (diffusion coefficient), U, and the degree of stirring. For the case of no stirring $k = 1$. As U is decreased and the stirring increased, k approaches k_0. It is evident that in cases where a large segregation is desired such as in zone melting a high degree of liquid agitation is required. Pfann[5] has given a rather complete survey of stirring methods for use in zone melting systems.

The plane interface described above will be a stable condition only in rather specialized situations. Since the interface is at the freezing

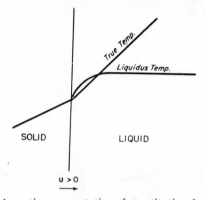

Fig. 2. A schematic representation of constitutional supercooling.

temperature of an alloy of composition C_i, the freezing temperature of the liquid ahead of the interface must rise as the concentration falls, as is indicated in Figure 1. As long as the temperature gradient in the liquid exceeds the initial slope of the curve marked "liquidus temp" a plane front will be stable. When the temperature gradient is less than this value a condition exists as illustrated in Figure 2. Chalmers and co-workers have referred to this situation as "constitutional supercooling." It can be seen that the interface will then degenerate with certain areas growing ahead of the main interface into the constitutionally supercooled region.

Tiller and Rutter[1] studied in detail the degradation of plane front interfaces in several dilute alloys of Pb in an unstirred system. Their findings justified the existence of the enriched boundary layer both qualitatively and quantitatively. The degradation of plane front solidification was found to show rather well defined stages as the amount of constitutional supercooling was increased. The initial breakdown showed the development of pock marks, followed by a cellular growth, with subsequent branching of the cells into dendrite projections from the interface.

The initial breakdown was found to correspond to the theoretically derived relation

$$G_L/U = [mC_0(1 - k_0)]/Dk_0 \tag{3}$$

where G_L is the temperature gradient in the liquid, and m is the slope of the liquidus line. The final breakdown was found to correspond to the relation,

$$G_L/U^{1/2} = BC_0 \tag{4}$$

where B is a proportionality constant depending on the alloy system.

Table I shows the maximum solute concentrations that can be tolerated in several alloy systems based on Eq. (3) and assuming a temperature gradient of 180°C/cm and a rate of advance U of 1.5×10^{-3} cm/sec. It can be easily seen that even with these rather conservative figures a plane front would be stable in most systems only in rather dilute alloys. In the case of zone melting, due to the very small solute concentrations and the slow growth rates used, interface stability is not a serious problem. However, for all common alloys

TABLE I

Comparison of Maximum Allowable Solute Concentration for Plane Front Solidification in Several Unstirred Systems
$(G_L = 180°C/cm; \quad U = 1.5 \times 10^{-3} \text{ cm/sec})$

Alloy base	Solute	$D \times 10^5$, cm²/sec	k_0	$-m$, °C/wt-%	$(C_0)_{max}$, wt-%
Al	Cu	7.2	0.171	3.38	0.50
Al	Zn	6.6	0.445	1.67	3.50
Al	Fe	1.4	0.018	2.94	0.01
Al	Mg	2.7	0.285	4.30	0.30
Pb	Ag	3.6	0.040	9.20	0.02
Cu	Mg	5.0	0.289	37.3	0.06
Cu	Sn	5.0	0.540	11.4	0.62
Cu	Zn	5.0	0.860	5.54	6.70

in ordinary casting processes interface instability is always encountered.

Equation (3) was derived for an unstirred liquid for which $C_l = C_s$ and $k = 1$. When the derivation is made for the case with liquid stirring a similar expression results,

$$G/U = [m(1 - k_0)]/Dk_0C_s \qquad (5)$$

This expression for the initial breakdown conditions differs from Eq. (3) only in that C_s appears instead of C_0. It can, therefore, be seen that agitation of the liquid allows less stringent conditions to be maintained without degeneration of the interface.

PRESENT WORK

Previous published experimental work on interface stability has been confined to several dilute alloys in unstirred systems. The present investigation deals with controlled solidification in more highly alloyed melts under conditions of violent bulk-liquid agitation. Under these conditions the interface instability and resulting structure and segregation are more closely related to those which might be met in continuous casting, centrifugal casting, and freezing in casting sprues. The alloy systems studied were Al-Cu, Al-Zn, and Al-Fe. These systems show large differences in the values of k_0, D, and m.

Experimental Apparatus and Procedure

Figure 3 is a pictorial drawing of the experimental apparatus. An insulated crucible was used to contain the melt to be studied. Power was supplied by an induction coil operating at a frequency of 960 cps. Heat was removed from the melt by a bottom plug made from an alloy of the system under study. A violent water spray on this plug was arranged at a preset distance below the heating coil. The interface position could be measured at any time by inserting a fine alumina-coated iron wire through the melt. With this apparatus the interface could be held under steady state heat flow conditions with a temperature gradient determined by the distance between the water spray and the coil. The magnitude of the temperature gradient in the liquid at the interface was determined by measuring the gradient in the solid G_s and making an appropriate correction (see

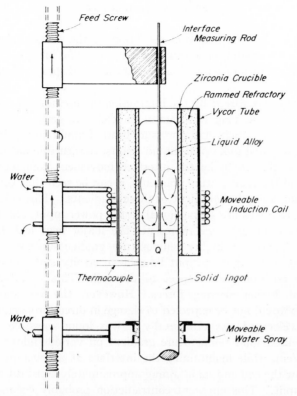

Fig. 3. Diagram of the basic elements of the apparatus.

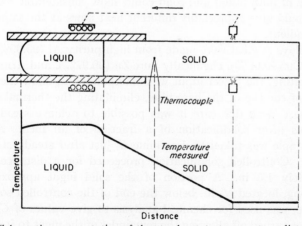

Fig. 4. Schematic representation of the steady state temperature distribution.

Table II). A schematic representation of the temperature distribution in the system is shown in Figure 4. The interface could be
moved at a known rate by advancing the coil and spray assembly on a
feed screw.

The melt was stirred by the interaction of the induced currents in
the melt with the magnetic field of the coil. In general, these magnetic forces were such that a pressure head of liquid metal about 6 in.
high was required to keep the liquid against the crucible walls. While
it was possible to make the interface movement completely independent of the temperature gradients, it can be seen that the stirring
is not completely independent of these gradients. This is true since
the stirring forces are proportional to the power input, and the heat
flow across the interface represents the major heat leak from the
system. Therefore, higher temperature gradients would require a
somewhat higher power input to achieve steady state at the same
interface position with respect to the coil. This would result in
somewhat higher stirring forces. However, the boundary layer
thickness would not be expected to change in direct proportion to the
stirring velocity.[4] Experimentally it was found possible to vary
the measured solid temperature gradient on various alloys from 54
to 76°C/cm, while maintaining the interface at a constant position
just below the coil and maintaining approximately constant electrical
power input. This apparent contradiction probably occurred since
many of the heats were highly alloyed and therefore the thermal conductivity in both liquid and solid could show considerable variation,
which would give appreciably different heat flows at the same measured gradient.

The alloys studied were made from high purity Al (99.99%), electrolytic Cu (99.92%), chemically pure Zn (99.97%), and Armco iron.
After melting, the power input was manipulated to allow the partial
melting of the top of the base plug, eliminating the thermal contact
resistance. With due care it was possible to achieve steady state
conditions after solidification of a fraction of an inch. A small
liquid sample was taken to determine C_0 just after steady state was
reached. Controlled solidification proceeded for a distance of approximately 1.5 in. A portion of the solid ingot approximately
$1/8$ in. long, located $3/4$ in. below the end of the controlled solidification zone, was used for chemical analysis to give values of C_s. The
power was turned off allowing the remainder of the ingot to freeze in a

TABLE II
Summary of Experimental Heats

Heat No.	Alloy	C_c, wt-%	C_e, wt-%	k	G_s, °C/cm	G_L,[a] °C/cm	$U \times 10^3$, cm/sec	$G_L/U \times 10^{-5}$, °C/cm²/sec	Structure
4	Al-Cu	0.65	0.30	0.46	61	160	1.4	1.2	Columnar
6	Al-Cu	0.69	0.28	0.41	60	160	3.0	0.52	Columnar
8	Al-Cu	0.91	0.20	0.22	62	160	0.45	3.6	Columnar
7	Al-Cu	0.98	0.53	0.54	60	150	2.9	0.54	Columnar
1	Al-Cu	1.02	0.44	0.46	76	200	1.6	1.2	Columnar
5	Al-Cu	1.02	0.30	0.30	62	160	0.88	1.8	Columnar
2	Al-Cu	1.08	0.57	0.53	67	170	1.8	0.97	Columnar
3	Al-Cu	1.45	0.82	0.57	67	170	1.7	1.0	Columnar
9	Al-Cu	1.67	0.81	0.49	54	140	1.6	0.87	Columnar
23	Al-Cu	1.43	1.00	0.70	56	140	3.2	0.46	Equiaxed
21	Al-Cu	1.84	1.02	0.55	70	180	2.0	0.92	Equiaxed
22	Al-Cu	2.84	1.79	0.63	68	180	1.5	1.2	Equiaxed
20	Al-Cu	3.64	2.18	0.60	73	190	1.9	1.0	Equiaxed
19	Al-Cu	4.32	2.81	0.65	72	190	1.6	1.1	Equiaxed
24	Al-Cu	9.90	5.32	0.54	58	150	1.6	0.94	Equiaxed
10	Al-Zn	1.98	1.35	0.68	72	190	0.42	0.45	Columnar
11	Al-Zn	4.00	3.01	0.75	68	180	1.0	1.8	Columnar
15	Al-Zn	5.18	3.93	0.76	64	170	2.2	0.77	Columnar
17	Al-Zn	5.23	3.30	0.63	60	160	0.55	2.8	Columnar
12	Al-Zn	5.33	3.20	0.60	60	160	0.96	1.6	Columnar
16	Al-Zn	5.42	2.91	0.54	61	160	0.28	5.7	Columnar
13	Al-Zn	6.99	5.41	0.78	63	160	1.6	1.0	Columnar
18	Al-Zn	8.86	4.75	0.54	59	150	0.94	1.6	Columnar
28	Al-Zn	9.86	7.72	0.78	66	170	2.8	0.60	Equiaxed
27	Al-Zn	16.10	11.54	0.72	65	170	1.4	1.2	Equiaxed
25	Al-Zn	20.25	14.13	0.70	64	170	0.78	2.1	Equiaxed
26	Al-Zn	29.50	19.95	0.67	67	180	1.1	1.5	Equiaxed
29	Al-Zn	48.35	32.86	0.68	71	180	0.95	2.0	Equiaxed
31	Al-Fe	0.037			70	180	1.5		Columnar
30	Al-Fe	0.044			70	180	1.5		Columnar
32	Al-Fe	0.057			70	180	1.5		Columnar
33	Al-Fe	0.123			70	180	1.5		Columnar
35	Al-Fe	0.156			70	180	1.5		Equiaxed
34	Al-Fe	0.229			70	180	1.5		Equiaxed

[a] Here, G_L was derived by assuming the heat of fusion to be negligible and assuming the ratio of the solid to liquid thermal conductivity for the alloys to be 2.6.

manner very much similar to chill casting. The ingots were sectioned in a longitudinal plane and examined for macro- and microstructure.

The range of U studied was from 0.45 to 3.2 $\times$ 10^{-3} cm/sec. The temperature gradient in the solid was varied from 54 to 76°C/cm. The initial concentrations were from 0.65 to 9.9, 1.98 to 48.35, and 0.037 to 0.229 wt-% for Al-Cu, Al-Zn, and Al-Fe, respectively.

Table II is a summary of the results for 34 heats.

Macrostructures

The macrostructures of the zones solidified under the controlled conditions were of two types. The first consisted of large columnar grains and the second fine equiaxed grains. Figure 5 shows these two typical types of structure for three Al-Cu heats. These ingots have been cut from the plug at a location corresponding to the beginning of the steady state zone of controlled solidification. In all cases the controlled zone showed no indication of gas porosity even though the melts undoubtedly contained a large amount of hydrogen.

The controlled zone extended to approximately 20% of the height of the ingot; above this zone a small region of equiaxed grains was always found, followed by a columnar zone and then a zone of large equiaxed grains. The zones above the controlled zone, formed when the power was turned off, correspond exactly to that expected in a chill casting of these alloys. The equiaxed zone at the top of the ingots showed considerable porosity.

The presence of the large columnar structure in the controlled zone was taken to mean the presence of plane front solidification. The shape of the interface (concave downward) can be deduced from some faintly visible bands which appeared after etching. These were undoubtedly the result of very small fluctuations in the growth rate, causing small changes in the solute concentration of the solid.

The appearance of the fine, equiaxed structure was taken to mean the complete degeneration of plane front solidification, with nucleation occurring a short distance ahead of the interface. The size of the equiaxed grains varied considerably for different heats in a given alloy system. Higher initial concentrations or faster growth rates at a given temperature gradient caused a finer grain size. Figure 5 shows an example of this variation. Too few heats were available to establish the effect for the individual variables mentioned. The

(a)   (b)   (c)

Fig. 5. (a) Heat 7 showing columnar growth. (b) Heat 21 showing equiaxed structure. (c) Heat 20 showing the effect of C_0 on equiaxed grain size.

columnar grains were found to vary in size but with no apparent
pattern. This size variation was probably due to the differences in
the crystallographic orientations of the grains present initially at the
plug melt interface. While no x-ray data were taken, it is probable
that many of the grains shown by etching differed very little from
one another in orientation.

Microstructures

The microstructure of the columnar-type heats showed no trapped
eutectic and no gas or shrinkage in the controlled zone. These facts
give an additional indication that plane front solidification was
achieved. Figure 6 shows a typical microstructure of a plane front
heat.

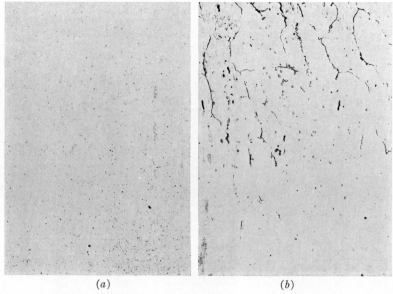

(a) (b)

Fig. 6. (a) Microstructure of heat 3 in controlled zone. (b) Microstructure of heat
3 at junction between controlled zone and chill layer. 75×.

Just at the boundary between the end of the columnar controlled
zone and the remaining ingot a very interesting type of microstructure
was observed. Figure 6 shows a typical case. Here the grains are
separated by solute-rich channels. Tiller and Rutter,[1] in describing
the degeneration of an interface into an unstirred liquid, have shown
that these areas result when the interface starts to grow into the
supercooled liquid adjoining it. These channels can extend a long
distance behind the advancing dendrite tips and the resulting solute
trapped probably accounts for inverse macrosegregation.

The equiaxed heats showed some areas resulting from the trapping
of high solute-content liquid between grains. However, these areas
were surprisingly few and very small. No continuous or nearly
continuous network was found. Figure 7 shows one area containing
some $CuAl_2$ trapped during freezing.

Interface Stability

In principle, it would be possible to predict from Eq. (5) the conditions where the interface first becomes unstable. However, in the

Fig. 7. Microstructure of heat 19 in equiaxed controlled zone.   Dark areas are
CuAl$_2$.   75$\times$.

systems studied many of the assumptions underlying Eq. (5) were not
fulfilled.

First, Eq. (5) was derived for the case of no constitutional supercooling, while the method used to detect instability in this work
would probably not correspond to this condition.   With very slight
amounts of supercooling the interface would develop cells and dendrite projections.   As long as these were small and were contained
wholly within the boundary layer at the interface, the resulting
structure would probably still show columnar growth.   Using the
segregation data it is possible to estimate from the development of
Burton et al.[4] that the thickness of this layer was approximately
0.05 cm for most of the runs.   In general, the structural change noted
would seem to correspond to severe enough supercooling within the
boundary layer to cause a new set of grains to nucleate a short distance from the main interface.

Also, Eq. (5) assumes the solid and liquid densities to be equal, and
m, k_0, and D to be independent of concentration.   All of these assumptions may be appreciably in error in view of the high solute concentrations undoubtedly present at the interface in many of the heats.
In order to test the relation, values of the temperature gradient

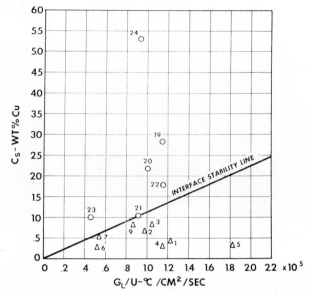

Fig. 8. Aluminum-copper alloys.   (O) equiaxed grains and (△) columnar grains.

in the liquid must be known.   To derive these values from the observed solid temperature gradient, reliable values for solid and liquid thermal conductivity as a function of solute content are needed, but lacking.

In spite of these objections it was found that after plotting values of C_s vs G_L/U for all the heats of a given system, a straight line could be drawn through the origin separating all the equiaxed heats from the columnar heats.   Figures 8 and 9 show these plots.   The slopes of the lines are considerably greater than obtained by assuming reasonable values for the required "constants."   It was found impossible to separate the two types of heats with a straight line if C_0 were plotted against G_L/U as would be required in the case of an unstirred system.

No values of C_s for the six Al-Fe heats were obtained, but all of these heats were run at the same gradient and velocity so that the breakdown point in terms of C_0 gives a relative measure of stability. Under conditions where 0.2 wt-% Fe would cause equiaxed grains, it was estimated with the aid of Figures 8 and 9, and an estimate of the expected segregation, that about 2.5% Cu and 11% Zn could be

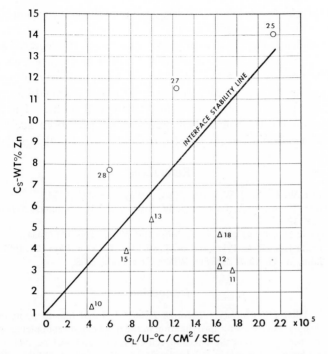

Fig. 9. Aluminum-zinc alloys.   (O) equiaxed grains and (△) columnar grains.

tolerated without instability.   A comparison of these values with those in Table I for the unstirred condition shows that substantially larger amounts of solute can be tolerated without interface instability when the melt is highly agitated.   While qualitative, these figures certainly bear out the prediction that would be made on the basis of Eq. (5) and the relative values of m, k_0, and D shown in Table I. The most important variation is undoubtedly in k_0.

Segregation

Values of k, which are a measure of the net segregation, are listed in Table II.   It was possible to approach k_0 at the lowest speeds used. The lowest values obtained for k were 0.22 and 0.54, compared with 0.171 and 0.445 for k_0 for Al-Cu and Al-Zn, respectively.   While k generally increased with U, the data showed many anomalies.   However, the values are in all cases less than one, the value expected in the absence of liquid agitation.

A somewhat surprising result is apparent from the segregation data for the equiaxed heats. These showed almost as much segregation as did the plane front heats. In view of the possibility of trapping liquid of high solute content between the grains it would be expected that very little, if any, macrosegregation would occur. The growth mechanism for these equiaxed grains must have been such that a minimum of liquid became isolated from the stirred bulk liquid.

References

1. Tiller, W. A., and J. W. Rutter, *Can. J. Phys.*, **34**, 234 (1956).
2. Tiller, W. A., K. A. Jackson, J. W. Rutter, and B. Chalmers, *Acta Met.*, **1**, No. 4, 428 (1953).
3. Wagner, C., *Trans. Am. Soc. Mining Met. Engrs.*, **200**, 154 (1954).
4. Burton J. A., R. C. Prim, and W. T. Slichter, *J. Chem. Phys.*, **21**, 1987 (1953).
5. Pfann, W. G., *Zone Melting*, Wiley, New York, 1958.

Discussion

W. A. Tiller (*Westinghouse Research Labs.*): I would like to point out that Eq. (3) is only a first-order approximation in the determination of planar interface stability since it neglects the effect of cell curvature and surface energy on the transition from a planar to a cellular interface. When these additional features are considered it is found that a certain degree of constitutional supercooling is required before a cellular interface will form. For the case of stirring Eq. (5), which has been treated by the discusser ("Alloy Crystal Growth," *Growth and Perfection of Crystals*, Wiley, New York, 1958), should be substituted by

$$G/U = [m(1 - k_0)]/Dk_0 \, C_s - \alpha\sigma \qquad (D1)$$

where σ is solid-liquid interfacial energy per unit area and α is a parameter that depends upon the freezing velocity and the convectionless layer thickness.

I do not think that it is wise to use Eq. (5) to represent the gross structure transition from columnar crystal growth to equiaxed crystal growth since it tends to cause some misunderstanding of equiaxed crystal formation. The formation of the equiaxed crystals occurs by heterogeneous nucleation when a certain degree of constitutional supercooling δT_c exists adjacent to the interface (Tiller, p. 855–63). Thus, the proper condition for describing this transition of grain structure morphology is

$$G/U = [m(1 - k_0)]/Dk_0 \, C_s - (\beta\delta T_c/U\Delta) \qquad (D2)$$

where β is a constant and Δ is the convectionless layer thickness. For certain special conditions of growth and stirring $\delta T_c/U\Delta$ may be a constant so that G/U

and C_s are linearly related; however, in general this is likely to be so only in the case of no stirring (p. 855–63).   It is interesting to note from Eq. (D2) that a study of this columnar-equiaxed transition as a function of the convectionless layer thickness Δ would yield information concerning the catalytic activity of the heterogeneous nuclei (i.e., the magnitude of δT_c).

M. C. Flemings: The authors are in basic agreement with the remarks of Dr. Tiller.   In discussing the experimental results in light of the development of Eq. (5), the authors hoped to convey that they did not feel these experiments were a critical test of this relation.   In fact, in the systems studied many of the uncertainties pointed out in the paper are such that they far overshadow the additional term suggested by Dr. Tiller.   In short, the only conclusion that the authors could draw from the data available was that it was *consistent* with Eq. (5).

It is indeed unfortunate that the experiments were completed before the development of many of the elements of the theory.   For this reason the experiments performed were not those which could properly and critically test the relations suggested by Dr. Tiller.

The Effect of an Electric Field on the Segregation of Solute Atoms at a Freezing Interface

JOHN ANGUS, DAVID V. RAGONE, and EDWARD E. HUCKE

University of Michigan, Ann Arbor, Michigan

Abstract

A steady state solution for the segregation occurring at a freezing interface has been given for the case where an electric diffusion flux has been added to the ordinary diffusion of solute away from the interface. The increase in segregation can be quite large for metallic systems when slow freezing rates are considered, when bulk agitation is moderate, and particularly when the equilibrium segregation coefficient is close to unity.

INTRODUCTION

In the past few years it has been learned that the diffusion of solute atoms ahead of a freezing interface is the controlling factor with respect to the segregation that takes place. Furthermore, the interrelation between the temperature gradient at the interface and the freezing temperature of the liquid ahead of the interface determines the stability of the interface. An excellent study of this behavior has been given in the literature.[1]

Briefly, the diffusion away from the interface cannot keep pace with the rejection of solute into the liquid unless a concentration gradient is set up. This results in a rise in the concentration in the liquid at the interface, and assuming partition equilibrium, a rise in the concentration of the solid. Agitation of the liquid can substantially aid the diffusion away from the interface, but there will always be a stagnant boundary layer where solute flow is by atomic diffusion. Stirring merely reduces the thickness of this layer. In the absence of any bulk liquid motion it has been shown[2] that no segregation occurs except for a very short transient period at the start and end of solidification.

Figure 1 shows the concentration profile schematically for an interface advancing at a constant rate, R centimeters per second, into a stirred liquid. It can be seen that in the general case some net segregation will occur since C_s is different from C_0. It is convenient to define

$$k = C_s/C_0 \tag{1}$$

as the segregation coefficient. The value of k will be a function of R, D (diffusion coefficient), the degree of stirring, C_0 and k_0. Where k_0 is the equilibrium segregation coefficient and is given by

$$k_0 = C_s/C_i \tag{2}$$

c_i is the solute concentration immediately adjacent to the solid. It will be assumed in the following treatment that k_c is independent of concentration.

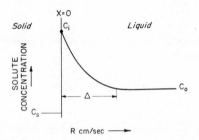

Fig. 1. Schematic concentration profile at a freezing interface.

The degree of stirring can conveniently be described in terms of Δ, the thickness of the hydrodynamic boundary layer. Burton et al.[3] have given a steady state solution for the segregation coefficient k as a function of Δ and the other pertinent variables. Their result is given in Eq. (3).

$$k = k_0/[k_0 + (1 - k_0) \exp \{-R\Delta/D\}] \tag{3}$$

Electric Diffusion

It has long been established that metallic conductors have a small component of ionic conductivity. That is, the presence of an electric field causes not only the flow of electrons but a small ionic mass flow as well.   In a given alloy it is possible to cause a net flow of solute atoms with respect to solvent atoms by application of an electric field.   Since the polarity of the field can be chosen, the direction of the "electric diffusion" flux can always be independently chosen with respect to the interface movement.

It is customary to define the electric mobility U as the steady state drift velocity of the solute atoms with respect to the solvent in a unit electric field.   The net electric flux may then be written as

$$J_e = UcE \qquad (4)$$

where c is the solute concentration and E is the electric field strength.

The passage of a large dc across the liquid-solid interface will then result in the addition of an electric flux to the ordinary diffusion flux provided the proper choice of polarity is made.   It is thereby possible to enhance the segregation and to relieve interface stability problems caused by the presence of the boundary layer.

The use of electric fields in zone melting, and crystal growing applications has been described by Ioffe[4] and by Pfann and co-workers.[5] Both groups have proposed the utilization of the Peltier heating at the interface for control of the thermal conditions, which in turn control the freezing rate, which influences the segregation.   Pfann[6] has also given an excellent summary of the methods by which Joule heating could be used to move a molten zone and also the methods of using the interaction between the current and magnetic fields for levitation and for electrodynamic stirring.   However, the mass flow caused by the passage of dc in these systems has not been treated. Under certain conditions this mass flow and its associated effect on segregation and stability can be significant.

Steady State Segregation with the Addition of an Electric Diffusion Flux

The total solute flux J_T away from a moving interface when an electric field is present may be written as

$$J_T = (-D\partial c/\partial x) + UEc - cR \qquad (5)$$

This equation neglects the diffusion of solute in the solid and chooses as a reference system $x = 0$ at the interface. The conservation of mass may be expressed as

$$\partial c/\partial t = -\text{div } J_T \tag{6}$$

When Eq. (5) is substituted into Eq. (6) the following differential equation results for the uniaxial case.

$$\partial c/\partial t = (D\partial^2 c/\partial x^2) + (R - UE)(\partial c/\partial x) \tag{7}$$

Equation (7) is the same as that solved by Burton et al.[3] with the exception of the addition of another velocity UE to the growth velocity R. However, the results obtained previously cannot be simply transformed by using an "equivalent velocity" equal to $R - UE$, since the boundary conditions used previously are not appropriate to the case with an electric flux except for the special case when k_0 is very small compared to unity.

The following boundary conditions are suitable for the case with combined fluxes

$$C = C_0 \qquad \text{at } x = \Delta \tag{8}$$

$$R(C_i - C_s) = [-D(\partial c/\partial x)] + UEC_i \text{ at } x = 0 \tag{9}$$

The first expresses the fact that a short distance ahead of the interface, the bulk liquid concentration is uniform due to stirring, while the second condition represents the conservation of solute atoms at the interface. After using Eq. (2), Eq. (9) becomes

$$-(\partial c/\partial x)_{x=0} = (C_s/Dk_0)[(1 - k_0)R - UE] \tag{10}$$

The steady state solution to Eq. (7) for the conditions (8) and (9) is given by

$$C = C_0 - \frac{C_s\{R(1 - k_0) - UE\}}{k_0(R - UE)} \exp\left\{\frac{-(R - UE)\Delta}{D}\right\} +$$

$$\frac{C_s\{R(1 - k_0) - UE\}}{k_0(R - UE)} \exp\left\{\frac{-(R - UE)x}{D}\right\} \tag{11}$$

Since the major interest is in the segregation coefficient k, Eq. (11) can be simplified by evaluating C at $x = 0$ and solving for k after making use of Eq. (1).

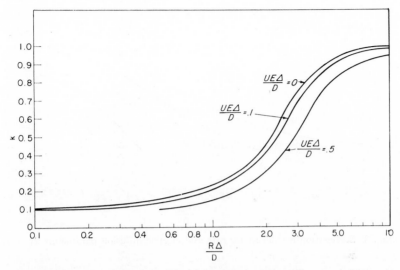

Fig. 2. Segregation coefficient for rate and electric diffusion parameters $k_0 = 1$.

$$k = \cfrac{k_0(R - UE)}{Rk_0 + R(1 - k_0) \exp\left\{\cfrac{-(R - UE)\Delta}{D}\right\} - \cfrac{UE}{R} \exp \left\{\cfrac{-(R - UE)}{D}\right\}} \quad (12)$$

It can be noted that Eq. (12) is identical with Eq. (3) when $E = 0$.

For evaluating the effect of the electric field it is useful to define the parameters,

$$X = UE\Delta/D \quad (13)$$

$$Y = R\Delta/D \quad (14)$$

and plot k vs $R\Delta/D$ for various values of $UE\Delta/D$. Figures 2 and 3 show such plots for $k_0 = 0.1$ and 0.7, respectively.

From Eq. (12) it can be found that k equals k_0 when $UE = R(1 - k_0)$. Increasing UE beyond this point would not result in a greater than equilibrium segregation since this would correspond to removing solute faster than it is rejected by the interface and consequently the rate would be limited by the solute diffusion in the solid just behind

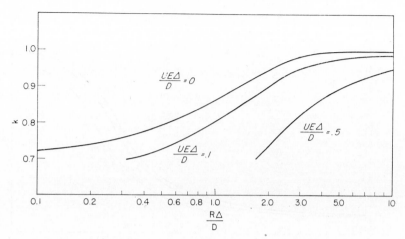

Fig. 3. Segregation coefficient for rate and electric diffusion parameters $k_0 = 7$.

the interface. The interface would simply continue to freeze with very nearly equilibrium segregation. It should be noted that the electric flux can also be made to oppose the ordinary diffusion flux.

DISCUSSION

Although a large number of metallic systems have been studied qualitatively with respect to electric diffusion, very little good quantitative data exist for the electric mobilities. Schwartz[7] has written a summary of the information available up to 1940. The range of values that might be expected is from 10^{-3} to 10^{-5} cm²/sec-v. The greater the dissimilarity between the atomic masses and the valences of the metal and solvent, the greater the expected mobility. The mobility is not very temperature sensitive, at least much less so than the diffusion coefficient.

The effect of the electric flux is obviously dependent on whether or not UE is comparable to $R(1 - k_0)$. In principle, E could be made very large but limitations develop due to Joule heating which increases as E^2. However, with small melts of reasonably high melting point metals it is possible to obtain E values of from 0.1 to 0.5 v/cm without undue cooling problems. With these values of E and U it can be seen that equilibrium segregation would be achieved at rates of the order of a fraction to 1 cm/hr for all cases except those where k_0 approaches unity.   In these cases equilibrium segregation would be obtained at much higher values of R.

Since the diffusion coefficient in liquid metals are all of the order 10^{-5} to 10^{-4} cm²/sec and the value of Δ ranges from 10^{-2} to 10^{-1} for moderate agitation, values of the parameter $UE\Delta/D$ from 0.1 to 0.5 are expected, with higher values distinctly possible.

From Figures 2 and 3 it can be seen that a significant improvement in segregation at a given speed is possible in certain ranges of the parameter $R\Delta/D$.   The value without the electric field is shown for comparison purposes.   The effect is of course more pronounced for the case where $k_0 = 0.7$.   It can also be seen that a rather significant increase in rate could be achieved at the same segregation.

Aside from the effect on segregation, the addition of the current would have an important effect on the stability of a plane front interface.   In zone melting or crystal growth in highly alloyed melts the presence of the solute-rich boundary layer causes the degeneration from plane to dendritic interfaces in all cases except those of very slow growth or where an extremely high temperature gradient is maintained ahead of the interface.   This behavior results from "constitutional supercooling" and has been described in literature by Tiller and Rutter.[1]   Briefly, the added component of mass flow away from the interface would allow plane front growth with smaller gradients, higher rates, or higher solute concentrations.   However, a more important effect of the electric current on interface stability is due to the Joule heating.   Since for most metals the resistivity of the solid is about half of that of the liquid, the development of dendritic projections on the interface would be curtailed since such a projection would immediately carry more of the current and therefore develop more Joule heat and melt.

All of the considerations of interface stability and segregation are predicted on the assumption that the partition at the interface is that given by the phase diagram.   It should be noted however that the phase diagram is a statement of the *bulk* concentrations of phases in equilibrium with each other at a given temperature.   It was recognized by Gibbs that interfacial regions will in general have associated with them *equilibrium* surface excesses of one or more components of the system.   These excesses exist within a region of the order of angstroms in thickness.   These regions are very thin with respect to the thickness of the diffusion boundary layer.   The presence of large excess concentrations at metallic interfaces has been verified in metallic systems from the Gibbs adsorption equation and measurements of the interfacial energy. Furthermore, it is known for many liquid-liquid interfaces from electric double layer measurements that a small change in the potential across the two adjoining phases can cause a major change in these surface excesses. Since the freezing solid is undoubtedly affected most by the concentration immediately adjacent to it, it is quite reasonable to expect that the presence of the electric field at the interface may have a larger effect on the segregation than expected on the basis of diffusion calculations. A series of experiments to clarify this point is needed.

SUMMARY AND CONCLUSIONS

In summary, it can be stated that the addition of an electric diffusion flux aiding ordinary diffusion would have a beneficial effect toward maintaining plane front solidification due to both mass flow and thermal considerations. In addition, an enhanced segregation can be expected particularly when k_0 approaches unity, when freezing rates are slow, and when the system is subject only to moderate agitation.

References

1. Bolling, G. F., W. A. Tiller, and J. W. Rutter, *Can. J. Phys.*, **34**, 234 (1956).
2. Tiller, W. A., K. A. Jackson, J. W. Rutter, and B. Chalmers, *Acta Med.*, **1**, 428 (1953).
3. Burton, J. A., R. C. Prim, and W. P. Slichter, *J. Chem. Phys.*, **21**, 1987 (1953).
4. Ioffe, A. F., *Zhur. Tekh. Fiz.*, **26**, 478 (1956).
5. Pfann, W. G., K. E. Benson, and J. H. Wernick, *J. Electronics*, **2**, 597 (1957).
6. Pfann, W. G., *Zone Melting*, Wiley, New York, 1958.
7. Schwartz, K. E., *Elektrolytische Wanderung in flussigen und festen Metallen*, J. A. Barth Co., Leipzig, 1940.

Discussion

H. W. Weart and **B. S. Chandresekhar** (*Westinghouse Research Labs., Pittsburgh, Pa.*): It is worthwhile noting that, in addition to the steady state electron-drag effect discussed by the authors, the flow of current through a solidifying metal can produce some rather more striking effects. By way of illustrating some of these effects, we would like to describe briefly the structure produced in a two phase alloy solidified under the influence of an electric field.

A long bar of Bi–Sn eutectic alloy was solidified unidirectionally while a steady current of 100 amp/cm² flowed through it parallel to the growth direction.   The structure obtained is shown in Discussion Figure 1 in which the growth direction is from left to right.

Three regions of the specimen can be distinguished.   Region I, in which the electric current and the motion of the liquid-solid interface are parallel, displays a structure consisting of unresolved eutectic (grey), and bands of Sn-saturated Bi (black).   Region II, in which the direction of current flow and of interface motion are opposed, consists of the eutectic, bands of Bi-saturated Sn (white) and Sn dendrites.   Region III, which was solidified more rapidly and without current, is essentially all eutectic in structure.   It should be noted that the bands which

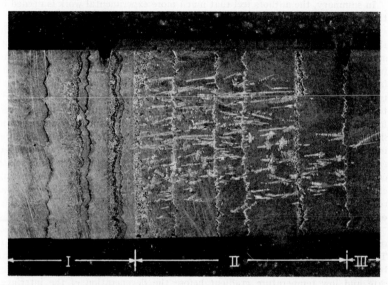

Discussion Fig. 1.   Structural inhomogeneities in Bi-Sn eutectic.   Growth is from left to right.   6×.

appear in the figure are actually layers of one phase, which completely cover the interface and temporarily separate the two phase solid from the melt.

There are several effects which may contribute to the observed structure, including electrolysis of the liquid alloy and the Peltier effect at the two liquid-solid interfaces.   An elucidation of the structure is presently being sought.

J. Angus: The experiments performed by Weart and Chandrasekhar are indeed extremely interesting and point to an intriguing area of research.   At first glance it would seem that the observed effects are somewhat more pronounced than would be anticipated from the magnitude of "electric mass transfer." Several investigators have noted that the passage of a current through a liquid alloy will cause a solid phase to form at one electrode.   In theory a eutectic alloy just above the eutectic temperature would precipitate its two solid phases at opposite electrodes with a vanishingly small net electric mass transfer. This is true since the movement of a very small amount of component A toward one end would cause the precipitation of the A-rich phase at that electrode, while the same movement would cause the precipitation of the B-rich phase at the other electrode.

That is, when the liquid is very close to saturation with respect to both phases a small net mass movement can cause the two phases to precipitate at two different locations. If the specific volumes of the two solid phases are much different from the liquid a bulk liquid flow would result. The flow could be additive with the electric mass flow.

In summary, the authors feel that much more experimental work is needed in this field before definite conclusions can be made.

W. A. Tiller (*Westinghouse Research Labs., Pittsburgh, Pa.*): I would question the statement that one effect of the electric field is to relieve the interface instability problems; in fact, I think that it might enhance the instability. Careful consideration of the "cell formation" problem indicates that a cellular interface will form if, by doing so, the caps of the cells are stable at a higher temperature than a planar interface. Since the effect of curvature and surface energy is to retard this transition and the change in cap solute concentration by enhanced lateral diffusion tends to aid the transition, any mechanism that increases the flux of solute away from the cap relative to the planar interface will increase the instability. In the presence of an electric field the "point effect" will give an enhanced electric field at the cell caps which may significantly decrease the solute concentration there. Such an effect will be in opposition to the Joule heating effect discussed by the authors and either may predominate. Likewise, field reversal may aid the situation but in general it probably will not. I think that only experiments will clear up this point.

J. Angus: The authors in discussing the interface stability problem have pointed out two factors which might be expected to promote plane front solidification. The first of these is the additional electric diffusion flux, which if made significant by the proper choice of freezing variables would undoubtedly allow faster freezing rate and low temperature gradient before the degeneration of the interface. The second factor concerns the influence of Joule heating under conditions where the interface has become unstable. The authors feel that this effect would be a major one.

Dr. Tiller's discussion does not deny that both of these factors would contribute in the direction of greater interface stability. His interjection of a possible non-uniform field due to a point effect would tend to oppose the second factor mentioned by the authors. However, it would in no way be concerned with the first factor. In addition, it would be important only in cases where projections were already present on the interface and only then if this enhanced electrical diffusion from the tip of the projection were appreciable.

In order to obtain a rough idea of the magnitude of this effect the authors asked Prof. A. D. Moore of the Dept. of Electrical Engineering, University of Michigan, to estimate the field intensity at the tips of series of roughly hemispherical bumps protruding from a plane. For a liquid to solid resistivity ratio of infinity; i.e., a conductor projecting into a nonconducting liquid, the field intensity was estimated to be less than a factor of two.   In the case where the resistivity ratio is about 2 the field concentration would certainly be much smaller.   In short, the point effect would be expected to be very small when the point protrudes into a good conducting medium.   While it is true that any point effect would cause a difference in the electric field between the tips and the crevices, an offsetting factor arises since the electric flux is given by the product of the field, concentration, and the mobility [Eq. (4)] ; and the crevice concentration would be higher than the tip concentration.   The concentration dependence of the mobility would also enter.

The heating effect mentioned by the authors wou'd be directly proportional to the difference of resistivity between the liquid and the solid.   Thus about twice as much power per unit volume would be generated in the solid projection as in the adjoining liquid.   The authors agree that experiments would be helpful in determining the magnitudes of the competing effects.   It is stated (W. G. Pfann, *Zone Melting*, Wiley, New York, 1958, p. 84) that in the case of Ge where the solid to liquid resistivity is about 17 (compared to normal metals of 0.5), the application of Joule heating caused a liquid area formed within a $10 \times 0.5 \times 0.5$ cm rod to progress nearly the entire length of the rod without melting the outside.   While this experiment in itself is not conclusive, it indicates that in a normal metal the Joule heating would be effective in diminishing the stability of a solid projection from the interface.

The Influence of Large Amounts of Undercooling on the Grain Size of Nickel

J. L. WALKER

General Electric Company, Schenectady, New York

Abstract

The dependence of the grain structure of nickel on undercooling has been determined experimentally. A marked decrease in grain size occurs in the range of 140 to 150°C undercooling. An hypothesis has been presented to explain the grain size transition in terms of the mechanical disturbance caused by the rapid change in volume at very high freezing rates.

INTRODUCTION

Metals normally freeze with only a few degrees undercooling. This behavior indicates that the grains nuclear on solid impurity particles frequently described as nucleation catalysts. Turnbull[1] has shown that very small droplets of metals can be undercooled considerably before nucleation occurs. When a metal sample is subdivided the probability of solid impurity inclusion in a given droplet is reduced. Some droplets, therefore, do not contain nucleation catalysts and consequently can be undercooled to the homogeneous nucleation temperature. When proper precautions are taken, it is possible to undercool large nickel samples (400 to 500 g) as much as 285°C. These samples are sufficiently large to permit determining the dependence of grain size on undercooling. This dependence will be described subsequently.

EXPERIMENTAL METHODS AND RESULTS

The apparatus used for the undercooling experiments is shown schematically in Figure 1. Fused silica crucibles approximately $1^1/_2$ in. in diameter by 3 in. high were used for all experiments.

845

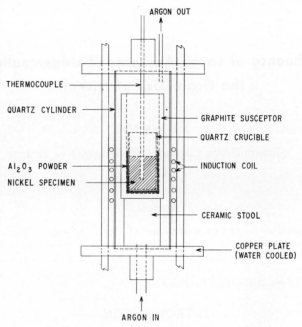

ARGON OUT

THERMOCOUPLE

QUARTZ CYLINDER

GRAPHITE SUSCEPTOR

QUARTZ CRUCIBLE

Al$_2$O$_3$ POWDER

INDUCTION COIL

NICKEL SPECIMEN

CERAMIC STOOL

COPPER PLATE
(WATER COOLED)

ARGON IN

Fig. 1. Apparatus used for undercooling experiments.

Fused silica has a number of advantages in this application. It is a glass and therefore should not be effective in promoting nucleation by a catalysis mechanism. The surface of fused silica is smooth compared to that of crucibles made with crystalline materials. Consequently, effects due to small cracks or trapped inclusions are minimized. The specimens were melted and solidified in an argon atmosphere, power being supplied by coupling a high frequency induction coil to the graphite cylinder containing the melting crucible. Temperatures were determined by means of an immersed platinum-platinum 10% rhodium thermocouple. The thermocouple was protected by a fused silica tube. A typical heating and cooling cycle is shown in Figure 2. It is observed that as soon as freezing starts the sample is heated very quickly to the melting point, indicating a very high freezing rate; i.e., a high rate of evolution of the heat of fusion.

Specimens obtained from similar experimental runs were sectioned and macro-etched to show the grain structure. The grain diameter

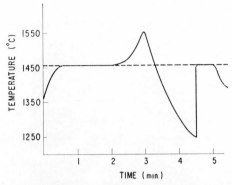

Fig. 2. Cooling curve for sample that undercooled 200°C.

so determined is plotted as a function of undercooling in Figure 3. Since the grains are columnar the parameter plotted is the grain diameter at the surface of the specimen. A longitudinal section is shown in Figure 4, indicating that the grains nucleated at the surface of the specimen. Specimens that solidified after undercooling to temperatures of 130 and 145°C are shown in Figure 5.

At undercoolings up to approximately 140°C the specimens contain only a few grains. Presumably the grains that form in the range

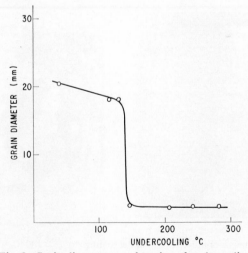

Fig. 3. Grain diameter as a function of undercooling.

Fig. 4. Longitudinal section of specimen solidified after undercooling 240°C.
1.20 ×.

up to 140°C nucleate on a few solid impurity particles accidentally included in the system. The grain size under these conditions is determined only by the number of particles that effectively promote nucleation.[2] There is a sharp decrease in grain diameter at undercoolings between 140 and 150°C, and at larger undercoolings the diameter remains relatively constant.

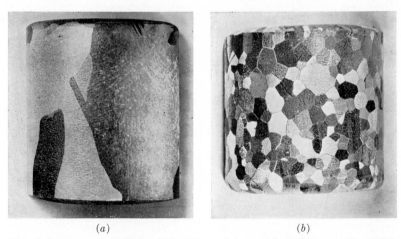

(a)   (b)

Fig. 5. Specimens solidified after undercooling to (a) 130°C and (b) 145°C.
1.20 ×.

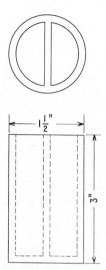

Fig. 6. Container used in split crucible experiments.

If these latter results are to be rationalized only in terms of nuclea-tion catalysis it must be assumed that the samples that undercool more than 150°C contain a uniform dispersion of nucleation catalysts. Further, it must be assumed these catalysts promote nucleation simultaneously in the liquid although the temperature is nonuniform. An alternative interpretation is that at some undercooling larger than 145°C very effective nucleation catalysts are precipitated in the liquid, and grains nucleate on those catalysts at the surface of the specimen. The results of freezing experiments performed in a "split" crucible indicate that some phenomenon other than or, at least, in addition to the precipitation of nucleation catalysts is involved in the very sharp grain size transition. Two nickel specimens were melted and undercooled in the split crucible shown schematically in Figure 6. The specimens were separated by a fused silica plate. At large undercoolings the specimens solidified simultaneously although they were at very different temperatures. A typical set of results of a split crucible experiment is shown in Table I. The simultaneous freezing behavior indicates that at large undercoolings some means of communication exists between the two separated specimens. It was observed that an audible click or bump is detected when freezing begins at large undercoolings. This sound indicates that freezing

TABLE I

| Undercooling, °C | | Freezing behavior |
Side A	Side B	
100	85	Not simultaneous
130	160	Simultaneous
150	181	Simultaneous
165	195	Simultaneous
68	93	Not simultaneous
70	100	Not simultaneous

produces a mechanical disturbance in the system. An attempt was made to measure the relative magnitude of the disturbance by placing the stylus of a phonograph cartridge in a small hole near the top of the thermocouple protection tube. The output from the cartridge was displayed on an oscilloscope and photographed. The maximum amplitude of the signal observed on the oscilloscope is plotted as a function of undercooling in Figure 7. It is observed that the mechanical disturbance increases sharply in the temperature range where the decrease in grain diameter occurs, suggesting a probable relationship between the two effects. It is proposed that the pressure disturbance indicated by the sound can account for the sharp decrease in

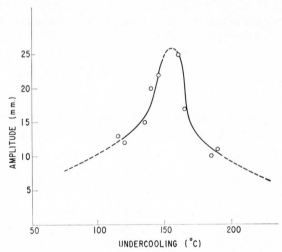

Fig. 7. Amplitude of the initial pulse as a function of undercooling.

grain size, by means of a sudden increase in nucleation rate stimulated by the increase in pressure.

DEPENDENCE OF NUCLEATION RATE ON TEMPERATURE AND PRESSURE

Turnbull[3] has observed that mild mechanical vibrations can induce nucleation of crystals in an undercooled liquid at a temperature several degrees higher than that at which nucleation would normally occur.   It was suggested that the effect is due to cavitation at the container wall or on other surfaces.   The collapse of a cavity can give rise to a very large pressure in the surrounding liquid as the liquid rushing in is stopped or slowed down.[4]   The effect of a pressure increase in liquids that contract on freezing is equivalent to an increase in the undercooling.   This is, in fact, the dependence of melting temperature on pressure described by the Clausius-Clapeyron equation:

$$dP/dT = \Delta H_V / T_0 V_V$$

where ΔH_V is the latent heat of fusion per unit volume and ΔV_V is the volume change per unit volume during solidification.   The effect of pressure on melting temperature follows from its effect on the volume free energy change ΔF_V during freezing.   This effect in turn can be included in the nucleation equation giving the dependence of nucleation rate on pressure and temperature.

The rate of nucleation of solid from liquid is given by[5]

$$I = (nkT/h) \exp\left\{ -K\sigma^3/(\Delta F_V)^2 kT - \Delta F_A/KT \right\}$$

where I is the rate of nucleation per unit volume, n is the atomic density, σ is the solid-liquid interfacial energy, ΔF_V is the free energy change per unit volume on freezing, ΔF_A is the free energy of activation for transferring an atom across the solid-liquid interface, K is a shape factor and k, T, and h have their usual meanings.   An approximate expression for the dependence of ΔF_V on pressure and temperature can be derived if it is assumed that the difference between the compressibilities of the liquid and solid is small relative to the volume contraction on freezing.   This relationship is

$$\Delta F_V = (\Delta H_V/T_0) \Delta T + \Delta V_V \Delta P$$

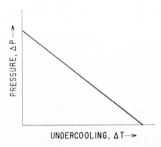

Fig. 8. Pressure required to nucleate as a function of undercooling.

where ΔT is the undercooling, ΔP is the pressure increase, and T_0 is the melting point. For a given sensible nucleation rate ΔF_V must have a finite negative value C. The pressure-temperature relationship for a fixed nucleation rate becomes:

$$\Delta P = (C/\Delta V_V) - (\Delta H_V/\Delta V_V T_0)\Delta T$$

The effect of having nucleation catalysts in the liquid is to decrease the absolute magnitude of the constant C. This dependence of undercooling on pressure is shown graphically in Figure 8.

If the pressure disturbance caused by freezing at any undercooling ΔT is larger than the corresponding value of ΔP, nucleation should occur spontaneously. It is proposed that this effect can account for the sharp drop in grain size observed in the experiments on the undercooling of nickel. This can be shown qualitatively by superimposing the experimentally determined disturbance amplitude vs

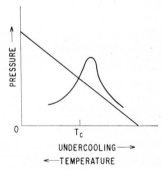

Fig. 9. Relationship between pressure required to nucleate and pressure increase that occurs during freezing.

undercooling curve shown in Figure 7 on the curve in Figure 8. This has been done in Figure 9 adjusting the curves so that they intersect at the temperature T_C, where the sudden drop in grain size occurs. It is assumed that the amplitude observed on the oscilloscope is a measure of the maximum pressure pulse in the undercooled liquid. At temperatures lower than T_C, the pressure is sufficiently high to promote nucleation. Therefore at undercoolings larger than $(T_0 - T_C)$, the nucleation of one crystal promotes the nucleation of many others. At higher temperatures the grain size depends only on the number of active nucleation catalysts contained in the liquid.

The mechanical disturbance very probably is a result of the rapid volume change that occurs during freezing in an undercooled liquid.

The author would like to thank R. L. Fullman, C. R. O'Clair, and P. G. Frisch-mann for the advice and assistance that they contributed to the preparation of this paper.

References

1. Turnbull, D., *J. Appl. Phys.*, **20**, 817 (1949).

2. Walker, J., "Structure of Ingots and Castings," *Liquid Metals and Solidification*, American Soc. for Metals, Cleveland, Ohio, 1958, p. 324.

3. Turnbull, D., "Principles of Solidification," *Thermodynamics in Physical Metallurgy*, American Soc. for Metals, Cleveland, Ohio, 1950, p. 286.

4. Crawford, A. E., *Ultrasonic Engineering*, Butterworths, London, 1955, pp. 26 and 40.

5. See ref. 3, p. 284.

Discussion

W. A. Tiller (*Westinghouse Research Labs.*): I wonder if the curve in Figure 7 is influenced by a resonance-type of vibration in the thermocouple tube? It is difficult to understand why the amplitude should increase until $\Delta T \sim 150°C$ and then decrease unless this is the case. Has the author produced such nucleating by an externally applied vibration to the system?

J. L. Walker: In reply to Dr. Tiller's question, I should point out that curves similar to that reproduced in Figure 7 were obtained using rods and tubes of varying diameters and lengths. The maximum does not appear to be effected by changes in the factors that determine the resonance of the probe.

I should point out that the decrease in amplitude at undercoolings larger than 150°C was not expected. One possible explanation which is being investigated is that the maximum disturbance that can occur in liquid is just that required to produce the phase change from liquid to solid. It would be expected then that the amplitude vs undercooling curve would decrease with undercooling as does the pressure vs undercooling curve shown in Figure 8.

In reply to Dr. Tiller's second question, it has been possible to induce nucleation in undercooled nickel by an externally applied vibration.

Grain Size Control during Ingot Solidification

W. A. TILLER

Metallurgy Department, Westinghouse Research Laboratories, Pittsburgh, Pennsylvania

Abstract

A qualitative description of the thermal and chemical factors controlling the ratio of equiaxed zone width to columnar zone width and the grain sizes in these zones is presented.

INTRODUCTION

It is well known that the grain structure developed during ingot solidification generally determines the degree of chemical inhomogeneity, the strength, and the strength anisotropy of the ingot. These are characteristics that greatly influence the workability of the ingot and its final properties. Thus, considerable effort is expended by industry to produce the best as-cast grain structure.

The three main types of ingot structures are illustrated in Figure 1. Neglecting a thin "chill" layer at the outer surface of the ingot which consists of equiaxed grains, the main volume of the ingot generally

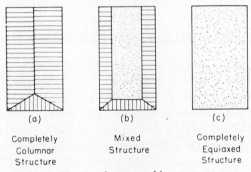

| (a) | (b) | (c) |
| Completely Columnar Structure | Mixed Structure | Completely Equiaxed Structure |

Fig. 1. Three main types of ingot structure.

consists of a zone of long columnar grains and a zone of equiaxed grains (Fig. 1b). In the extreme cases, the ingot may be either wholly columnar (Fig. 1a) or wholly equiaxed (Fig. 1c). In practice, one wishes to control the solidification of the ingot so as to produce one of the extremes depending upon the type of properties desired. One wishes the ingot to be either wholly equiaxed for isotropic properties or wholly columnar for anisotropic properties.

This article will be devoted to the application of present-day knowledge of nucleation and growth to qualitatively explain the general ingot structure (Fig. 1b) and to point out the type of information needed for the control of ingot grain structure. We wish to know what determines the ratio of equiaxed zone width to columnar zone width (we would like this ratio to be either zero or infinite) and what determines the size of the grains in these zones.

Cibula[1] has shown on aluminum that the presence of certain heterogeneous nuclei in the liquid will lead to the virtual suppression of undercooling in the melt. He found that such melts of aluminum could not be undercooled by more than a fraction of a degree. However, such an effect only changes a coarse columnar structure to a much finer, but still columnar structure. To produce an equiaxed grain structure he found that it was necessary to have an appropriate solute element, for example Cu, present in the melt. He postulated that concentration gradients were produced which hindered the growth of the grains and thus concluded that both heterogeneous nuclei and solute elements were necessary prerequisites for a fine-grained equiaxed structure. Let us now see how the heterogeneous nuclei interact with the concentration gradients and the thermal properties of the alloy to produce the various grain structures.

NUCLEATION CATALYSTS

Before considering the freezing of an ingot some understanding of the heterogeneous nuclei is mandatory. The heterogeneous nuclei, or catalysts, are small particles of insoluble impurity in the melt which may, or may not, have been added intentionally. At some degree of undercooling of the melt, a certain type of catalyst will be beneficial for the nucleation of the solid phase; i.e., a particle of solid can form more readily on the surface of the catalyst than in the homogeneous liquid. It is found that homogeneous nucleation in the liquid may require undercoolings as large at 250°C,[2] whereas heterogeneous nucleation can occur at undercoolings as small as 0.1°C.[1] For particular catalysts the rate of nucleation vs undercooling will be as illustrated in Figure 2; a high nucleation rate for a specific catalyst will occur at a critical undercooling δT_c. Since an appreciable nucleation rate occurs over a temperature range of only a few degrees, a particular catalyst may be characterized by the undercooling at which it produces a high nucleation rate. This nucleation rate N depends also upon the number of these catalytic particles N_0 per unit volume of the melt in the following way.

$$N = N_0 \exp\left\{-A/\delta T^2\right\} \qquad (1)$$

where A is a constant for the particular catalyst. If there are several different catalysts present in the same melt, only the one which has the smallest δT_c will catalyze the nucleation since the melt will never undercool more than that necessary for the first catalyst to operate.

We do not know, in any rigorous way, how to go about producing a catalyst with a small δT_c. We expect that if the catalyst has a lattice arrangement and lattice spacing which is close to that of the nucleating solid, then δT_c will be small.[3] However, the catalyst surface generally has a layer for foreign atoms chemisorbed on it which may either increase or decrease this disregistry. Thus, a small amount of

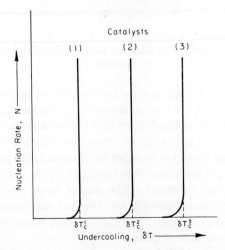

Fig. 2. Nucleation characteristics of three catalysts.

solute added to the melt may either increase or decrease the catalytic activity; i.e., change δT_c of the catalyst.   The gap in our knowledge centers around the physical forces which lead to the chemisorbed layer, the kinetics of its formation, and the epitaxial arrangement it makes with the catalyst surface.   At present we must determine the catalytic activity by empiricism.

INGOT SOLIDIFICATION

In the conventional method of casting, the alloy (see Fig. 3) having a certain degree of superheat is poured to fill a mold.   The outer

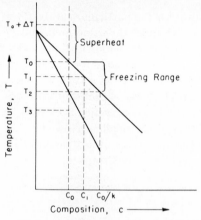

Fig. 3. Portion of equilibrium diagram used to describe freezing of alloy of composition C_0.

rim of liquid metal cools rapidly to the melting temperature T_0 and begins to undercool.   At some degree of undercooling δT_c, nuclei of solid begin to form at random in this thin chilled layer at the mold surface.   The number of grains formed per unit area of the outer surface will depend upon the number of the catalysts per unit volume and upon δT_c.   If this number is large and δT_c is small, the grains in the chill layer will be small.   The size of these grains will also be influenced by the constitutional and thermal parameters of the alloy; however, these effects will be discussed later when we consider the grain size of the equiaxed grains.

The grains in the chill layer are randomly oriented and begin to grow inward due to the heat conduction through the mold.   As the grains become columnar several things happen:

1.   Because of the slow diffusion rate of solute in the liquid, the solute builds up rapidly at the interface[4] to the value of $\alpha C_0/k$, where C_0 is the initial concentration of solute in the melt, k is the ratio of the solubility of solute in the solid to the solubility in the liquid at a certain temperature, and α is a constant which depends on the detailed interface morphology.   As the solute buildup occurs, the interface temperature decreases along the liquidus line.

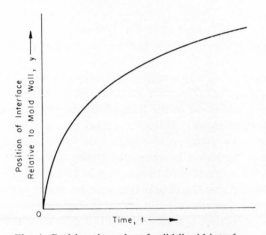

Fig. 4. Position-time plot of solid-liquid interface.

2.   For most alloys the interface will have a dendritic morphology. Because of this morphology, a preferred orientation will develop in the columnar grains which increases the grain width by a factor of 5–10 over that in the chill zone.[5]

3.   The temperature gradient in the solid conducts away not only the latent heat of fusion but some of the superheat from the liquid as well; thus, the temperature gradient in the liquid at the interface decreases as the interface advances inward.

Depending upon the thermal parameters of the alloy and mold, the interface advances inward from the mold wall in a manner depending on time as illustrated in Figure 4.   Since the velocity of freezing is decreasing with the distance of the interface from the mold wall, the solute distribution in the liquid ahead of the interface will be as illus-

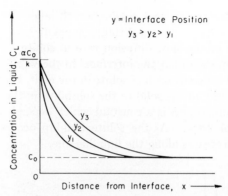

Fig. 5. Solute distribution ahead of interface as a function of interface position.

trated in Figure 5 as a function of interface position.   This assumes that the interface concentration remains constant which is not quite true.   Since every point in the liquid has a definite concentration of solute then, from the equilibrium diagram, it has a definite freezing temperature.   We shall speak of this as the equilibrium temperature distribution in the liquid as contrasted to the actual temperature distribution which is determined by heat flow.   The equilibrium temperature distribution and the actual temperature distribution as a function of interface position are illustrated in Figure 6.

It can be seen that a region of liquid exists in which the actual temperature is below the liquidus temperature.   This liquid is said to be constitutionally supercooled and is therefore unstable with

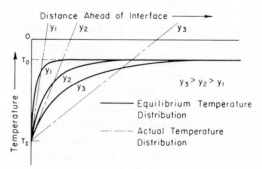

Fig. 6. Degree of constitutional supercooling ahead of interface as a function of interface position.

respect to the nucleation of new grains. When the critical value of supercooling, δT_c, is reached at some point in the liquid, nucleation will be catalyzed and grains will form in the liquid ahead of the interface, thus prohibiting further growth of the columnar grains. This is illustrated in Figure 7 and constituted the onset of equiaxed nucleation.

A quantitative treatment of this problem[6] shows that the ratio of equiaxed zone width to columnar zone width varies in the following way: (a) inversely proportional to the effective superheat which is equal to the actual superheat plus the freezing range; (b) inversely proportional to a function of the thermal parameters of the alloy. For example, as the thermal conductivity of the solid decreases due

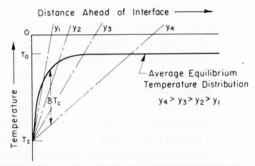

Fig. 7. Approximate description of constitutional supercooling increase in liquid to the critical value needed for equiaxed crystal nucleation.

to the alloying this function decreases; (c) inversely proportional to δT_c; (d) proportional to the freezing range of the alloy.

This variation of the ratio of equiaxed zone width to columnar zone width agrees with the available facts.[7,8]   The quantitative treatment[6] also shows that, to a first approximation, it is the ratio of the temperature gradient in the liquid at the interface to the velocity of freezing that determines the onset of equiaxed nucleation, a prediction that is also in agreement with experiment.[9]

Let us now consider the grain size of the equiaxed crystals.   First, consider the nucleation and growth of a grain in an infinite bath of liquid which is undercooled.   If the grain nucleates at the temperature T_3 in Figure 3, the departure from equilibrium at the interface causes it to grow very rapidly (about 10^4 cm/sec).   After it has grown a few atomic layers its interface temperature and concentration lie on the liquidus line below T_0, and the particle still grows rapidly but now at a rate determined by the rate at which heat can be conducted away (about 10–1 cm/sec). As it grows the solute concentration at the interface increases to C_0/k and thereafter the particle grows at the constant interface concentration C_0/k at a rate which depends on the rate of heat conduction (still about 1–0.1 cm/sec).

If, however, the grain nucleates at temperature T_1, it follows the same initial growth rate path but quickly slows down as the interface concentration approaches C_1. The concentration cannot build up to C_0/k in this case; it cannot be greater than C_1 as the interface temperature cannot be below the bath temperature. The grain then grows at a rate determined by the diffusion of solute in the liquid (about 10^{-3}–10^{-4} cm/sec). We may consider that the grain has essentially stopped growing when it reaches this state and this will be its ultimate grain size. Its size depends upon the distance it must grow in order to build up the concentration to C_1 at the interface. A quantitative treatment of this problem[10] shows that the grain size varies in the following way: (a) proportional to δT_c, (b) proportional to the partition coefficient k, and (c) inversely proportional to the liquidus slope.

The preceding discussion leads to the minimum possible grain size since it assumes that all the latent heat can be conducted away. In an actual ingot, a number of grains will nucleate when the undercooling $\delta T_c^{°}$ is reached ahead of the columnar interface. These grains will rapidly grow to the size d provided the latent heat can be conducted away. In adjoining volumes of liquid undercooling δT_c still exists, so nuclei will form here and grow to the size d. In this way the ultimate grain size in the equiaxed zone will be d. However, if the rate of heat conduction is poor, the first few grains to nucleate will raise the local temperature above T_1 due to their latent heat evolution and thus no new grains can nucleate. These primary grains may grow to a large size before regions of liquid are again undercooled to δT_c so that new grains may nucleate. This leads to an ingot size effect; i.e., the larger the ingot, the slower the heat transfer in the central regions and the larger the grains. Thus, the grain size d also varies inversely as the heat transfer capacity.

CONCLUSIONS

From the foregoing we can see that columnar ingots will be produced if the alloy is cast with a large superheat and if the efficient catalysts are eliminated from the melt (δT_c must be greater than the freezing range).   On the other hand, fine-grained equiaxed ingots will be produced by casting with a low superheat, by adding an effective catalyst to the melt ($\delta T_c < 1\,°\mathrm{C}$), and by adding an appropriate solute element to the melt.   In the future we may thus have, neglecting the ingot size limitation, complete control of the ingot structure and grain size if we know how to produce catalysts with the appropriate δT_c.

References

1. Cibula, A., *J. Inst. Metals*, **76,** 321 (1949).

2. Turnbull, D., "Principles of Solidification," *Thermodynamics in Physical Metallurgy*, American Soc. for Metals, Cleveland, Ohio, 1950, p. 282.

3. Turnbull, D., and B. Vonnegut, *Ind. Eng. Chem.*, **44,** 1292 (1952).

4. Tiller, W. A., K. A. Jackson, J. W. Ritter, and B. Chalmers, *Acta. Met.*, **1,** 428 (1953).

5. Tiller, W. A., *Am. Inst. Mining, Met. Petrol. Engrs.*, **209,** 847 (1957).

6. Tiller, W. A., to be published.

7. Northcott, L., *J. Inst. Metals*, **65,** 173 (1939).

8. Walker, J. L., *Structure of Ingots and Castings, Liquid Metals and Solidification*, American Soc. for Metals, Cleveland, Ohio, 1957, p. 319.

9. Plaskett, T. S., and W. C. Winegard, *Trans. Am. Soc. Metals*, **51,** (1958); Preprint No. 77.

10. Tiller, W. A., to be published.

A Study of the Morphological and Distributive Features of the Solidification Process in Chill-Cast Aluminum-Copper Ingots*

W. V. YOUDELIS

University of Alberta, Edmonton, Alberta

J. U. MacEWAN

McGill University, Montreal, Quebec

and

J. S. KIRKALDY

McMaster University, Hamilton, Ontario

Abstract

A theoretical and experimental study of the processes involved in the formation of chill-cast aluminum-copper ingots has been made. The study includes morphology, temperature distributions, and solute distributions (including inverse segregation and eutectic exudations). The morphological features of the solidification process are attributed to the thermodynamic requirement that the system pass through states of minimum or decreased integrated entropy production rate. This decreased entropy production rate, as compared to a flat interface, is manifested in the final microstructures by remnant available energy in the form of surface free energy, solute segregation, and crystal defect structures.

Experimental evidence is presented in support of numerical calculations of solute distributions in the ingot. A model for eutectic exudations is proposed.

INTRODUCTION

An examination of a recent survey on metal solidification[1] indicates that our knowledge of certain particulars of the process is well ad-

* Most of the work on this paper was carried out in the Department of Metallurgical Engineering, McGill University, Montreal, Quebec.

vanced. It is, however, apparent that no general principle is widely known which unifies the various macroscopic aspects of the phenomenon—morphology, temperature distributions, and concentration distributions. One of the authors has recently suggested such a thermodynamic principle.[2] This suggestion will be examined in some detail here and the results applied to various aspects of the solidification problem. New experimental observations on morphology and solute distributions are presented in support of the theoretical description.

THE VARIATION PRINCIPLE

In our earlier communication,[2] it was presumed that the progress of a steady state irreversible process, proceeding within well-defined boundary conditions, follows a configuration defined by the state of minimum rate of entropy production. This can be described by the variation principle,

$$\delta \int_V \sigma dV = 0, \text{ minimum} \tag{1}$$

where V is the volume and σ is the instantaneous rate of entropy production per unit volume. If T is the absolute temperature, then $T\sigma$ is the energy dissipation rate, or roughly speaking, the rate of conversion of available energy into dissipated thermal energy.

Relation (1) is applicable to steady state systems involving simultaneous diffusion, thermal conduction, and near-equilibrium homogeneous chemical reaction, as Brown has demonstrated,[3] and although it has not as yet been proved, we believe that it is applicable to systems involving heterogeneous reactions as well. Accordingly, it is used here for the description of steady state crystal growth.

In the usual phenomenological scheme, the rate of entropy production is given by the relation[4]

$$\sigma = \sum_i J_i X_i, \tag{2}$$

where the J_i and X_i are suitably conjugated fluxes and forces (heat flows, diffusion currents, and reaction rates; thermal gradients, chemical potential gradients, and chemical affinities). Because the leading term of each flux is proportional to its conjugate force, the main contribution to the entropy production will be a sum of positive terms, each proportional to the square of a driving force. de Groot[4] has summarized the methods of determining the appropriate fluxes and forces.

Relation (1) applies only to steady state processes, and since these usually only occur in experimental situations, it is desirable to have a generalization of (1) which applies to nonsteady state processes. Onsager[5] has shown that the field equations for isothermal diffusion can be derived from the variation principle

$$\delta[-(1/T)(dF/dt) - \int_V \sigma dV] = 0, \text{ maximum} \qquad (3)$$

where $-dF/dt$ is the rate of decrease of the Gibbs free energy. This suggests that in a general dissipative process, the rate of entropy production will be as small as possible, consistent with the maximum rate of decrease of some generalized potential function. Accordingly, σ will not be a minimum but will only tend that way. We will summarize this with the postulate that any nonsteady dissipative process passes through states in which the integrated entropy production rate tends toward a minimum; i.e.,

$$\int_V \sigma dV \longrightarrow \text{minimum} \qquad (4)$$

MORPHOLOGICAL CONSIDERATIONS OF METAL SOLIDIFICATION

The popular approach to the problem of morphology in metal solidification is to consider the crystallographic features of the solid-liquid interface and the associated diffusion and thermal fields. It is immediately appreciated that the differential phenomenological equations combined with the boundary conditions and the interface continuity and supersaturation relations do not uniquely determine the morphology. It therefore becomes necessary to impose at least one more condition on the system to obtain a unique solution. The most successful procedure of this type is due to the Chalmers school.[6,7] It is noted that a virtual flat interface advancing into an alloy melt at a rate in excess of a certain critical value, piles up solute to such an extent that the interfacial liquid layer becomes "constitutionally supercooled." The interface therefore advances by cellular or dendritic growth to eliminate this supercooling by an amount consistent with the associated increase in interfacial energy. Although it is not explicit stated, the implication here is that the system passes through states which minimize, or tend to minimize, some potential function.

The practical value of this concept in correlating the results of experiments has been adequately demonstrated. One, however, feels that the approach is theoretically unsatisfactory since it does not seem to be possible to specify an appropriate potential function. The obvious ones to try are the Gibbs free energy or the enthalpy, but these tend to a minimum only at the equilibrium end of a constant pressure, isothermal or constant pressure, isentropic process, respectively. We have therefore turned from early attempts in this direction to seek a general principle involving the variables common to the thermodynamics of irreversible processes. Equation (1) is our choice for steady state processes.

It should be appreciated that the variation principle, insofar as it is valid, is a far more powerful statement than any subsidiary condition imposed on the under-determined system. In principle, it is possible to derive the morphology, the field equations and their solutions and the supersaturation relations from the variation principle, provided it is combined with the boundary conditions and the mass and heat continuity equations. For the steady state system considered by Brown,[3] this can in fact be done, but because of the complexity of the system considered here it is most convenient to combine our independent knowledge of the diffusion and thermal fields with the variation principle. Although our system is now over-determined, this seems to be the most economic method for defining the theoretical basis of morphological variation.

It has been tacitly assumed thus far that for given precise initial conditions, the subsequent morphological development of the solid-liquid distribution is unique. Clearly, this must be mitigated against to some extent by nucleation and defect-dependent processes which occur during the growth processes. We will accordingly assume that heterogeneous nucleation in the liquid does not occur, that interface nucleation is homogeneous within areas small relative to the area of morphological units (or that defect densities are high within such units if they play an important role), and, if mold surface nucleation is involved, that the initial conditions are specified just subsequent to the completion of such nucleation processes. The qualitative descriptions to follow will not be seriously in error if these conditions are not met, but it seems worthwhile to anticipate at this point any criticism of the procedure which might arise.

Cellular Growth in Alloys

Consider the steady state growth of a metal single crystal into a binary alloy melt and assume that relation (1) correctly describes the process. We will ignore for the moment any crystallographic effects and consider the thermodynamics of a typical volume V (shown in Fig. 1) which migrates at the same rate as the solid-liquid interface. We may think of the cuspoidal indentations shown as the elevation of an array of cell boundaries. For convenience, the test variation is made from this configuration to that of a flat interface advancing at the same rate within the same boundary conditions.

In this variation the entropy production due to chemical reaction remains unchanged to the first order. It seems plausible that the contribution from the liquid diffusion field (the solid makes a negligi-

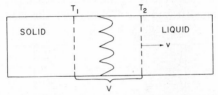

Fig. 1. Schematic advancing steady state solid-liquid interface.

ble contribution) is increased since the effective volume of integration for this term is increased, thus favoring a nonplanar morphology. Furthermore, in consideration of the contribution of the thermal fields, particularly in the solid, we might again conclude that the cellular interface is thermodynamically favored since it appears to position the average latent heat source nearer to the sink at temperature T_1. This shortens the average transport path in the solid for latent heat, and correspondingly, lessens the value of the variation integral.

A further role of the solute in this description is to supply a pile-up of solute between the cells which constitutionally matches the interface temperature variation. The length of the cells will be determined by the concentration of solute which can be piled up at the cusps through lateral flow from the tips. There will be a critical growth velocity for each alloy below which the solute pile-up is insufficient to assure substantial equilibrium along interfaces parallel to the growth direction, and for these conditions the interface will remain flat.[7]

The lateral cell dimensions will be determined mainly by the lateral diffusion flow and the growth velocity and, as usually observed, will be of the order of magnitude of the diffusion length

$$d \sim D/v \qquad (5)$$

where D is the liquid diffusion coefficient and v is the growth velocity.

Dendritic Growth in Alloys

In the discussion thus far we have ignored any crystallographic effects at the interface. This is a reasonable approximation for slight changes in the profile of the interface since the supersaturation required to maintain steady state growth is relatively constant over the whole interface. The observations bear this out since, for conditions slightly more severe than the critical ones, the corrugations or cells are quite smooth and featureless, and the crystallography ap-

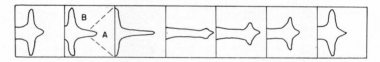

Fig. 2. Representative cyclic configuration near an advancing dendrite tip.

pears only in the orientation of their boundaries. We naturally expect crystallographic effects to appear as soon as the cusps are deep enough to bare an appreciable area of different low index plane to the liquid. This is because the supersaturation conditions are different for different crystal faces. The system might adjust to this by altering the diffusion and thermal fields, maintaining the simple form of the cusps. However, this tendency would lead to incompatibility with the transport equations. Accordingly, the morphology must alter and it does so by incipient side branching on preferred crystallographic planes. As the growth conditions become more severe, the field components at right angles to the growth direction approach a condition wherein projectional growth can be supported in that direction, and there will be then a tendency to reduce σ locally by side branching from the points of incipient branching. Branching, however, is inconsistent with local steady state so instability sets in. In spite of this, we can preserve our variational principle by allowing the system to enter an oscillatory mode in which Eq. (1) still holds but in which there are local changes of entropy production rate. Consider Figure 2 which shows a series of pictures of a dendrite tip, equally spaced in time. The frames are moving with the average interface. The previous considerations indicate that there is an alternating transfer of a high local rate of entropy production between regions A and B in Figure 2, and if we presume that

$$\int_A \sigma dV + \int_B \sigma dV = \int_{A+B} \sigma dV = \text{const} \tag{6}$$

the variational relation is preserved.

There is a useful, nontrivial analogy between this behavior and that of the lossless electrical tuned circuit. In the latter case, the energy E is transferred between the condenser and inductance by the action of the oscillatory potential difference in such a way that

$$E = E_1 + E_2 = \text{const} \tag{7}$$

Now since there is also a natural tendency or "force" for reduction of entropy production we can formally define a potential difference corresponding to the different states of entropy production in A and B (the amount of constitutional supercooling might be a suitable potential function) and a transfer law to go with it. In principle, the system can then be analyzed to obtain the oscillation frequency in terms of the growth rate, thermal gradients, thermal conductivity, and diffusion coefficient, and thence the branch spacing. In fact, since diffusion is appreciably slower than thermal conduction, it will be the former which determines the relaxation time τ of a configuration and therefore the oscillation frequency ν. This time is roughly that to transmit an interaction across the dendrite spacing so that

$$\nu = 1/\tau \sim D/d^2 \tag{8}$$

with the branch spacing

$$a = v/\nu \sim (Vd/D) \cdot d \tag{9}$$

Thus, from estimate (5), which applies to dendrites as well as cells, the branch and core spacings should be the same order of magnitude, as in fact is observed.

Dendritic Growth of Pure Metals

Weinberg and Chalmers[8] have demonstrated that melt supercooling is a requisite to dendritic growth into a pure melt. The most prevalent occurrence of such a phenomenon is in the top center of an ingot where supercooling has occurred by radiation and convection.

Under these practical circumstances, the solid-liquid interface advances uniformly by transfer of heat through the mold wall. When this interface meets the supercooled region, its rate of advance will accelerate, and heat will be dissipated into, as well as away from, the liquid. Now statement (4) requires that the integrated rate of entropy production be as small as possible consistent with the optimum rate of change of some potential function. Thus, dendrite growth is favored since this mechanism distributes the average latent heat source uniformly within the sink, tending to reduce the average length of thermal transfer paths, and thus the integrated rate of entropy production. If the process is controlled entirely by thermal effects then one can estimate that the dendrite and branch spacings will be of the order of the thermal transport length,

$$1 \sim k/Cp\delta v \qquad (10)$$

where k is the thermal conductivity, Cp the specific heat of the liquid δ the density, and v the mean rate of dendrite advance.

Observational Support for the Variation Principle

In concluding this section on morphology we note that the qualitative aspects of the principle of minimum entropy production can be deduced from the observations of an actual steady state interface and the inferred properties of a corresponding virtual plane interface. By "corresponding" we mean that which would be obtained theoretically by moving the same two interface bracketing temperature points (T_1 and T_2 on Fig. 1) uniformly through the sample in the same fixed spacial relationship. This correspondence assures that the growth rate is the same, the initial liquid state is identical, and the change in the thermal energy content per unit volume between T_2 and T_1 is almost identical in the actual and virtual states. As a result of these conditions we can write for the difference between the virtual and actual process,

$$\Delta \int_V \sigma dV = vA \Delta S \qquad (11)$$

where A is the cross-sectional area and S is the specific entropy corresponding to temperature T_1.   The flat interface evidently leads to the highest final entropy state since the other has its entropy decreased relatively by the solid solute segregation and the associated dislocation network.   Thus, ΔS is positive, and the nonplanar configuration must have the smaller entropy production rate.   The free energy difference ΔF corresponding to ΔS is given approximately by

$$\Delta F = -T_1 \Delta S \qquad (12)$$

We can therefore make an alternative, qualitative, statement of our principle to the effect that for given boundary conditions nature chooses that path which conserves the maximum amount of free energy in a given time.   Dendritic growth with its attendant solid solute segregation and interfacial energy production in the form of dislocation nets or solid phase interfaces is a clear expression of this thermodynamic principle.

The results of this comparison of "observed" final states are of course quite consistent with our earlier statement that the entropy production rate is reduced within a test volume with nonplanar interface by reduction of the effective volume of integration in the diffusion field.   This reduction in entropy production is manifested in the production of surface free energy and solute segregation in the same region.

If we accept the principle of minimum entropy production as an accurate statement for the complex systems in question, then for truly steady state growth of a cellular interface, it appears that constitutional supercooling must be eliminated at the cell tips.   This follows from the presumption that the cells will take the maximum length compatible with the constraints in order to assure the maximum segregation of solute with its attendant conservation of free energy.

MORPHOLOGICAL OBSERVATIONS IN ALUMINUM-RICH, ALUMINUM-COPPER ALLOYS

The most striking feature of metallographic studies in unidirectionally solidified ingots of aluminum-copper is the regularity of the structures.   Figures 3 and 4 show, respectively, a basal and longitudinal section in an aluminum, 5% copper crystal, while Figure 5 shows the chill-face development of an aluminum, 10% copper crystal.   It is

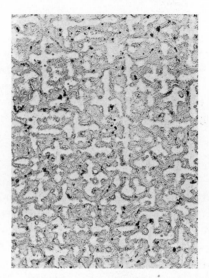

Fig. 3. Microstructure of 5% copper ingot. Plane of polish perpendicular to solidification direction, showing pattern of dendrite cores. 230×.

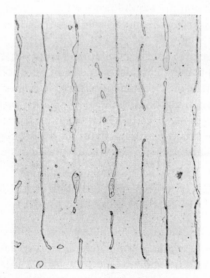

Fig. 4. Microstructure of 5% copper ingot. Plane of polish parallel to solidification direction, showing long continuous eutectic channels. 720×.

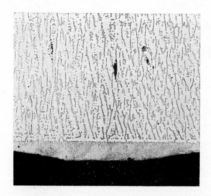

Fig. 5. Microstructure of base of 10% copper ingot fast-cooled and cast at atmospheric pressure, showing massive sweat beads formed during reheating. 90×.

evident that the early history of such crystals must have been close to the ideal shown in the sketch of Figure 6.   We imagine that an initial nucleus of suitable orientation at the chill-face side of a narrow supercooled region expands parallel and perpendicular to the chill face in a fashion similar to that of a dendritic crystal growing into the supercooled pure melt described above. Of course, in the present case,

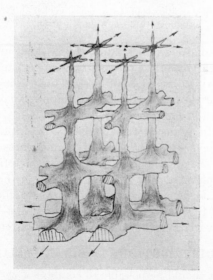

Fig. 6. Schematic perspective view of growing dendrites.

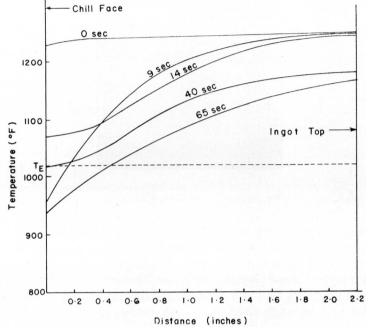

Fig. 7. Thermal history of 10% copper ingot, fast cooled and cast at atmospheric temperature, showing reheating.

solute redistribution occurs simultaneously and undoubtedly influences the dimensions of the primary dendritic units. At a slightly later stage, following dissipation of most of the thermal supercooling, the perpendicular growth settles into an approximate steady state much as described in the previous theoretical discussion of alloy dendritic growth. In terms of the oscillatory description of dendrite branching and the postulate of substantial uniqueness of morphology, the regularity of the observed structures is satisfactorily rationalized. It should be emphasized that dendritic growth in the later approximately steady state stages is not a manifestation of efficient heat dissipation from the tips as has sometimes been stated but is rather a thermodynamic variation which conserves available energy.

THERMAL DISTRIBUTIONS IN BINARY ALLOY INGOTS

In principle, it should be possible to combine a variation principle with the boundary conditions to obtain simultaneously the mor-

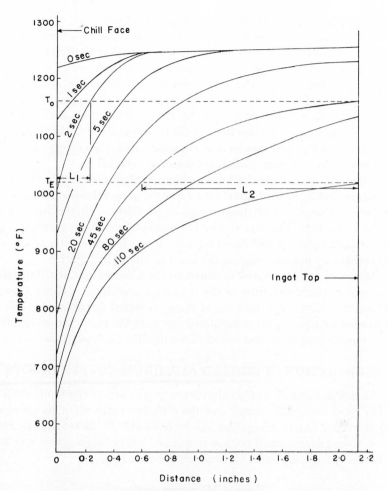

Fig. 8. Thermal history of 10% copper ingot (2A1A), fast cooled and cast at 50 psig argon.

phology and concentration and temperature distributions. In practice, however, this is not feasible, so we must make suitable approximations and calculate each feature separately. Fortunately for us, in fast-cooled ingots nature contrives to simplify the macroscopic distributions by providing microscopic morphologic units. In the case of the temperature distribution, this fine structure is so effective that the distribution becomes, for all practical purposes, smooth and continuous. This observation has important consequences. First of all, it allows us to regard the liquid-solid mass distribution in the ingot as a smooth function of temperature and therefore of time and position in the ingot. This result will be used effectively in the later segregation calculations. Secondly, it allows us to express the average thermal conductivity, specific heat, and latent heat source strength as continuous functions of the temperature and its derivative so that the thermal conduction equation with source term can be solved subject to given initial and boundary conditions.

Figures 7 and 8 show the measured temperature distributions in two unidirectionally chilled aluminum-copper ingots, solidified at atmospheric pressure and 50 psig argon, respectively. In the first case (Fig. 7) the ingot has parted from the mold at an early stage, resulting in a reheating of the chill-face regions. It was found possible to avoid this effect by pressure casting the ingot as shown in Figure 8.

We have not attempted to calculate the temperature distributions because of the uncertainty of the boundary conditions. However, in the next sections, we make use of these measured distributions to determine the liquid-solid mass distributions in the ingot and to clarify the mechanisms of inverse segregation and eutectic exudations.

SEGREGATION IN CHILLED ALUMINUM-COPPER INGOTS

In unidirectionally chilled aluminum-copper ingots the liquid diffusion rates are small enough and the diffusion paths tortuous enough that normal macrosegregation can be ignored.[9-11] It remains therefore to consider normal microsegregation, inverse segregation due to volume change, and eutectic exudation or sweating.

Normal Microsegregation

If one assumes in the usual approximation that diffusion in the solid is negligible while in the liquid it is fast enough to attain local equilibration of the interdendritic liquid with its immediately adjacent interface,[9-11] one can use a relation due to Hayes and Chipman[12] to calculate the nonequilibrium amount of eutectic which appears in hypoeutectic alloys. This has been discussed by Scheil on several occasions,[9,13] and successful comparative experiments in aluminum-copper have been carried out by Michael and Bever.[10] The differen-

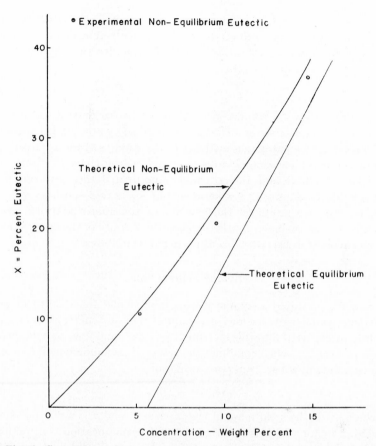

Fig. 9. Comparison of the theoretical and experimental amounts of non-equilibrium eutectic as a function of alloy concentration. The equilibrium values from the phase diagram are also shown.

tial equation relating liquid mass m_L and liquid concentration c_L is, neglecting volume change,

$$dm_L/m_L = -(dc_L)/c_L^{(1-k)} \qquad (13)$$

with the solution

$$c_L = c_0(m_L/m_0)^{-(1-k)} \qquad (14)$$

where c_0 is the alloy concentration, m_0 is the initial liquid mass in the volume element under consideration, and k is the distribution coefficient or equilibrium ratio of the solute concentration in the solid to that in the liquid. Evaluating Eq. (14) at the eutectic concentration gives the nonequilibrium eutectic ratio

$$X = (m_{LE}/m_0) = (c_{LE}/c_0)^{-1/(1-k)} \qquad (15)$$

Figure 9 shows a comparison of our calculated and experimental values of X for a series of aluminum-copper, water-chilled ingots. The good agreement here is evidence of the validity of the approximations for the high cooling rates and high solute concentrations involved. Michael and Bever[10] have investigated this behavior for rather dilute alloys over a wide range of cooling rate and have determined the rate limits on the validity of the approximations. By extrapolation, their results also support the validity of the approximations involved in Eq. (13) for our particular conditions.

Inverse Segregation

Scheil[9] has stated a similar solute mass balance for a chill-face increment which takes account of volume change and therefore of excess solute transported into this increment via the liquid flow, as solidification proceeds. Scheil combines the result of a volume balance based on complete flow-back (no pore formation)

$$dm_L = -a\,dm_S \qquad (16)$$

(where m_S is the solid mass in the increment and a is a volume contraction factor which is less than unity for solidification contraction and which depends on the specific volumes of solid and liquid), with the solute balance

$$dm_L/m_L = -a[(dc_L)/c_L^{(1-k)}] \qquad (17)$$

to evaluate the segregation defined by

$$\Delta c = [(m_{LE}c_{LE})/1 - a_E] \\ + m_{SE}C_{SE}/[(m_{LE})/1 - a_E] + m_{SE} - c_0 \qquad (18)$$

The subscript E refers to eutectic values and the concentration C_{SE} is the average for the cored solid, exclusive of the eutectic.

Figure 10 shows Scheil's theoretical plot of the maximum segregation Δc vs c_0 for aluminum-copper in the composition range up to the

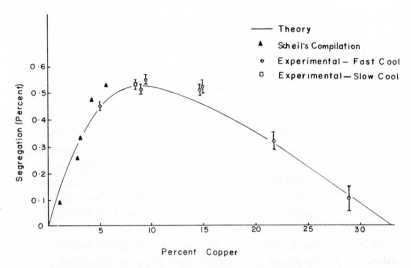

Fig. 10. Scheil's theoretical segregation curve and experimental results for aluminum-copper alloys.

eutectic. Also plotted are the confirmatory experimental results of the authors and other workers.

Kirkaldy and Youdelis[11] have extended Scheil's calculation to give not only the surface concentration but also the concentration at inner points of the ingot. As before, this calculation involves Eqs. (16) and (18), but Eq. (17) must now be modified to account not only for excess inflow of liquid to a given volume increment but also for the continuous flow of liquid right through the volume element which is caused by contraction at inner points of the interdendritic channels. This flow carries with it an average solute gradient of such sign that the solute concentration of every volume increment except the chill-face one is being continuously diluted. This dilution becomes increasingly effective as we move toward the hot end of the ingot and the term representing this in the differential equation assures the necessary reversal of the sign of the segregation in that region.

The dilution phenomenon, since it depends not only on conditions at a given position L in the ingot but also on those conditions which are occurring simultaneously at all points along the inner channels, must be described by an integro-differential equation. The authors have demonstrated[11] that the appropriate modification of Eq. (17) is to

$$dm_L/m_L = -K[(dc_L)/c_L^{(1-k)}] \qquad (19)$$

where

$$K = a[1 - 1/v_L m_L \int v_L'(1 - a')/a'(dm_L''/dm_L')dm_L'] \quad (20)$$

In this, v_L is the specific volume of the liquid and (dm_L''/dm_L') is a transformation factor expressing the relative rate of expansion or contraction of the mixed (mushy) zone of the ingot. It is less than unity if the zone is expanding and more than unity if contracting.

If a reasonably accurate model of the liquid-mass distribution as a function of time can be specified it is possible to specify the limits of the integral and the functional variation of (dm_L''/dm_L') and thence to iterate simultaneous solutions of Eqs. (16) and (19) for evaluation of Δc.

We have chosen for simplicity to represent the liquid-solid mass distributions in the mixed zone by straight lines varying in slope continuously in such a way as to agree as closely as possible with the observed temperature distribution and the phase diagram. Figure 11 shows the assumed distribution for ingot (2A1A) containing 10% copper corresponding to the temperature distributions of Figure 8. Figure 12 shows the solute distribution calculated on the basis of Sauerwald's volumetric data[14] along with our experimental solute distribution for this ingot. Figure 13 shows a similar curve for a 15% copper ingot. Apart from the anomalies near the chill face, the agreement is rather better than expected for the approximate model used in the calculation. The high surface values of the segregation are due to eutectic exudation, and these had to be corrected with the help of metallographic studies before inclusion on Figure 10. The anomalous segregation values near $L = 0.3$ on both sets of curves may be due to a sudden change in dendrite length associated with a change in the surface heat transfer coefficient at the time of exudation or to dilution at inner points attending the exudation of rich material at the surface.

The theory demonstrates that positive segregation will persist as long as the mushy zone in the ingot continues to increase its length. Such a morphological behavior is characteristic of the flattening temperature distributions extent in ingots solidified in the unsteady manner of our experiments, so we always observe this flat region of positive segregation extending well into the ingot. It would only be if the

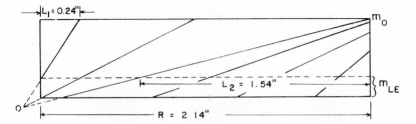

Fig. 11. Approximate mass distributions in the 10% copper ingot (2A1A) as determined from the thermal distributions of Fig. 8. The critical dendrite lengths L_1 and L_2 are indicated in both figures.

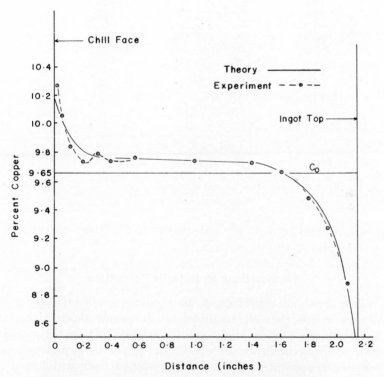

Fig. 12. Theoretical and experimental segregation distributions for the 10% copper, pressure-cast ingot (2A1A).

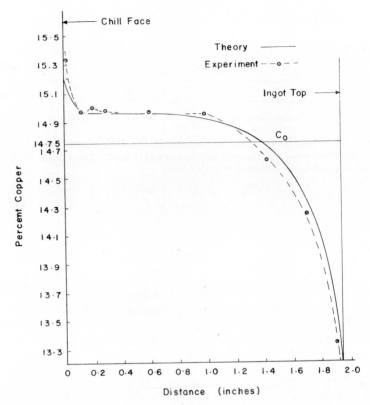

Fig. 13. Theoretical and experimental segregation distributions for a 15% copper pressure-cast ingot.

growth attained a true steady state that we would observe an extensive central region of zero segregation.

Observations on Eutectic Exudations

When aluminum-copper ingots are solidified unidirectionally as in our experiments, the chill face invariably shows eutectic exudations in the form of sweat or a continuous eutectic layer. The massive sweat beads which occur in ingots solidified at atmospheric pressure can definitely be attributed to the reheating which attends withdrawal of the ingot from the mold at an early stage of the solidification.[15] Figure 5 shows a micrograph of the base of a 10% copper ingot which has massive sweat beads, and Figure 7 shows the corresponding thermal history of this ingot. The latter indicates that reheating occurs very soon after the base layer completely solidifies. Evidently, as soon as the base attains the ability to support mechanical stress due to thermal gradients and solidification contraction, it buckles and parts here and there from the mold. The pressure buildup in the liquid which attends the melting and expansion on reheating drives the interdendritic liquid through the low resistance channels to the chill surface of the ingot. The fact that appreciable flow is toward the chill face can be attributed to the fact that the viscosity of interdendritic liquid decreases toward the chill face due to the composition dependence of the liquid viscosity[16] and, perhaps more important, due to the superheat of the remelted material which exists simultaneously with the expansion.

Youdelis[17] has estimated the expansion in the chill zone of the 10% copper ingot of Figure 5 corresponding to the reheat cycle of Figure 7. Assuming the associated flow is toward the chill face he calculates an average exuded layer of 0.0012 in. thickness. The average thickness as determined metallographically was equal to 0.0011 in. Similar procedures for a 5% copper ingot led to values of 0.00045 and 0.00067 in., respectively. These results lend numerical support to the role of the reheat mechanism in sweating.

The role of ingot withdrawal in the phenomenon of sweating suggested that exudations might be avoided by pressure casting. Accordingly, a mold was designed which would sustain a hydrostatic pressure on the top of the liquid metal during solidification. When a head of 50 psig argon was applied, the temperature inversion usually observed at atmospheric pressure was absent, due no doubt to the maintenance of thermal and mechanical contact. As expected, sweat was no longer observed, but surprisingly, a uniform layer of eutectic still persisted at the chill face. Figure 8 shows the inversion free thermal history of the 10% copper ingot (2A1A) and Figure 14 shows a representative chill face microstructure. These observations were duplicated on ingots of 5%, 15%, 22%, and 30% copper, all cast at 50 psig pressure on a polished steel base plate.

In the absence of a thermal inversion, one must attribute these exudations to surface tension effects. If, for example, the interfacial free energy of the mold to primary solid interface is greater than that for the mold to eutectic liquid plus eutectic liquid to primary solid

Fig. 14. Microstructure of base of the 10% copper ingot (2A1A), pressure cast on a polished steel base. 720×.

interfaces, there will be a tendency to draw eutectic liquid out of the near interdendritic channels and along the solid-mold interface. This can proceed until a minute layer forms. The further growth of the exuded layer might then be attributed to the tendency of the system to equilibrate the eutectic layer and the adjacent low concentration solid by drawing some further noneutectic liquid. The metallographic evidence is consistent with this since in all surfaces observed, the original primary interface has apparently advanced by projection into the exuded layer on final solidification. Alternatively, all or

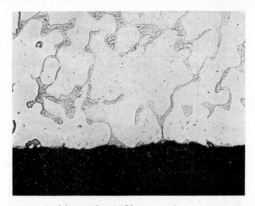

Fig. 15. Microstructure of base of a 10% copper ingot pressure cast on an alundum-coated base. 720×.

part of the layer growth might have been due to the buoyant force on the primary dendrites in the heavier eutectic liquid which becomes effective as soon as the resultant downward force on the dendrites is nullified by the completion of a eutectic liquid layer along the chill face.   If the layer were to remain liquid for the order of a second, numerical estimates of layer growth rates based on the buoyancy mechanism lead to sensible values.   Although the cooling curves of Figure 8 indicate that the eutectic isotherm passes through the observed thickness in about 0.001 sec it may be that liquid supercooling provides the necessary time delay for this mechanism to operate.

The appearance of an impoverished zone adjacent to the exuded regions as in Figures 5 and 14 is also to be understood in terms of the eutectic liquid flow mechanism.   We can imagine that just prior to exudation there exists a layer adjacent to the chill face having a width the order of magnitude of the diffusion length D/v in which the liquid concentration is near the eutectic value.   When the liquid from this region is exuded, other liquid is drawn in of appreciably lower concentration which lowers the final mean concentration of the region.   Because of their lower initial enrichment, the deeper regions are not noticeably affected by this dilution.   As might be expected on the basis of simple volumetric considerations, the effect is not evident in alloys of 15% mean concentration or greater.

The inferred role of surface tension in these phenomena suggested that layer exudation might be prevented by choosing a liquid metal-mold interface of high interfacial energy.   Accordingly, the steel base plate was coated with commercial alundum, and a 10% copper ingot was cast on it at 50 psig.   This combination was suggested by the strong convex meniscus observed between the alloy melts and our standard alundum-coated mold walls, evidently caused by the high mold-liquid interfacial energy.   As anticipated, layer exudations were inhibited as shown in the micrograph of Figure 15.   Although this result is by no means unequivocal, it suggests the possibility of prevention of eutectic layer formation in pressure castings by the choice of suitable mold dressings or materials.

SUMMARY

The principle of minimum rate of entropy production has been applied to steady state transport processes in the neighborhood of a growing crystal face.   The decreased entropy production rate of a dendritic interface, as compared to a flat one, is manifested in the final microstructure by remnant available energy in the form of surface free energy, solute segregation, and crystal defects. The principle therefore provides a satisfactory rationale of the observed morphology and a unifying statement for all the macroscopic features of growth: morphology, solute distributions, and temperature distributions.

In the detailed calculations, the solute and mass balances for a representative volume increment within a unidirectionally fast-cooled ingot have been described and two differential equations obtained relating the volume changes, the phase concentrations, and the phase masses in the system. The solution of these equations using a morphological model based on measured temperature distributions leads to quantitative relations for: (a) the fraction of nonequilibrium eutectic in the microstructure as a function of alloy concentration, (b) the maximum segregation occurring at the surface due to volume contraction, and (c) the segregation distribution throughout the ingot.

The calculations in all cases show quantitative agreement with the authors' measurements for the aluminum-rich, aluminum-copper alloys in the concentration range up to the eutectic. This agreement in respect to (b) and (c) demonstrates that volume contraction with flowback of enriched interdendritic liquid is the primary cause of inverse segregation in these alloys.

The formation of chill surface layers of eutectic which accompanies inverse segregation and derives from exudation on solidification has been studied as a function of casting pressure and mold dressing. In agreement with Adams,[15] it has been ascertained that massive exudation in the form of sweat is due to reheating and expansion of the dendritic shell as a result of ingot withdrawal. When this withdrawal is restricted by pressure casting at 50 psig, a smooth surface eutectic layer still persists, and because no reheating occurs it can only be attributed to surface tension effects. The fact that this exudation can be prevented to a certain extent by suitable mold dressing bears out the postulated role of surface tension in the phenomenon.

The authors are grateful to Aluminium Laboratories, Ltd., for support in the form of research funds, technical advice, and a fellowship to one of us (W.V.Y.).

References

1. *Liquid Metals and Solidification*, American Soc. for Metals Seminar, Cleveland, Ohio, 1958.

2. Kirkaldy, J. S., *Trans. Am. Soc. Metals*, **51,** 229 (1959), discussion to paper by T. S. Plaskett and W. C. Winegard.

3. Brown, W. Byers, *Trans. Faraday Soc.*, **54,** 772 (1958).

4. de Groot, S. R., *Thermodynamics of Irreversible Processes*, North-Holland Publishing Co., Amsterdam, 1952.

5. Onsager, L., *Ann. N. Y. Acad. Sci.*, **46,** 241 (1945–46).

6. Rutter, J. W., and B. Chalmers, *Can. J. Phys.*, **31,** 15 (1953).

7. Walton, D., W. A. Tiller, and W. C. Winegard, *Trans. Am. Inst. Mining Met. Engrs.*, **203,** 1023 (1955).

8. Weinberg, F., and B. Chalmers, *Can. J. Phys.*, **29,** 382 (1951).

9. Scheil, E., *Z. Metallk.*, **38,** 69 (1947).

10. Michael, A., and M. Bever, *Trans. Am. Inst. Mining Met. Engrs.*, **200,** 47 (1954).

11. Kirkaldy, J. S., and W. V. Youdelis, *Trans. Am. Inst. Mining, Met. Petrol. Engrs.*, **212,** 833 (1958).

12. Hayes, A., and J. Chipman, *Trans. Am. Inst. Mining Met. Engrs.*, **135,** 85 (1939).

13. Scheil, E., *Z. Metallk.*, **34,** 70 (1942)

14. Sauerwald, F., *Metallwirtschaft*, **22,** 543 (1943).

15. Adams, D. E., *J. Inst. Metals*, **75,** 809 (1948).

16. Jones, W. R. D., and W. L. Bartlett, *J. Inst. Metals*, **81,** 145 (1952–53).

17. Youdelis, W. V., Ph.D. thesis, McGill Univ., 1958.

Discussion

W. A. Tiller (*Westinghouse Research Labs., Pittsburgh, Pa.*): The principle of minimum entropy production in nonequilibrium systems, like the principle of minimum free energy in equilibrium systems, represents the optimum thermodynamic state of the system but it does not indicate the probability of reaching this state in a finite time. A severely segregated freezing crystal exhibits a lower rate of entropy production than a crystal freezing homogeneously and is therefore preferred. However, if no constitutional supercooling exists in the liquid, the interface remains planar and the crystal is homogeneous; i.e., the crystal continues to freeze in a nonoptimum manner. At a certain degree of constitutional supercooling a cellular interface forms, and a segregated crystal is produced. It is through the existence of the constitutional supercooling that the desired end state is reached. Without it the interface morphology could not change from the planar shape.

The interface morphology does not change in order to eliminate the constitutional supercooling although the discussor once thought this was the reason for the change. It has recently appeared to G. F. Bolling and the discussor that the interface morphology changes through the aid of the constitutional supercooling to produce the segregated state of a lower rate of entropy production. In fact, very little constitutional supercooling is eliminated when cells form and it can be easily shown that the constitutional supercooling is definitely *not* eliminated at the cell caps. Thus, the cells will adopt that morphology compatible with thermal and constitutional constraints that produces the minimum rate of entropy production.   The constitutional supercooling acts as a bridge for this morphology change.   After the interface morphology change the constitutional supercooling still remains.

J. S. Kirkaldy: Dr. Tiller has adequately summarized our thermodynamic description of the morphological aspects of solidification.   We prefer not, however, to use the term "constitutional supercooling" in the description of these phenomena since it has, through the years, attained causal attributes of a highly misleading character.   Our equivalent statement in this respect was that the cells or dendrites will attain a maximum length (for maximum segregation) compatible with the constraints, and the important constraint noted was that substantial equilibrium be maintained at the interface.   Such equilibrium can only be maintained along a temperature gradient if there is sufficient solute pile-up.   If there are no other constraints then the projections will be formed in such a way and of such a length that the liquidus line corresponding to the diffusion field parallels the actual thermal field at the tip.   This is equivalent to the vanishing of "constitutional supercooling."

Drs. Tiller and Bolling object strenuously to this latter deduction, and we look forward to the publication of their detailed discussion of this descriptive detail. Whatever the resolution of this point, it cannot detract from the general thesis of our paper.

SECTION IX: THE PROPER-
TIES OF HALIDES AND
SULFIDE MELTS

. . . . c

The Constitution of Cryolite and NaF-AlF$_3$ Melts

W. B. FRANK and L. M. FOSTER

*Alcoa Research Laboratories, Aluminum Company of America,
New Kensington, Pennsylvania*

Abstract

The composition of molten cryolite is considered from the standpoint of dissociation to logical products. Calculations employing experimental densities provide an excellent fit with the data for dissociation to NaF and NaAlF$_4$, with $K = 0.09$ at 1000°. Densities for Na$_3$AlF$_6$ and NaAlF$_4$ of 2.210 and 1.873 g/ml, and gram ion volumes for Na$^+$, F$^-$, AlF$_4^-$, and AlF$_6^{3-}$ of 5.7, 15.8, 61.6, and 77.9 are derived. Molten cryolite at 1000° has the following composition by mole fraction: Na$_3$AlF$_6$, 0.384; NaF, 0.411; and NaAlF$_4$, 0.205. The heat of dissociation of cryolite is $\Delta H = 22$ kcal/mole.

INTRODUCTION

When a sodium fluoride-aluminum fluoride mixture in the stoichiometric ratio of cryolite (3NaF·AlF$_3$) is fused and solidified, the product is entirely cryolite by x-ray and petrographic examination. Phase diagrams of the NaF–AlF$_3$ system have been reported by Fedotieff and Iljinskii,[1] Puschin and Baskow,[2] Hardouin,[3] Lorentz et al.,[4] and recently by Grjotheim.[5] Cryolite melts congruently. The compound maximum is broad, indicating partial dissociation into simpler species in the molten state. Grjotheim[5] calculated the liquidus curve in the vicinity of the cryolite composition according to the following four schemes (sodium was assumed to be completely ionized in all cases):

$$2AlF_6^{3-} = Al_2F_{11}^{5-} + F^- \tag{1}$$

$$AlF_6^{3-} = AlF_5^{2-} + F^- \tag{2}$$

$$AlF_6^{3-} = AlF_4^- + 2F^- \tag{3}$$

$$AlF_6^{3-} = Al^{3+} + 6F^- \tag{4}$$

It was necessary in the calculation to assume the heat of dissociation to be zero so the dissociation constant would be independent of temperature. Also, ΔC_P was assumed to be zero, and no dissociation was considered in the solid.

By trying various degrees of dissociation, arbitrarily chosen, for each scheme, and comparing the calculated with the observed curve, Grjotheim eliminated (1) and (2). Scheme (3) gave a somewhat better fit than (4), but he stated that the choice between these would have to be substantiated by other information, and suggested that both schemes may be operative simultaneously.[6] The best fit for scheme (3) was obtained with $\alpha = 0.3$ and $K = 0.06$.

Some of the quantities employed in Grjotheim's calculations have since been revised. The heat of fusion of cryolite has now been reported as about 28 kcal/mole (vs 20.85 used by Grjotheim), and the heat capacity of the liquid has been found to be higher than that of the solid.[7,8] Moreover, there is now evidence of partial dissociation in the solid.[9]

Grjotheim clearly recognized the sources of error in his method and particularly pointed out the difficulty in taking cognizance of nonideal behavior at the melting point where all of the calculations were made.

The present work treats the composition of these melts from the standpoint of melt densities corresponding to various dissociation schemes. The calculations are no less arduous than Grjotheim's but involve fewer assumptions and provide more detailed information.

EXPERIMENTAL

Composition of NaF-AlF$_3$ Melts

Several investigators[10-12] observed a maximum in the density curve of sodium fluoride-aluminum fluoride melts at approximately 33 wt-% (20 mole-%) aluminum fluoride. Vajna[13] found a similar maximum but at 37 wt-% aluminum fluoride. While the absolute values of the densities vary, there is good agreement, with the exception of Vajna's results, as to the composition of the melt at maximum density. Calculations are presented here to explain this variation of density with composition in terms of an equilibrium between cryolite and logical dissociation products.

The method consists of the following steps:

1. Three dissociation schemes are considered

Scheme I

Dissociation to sodium fluoride and aluminum fluoride

$$Na_3AlF_6 = 3NaF + AlF_3$$

$$K_I = [a_{NaF}]^3 [a_{AlF_3}]/[a_{Na_3AlF_6}] \tag{5}$$

Scheme II

Dissociation to sodium fluoride and chiolite

$$3Na_3AlF_6 = 4NaF + Na_5Al_3F_{14}$$

$$K_{II} = [a_{NaF}]^4 [a_{Na_5Al_3F_{14}}]/[a_{Na_3AlF_6}]^3 \tag{6}$$

Scheme III

Dissociation to sodium fluoride and sodium tetrafluoaluminate

$$Na_3AlF_6 = 2NaF + NaAlF_4$$

$$K_{III} = [a_{NaF}]^2 [a_{NaAlF_4}]/[a_{Na_3AlF_6}] \tag{7}$$

2. The composition of the melt is calculated for a series of arbitrarily chosen equilibrium constants K for each scheme as follows: Let N be the weighed-in mole fraction of NaF on a sodium fluoride-aluminum fluoride basis and n the moles of undissociated cryolite at equilibrium.

Assuming that the activity of each component is equal to its mole fraction, the expressions for activities of the species for each scheme become:

Scheme I

$$[a_{NaF}] = (N - 3n)/(1 - 3n)$$
$$[a_{AlF_3}] = (1 - N - n)/(1 - 3n) \tag{8}$$
$$[a_{Na_3AlF_6}] = n/(1 - 3n)$$

Scheme II

$$[a_{NaF}] = (8N - 5 - 4n)/(7N - 4 - 2n)$$
$$[a_{5NaF.3AlF_3}] = (1 - N - n)/(7N - 4 - 2n) \tag{9}$$
$$[a_{Na_3AlF_6}] = 3n/(7N - 4 - 2n)$$

Scheme III

$$[a_{NaF}] = (2N - 1 - 2n)/(N - 2n)$$
$$[a_{NaAlF_4}] = (1 - N - n)/(N - 2n) \qquad (10)$$
$$[a_{Na_3AlF_6}] = n/(N - 2n)$$

Substituting into (5), (6), and (7), and simplifying

$$K_I = [(N - 3n)^5 (1 - N - n)/[n(1 - 3n)^3] \qquad (11)$$
$$K_{II} = [(8N - 5 - 4n)^4(1 - N - n)/27n^3(7N - 4 - 2n)^2] \qquad (12)$$
$$K_{III} = [(2N - 1 - 2n)^2 (1 - N - n)]/[n(N - 2n)^2] \qquad (13)$$

The resulting fourth power, fifth power, and cubic equations are solved for the moles of undissociated cryolite, n, at a number of different compositions for each selected equilibrium constant by the method of successive approximations. The activities are then calculated for each of the three components from (8), (9), and (10), and the compositions are expressed as weight-% of each of the three components.

3. Series of melt densities are calculated for the series of compositions determined for each equilibrium constant by assigning a series of arbitrary but reasonable densities to the second dissociation product (i.e., AlF_3, $Na_5Al_3F_{14}$, or $NaAlF_4$) and to the undissociated cryolite. (The density of pure molten sodium fluoride is known from direct measurement.) If volumes are additive, the density of the melt is

$$d = \frac{100}{\dfrac{\text{wt-\% } Na_3AlF_6}{\text{density } Na_3AlF_6} + \dfrac{\text{wt-\% NaF}}{\text{density NaF}} + \dfrac{\text{wt-\% } AlF_3,\ Na_5Al_3F_{14},\ \text{or } NaAlF_4}{\text{density } AlF_3,\ Na_5Al_3F_{14},\ \text{or } NaAlF_4}} \qquad (14)$$

4. The value of K and the densities of undissociated cryolite and the second dissociation product that give the best agreement with the experimental curve are chosen for each scheme.

5. The best fits for three dissociation schemes are compared to give the most probable composition of molten cryolite.

The experimental densities used were those of Edwards et al.,[12] which were the most recent values.

It was found empirically that the value of the equilibrium constant determines the sharpness of the density maximum and the composition of the melt at maximum density. The density of the undissociated cryolite determines the value of the density maximum

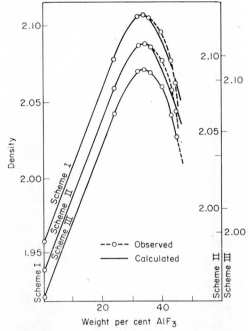

Fig. 1. Densities of NaF-AlF₃ melts at 1000°.

and, to a lesser degree, the composition of maximum density.   The density of the second dissociation product determines the slope of the right branch of the curve and, to some extent, the composition of maximum density.   Although it would be difficult to prove mathematically, values for these parameters that give the best fit with the measured densities appear to provide a unique solution to the problem.

The best fit to the experimental data for each scheme is shown for 1000° in Figure 1.   It is seen that in each case there is general conformity to the experimental curve, particularly on the sodium fluoride side of the maximum.   There is no basis for discarding the data point on the right-hand branch that is missed in schemes I and II, however, and in these cases it was impossible to adjust the parameters so as to give a better fit to the right-hand branch without greatly distorting other parts of the curve.

Almost perfect agreement with measured densities is obtained by dissociation into sodium fluoride and sodium tetrafluoaluminate, NaAlF₄ (scheme III), with an equilibrium constant of 0.090, and densities of undissociated molten cryolite and molten sodium tetra-fluoaluminate of 2.210 and 1.873 g/ml, respectively. (Edwards' density for sodium fluoride at 1000° was 1.957 g/ml.) This scheme is also the one favored by Grjotheim.

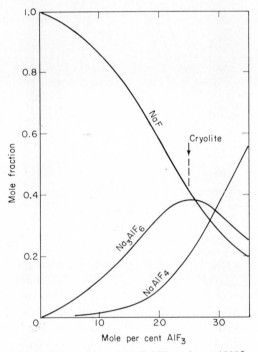

Fig. 2. Composition of NaF-AlF₃ melts at 1000°.

From the constant K for this dissociation it is possible to calculate the composition of the melt at other NaF–AlF₃ ratios. Figure 2 gives these calculated melt compositions at 1000°, as a function of the weighed-in composition. The compositions are shown only to 35 mole-% AlF₃. The proposed dissociation scheme does not apply to melts richer in AlF₃ than the NaAlF₄ composition and probably would cease to apply somewhat before that. (The experimental density data were carried only to 29 mole-% AlF₃.)

The Effect of Temperature on the Dissociation

Edwards et al.[12] determined melt densities from approximately 950 to 1090°, where permitted by the liquid range. Their data were reported as empirical equations giving the density as a function of temperature at each composition. The procedure outlined in the preceding section was also employed to determine the dissociation constant at 1030, 1075, and 1090° according to dissociation scheme III, which had provided the best fit to the experimental data at the lower temperature. An excellent fit of the calculated curves to the experimental data was likewise obtained at these temperatures. The dissociation constant K and α the degree of dissociation calculated from

$$K = 4\alpha^3/[(1 - \alpha)(2\alpha + 1)^2] \tag{15}$$

are given in Table I.

TABLE I
The Dissociation of Cryolite at Different Temperatures

Temp., °C	K	α
1000	0.09	0.35
1030	0.11	0.38
1075	0.15	0.42
1090	0.16	0.43

From

$$d \ln K/dT = \Delta H/RT^2 \tag{16}$$

Here, ΔH, the heat of dissociation per mole of dissociating cryolite, was calculated. The plot of log K versus $1/T$ is shown in Figure 3. There is no consistant deviation from a straight line, indicating that ΔH is insensitive to temperature over the range studied. A heat of dissociation of $\Delta H = 22$ kcal/mole is calculated from the slope.

Molar Volumes

The following molar volumes are calculated from the densities of the three species at 1000°: NaF = 21.5, NaAlF$_4$ = 67.3, and Na$_3$-AlF$_6$ = 95.0. If the ion volumes of Na$^+$ and F$^-$ are taken to be proportional to the cube of their crystal radii (r_{Na^+} = 0.97 A., r_{F^-} =

1.36 A), gram ion volumes of 5.7 and 15.8 are obtained for Na^+ and F^-, respectively. By subtracting the sodium volume from the volumes of the other two species, the gram ion volumes of the fluo-aluminate ions are: $AlF_4^- = 61.6$ and $AlF_6^{3-} = 77.9$.

DISCUSSION

Whereas exact agreement with experimental densities could be obtained only for scheme III, fair agreement was also obtained for the other two schemes. The choice of scheme III is supported by considerable other evidence, however. The work of Grjotheim has already been mentioned. Howard[14] identified $NaAlF_4$ in quenched

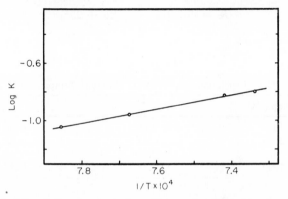

Fig. 3. Dissociation constant of cryolite as a function of temperature.

vapor from molten cryolite. On reheating, the material dispro-portionates to chiolite and aluminum fluoride, but it can be retained at room temperature and some of its properties have been deter-mined. The existence of a species in the vapor does not necessarily imply that the same species is a major component of the liquid. (From thermodynamic considerations, the same species must be present in the melt, but the activity coefficient may be very large.) As will be shown in a subsequent paper, however, the $NaAlF_4$ pres-sure from cryolite is many-fold greater than that of any other spe-cies, and it depends on the $NaF-AlF_3$ ratio of the melt in a manner predictable from the compositions calculated here.

A final argument supporting the dissociation to $NaAlF_4$ is the reasonable change in coordination number of aluminum from 6 in AlF_6^{3-} to 4 in AlF_4^- at high temperature.

There are, on the other hand, arguments against the other two dissociation schemes. Chiolite, $5NaF.3AlF_3$ (scheme II) is a lattice-type compound, and as such has parallels of equal or greater complexity in other solid systems. The existence of the very large $Al_3F_{14}^{5-}$ ion in solution is highly unlikely, however.

Aluminum fluoride cannot be passed off as an illogical component of melts, and, in fact, scheme I is generally accepted in the older literature. Aluminum fluoride is volatile, however, and, if present

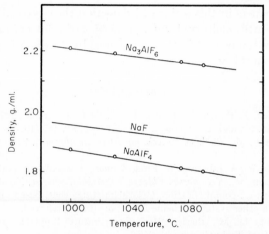

Fig. 4. Densities of the components of molten cryolite (NaF experimental, NaAlF₄ and Na₃AlF₆ calculated at temperatures shown).

as such, should appear in the vapor. Furthermore, the density that had to be assigned to AlF_3 (1.711 at 1000°) to give the best fit to the experimental curve seems much too low in view of its high density at room temperature compared to sodium fluoride and cryolite. (It should be pointed out that scheme I cannot be distinguished from Grjotheim's fourth scheme—dissociation to Na^+, Al^{3+}, and F^-—by density calculations alone, since the degree of ionization of the various species is not considered. However, transport experiments in cryolite-alumina melts[15] showed Al^{3+} to be essentially absent, and Grjotheim's fourth scheme can be eliminated on that account.

The assumption of additive volumes that was necessary for the calculations might be questioned. If the system were nonideal in this respect, however, departure from ideality should be greater as the melting point is approached. Figure 4 shows the densities of undissociated cryolite and sodium tetrafluoaluminate that provided the best fits to the experimental density curves at four temperatures. The curves are straight lines showing constant expansion coefficients and are roughly parallel to the curve for sodium fluoride, which was experimentally determined. If there were a departure from additive volumes that was temperature dependent, it would be evident in these curves.

Future papers in this series will show that the electrical conductivity of NaF–AlF$_3$ melts and some properties of solid cryolite at high temperature can be satisfactorily explained by the dissociation scheme deduced from this work.

References

1. Fedotieff, P. P., and W. P. Iljinskii, *Z. anorg. Chem.*, **80,** 121 (1913).
2. Puschin, N., and A. Baskow, *Z. anorg. Chem.*, **81,** 347 (1913).
3. Hardouin, M., *Publ. sci. et tech. ministère air (France)*, 34 (1933) (see ref. 5, p. 10).
4. Lorentz, R., A. Jabs, and W. Eitel, *Z. anorg. Chem.*, **83,** 39 (1913).
5. Grjotheim, K., *Kgl. Norske Videnskab. Selskabs, Skrifter*, No. 5 (1956).
6. In a private communication, Grjotheim states that, based on similar calculations with other systems, scheme III is now much preferred.
7. Albright, D. M., thesis, "High Temperature Properties of Cryolite," Carnegie Inst. of Technol., Jan. 31, 1956.
8. O'Brien, C. J., and K. K. Kelley, *J. Am. Chem. Soc.*, **79,** 5616 (1957).
9. Alcoa Research Labs., to be published.
10. Lundina, Z. F., *Trans. All-Union Aluminum and Magnesium Inst.*, **13,** 5 (1936); see *Discussions Faraday Soc.*, No. 1, 311 (1947).
11. Abramov, G. A., and P. A. Kozunov, *Trans. Leningrad Ind. Inst.*, No. 1, 60 (1939).
12. Edwards, J. D., C. S. Taylor, L. A. Cosgrove, and A. S. Russell. *J. Electrochem. Soc.*, **100,** 508 (1953).
13. Vajna, A., *Alluminio*, **19,** 541 (1950).
14. Howard, E. H., *J. Am. Chem. Soc.*, **76,** 2041 (1954).
15. Frank, W. B., and L. M. Foster, *J. Phys. Chem.*, **61,** 1531 (1957).

The Heats of Formation of Cryolite and the Aluminum Fluorides

P. GROSS, C. HAYMAN, and D. L. LEVI

Fulmer Research Institute, Ltd., Stokes Poges, Bucks, England

Abstract

The heat of reaction $^3/_2PbF_2 + Al + 3NaF = {^3/_2}Pb + Na_3AlF_6$ has been measured calorimetrically. With the standard heats of formation for PbF_2 and NaF of -158.5 and -136.3 kcal, respectively, a value of -784.95 kcal is derived for the standard heat of formation of Na_3AlF_6. The agreement with the value of -784.8 recently obtained by Coughlin confirms the value for PbF_2 which formed the basis for our previously published value for AlF_3, since slightly corrected by recalibration to -356.3 kcal. The heat of formation of AlF is recalculated using recent specific heat data.

INTRODUCTION

Apart from its main use as electrolyte in the aluminum electrolysis, cryolite is also used as a flux component in the aluminum industry, Its heat of formation is therefore of considerable metallurgical interest in the aluminum and light metal industry.

The only direct measurements on the heat of combination of sodium and aluminum fluorides to form cryolite previously published are those of Baud[1] who measured the heat evolved in precipitating the hydrated double fluoride from solutions of the two fluorides. Since these results appeared to be unreliable, new measurements not involving aqueous solutions were undertaken. After this work had been completed, Coughlin[2] published the results of a determination of the standard heat of formation of cryolite from a series of solution measurements. Coughlin's data can be used to evaluate the relatively small heat of combination of the two fluorides only by utilizing existing data on aluminum and sodium fluorides, so that the measurements reported here are of particular value in providing a check on

903

the accuracy both of Coughlin's data for cryolite and our own earlier measurements on the heat of formation of aluminum fluoride.[3]   On the other hand, the latter measurements with Coughlin's data and the measurements reported here provide a value for the heat of formation of aluminum trifluoride which is not dependent on the heat of formation of lead fluoride, as was our previously published value.

The method used was based on that previously applied to measurements on aluminum fluoride,[3] in which the aluminum fluoride was formed by the strongly exothermic reaction between lead fluoride and aluminum powders.   For the measurements on cryolite, powdered sodium fluoride was added to the reaction mixture so that cryolite, instead of aluminum fluoride, was formed.   The reaction used was thus:

$$^3/_2PbF_2 + Al + 3NaF = {}^3/_2Pb + Na_3AlF_6 \qquad (1)$$

The reaction mixture however was in the form of a lightly compressed powder and not a briquette as in the measurements on aluminum fluoride, since initiation of reaction in briquettes was found to be unsatisfactory in this case.

EXPERIMENTAL

The experimental procedure was generally similar to that used in our measurements on aluminum fluoride.[3]

Apparatus

The calorimeter consisted of an inner water bath (capacity 2000 ml) separated by a 8-mm air gap from the outer bath, the temperature of which was kept constant to $\pm 0.001 °C$.   The inner bath temperature was measured by a calibrated Stantel thermistor (type F2311/300) to within $0.0003 °C$.

The reaction was carried out in a small brass bomb fitted with electrical contacts and a needle valve, to permit filling with argon.   The reaction mixture was contained in an alumina crucible fitted with a aluminum cover to prevent the contents being scattered during reaction.   The crucible fitted closely inside a thick copper cylinder connected to the bomb wall by copper strips.   A tungsten wire attached to the electrical contacts was embedded in the reaction mixture, and the reaction was initiated electrically by connecting this wire with a 12-v battery.

Materials

The purity of the aluminum powder exceeded 99.96% apart from a slight oxide content which could not influence the results significantly. Before use the powder was treated as described previously.[3]

Lead fluoride was made as before[3] from spectrographically pure lead, and in deriving the heats of reaction given in the final column of Table I allowance was made for the small aluminum fluoride content of the lead fluoride.

The sodium fluoride (A. R. grade) was heated in a stream of hydrogen fluoride to 800°C to remove water. To avoid combination between hydrogen fluoride and sodium fluoride on cooling, the hydrogen was replaced with purified argon at 800°C and the salt allowed to cool in an argon stream.

Procedure

Weighed quantities of the purified reactants, in the form of fine powders, were carefully mixed together and placed in the alumina crucible. The crucible was fitted into the bomb, which was then filled with purified argon.

After equilibration in the calorimeter bath the reaction was started by connecting the tungsten wire momentarily with the battery, the reaction being completed in a few seconds. The energy required for igniting the mixture was deduced from the deflection of a ballistic galvanometer in circuit with the ignition wire, the deflection having previously been correlated (in blank experiments) with a directly measured quantity of heat. (The uncertainty in this measurement corresponded to a temperature change not greater than about 0.001°C.)

In all experiments an excess of aluminum over lead fluoride was used, it being assumed on the basis of our earlier work that all the lead fluoride was reduced. An excess of sodium fluoride over the amount required to convert the aluminum fluoride to cryolite was used in all cases, this excess varying in different experiments. Since the sodium fluoride-aluminum fluoride system[4] contains no compounds or solid solutions at the standard temperature having a sodium fluoride/aluminum fluoride ratio greater than that of cryolite itself, no correction is required on this account. The consistency in the heat data derived from experiments with mixtures of different composition indicates that reaction was in all cases essentially complete. X-ray examination of the products showed that the cryolite formed was crystalline and was the α low temperature form.

Calibration

The heat capacity of the calorimeter was measured by an electrical method, as was previously done. The value obtained was 2305 ± 0.0019 kcal/°C. This value is based on a redetermination thereby eliminating a source of error[5] previously present in the electrical equipment. The change made in the heat capacity requires revision of our original value for the standard heat of formation of aluminum fluoride, which becomes −356.3 kcal/mole instead of −355.7 kcal/ mole.

RESULTS

The results of the individual measurements are given in Table I and give $-138.3_1 \pm 0.1_1$ kcal/mole Na_2AlF_6.

TABLE I

Expt No.	Wt PbF_2, g	Wt Al, g	Wt NaF, g	Ignition correction, °C	Corrected temp. rise, °C	Heat of reaction, kcal/mole
12	4.633	0.924	2.177	0.006	0.759	138.11
13	4.652	0.913	1.991	0.002	0.760_5	138.56
14	6.971	1.382	2.983	0.002	1.139	138.59
15	7.008	1.417	2.998	0.002	1.141_5	138.18
16	7.023	1.369	3.020	0.001_5	1.142_5	138.10

DISCUSSION

Cryolite

The value of $138.3_1 \pm 0.1_2$ kcal for the heat of reaction (1) and the value for the heat of the reaction

$$^3/_2 \, PbF_2 + Al = AlF_3 + {}^3/_2 \, Pb \qquad (2)$$

previously reported and since corrected (see above) to $118.5_3 \pm 0.08$ kcal gives $19.7_8 \pm 0.14$ kcal for formation of cryolite from aluminum

fluoride and sodium fluoride.   Taking the value of 0.158.5 kcal for
the heat of formation of lead fluoride given in ref. 6 the value of
-136.3 kcal/mole for the heat of formation of sodium fluoride recently determined by Coughlin,[2] and the value of -138.3 kcal for
the heat of reaction (1), the standard heat of formation of cryolite
becomes -784.9_5 kcal/mole.

   The value thus obtained is in very satisfactory agreement with that
of -784.8 kcal/mole derived by Coughlin[2] from measurements on a
natural cryolite crystal with a composition corresponding to $Na_{2.96}$-
$AlF_{5.96}$.   In calculating this heat of formation, Coughlin assumed
that the dissolution of 0.04 mole aluminum trifluoride in 1 mole of
cryolite occurs without heat change; he also assumed our own earlier
value[3] for the standard heat of formation of aluminum fluoride, although the resulting heat of formation of cryolite would be scarcely
influenced by adoption of a widely different value.   The agreement is
indeed better than one could have expected considering that the
spread among various determinations of the heat of formation of lead
fluoride amounts to 1 kcal,[3] and that the accepted value cannot be
assumed to be accurate to within limits of much less than 1 kcal.

Aluminum Fluoride

   It may therefore be considered to be preferable to derive the heats
of formation of both aluminum trifluoride and lead fluoride from the
experimental data presented here, together with Coughlin's measurements and our previous[3] measurements on the heat of reaction (2).
The values thus obtained, -158.4 kcal/mole for lead fluoride and
-356.1_5 kcal/mole for aluminum fluoride, will clearly be almost
identical with the values for these substances previously referred to in
this paper.   Although the agreement within the set of values thus
provided is most satisfactory, they all appear to be dependent on the
accepted value of the heat of formation of hydrogen fluoride.   It
would therefore be of interest to compare the heat of formation of any
of the metal fluorides for which values are at present linked with that
of hydrogen fluoride, with an experimental value obtained directly by
combustion of the metal in fluorine.   We have almost completed
measurements on the heat of formation of titanium tetrafluoride by
direct combination of the elements, and the essential procedure involved could be extended to other fluorides.

Aluminum Monofluoride

The heat of formation of aluminum trifluoride being thus confirmed, it appears worthwhile to use recently measured values for the specific heat of aluminum trifluoride,[7,8] and the more recent spectroscopic data for the specific heat of aluminum monofluoride[9] for a recalculation of the heat of formation of aluminum monofluoride on the basis of the experiments described some time ago[10] in which the aluminum monofluoride pressure of the reaction $AlF_3 + 2Al = 3AlF$ was measured by comparing it with the vapor pressure of lead at 920°C. The ratio of lead/aluminum of 1.92 and the standard entropy of aluminum trifluoride of 15.89 e.u.,[7] instead of the previously used estimated value of 12.5 e.u., lead to a standard heat of formation of aluminum monofluoride vapor of −61.4 kcal/mole. With a heat of evaporation for aluminum of 77.4 kcal/mole[11] and a heat of dissociation of fluorine of 37.9 kcal/mole fluorine,[12,13] this leads to a value of 157.4 kcal/mole for the energy of dissociation of AlF. This is higher than the lower limit of 156.4 kcal/mole recently given by Barrow et al.[9] but noticeably lower than the minimum extrapolated value found acceptable by these authors, who tend to explain the discrepancy by the assumption of a maximum in the potential curve for AlF.

References

1. Baud, E., *Ann. chim. et phys.*, **1**, No. 8, 58 (1904).
2. Coughlin, J. P., *J. Am. Chem. Soc.*, **80**, 1802 (1958).
3. Gross, P., C. Hayman, and D. L. Levi, *Trans. Faraday Soc.*, **50**, 477 (1954).
4. *Gmelins Handbuch der anorganischen Chemie, Aluminum*, Vol. B2, Berlin, 1934, p. 367.
5. Gross, P., C. Hayman, and D. L. Levi, *Trans. Faraday Soc.*, **53**, 1601 (1957).
6. *Selected Values of Chemical Thermodynamic Properties*, Circ. 500, Natl. Bureau of Standards, Washington, D. C., 1952.
7. King, E. G., *J. Am. Chem. Soc.*, **79**, 2056 (1957).
8. O'Brien, C. J., and K. K. Kelley, *J. Am. Chem. Soc.*, **79**, 5616 (1957).
9. Barrow, R. F., J. W. C. Johns, and F. J. Smith, *Trans. Faraday Soc.*, **52**, 913 (1956).
10. Gross, P., C. S. Campbell, P. J. C. Kent, and D. L. Levi, *Discussions Faraday Soc.*, **4**, 206 (1948).
11. Brewer, L., and A. W. Searcy, *J. Am. Chem. Soc.*, **73**, 5308 (1951).
12. Barrow, R. F., and A. D. Caunt, *Proc. Roy. Soc. (London)*, **219**, 120 (1953).
13. Wise, H., *J. Phys. Chem.*, **58**, 389 (1954).

Metal-Molten Salt Solutions. I. Phase Equilibria in the Systems Mg + MgCl$_2$ and Ca + CaF$_2$

P. S. ROGERS

British Iron and Steel Research Association, London, England

J. W. TOMLINSON and F. D. RICHARDSON

Department of Metallurgy, Imperial College, London, England

Abstract

The solubility of Mg in MgCl$_2$ has been found to be 0.30 and 0.69 mole-% at 800 and 1000°C, respectively. Studies of the solubility as a function of Mg activity have shown that Mg in solution in MgCl$_2$ obeys Henry's law at these temperatures.

The system Ca + CaF$_2$ has been studied by differential thermal analysis and solubility measurement. A monotectic and a eutectic were found, at 25.5 mole-% Ca and 1290°C and at 98.6 mole-% Ca and 821°C separated by a two liquid region terminated by a consolute point at 1322°C. The melting points of the pure salt and metal were found to be 1411 ± 3 and 837 ± 1°C, respectively.

INTRODUCTION

In recent years much interest has been attached to the study of the properties of solutions of metals in molten halides since these systems play an important part in processes for the extraction of the nuclear metals (e.g., uranium, thorium, and zirconium) both by bomb reduction and electrodeposition.

In this laboratory, work has been in progress since 1953 on systems involving metals of group IIA. Considerable difficulty has been experienced in making the measurements, due to the reactivity and volatility of both metals and salts and it has been necessary to develop new techniques. The experimental work will therefore be described in some detail.

909

EXPERIMENTAL

Materials

The magnesium was kindly given by Magnesium Elektron Ltd., who provided the following analysis of the metal in wt-%;

Na	0.01	Zn	0.001
Al	0.005	Cu	0.001
Mn	0.004	Pb	0.001
Ca	0.004	Ni	0.0005
Fe	0.001	Si	0.006
		P	<0.001

Specimens were cut from a block and their surfaces cleaned with a file immediately before use, to remove the oxide film.

Calcium was given by the U.K.A.E.A., Risely, and was in granular form. The major impurities were in wt-%:

Cl	0.2	Na	0.02
Mg	0.02–0.08	N	<0.002
C	0.05	Other metals	<0.01

The metal was kept in a closed tube filled with argon until required, when individual bright grains were selected for use. They could be transferred and weighed in a closed bottle without detectable oxidation occurring. A test for nitrogen made on a sample immediately before use, showed that <0.005 wt-% was present.

The aluminum used was Hopkin and Williams 99.99% "super pure" metal in the form of $1/8$ in. wire.

Attempts to produce anhydrous $MgCl_2$ by heating the hexahydrate or the double salt $MgCl_2 \cdot NH_4Cl \cdot 6H_2O$ in air and by heating the hexahydrate *in vacuo* were unsuccessful. The method finally developed was to heat the hexahydrate in batches of about 20 g to 400 °C over a period of about 8 hr in a stream of dry hydrogen chloride (2–300 ml/min). Care was taken to prevent melting of the hydrated salt because this led to the formation of some oxide. Later, $MgCl_2$ containing about 1% of water was obtained from Magnesium Elektron Ltd. and this could be successfully dehydrated in about $2^1/_2$ hr by the same procedure. The main impurities in the salt supplied were in wt-%:

Mn	Ca	Fe
0.036	0.8	0.02

Although it was a by-product of the reduction of $TiCl_4$ by Mg, no Ti could be detected in the sample.

The anhydrous salt was stored in an evacuated tube and handled only in a dry box or closed container.   Frequent analyses for moisture were carried out by titrating samples of the salt dissolved in methanol with Karl Fischer reagent.   Magnesium chloride was never used if it appeared to contain more than 0.05% H_2O.   This is a maximum figure since some moisture was inevitably picked up by the salt during analysis.

Analar "dry" $CaCl_2$ which contained about 25 wt-% of water was dehydrated by heating the powdered salt to 400°C *in vacuo* over the course of an hour and then maintaining this temperature for a further four hours.   This was done in the iron crucibles in which experiments were later to be carried out, and after dehydration the salt was fused by heating the crucibles *in vacuo* in a high frequency furnace.   This effectively prevented rehydration during momentary exposure to the air.   No oxide could be detected in samples of salt treated in this way and the iron crucibles were quite unattacked.

Commercial CaF_2 was dried by heating it for one hour at 1000°C. The analysis in wt-% was as follows:

CaF_2	SiO_2	Fe	Cl	SO_4
99.9	<0.02	0.0015	0.001	0.01

Commercial NaF was dried at 130°C for an hour.   The impurities present were in wt-%:

Cl	PO_4	SiO_2	SO_4
0.002	0.001	0.05	0.01

Solubility Measurements

These measurements were made by bringing the appropriate salt and metal phases to equilibrium in a small crucible, and then quenching rapidly in water.   This method is known to lead to errors in some systems[1] due to segregation on cooling.   In the case of Mg + $MgCl_2$, however, the metal solubility is so small that it is improbable that much segregation could have taken place.   In addition, analysis of salt from different parts of the crucible failed to reveal any evidence of nonuniformity.   In the case of the Ca + CaF_2 mixtures the agreement between the solubility measurements and the D.T.A. measurements is good evidence that no segregation took place.   In all cases it

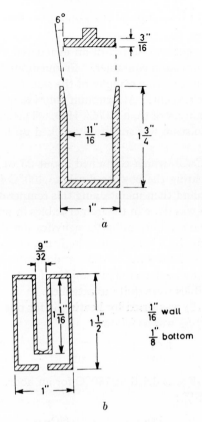

Fig. 1. Crucible with tapered lid used as container (*a*) and crucible with thermo-couple well for thermal analysis (*b*).

was necessary to seal the small crucibles within an outer container to prevent loss of the metal by volatilization. The containers (Fig. 1) were made of mild steel and before use were heated overnight in hydrogen at 900 °C to remove sufficient carbon, phosphorus, and oxygen to eliminate interference from such impurities during the experiment. After filling, the lid of the containers was pressed into the taper and the joint arc-welded under a rough vacuum with a tungsten electrode. The filled, sealed containers were suspended in a furnace by means of an iron wire, and the experiments were carried out in an atmosphere of purified, dried argon. The temperature was measured by a Pt-13% Rh/Pt thermocouple, being controlled to $\pm 0.25°$ at 1000°C and $\pm 0.75°$ at 1300°C.

For experiments in the Mg + MgCl$_2$ and Mg + Al + MgCl$_2$ systems the inner crucibles were made by Murex Ltd., from tantalum carbide containing about 4% niobium carbide. They were 20 mm high by 15 mm O.D. with 2 mm walls and had been sintered to a high density. It was necessary to remove small traces of iron and organic matter by washing in acid and carbon tetrachloride and small quantities of a black powder (possibly a higher carbide of tantalum) by melting some magnesium chloride in the crucible. Tantalum carbide was the only material of a number tested (Fe, Ir, Pt, Mo, TiC, and WC) which was unattacked by Mg, Al, and MgCl$_2$.

A blank run in which magnesium chloride only was used showed that no water was picked up during handling. After equilibration the magnesium chloride, which is a soft waxy solid, could easily be scraped out of the crucibles since it floated on both Mg and Mg + Al alloys. The separation was carried out in a dry box and samples of the salt were analyzed for excess magnesium by dissolving them in water or dilute acid and measuring the volume of hydrogen evolved.[2]

For experiments on the Ca + CaF$_2$ system, pure iron inner crucibles were used, 0.5 in. in diameter and 1.25 in. high. After equilibration and quenching the inner crucible was sawed down the long axis and the faces polished under paraffin to enable the phase boundary to be distinguished; the calcium rich phase was found to be on top. Samples were taken for analysis by sawing laterally. No satisfactory wet method was found for analyzing Ca + CaF$_2$ mixtures due to the general insolubility of CaF$_2$. A method was developed in which the samples were analyzed by heating them in an iron crucible at 980°C in a vacuum of 10^{-5} mm Hg. The vapor pressure of Ca at 980°C is about 10 mm Hg and all the metal volatilized in two hours. Analyses of standard mixtures of Ca + CaF$_2$ showed that the method was accurate to better than $\pm 1\%$.

Differential Thermal Analysis

Preliminary experiments with the Ca + CaF$_2$ system showed that the components were completely miscible at 1402°C, and in experiments at lower temperatures difficulty was experienced in separating the phases. It was therefore decided to study the phase diagram by thermal analysis. It was necessary to use a differential method because of complications arising from the need to hold each mixture in a sealed iron crucible. The crucibles had a heat capacity large in comparison with that of the mixture; there was no possibility of stirring and it was impossible to bring the thermocouple into direct contact with the melt.

Two identical mild steel crucibles of the type shown in Figure 1 were used, one contained the mixture to be studied and the other was empty and served as a thermal reference. They were arranged in the constant temperature zone of a molybdenum wound furnace as shown in Figure 2. The crucibles pretreated as described above were filled with weighed quantities of CaF_2 and Ca. A small mild steel plug was then sealed into the filling hole, using the welding technique previously referred to. Two Pt-13% Rh/Pt thermocouples in-

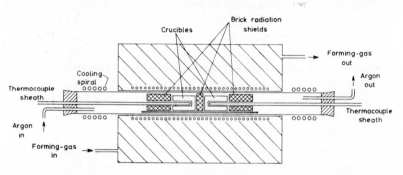

Fig. 2. Experimental arrangement for differential thermal analysis.

sulated by mullite sheaths were placed in the wells and their outputs, opposed in series, were fed into a dc. amplifier and recorder. Cooling curves were found to be unsatisfactory because the melts always supercooled, often by as much as 40°C, and heating curves were therefore employed. The crucibles were first heated above the estimated liquidus temperature and then rapidly cooled to disperse the phases as much as possible. A heating curve was then recorded over the temperature range of interest, using a heating rate of about 6°/min. Experiments with NaCl showed that the temperature at which an isothermal phase change took place corresponded to the peak on the D.T.A. curve rather than to the first inflection. This was probably due to the unavoidable thermal lags in the system and no means of overcoming this difficulty could be found. The differential curves for the CaF_2-Ca mixtures were therefore interpreted in the light of this information and the limitations of the method are reflected in the accuracy attached to the results discussed below.

Several determinations of the melting point of NaCl gave a value of 800 ± 1° which may be compared with the accepted value of 801 ± 1.°C.

RESULTS AND DISCUSSION

The Systems Mg + $MgCl_2$ and Mg + Al + $MgCl_2$

The solubility of Mg in $MgCl_2$ has been measured by Zhurin,[3] and preliminary series of experiments were carried out at 800 and 1000°C in an attempt to confirm these results. The figures obtained from runs of 2 to 70 hr duration showed considerable variation not only from run to run but also from sample to sample within each run. At 800°C thirteen separate experiments gave magnesium solubilities ranging from 0.62 to 1.36 mole-%[*] and at 1000°C eight experiments gave from 0.9 to 2.4 mole-%. The mean values were not very different from the solubilities of 0.90 and 1.24 mole-% for the same temperatures reported by Zhurin in 1935. Close examination of the results showed that the apparent solubility increased as the age of the salt increased, ie., as the water content increased. A detailed analysis of one sample apparently containing 1.2 mole-% Mg, showed that 0.12 wt-% of finely divided metallic iron (which would appear as 0.2 mole-% Mg in the analysis) and 2.2 wt-% MgO were present. An experiment at 800°C in which 14 wt-% water was added to the salt, gave an apparent solubility of 4.3 mole-% Mg. It was therefore concluded that at least part of the scatter in the results was due to the presence of iron in the samples, arising from water in the salt. Kremnev[4] has shown that emulsions of Mg metal in $MgCl_2$ can be stabilized by solid oxide particles; this suggests an explanation which may account for the remainder of the scatter.

Precautions were therefore taken to exclude moisture at all stages of the experimental procedure as described above and the consistency of the experimental results was improved. An extensive series of experiments was undertaken at 1000°C, using 50, 80, and 100

---

[*] Throughout this paper mole-% is taken to mean:

$$[\text{g atoms metal}/(\text{g atoms metal} + \text{moles salt})] \times 100$$

atomic-% Mg-Al alloys. Duplicate analyses were made of the quenched salt in each case and experiments were carried out for periods up to 17.5 hr to determine the time required for the system to reach equilibrium. This proved to be less than 3 hr in all cases. The results are summarized in Table I.

TABLE I
Solubility of Mg in $MgCl_2$ from Mg + Al Alloys at 1000°C

Atomic-% Mg in alloy	Mean solubility, mole-%	No. of expts	Std error
50	0.416	5	0.015
80	0.635	16	0.005
100	0.691	7	0.011

A few experiments were carried out at 800 and 1182°C to determine the temperature coefficient of the solubility. Those at 800°C were successful; those at 1182°C were inconsistent for reasons which are not clear and may be in part due to the high vapor pressure of the magnesium (about 3 atm) and the difficulty of obtaining absolutely gas tight welds in the crucibles. The value obtained at 1182°C using pure Mg, 1.8 mole-%, is thought to be too high by about 20%. The results for 800 and 1000°C are summarized and compared with those of Zhurin in Table II. The figures have been rounded off and

TABLE II
Summarized Solubilities of Mg in $MgCl_2$ (mole-%)

Atomic-% Mg in alloy	This work		Zhurin[a]	
	800°C	1000°C	800°C	1000°C
50	0.16±0.008	0.42±0.02	0.43	—
80	0.25±0.013	0.64±0.03	0.78	—
100	0.30±0.015	0.69±0.03	0.90	1.24

[a] Cited from ref. 3.

the accuracies assigned take into account the random errors shown above, plus an additional uncertainty to allow for the possible effects of impurities in the metal and salt phases.*

* Based on the reduction of the Mg activity by impurities and the effect of KCl on the solubility as determined by Zhurin.[3]

The salt from an experiment at 1000°C using an 80% Mg alloy contained less than 0.005 mole-% Al. Samples of the magnesium phase, after equilibration with $MgCl_2$ at 800 and 1000°C contained less than 0.002 mole-% of $MgCl_2$.

Zhurin's results are three times greater than those obtained in this work at 800°C and twice those at 1000°C. For the reasons discussed above the discrepancy may well be due to the high MgO content of the $MgCl_2$ used by Zhurin (up to 1% is quoted) and the presence of water in the containers, since no reference was made by Zhurin to precautions for handling the material out of contact with the air.

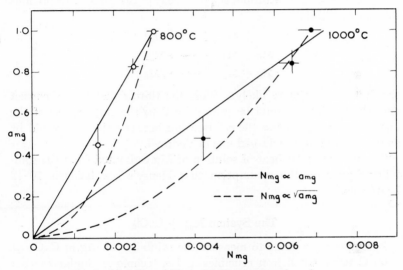

Fig. 3. Solubility of Mg in $MgCl_2$ as a function of a_{Mg}.

At the time the experiments using Mg + Al alloys were carried out, it was intended to use the measurements made by Schneider and Stoll[5] of the vapor pressures of Mg over these alloys to calculate the Mg activities. A detailed study recently made by Alcock and Hooper[6] of the transportation technique for measuring vapor pressures indicates that the extrapolation to zero flow rate, used by Schneider and Stoll, makes their pressures unreliable. Activities have therefore been calculated from the boiling point measurements of Leitgebel[7] and the heat of vaporization and partial molar heats of solution recommended by Kubaschewski and Evans.[8] The solubility of Mg in $MgCl_2$ is shown as a function of magnesium activity at 800 and 1000°C in Figure 3. The relationship supports the view that no serious segregation took place during quenching and that the measured solubility is not due to the formation of a dispersion of Mg metal.

Unfortunately the activity data are not accurate enough to allow any detailed conclusions to be drawn concerning the nature of the solutions. The fact that the solubility is approximately proportional to the Mg activity and that at such low concentrations the activity coefficient of the dissolved metal would be expected to be substantially independent of concentration, suggests that of the three most obvious solution equilibria

$$Mg \longrightarrow Mg^0$$
$$Mg + Mg^{2+} \longrightarrow Mg_2^{2+}$$
$$Mg + Mg^{2+} \longrightarrow 2Mg^+$$

the first two are more likely. Were the third equation the correct one, the solubility would be proportional to the square root of the magnesium activity and the relationship between the two would be as represented by the dashed line in Figure 3.

The partial molar heat of solution of Mg estimated from the solubility figures on the assumption that Henry's law holds is 10–12 kcal/mole.

The System Mg + $CaCl_2$

Attempts were made to measure the solubility of Mg in $CaCl_2$ at 1100°C using small iron crucibles and a technique similar to that described for the Mg + $MgCl_2$ system. The volumes of hydrogen evolved from the samples in the analysis apparatus were only slightly larger than the blank value so that no accurate analyses could be obtained. The solubility is less than 0.05 mole-%.

The System Ca + CaF_2

Preliminary experiments at 1402°C indicated that Ca and CaF_2 were completely miscible at this temperature and a quenched specimen containing 59 mole-% Ca had a structure consisting of dendrites of a metallic phase embedded in a granular matrix. All the results obtained both by solubility and thermal analysis measurements are

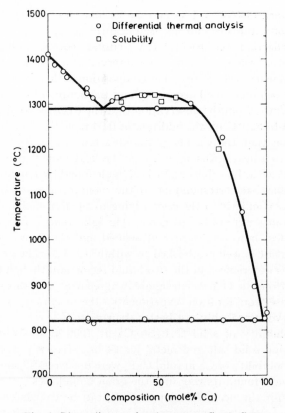

Fig. 4. Phase diagram for the system Ca + CaF₂.

shown in Figure 4.   The system consists of a eutectic and a monotectic separated by a two-liquid region.   The monotectic occurs at
1290 ± 5°C and 25.5 mole-% Ca and the eutectic at 821 ± 3°C and
98.6 moles-% Ca; the miscibility gap closes at 1322 ± 10°C.

The melting point of the pure salt was found to be 1411 ± 3°C.
The only reliable previous value for the melting point of CaF₂ is
the value of 1418°C given by Naylor.[9]   He obtained this figure from
the break in a heat content versus temperature curve, but since no
determinations were reported between 1411 and 1425°C, the value
obtained in the present work is consistent with his observations.

The value generally accepted for the melting point of Ca is that due
to Hoffmann and Schulze,[10] 851 ± 1°C.   The value obtained in the

present work of 837 ± 1°C may be as much as 5° low, due to the presence of impurities, but not significantly more.

The inflection on the D.T.A. curves corresponding to the eutectic was always sharp and was observed at a number of compositions as shown in the figure. The composition of this eutectic (821°C) could not be determined accurately and the figure of 98.6 mole-% Ca was calculated from the observation that the freezing point of Ca was depressed to 826°C by the addition of 0.94 mole-% of CaF_2, and the assumption that the Ca obeys Raoult's law. This depression corresponds to a heat of fusion of Ca of 2.08 kcal/mole which is in close agreement with the value of 2.07 kcal/mole found by Kubaschewski.[11]

The inflection corresponding to the monotectic was not easy to observe, particularly in the region lying to the left of the monotectic and no points were obtained here. The inflections corresponding to the liquidus, however, were well defined and the depression of the freezing point is well established to within ±3°C. The greatest difficulty was experienced in the two-liquid region and though the points obtained from the D.T.A. curves are in agreement with those obtained from phase equilibration experiments, the accuracy of the two liquid curve is probably not better than ±10°C.

The solubility of solid CaF_2 in Ca at 1200°C was obtained by equilibrating solid salt and metal for 24 hr. Experiments to determine the solubility of Ca in solid CaF_2 were unsuccessful since free Ca metal always found its way into the grain boundaries.

Values for the heat of fusion of CaF_2 can be calculated from the depression of the freezing point by Ca, if it is assumed that the CaF_2 behaves ideally and no solid solution of Ca in CaF_2 is formed. The values depend on the mechanism of solution and are as follows for the three simplest cases (see Grjotheim et al.[12])

$$C \longrightarrow Ca^0 \text{ (atomic solution)} \quad \Delta H_f = 10.5 \pm 0.75 \text{ kcal/mole}$$

$$Ca + Ca^{2+} \longrightarrow Ca_2^{2+} \quad \Delta H_f = 11.0 \pm 0.75 \text{ kcal/mole}$$

$$Ca + C \longrightarrow 2Ca \quad \Delta H_f = 20 \quad \pm 1.5 \text{ kcal/mole}$$

Only data for solutions containing up to 8.37 mole-% Ca were used for these calculations. None of these figures is in agreement with the heat of fusion determined directly by Naylor[9] (7.1 kcal) though a value close to this can be obtained in the case of the first two solution mechanisms from the limiting slope of the liquidus if it is drawn with a slight upward curvature. It was therefore decided that it would be better to compare these heats with a value determined by a cryoscopic method. Three values were therefore obtained for the depression of the freezing point of CaF_2 by NaF which are shown in Table III.

TABLE III

Composition, mole-% NaF	Freezing points, °C
0	1411
2.71	1401
7.01	1370
13.89	1327

Provided that CaF_2 behaves ideally in the melt and there is no solid solution of NaF in CaF_2 a value of 9.8 ± 0.3 kcal/mole can be calculated for the heat of fusion of CaF_2 from these results. It is seen that the data are consistent with a solution mechanism involving either Ca atoms or Ca_2^{2+} ions. Similar conclusions have been draw from the results of work on the systems Cd + $CdCl_2$[12] and Ca + $CaBr_2$.[13]

There is no obvious reason for the discrepancy between the heat of fusion calculated from the cryoscopic data and the directly measured value, but this clearly does not affect the structural conclusions.

The value of the partial molar heat of solution of solid CaF_2 in liquid Ca calculated from the slope of a plot of log N_{CaF_2} vs $1/T$ is 14.3 ± 0.5 kcal/mole. The plot is linear within the limits of experimental error which is surprising since the solutions contained up to 20 mole-% CaF_2 and Henry's law would not be expected to hold up to this composition. Similar linear plots were obtained by Bredig et al.[14] for alkali metal systems.

The Nature of Metal-Molten Salt Solutions

Some forty systems in which metals dissolve in molten salts have so far been studied, but in most of these cases the solubility has either been small or only measured under very limited conditions. In a number of cases where substantial miscibility occurs, detailed phase equilibrium diagrams have been published. Systematic studies have been carried out for the alkali metals and their halides by Bredig and his co-workers,[1,14] and a similar program on the alkaline earth metals is being pursued in this laboratory.

Too much significance must not be attached to early work in which the melts were samples after quenching. The results obtained by Schäfer and Niklas with $Ba + BaCl_2$,[15] by Bredig with $Na + NaCl$,[1] and unpublished work in this laboratory with $Ca + CaCl_2$ and $Ca + CaBr_2$[13] show that errors due to segregation can occur in spite of very rapid cooling and errors in the opposite direction can arise due to imperfect separation of the phases when the difference in density is small or when one phase wets the crucible much better than the other.

There has been some discussion of the nature of these solutions, and several descriptive models have been proposed. The present authors do not consider this a fruitful subject for extended discussion at this stage since there is an almost complete lack of experimental work which could give information about the structure or thermodynamic behavior of the solutions. Measurements of heats of mixing and activities are needed to form a basis for the development of models in terms of which entropies of mixing can be calculated and compared with measure values. X-ray studies and measurements of structure sensitive properties (e.g., electrical conductivity and transport[16] diffusion, viscosity, and density,[17]) should enable a more detailed structural description to be given.

One generalization which arises out of all the work so far reported, is that miscibility is often limited when the ratio of the radii of the cation to the anion in the salt r_+/r_-, is less than about 0.42 and is substantial when r_+/r_- is greater than this value, tending to increase as r_+/r_- increases. The systems $Mg + MgCl_2$ and $Ca + CaF_2$ represent two extreme examples of this situation, the values of r_+/r_- being 0.36 and 0.74, respectively.

The significance of the change in behavior at $r_+/r_- = 0.42$ may be explained in the following way. Due to the strong coulombic forces between anions and cations, substantial miscibility will only occur in a metal-molten salt system if a strong interaction takes place between the added metal atom and the cations of the salt. For this to be so, two conditions must be met; firstly, the internuclear separation of the added metal atom and the cations must have an optimum value and secondly, suitable electronic energy levels must be available for chemical binding. The first condition is reflected in the dependence on the value of r_+/r_- since when this falls below about 0.42, anion-anion contact occurs (see Pauling[18]); extra metal atoms introduced into the melt would then be unable to approach close enough to the cations to interact sufficiently with them. The second is reflected in the fact that metals do not in general dissolve in salts of other metals, e.g., the system $Mg + CaCl_2$ described in this paper. Exceptions to the first condition would be likely to occur when there is considerable short range ordering in the melt and the anions are complex and to the second when there are strong interactions between the two metals, e.g., when a stable intermetallic compound is formed. In such cases the two metals have been found to dissolve together in the salt of one of them.[19]

A description in these terms may be more fruitful than the narrower one in terms of lower valence states, M_2^{2+} ions or subhalide formation insofar as it should permit a consistent description of solutions over the complete range from salt to metal.

Thanks are due to the United Kingdom Atomic Energy Authority for support of this work including a bursary to one of us (P.S.R.).

References

1. Bredig, M. A., *High Temperature—a Tool for the Future*, Stanford Research Inst., Univ. of California, 1956, p. 111.

2. Rogers, P. S., D. J. M. Bevan, and J. W. Tomlinson, *Mikrochim. Acta*, **1956**, 1839.

3. Zhurin, A. I., *Metallurg.* **10**, No. iv, 87 (1935).

4. Kremnev, L. J., K. P. Mischenko, and A. J. Foklinov, *Zhur. Priklad. Khim.*, **19**, 363 (1946).

5. Schneider, A., and E. K. Stoll, *Z. Elektrochem.*, **47**, 519 (1941).

6. Alcock, C. B., and G. W. Hooper, this Symposium.

7. Leitgebel, W., *Z. anorg. Chem.*, **202**, 305 (1931).

8. Kubaschewski, O., and E. Ll. Evans, *Metallurgical Thermochemistry*, Pergamon, London, 1958.

9. Naylor, B. F., *J. Am. Chem. Soc.*, **67**, 150 (1945).

10. Hoffmann, F., and A. Schulze, *Physik. Z.*, **36**, 453 (1935).

11. Kubaschewski, O., *Z. Elektrochem.*, **54**, 275 (1950).

12. Grjotheim, K., F. Grönvold, and J. Krogh-Moe, *J. Am. Chem. Soc.*, **77**, 5824 (1955).

13. Staffansson, L. I., J. E. Taylor, J. W. Tomlinson, and F. D. Richardson, unpublished work.

14. Bredig, M. A., J. W. Johnson, and Wm. T. Smith, Jr., *J. Am. Chem. Soc.*, **77**, 307 (1955); M. A. Bredig, H. R. Bronstein, and Wm. T. Smith, Jr., *J. Am.*

Chem. Soc., **77**, 1454 (1955); J. W. Johnson and M. A. Bredig, *J. Phys. Chem.*, **62**, 604 (1958).

15. Schäfer, H., and A. Niklas, *Angew. Chem.*, **64**, 611 (1952).
16. Bronstein, H. R., and M. A. Bredig, *J. Am. Chem. Soc.*, **80**, 2077 (1958).
17. Keneshea, F. J., Jr., and D. Cubicciotti, *J. Phys. Chem.*, **62**, 843 (1958).
18. Pauling, L., *The Nature of Chemical Bond*, Cornell Univ. Press, New York, 1945, p. 352.
19. Heymann, E., R. J. L. Martin, and M. F. R. Mulcahy, *J. Phys. Chem.*, **47**, 473 (1943); E. Heymann and P. Weber, *Trans. Faraday Soc.*, **34**, 1492 (1938).

A Study of Equilibrium between Metals and Their Polyvalent Chlorides in LiCl-KCl Eutectic Melt

LING YANG, ROBERT G. HUDSON, and CHIEN-YEH CHIEN

Metals Research Laboratory, Carnegie Institute of Technology, Pittsburgh, Pennsylvania

Abstract

Dilute solutions of uranium, thorium, zirconium, and columbium chlorides in LiCl-KCl eutectic melts were made by anodic dissolution of these metals. After equilibrium was reached between the solution and the metal, the electrode potential was measured relative to a AgCl reference electrode. The nature of the metal ions in the equilibrated melt was determined either from the slope of the isothermal plots of potential versus the logarithm of concentration, or by using Faraday's law. It was found that in the temperature range of 760 to 830°K, U^{+3}, Th^{+4}, Zr^{+4}, and Cb^{+3} are the predominant species existing in the uranium chloride (0.26–2.08% U), thorium chloride (0.19–1.47% Th), zirconium chloride (0.07–0.86% Zr), and columbium chloride (0.13–0.43% Cb) melts, respectively. For columbium chloride melts of higher concentrations than that shown above, other species of columbium ions, probably Cb^{+4}, coexist with Cb^{+3} in appreciable amounts. The results are explained on the basis of the magnitude of the free energy of formation of the chlorides of these metal ions of different valence states and the tendency for these metal ions to form complex ions with the chloride ions in the melt.

INTRODUCTION

Generally speaking, metal halides dissolved in molten halide solvents can be divided into three groups according to the valence state of their metal ions present in the melt in equilibrium with the same metals. For some, the metal ions possess only one stable valence state under the given conditions. For others, the metal ions, though capable of existing in more than one valence state, are present predominantly in one of these states in the equilibrated melt. A third possibility lies with those metal halides for which metal ions of dif-

925

ferent valence states can coexist in appreciable amounts in the equilibrated melt.   For electrodeposition in molten halide systems, better
control of the operations requires a thorough understanding of which
group each metal halide belongs to and the equilibrium electrode
potentials between the metals and their ions in the solvent chosen.
In addition, it is also desirable to know the coexisting valence states
and how the relative amounts of each vary with the temperature and
the concentration of the melt.   Previously, we have studied the
equilibrium electrode potentials between metals and their ions for a
number of single valence metal chlorides in LiCl-KCl eutectic melts.[1]
It is the purpose of this work to extend the investigations to some
polyvalent metal chlorides in the same solvent and to find out the nature of the metal ions present in the melts equilibrated with the corresponding metals.

EXPERIMENTAL

Cell Arrangements

Figure 1 shows the arrangements used for these studies.   The
metal electrode consists of a piece of pure metal rod, usually $^3/_{16}$ in. in
diameter and $1^1/_2$ in. long, hanging at the end of a 5-mil tungsten
spring.   The surface of the rod is finished with fine emery paper,
lightly etched in dilute HF, washed, and dried.   To avoid contamination of the metal surface, the metal rod is enclosed in purified argon
gas in a 10-mm Pyrex tube the bottom of which is sealed and blown
thin.   Outside of this tube there is a 14-mm Pyrex tube containing
about 8 g of LiCl-KCl eutectic melt in a purified argon atmosphere.
By shaking the assembly slightly, the spring is made to oscillate and
the thin bottom of the 10-mm tube becomes broken when the metal
rod strikes it.   The length of the spring is usually adjusted so that
when the glass membrane is broken, the end of the metal rod is about
$^1/_4$ to $^1/_2$ in. beneath the surface of the melt.   A desired amount of
the metal chloride is then introduced into the melt by anodic dissolution of the metal rod, the cathode being an Ag wire (0.05 in. diam)
immersed in about 20 g of LiCl-KCl eutectic melt containing a known
amount of AgCl in purified argon gas.   Although the metal anode
and the Ag cathode are separated by a glass membrane and Li^+ is the
predominate current carrier through the glass, the change of the
Li/K ratio in both compartments is negligible because the amount of

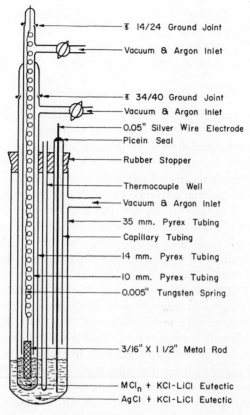

Fig. 1. Cell arrangement.

current used for the anodic dissolution of the metal is small, i.e., the concentration of the metal chloride MCl_n in the melts studied in this work is low (less the 0.5 mole-%).   The Ag reference electrode thus serves a dual function, as the cathode in the preparation of the metal chloride melt and as a reference for the subsequent potential measurement.

In some measurements, in addition to the Ag reference electrode, a bubbling chlorine reference electrode (not shown in Fig. 1) is also immersed in the melt.   This consists of a graphite rod ($1/8$ in. diam and 12 in. long) surrounded by a 7-mm Pyrex tube, with the end of the rod dipped in LiCl-KCl eutectic melt.   Dry chlorine gas passes around the rod and bubbles continuously through the melt. The assembly is enclosed in a 12-mm Pyrex tube with an outlet for the chlorine. The graphite rod is saturated with chlorine by anodic polarization, with the Ag wire as the cathode.

Potential Measurements

As soon as enough metal chloride is introduced into the melt surrounding the metal rod, the current is switched off. The Ag electrodes in the Ag coulometer are washed and weighed for the determination of the amount of current passed through the melt. The potential between the metal electrode and the AgCl reference electrode (or the chlorine reference electrode) is then followed until a steady value is obtained. In case the metal ions in the melt equilibrated with the metal are predominately of the same valence state in the temperature range used in this work (490–560°C), the equilibrium electrode potentials at various temperatures in this range can be determined by using the same sample. However, if more than one valence state of the metal ions is present in the equilibrated melt and the relative amounts change with temperature, then individual samples have to be used for the determination of the equilibrium potentials at different temperatures. This is because in the latter case the concentration of the metal chloride in the melt in contact with the metal changes with temperature, while in the former case it stays constant when the temperature of the melt is changed. After the potential measurements have been accomplished, the metal electrode is lifted out of the melt. Both the MCl_n and the AgCl melts are then frozen quickly and analyzed for the MCl_n and the AgCl contents, respectively.

The equilibrium electrode potentials obtained relative to the AgCl reference electrode, after correcting for the thermal emf of the Ag-W thermocouple, can be converted to those based on the chlorine reference electrode, i.e., potentials of cells of the type

$$M/MCl_n \text{ in LiCl-KCl eutectic}/Cl_2 \qquad (1)$$

in the manner shown previously.[2] Owing to the presence of a glass membrane between the MCl_n and the AgCl compartments, the values thus obtained are higher than the true values. However, since the concentrations of MCl_n in the melts studied in this work are less than 0.5 mole-%, it is concluded on the basis of our previous studies of this reference electrode[2] that the difference cannot be more than 5 mv. In case measurements have been made by using the chlorine reference electrode the potential data obtained, after correcting for the thermal emf of the graphite-W thermocouple, represents the potentials of cells of the type:

$$M|MCl_n \text{ in LiCl-KCl}|\text{Pyrex}|\text{LiCl-KCl}|Cl_2 \qquad (2)$$
$$\text{eutectic} \quad \text{membrane} \quad \text{eutectic}$$

These are not the same as that for cell type (1). The difference, however, is probably very small in view of the low concentrations of MCl_n in the MCl_n melts studied in this work. As the AgCl reference electrode is easier to construct and the Ag wire is needed as a cathode in the preparation of the MCl_n melt by anodic dissolution, this reference electrode was used in all of the melts studied except the UCl_3 melts for which both the AgCl and the chlorine reference electrodes were used. Methods for heating the cell, preparing the LiCl-KCl eutectic and the reference electrodes, and measuring the potentials are the same as those described previously.[1,2]

Study of the Nature of Metal Ions in Equilibrium with the Metal Electrode

In general, the nature of the metal ions in the melt in equilibrium with the metal electrode can be determined if specific chemical methods are available for the quantitative estimation of each of the valence states of the metal ions.[3,4] Unfortunately these methods are not always available. For the metal chlorides studied in this work, the following two ways have been tried.

1. Using the slope of the isothermal plot of E versus $\ln N_{MCl_n}$, E is the equilibrium electrode potential between the metal and the metal ions in the melt relative to the chlorine reference electrode and N_{MCl_n} is the mole fraction of the metal chloride in the melt, evaluated from analytical data by assuming the metal ions exist only as M^{+n} in the melt. If this assumption is true and the melt obeys Henry's law in the range of concentrations studied, then following the Nernst equation, for constant temperature,

$$dE/d \ln N_{MCl_n} = RT/nF \qquad (3)$$

where R is the gas constant, T is the temperature of the melt in °K, and F is the Faraday constant. The value of n can therefore be evaluated from the slope of the isothermal plot of E vs $\ln N_{MCl_n}$.   It should be a small integer or very close to it and can be compared with the assumed value.   A good agreement between them means M^{+n} is the predominating ion species in equilibrium with the metal.   If the melt does not obey Henry's law in the concentration range studied or if more than one valence state of the metal ions coexists in the melt, this method is not applicable.

2.   Using Faraday's law: if the metal chloride in the melt is introduced by anodic dissolution of the metal, it is possible to study the nature and the amount of each coexisting metal ion in the equilibrated melt by measuring the amount of the current used and the amount of metal in the equilibrated melt. If an amount of current Q (in coulombs) is used in the anodic dissolution of the metal, the amount of metal w (in g) in the equilibrated melt is

$$w = (Q/F)M/n \tag{4}$$

where M is the atomic weight of the metal and n is the apparent valence of the metal ions in the melt.   If there are m predominating valence states of the metal ions in the melt, namely $n_1, n_2, n_3 \ldots n_m$, then

$$1/n = (f_1/n_1) + (f_2/n_2) + (f_3/n_3) + \ldots f_m/n_m \tag{5}$$

where f represents the fractions of the metal ions in each valence state and

$$f_1 + f_2 + f_3 + \ldots f_m = 1 \tag{6}$$

It must be pointed out that at the moment the current is switched off, the amount of metal in the melt is not w and the apparent valence of the metal ions is not n.   As the equilibrium conditions are gradually approached, more metal may be dissolved into the melt by the reaction

$$(n_2 - n_1)\,M + n_1 M^{+n_2} \longrightarrow n_2 M^{+n_1} \tag{7}$$

or some metal may be precipitated out by the reaction

$$n_2 M^{+n_1} \longrightarrow (n_2 - n_1)M + n_1 M^{+n_2} \tag{8}$$

What actually happens depends on how the initial conditions in the melt may deviate from the equilibrium conditions.   This probably varies with the current density of the electrolysis.   It is only when true equilibrium has been established between the metal and the melt that the values of w and n are reached.   The attainment of the equilibrium conditions is ascertained by the constant value of the electrode potential.

If we determine w by chemical analysis and Q by an Ag coulometer, n can be calculated by Eq. (4).   Calculation of the fractions of metal ions existing in various valence states by Eqs. (5) and (6) depends upon the value of m.   If $m = 1$, then $n = n_1$ and $f_1 = 1$.   This is the case where the metal ions exist predominately in the melt in a single valence state.   The conformity to Henry's law by the melt is not a prerequisite when this method is used.   If $m = 2$, then

$$1/n = (f_1/n_1) + (f_2/n_2) \qquad (9)$$

$$f_1 + f_2 = 1 \qquad (10)$$

The fractions of metal ions existing in the valence states n_1 and n_2 in the melt can be determined from these equations.   If $m > 2$, this method is not applicable unless supplemented by some chemical methods.   Even if $m = 2$, it is always desirable to check the results by chemical analyses.   Moreover, it must be assured that the metal does not dissolve physically in the melt or react with the solvent. In addition, local cell actions on the metal surface should be absent or negligible and the anodic reaction during the electrolysis should consist of only the dissolution of the metal.   All these can be proved experimentally by the lack of solubility of the metal in the solvent, the constancy of the composition of the equilibrated melt even if the metal is left in contact with it for long periods of time, and the yield of reasonable n values.   Complication due to physical dissolution of metal in the metal chloride itself should not arise because the concentrations of metal chloride in the melts studied are very low.

The metal rods used are of the following origins: uranium, super-pure grade kindly donated by Dr. Irving Johnson of Argonne National Laboratory; thorium, iodide grade supplied by Metal Hydrides Inc.; zirconium, iodide grade (Hf less than 100 ppm) supplied by the Navy Reactors Operations Office in Pittsburgh; columbium, Wah Chang Co. pure grade (99.8% Cb).   The lack of appreciable solubility of these metals in LiCl-KCl eutectic melt was established by the failure of detecting them (less than 0.1 mg in 8 g of melt) in melts which have been in contact with these metals at 823°K in pure argon for 10–40 hr.

RESULTS AND DISCUSSION

Studies have been made on melts containing uranium chloride, thorium chloride, zirconium chloride, and columbium chloride in the temperature range 760–830°K. The results are summarized as follows.

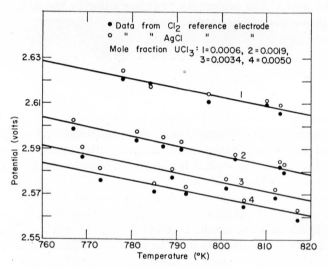

Fig. 2. Potentials of uranium-chlorine cells in LiCl-KCl eutectic melts containing UCl₃.

1. Uranium chloride melts (0.26–2.08% U). The potential data are shown in Table I and plotted as a function of T in Figure 2 after those obtained by using the chlorine reference electrode have been corrected to that for $p_{Cl_2} = 1$ atm. The potentials obtained by using the AgCl reference electrode are a few millivolts higher than those obtained by using the chlorine reference electrode. This is what would be expected on the basis of our previous investigations of the AgCl reference electrode.[2] The potentials obtained by using the chlorine reference electrode, however, may also deviate slightly from the true values because of the presence of a glass membrane between the

TABLE I
Equilibrium Electrode Potentials of the Uranium-Chlorine Cells

Mole fraction, N_{UCl_3}	Temp., °K	Cl$_2$ reference electrode		Mole fraction, N_{AgCl}	AgCl reference electrode		$E_{UCl_3} = E_{AgCl}$ $E_{obs.}$, volts
		P_{Cl_2}, atm	$E_{UCl_3 \, obs.}$, volts		E_{AgCl}, volts	$E_{obs.}$, volts	
0.00062	778	0.971	2.6206	0.0370	1.0826	1.5421	2.6247
	784		2.6189		1.0825	1.5351	2.6176
	797		2.6108		1.0823	1.5323	2.6146
	810		2.6093		1.0821	1.5295	2.6116
	813		2.6058		1.0821	1.5274	2.6095
0.00188	767	0.969	2.5987	0.0365	1.0837	1.5188	2.6025
	781		2.5938		1.0835	1.5141	2.5976
	787		2.5910		1.0835	1.5117	2.5952
	791		2.5899		1.0834	1.5097	2.5931
	803		2.5856		1.0833	1.5054	2.5877
	813		2.5820		1.0832	1.5011	2.5843
	814		2.5793		1.0832	1.4999	2.5831
0.00342	769	0.982	2.5863	0.0347	1.0861	1.5045	2.5906
	789		2.5771		1.0859	1.4952	2.5811
	801		2.5728		1.0858	1.4911	2.5769
	812		2.5683		1.0857	1.4886	2.5723
0.00502	773	0.973	2.5762	0.0347	0.0861	1.4955	2.5816
	785		2.5715		1.0860	1.4886	2.5746
	792		2.5702		1.0859	1.4872	2.5731
	805		2.5647		1.0858	1.4821	2.5679
	817		2.5584		1.0857	1.4775	2.5632

metal and the chlorine compartments. In drawing the lines showing the temperature dependence of the potentials E, both sets of data are taken into consideration. The slopes of the isothermal plots of E vs $\ln N_{UCl_3}$ constructed by using data shown in Figure 2 yield $n = 3.05$, 3.07, and 3.09 for 770, 790, and 810°K, respectively. The n values obtained by using Faraday's law, as shown in Table VII(a), are also very close to 3. It is therefore concluded that Henry's law is approximately obeyed in the range of concentrations studied and that U^{+3} is the predominant species of uranium ions existing in these melts in equilibrium with uranium metal. In Table II are shown the activities a and the activity coefficients γ of UCl_3, calculated from E values interpolated from Figure 2 at 770, 790, and 810°K and by using the standard electrode potentials $E°$ evaluated from the $\Delta F°$ values of solid UCl_3.[5] It can be seen that all the γ-values are close to unity.

TABLE II

Activities and Activity Coefficients of UCl_3 in LiCl-KCl Eutectic Melts

Mole fraction, N_{UCl_3}	Temp., °K	E,[a] volts	$E°$,[b] volts	$10^3 a_{UCl_3}$	γ_{UCl_3}
0.00062	770	2.625	2.459	0.55	0.89
	790	2.617	2.447	0.56	0.91
	810	2.609	2.432	0.50	0.81
0.00188	770	2.599	2.459	1.78	0.95
	790	2.592	2.447	1.70	0.90
	810	2.584	2.432	1.45	0.77
0.00342	770	2.587	2.459	3.09	0.90
	790	2.579	2.447	3.02	0.88
	810	2.572	2.432	2.45	0.72
0.00502	770	2.580	2.459	4.22	0.84
	790	2.573	2.447	3.98	0.75
	810	2.565	2.432	3.31	0.66

[a] Here, E is interpolated from Figure 2.

[b] Here, $E°$ is calculated from the $\Delta F°$ values evaluated by Glassner.[5]

Since γ is very sensitive to any slight uncertainty in $E°$ values, the only conclusion that can be drawn is that U^{+3} does not show a strong tendency of forming complex ions with the chloride ions in the melt under these conditions. This is presumably due to the big size of the U^{+3} ion (radius = 1.04 A). The approximate conformity to Henry's law by these melts is apparent on comparing the γ-values of these melts at the same temperature.

2. Thorium chloride melts (0.19–1.47% Th).   The potential data obtained by using AgCl reference electrode are shown in Table III

TABLE III
Equilibrium Electrode Potentials of Thorium-Chlorine Cells

Mole fraction, N_{ThCl_4}	Temp., °K	AgCl reference electrode			
		Mole fraction, N_{AgCl}	E_{AgCl}, volts	$E_{obs.}$, volts	$E_{ThCl_4} = E_{AgCl} + E_{obs.}$, volts
0.00048	763	0.0800	1.0361	1.6973	2.7334
	775		1.0353	1.6931	2.7284
	787		1.0344	1.6881	2.7225
	804		1.0332	1.6817	2.7149
	825		1.0317	1.6729	2.7046
0.00190	768	0.0762	1.0386	1.6689	2.7075
	769		1.0386	1.6679	2.7065
	786		1.0375	1.6615	2.6990
	797		1.0368	1.6587	2.6955
	803		1.0364	1.6539	2.6903
	824		1.0350	1.6454	2.6804
0.00377	772	0.0805	1.0349	1.6515	2.6864
	774		1.0347	1.6509	2.6856
	777		1.0344	1.6473	2.6817
	801		1.0328	1.6393	2.6721
	828		1.0309	1.6266	2.6575

and plotted as a function of T in Figure 3.   Unlike the uranium chloride melts, Henry's law is not obeyed for the whole range of compositions studied, although it is approximately obeyed by the two more dilute melts studied.   The n values obtained by using Faraday's law, as shown in Table VII(b), are very close to 4, indicating that the predominant species of thorium ions in equilibrium with thorium metal in these melts is Th^{+4}.   The activities a and the activity coefficients γ of $ThCl_4$ are calculated from $E°$ values evaluated from $\Delta F°$ values of solid $ThCl_4$[5] and shown in Table IV.   All the γ-values obtained are of the order of 10^{-3} and increase with the increase of temperature.   This indicates that the Th^{+4} ions have a strong tendency of forming complex ions with the chloride ions in the melt.

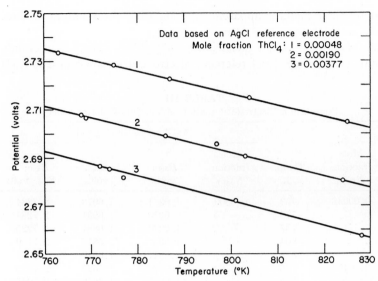

Fig. 3. Potentials of thorium-chlorine cells in LiCl-KCl eutectic melts containing ThCl₄.

TABLE IV

Activities and Activity Coefficients of $ThCl_4$ in KCl-LCl Eutectic Melts

Mole fraction, N_{ThCl_4}	Temp., °K	E, volts	$E°$,[a] volts	$a \times 10^6$	$\gamma \times 10^3$
0.00048	763	2.7334	2.4859	0.28	0.59
	775	2.7284	2.4806	0.36	0.74
	787	2.7225	2.4752	0.46	0.95
	804	2.7149	2.4675	0.60	1.26
	825	2.7046	2.4581	0.93	1.95
0.00190	768	2.7075	2.4837	1.32	0.69
	769	2.7065	2.4832	1.38	0.73
	786	2.6990	2.4756	1.90	1.00
	797	2.6955	2.4707	2.00	1.05
	803	2.6903	2.4680	2.45	1.29
	824	2.6804	2.4585	3.71	1.96
0.00377	772	2.6864	2.4819	4.37	1.16
	774	2.6856	2.4810	4.58	1.21
	777	2.6817	2.4797	5.63	1.49
	801	2.6721	2.4680	7.59	2.02
	828	2.6575	2.4567	12.60	3.34

[a] Here, $E°$ is calculated from the $\Delta F°$ values evaluated by Glassner.[5]

3. Zirconium chloride melt (0.07–0.86% Zr). The potential data obtained by using the AgCl reference electrode are shown in Table V and plotted in Figure 4 as a function of temperature. Like the tho-

TABLE V
Equilibrium Electrode Potentials of Zirconium-Chlorine Cells

Mole fraction, N_{ZrCl_4}	Temp., °K	AgCl reference electrode			
		Mole fraction, N_{AgCl}	E_{AgCl}, volts	$E_{obs.}$, volts	$E_{ZrCl_4} = E_{AgCl} + E_{obs.}$ volts
0.00048	763	0.0633	1.0510	1.1469	2.1979
	775		1.0493	1.1450	2.1943
	790		1.0486	1.1447	2.1933
	802		1.0479	1.1420	2.1899
	822		1.0473	1.1408	2.1881
0.00301	767	0.0708	1.0444	1.1262	2.1706
	783		1.0432	1.1233	2.1665
	799		1.0420	1.1198	2.1618
	817		1.0409	1.1163	2.1572
0.00541	771	0.0631	1.0501	1.1064	2.1565
	789		1.0491	1.1010	2.1501
	800		1.0484	1.0980	2.1464
	823		1.0470	1.0905	2.1375

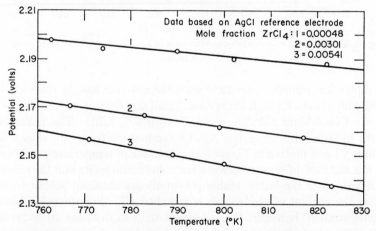

Fig. 4. Potentials of zirconium-chlorine cells in LiCl-KCl eutectic melts containing ZrCl₄.

rium chloride melts studied, the zirconium chloride melts do not obey
Henry's law for the whole range of the compositions studied. The n
values obtained by using Faraday's law, as shown in Table VII(c),
are very close to 4, indicating that Zr^{+4} is the predominant species of
zirconium ions present in equilibrium with zirconium metal in these
melts. No attempt has been made to calculate the activities and the
activity coefficients of $ZrCl_4$ in these melts because of the uncertainty
in the $\Delta F°$ values. However, if the extrapolated $\Delta F°$ values from
Glassner's plot[5] are used, it is estimated that the activity coefficients
should be of the order of 10^{-5} to 10^{-6}. The strong tendency for

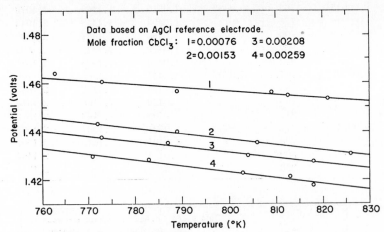

Fig. 5. Potentials of columbium-chlorine cells in LiCl-KCl eutectic melts containing CbCl₃.

complex ion formation by Zr^{+4} with the chloride ions in the melt is
probably due to its high charge and small size (radius = 0.8 A).

4. Columbium chloride melts (0.13–0.43% Cb). The potential
data obtained by using the AgCl reference electrode are shown in
Table VI and plotted in Figure 5 as a function of temperature. There
is one distinct difference between the columbium melts and the others
studied. For the latter, stable potentials are obtained within $1/2$ hr
after the current of electrolysis is switched off. For the columbium
melts studied, however, the potentials tend to drift for 10 to 20 hr
after the electrolysis before they reach stable values. For melts of
low concentrations such as those shown here, once equilibrated with

TABLE VI

Equilibrium Electrode Potentials of Columbium-Chlorine Cells

Mole fraction, N_{CbCl_3}	Temp., °K	AgCl reference electrode			
		Mole fraction, N_{AgCl}	E_{AgCl}, volts	$E_{obs.}$, volts	$E_{CbCl_3} = E_{AgCl} + E_{obs.}$ volts
0.00076	763	0.0279	1.0998	0.3642	1.4640
	773		1.1002	0.3605	1.4607
	789		1.1006	0.3559	1.4565
	809		1.1012	0.3549	1.4561
	813		1.1013	0.3538	1.4551
	821		1.1015	0.3518	1.4533
0.00153	772	0.0812	1.0347	0.4064	1.4431
	789		1.0335	0.4047	1.4402
	806		1.0321	0.4013	1.4354
	826		1.0310	0.3972	1.4302
0.00208	773	0.0538	1.0599	0.3775	1.4374
	787		1.0595	0.3756	1.4351
	804		1.0590	0.3711	0.4301
	818		1.0586	0.3690	1.4276
0.00259	771	0.0316	1.0922	0.3372	1.4294
	783		1.0924	0.3357	1.4281
	803		1.0926	0.3303	1.4229
	813		1.0928	0.3284	1.4212
	818		1.0929	0.3245	1.4174

columbium metal at one temperature, no further waiting period is needed for obtaining stable potentials at other temperatures. For melts of concentrations higher than those shown here, e.g., 1% Cb, even though they have been equilibrated with columbium metal at one temperature, a long waiting period of 10 to 20 hr is needed before the potential becomes stable at another temperature. If the waiting period is not long enough, the potential versus temperature curve obtained has an abnormal shape. Figure 6 illustrates such a curve obtained from an unequilibrated melt containing about 0.8% Cb, with a waiting period of about $1/2$ hr for each point shown. The potentials thus obtained obviously have no thermodynamic significance. The dilute melts shown in Table VI do not obey Henry's law over the whole range of concentrations studied. However, for these dilute equilibrated melts, the n values obtained by using Faraday's law are very close to 3, as shown in Table VII(d). For equilibrated melts of

TABLE VII

Determination of the Valence of Metal Ions in LiCl-KCl Eutectic Melt in Equilibrium with Metals by Using Faraday's Law

Element	Concn., wt-% M	N_{MCl_n}	Temp. range, °K	Q, coulombs	w, mg	n
(a) Uranium	0.26	0.00062	778–813	25.2	20.6	3.02
	0.80	0.00188	767–814	74.7	61.8	2.98
	1.43	0.00342	769–812	141.6	114.8	3.05
	2.08	0.00502	773–817	206.0	169.0	3.01
(b) Thorium	0.19	0.00048	763–825	13.45	7.9	4.07
	0.76	0.00190	768–824	49.3	29.1	4.07
	1.47	0.00377	772–828	106.2	63.1	4.05
(c) Zirconium	0.07	0.00048	763–822	26.9	6.4	4.00
	0.48	0.00301	767–817	150.0	35.2	4.03
	0.86	0.00541	771–823	273.0	65.0	3.98
(d) Columbium	0.13	0.00076	763–821	13.4	4.3	2.99
	0.25	0.00153	772–826	64.8	20.9	2.98
	0.35	0.00208	773–818	101.5	30.7	2.96
	0.43	0.00259	771–818	119.5	38.4	3.00

higher Cb concentration and for all unequilibrated melts studied (containing less than 1.2% Cb), the n values obtained lie between 3 and 4. It is therefore concluded that Cb^{+3} is the predominant species of columbium ions present in these dilute equilibrated melts over the whole range of temperature used in this work (760–830°K) and that for all the unequilibrated melts and equilibrated melts of higher Cb concentrations studied, other species of columbium ions also exist in appreciable amounts. The relative amounts of the coexisting species initially present in the melt after electrolysis should depend on the current density used for the anodic dissolution and that in equilibrated melts should vary with their temperature and Cb concentration. The long waiting periods needed before obtaining stable potentials after electrolysis or after a change of the temperature of the melt are associated with the establishment of the relative amounts of the coexisting species corresponding to the equilibrium conditions. It is highly possible that the species coexisting with Cb^{+3} is Cb^{+4}, although the presence of Cb^{+5} or a mixture of Cb^{+4} and Cb^{+5} can also explain why the values of n lie between 3 and 4. The data concerning columbium melts of mixed valence states will be presented in the future after the results already obtained have been checked with chemi-

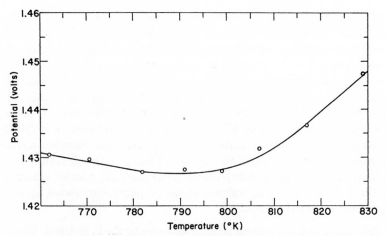

Fig. 6. Abnormal shape of the potential-temperature curve obtained when mixed valence states exist in the melt containing columbium chloride.

cal methods and more information is available to show how the relative amounts of each coexisting species of columbium ions vary with the temperature and the concentration of the melt.

The equilibrium between the chlorides of metal ions of two different valence states i and j $(j > i)$ with the metal M can be represented by the equation:

$$(j - i)M + iMCl_j = jMCl_i \qquad (11)$$

If their mole fractions and activity coefficients are represented by N and γ, respectively, then:

$$\Delta F° = ij(\Delta F_i° - \Delta F_j°) = -RT \ln (N_i \nu_i)^j / (N_j \nu_j)^i \qquad (12)$$

where $\Delta F°$ is the standard free energy change of the reaction, and $\Delta F_i°$ and $\Delta F_j°$ are, respectively, the free energy of formation of MCl_i and MCl_j per Cl atom. The relative amounts of M^i and M^j in the equilibrated melt, i.e., the ratio N_i/N_j, depend both on $(\Delta F_i° - \Delta F_j°)$ and on γ_i and γ_j. In general, $\Delta F_i°$ is more negative than $\Delta F_j°$, thus favoring the presence of the lower valence state in the equilibrated melt. On the other hand, ions of the higher valence state, owing to their higher charge and smaller size, have a greater tendency for forming complex ions, i.e., γ_j is much smaller than γ_i, and thus favors the presence of the higher valence state in the equilibrated melt. For the uranium chloride melts, the former outweighs the latter and therefore U^{+3} is the predominant species present. For the thorium chloride and the zirconium chloride melts, the opposite is true and therefore Th^{+4} and Zr^{+4} are the predominant species present. For the columbium chloride melts, the two (referring to the coexisting valence states) probably are of the same magnitude at higher Cb concentrations but with the former outweighing the latter at lower Cb concentrations. Thus, Cb^{+3} is the predominant species in dilute melts and mixed valence states prevail in more concentrated melts. In general, the ΔF° values and the γ values are either inaccurate or unknown. It is therefore impossible to calculate the relative amounts of the various coexisting valence states of polyvalent metal ions in equilibrium with the metal.

This work is part of a research program sponsored by the U. S. Atomic Energy Commission.

References

1. Yang, L., and R. G. Hudson, "Equilibrium Electrode Potentials of Some Metal-Chlorine Galvanic Cell and Activities of Some Metal Chlorides in LiCl-KCl Eutectic Melts," *Trans. Met. Soc. AIME*, to be published.

2. Yang, L., and R. G. Hudson, "Some Investigations of the [Ag/AgCl + LiCl-KCl Eutectic] Reference Electrode," *J. Electrochem. Soc.*, to be published.

3. Mellgren, S., and W. Opie, *Trans. Am. Inst. Mining, Met. Petrol. Engrs.*, **209**, 266 (1957).

4. Kellogg, H. H., et al., ONR Rept. Nonr 266 (24), June, 1956. Columbia Univ., School of Mines.

5. Glassner, A., U. S. Atomic Energy Commission, Rept. ANL-5750. "The Thermodynamic Properties of the Oxides, Fluorides and Chlorides to 2500°K."

Discussion

T. A. Henrie (*Bureau of Mines, Nevada*): In fused chloride salts which contain titanium di- or trichloride, it is well known that there are reactions with oxide materials such as quartz, alumina, and zirconia which produce a metal mirror on the ceramic surface and, no doubt, oxide impurity in the fused salt. In some instances it has been observed that the ceramic surfaces become electrical conductors when exposed to an atmosphere containing the vapors of these salts, even at temperatures as low as 400 to 500°C. An equation which could represent the reaction would be

$$7TiCl_2 + SiO_2 \longrightarrow 2TiOCl + TiSi + 4TiCl_3$$

Shaefer and his associates [*Angew. Chem.*, **69**, No. 13/14, 479 (1957)] found that there is some reaction between titanium trichloride and quartz to produce titanium oxychloride and found titanium oxychloride to be relatively stable.   It is possible that the TiOCl produced by reactions with oxides could diffuse to the metal surface (metal anode in your apparatus) and contaminate the surface with oxygen by the following reaction (if titanium were the metal)

$$2TiOCl + Ti \longrightarrow 2Ti(O)_{ad.} + TiCl_2$$

The metals you have worked with have a great affinity for oxygen similar to titanium.   Since the metals are at relatively low temperatures the diffusion of contaminating oxygen atoms into the metal would be relatively slow; therefore, a very small amount of oxygen could contaminate the metal surface.   This would alter the equilibrium and therefore calculated results such as activity coefficients could be erroneous.   It is possible that any similar equilibrium measurements made in glass apparatus may also be in error.   It is felt that only relatively noble metals or other inert materials should contact fused salt mixtures containing metals of this type in equilibrium determinations.

Thermodynamic Studies on Pyrrhotite

KICHIZO NIWA

Department of Chemistry, Faculty of Science, Hokkaido University, Sapporo, Japan

and

TSUGUYASU WADA

The Research Institute for Iron, Steel and Other Metals, Tôhoku University, Sendai, Japan

Abstract

The activities of sulfur in pyrrhotite are precisely determined by measuring the equilibrium of H_2S/H_2 over pyrrhotite of various compositions using a new method. The thermodynamical quantities derived from the measurements are discussed from the viewpoint of the nonstoichiometry, and discussion is also offered as to the decomposition of pyrite and the oxidation of pyrrhotite.

INTRODUCTION

Pyrrhotite, FeS_{1+x}, is a typical nonstoichiometric compound existing over the composition range from $x = 0.0$ to about 0.14.[1,2] Studies of its crystal structure[1,3,4] have shown that the lattice parameters and the unit cell volume contrast when x is increased, and as Hägg and Sucksdorff[3] have first ascertained, the nonstoichiometry is due to the formation of cation vacancies at the iron lattice sites rather than to the formation of interstitial or substitutional defects.

In contrast with the satisfactory information on the structure, there are only a few reports concerning the thermodynamic properties of pyrrhotite. Sano and Okajima[5] studied the activity of sulfur in pyrrhotite by measuring the equilibrium of H_2S/H_2 as a function of the solid composition. The results obtained by them are somewhat scattered, however. In general, there are many difficulties in such a measurement, especially in the accurate determination of the composition of the solid phase. Rosenqvist[6] measured the equilibrium of H_2S/H_2 over pyrrhotite phase. But this work is a part of the systematic investigation of the thermodynamics of iron, cobalt, and nickel sulfides, so the data are not sufficient to enable discussion of the properties of pyrrhotite in detail.

Three groups of investigators have reported thermodynamic or statistical thermodynamic studies on the nonstoichiometric compounds by their respective methods. Anderson[7] discussed the activities of components and phase separation by a statistical thermodynamical method which is essentially based on that developed by Fowler and Guggenheim.[8]

Anderson's theory was derived by considering the interaction energies between vacancies or between interstitial atoms in addition to the energies of formation of a vacancy or an interstitial atom, when the grand partition function for defects is computed. Recently, Libowitz[9] reported a successful application of this theory on the problem of nonstoichiometry in uranium hydride. Next, Takeuchi and Igaki[10] reported a statistical thermodynamical theory by which a quantitative interpretation was given as to the activity of oxygen in wüstite phase. These authors computed a partition function by considering that in addition to the formation of cation vacancies the excess electron defects which are created by the deficiency of cations are distributed at random among the rest of the cations. A good agreement was observed between the activity of oxygen thus calculated and that obtained experimentally by Sambongi.[11] Sano and Okajima[5] stated that the activities of sulfur in pyrrhotite which were observed in the course of their experiments also obey Takeuchi's theory. Not too long ago, Wagner et al.[12-14] measured the chemical potentials of silver or copper in Ag_2S, Cu_2S, and copper chalcogenides as a function of composition, by means of an electrochemical method called "coulometric titration." The results were discussed under the postulation that the changes in activities of silver or copper are entirely attributed to the change in activity of electrons, the activity of silver ions or copper ions being considered to be constant. This is rather a special case, however, arising from the peculiarity of the structures, the so-called "averaged structure," of these compounds.

In the present paper, the activities of sulfur in pyrrhotite are precisely determined by measuring the equilibrium of H_2S/H_2 over pyrrhotite of various compositions using a new method. The thermodynamical quantities derived from the measurements are discussed from the viewpoint of nonstoichiometry, and discussion is also offered as to the decomposition of pyrite and the oxidation of pyrrhotite.

EXPERIMENTAL

Two methods were employed in the present work, both based essentially on a circulation method. The apparatus of these two methods are the same, except for a difference of reaction tubes.

Method I

In the first method, a quartz spring balance was set in the reaction tube in order to determine *in situ* the weight of sample which is in equilibrium with a H_2S/H_2 mixture. Since the amount of iron is known and not changed, the ratio Fe:S in pyrrhotite can be determined from the weight of the sample.

Figure 1 shows the apparatus used in method I. Here, R is the reaction tube of quartz glass, in which the sample is suspended by a quartz spring and fiber, D is a phosphorus pentoxide drier, and P_1 and P_2 are the circulation pumps (the former was used for the circulation during the reaction, and the latter for the gas analysis).

The starting material of sample was ferric oxide. About 120

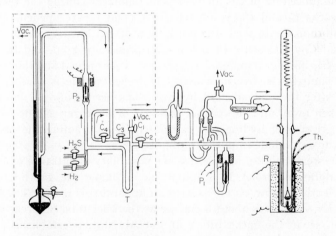

Fig. 1. Apparatus of measurement (method I).

mg of ferric oxide was weighed into the quartz bucket and hung in the reaction tube. The oxide was then reduced to metallic iron by hydrogen at about 600 to 800°C. The decrease of weight during the reduction was in good agreement with the calculated value. After the reduction had been finished, the excess hydrogen was removed and hydrogen sulfide was introduced to sulfurize the iron to pyrrotite. The total pressure at equilibrium was 200 to 400 mm Hg for most runs. The attainment of equilibrium was found by the cessation of increase in the weight of sample; usually this took a few hours. After the weight had become constant, the sample was maintained for about the same duration as that required to reach it, in order to assure the arrival at equilibrium. Finally, the weight of the sample was measured and the partial pressures of hydrogen sulfide and hydrogen were determined as described below.

When one run had thus been finished, the next run could immediately be started, using the same sample, by adding or removing hydrogen or hydrogen sulfide and, if it was necessary, by varying the reaction temperature.

The spring used had a sensitivity of about 3 mg/1 mm, and its elongation could be measured to 0.05 mm by a cathetometer. So the change of weight can be observed with accuracy of ±0.15 mg. From the amount of sample used, this accuracy corresponds to ±0.003 for $1 + x$ in $FeS_{1 + x}$ or to 0.15 atomic-% of sulfur.

The procedure of gas analysis is as follows: During the reaction, the cocks C_3 and C_1 are closed and C_2 and C_4 are opened. When equilibrium is attained, the circulation of gas is stopped and cocks C_2 and C_4 are closed. First the total pressure is read, and then the trap T is immersed in liquid air, the cock C_3 is opened and the circulation pump P_2 is driven, whereby hydrogen sulfide is condensed in T. After the uncondensed hydrogen has been removed, liquid air is taken away and the partial pressure of hydrogen sulfide is read. The pressure of hydrogen is calculated by subtracting the pressure of hydrogen sulfide from the total pressure.

The weak point of method I is the possibility of entrance of a thermal diffusion error. It is impossible to make the gas inlet tube sufficiently narrow, as far as such an apparatus is used. The linear velocity of gas was about 3 cm/sec at the inlet tube, whereas it was 50 cm/sec at the outlet tube. If a steady state is established, however, there should be no difference between the composition of gas at the sample and that at the gas analysis apparatus, since the velocity of gas flow in the outlet tube is so large that the thermal diffusion can be eliminated.   This will be confirmed by method II.

Method II

To check the results obtained by the above method, alternative measurements were carried out by use of a reaction tube which is shown in Figure 2.   It is made of quartz or Pyrex glass, and the gas inlet and outlet tubes are made narrow enough to eliminate thermal diffusion.   About 50 cm/sec of linear velocity of gas flow is obtained in the outlet and inlet tubes by circulating the gas at volume velocity of 300 cc/min.

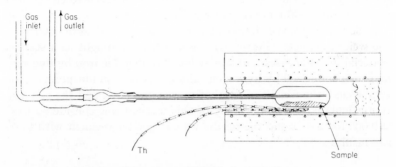

Fig. 2. Apparatus of measurement (method II).

About 0.5 g of sample was taken; after the 24- to 30-hr reaction the gas was analyzed by the same procedures as method I.   Composition of the solid phase was determined by chemical analysis and an x-ray analysis was made as follows.

To determine the solid composition by chemical analysis, about 0.1 g of pyrrhotite was dissolved in aqua regia; iron was first precipitated by ammonium hydroxide and determined as Fe_2O_3.   From its filtrate sulfate ions were separated as barium sulfate and then weighed.

Unfortunately, it was found that the chemical analysis did not possess the accuracy required in the present work.   The results were reproducible only within ± 0.02 of $1 + x$, and often tended to yield high values in the percentage of sulfur.   Thus, the compositions calculated from lattice constants measured by x-ray diffraction were regarded to be more reliable.

The relation between lattice constants and sulfur content of pyrrhotite has been determined by Haraldsen[1]; this relation was employed in the present work to determine the composition. X-ray diffraction photographs were taken by using a Debye-Scherrer camera of 90 mm diam and $CoK\alpha$-ray. Since pyrrhotite has a hexagonal lattice,

$$\sin^2 \theta = \alpha(h^2 + hk + k^2) + \beta(l^2) \qquad (1)$$

where α and β are constants related respectively to the lattice constants a_0 and c_0 as

$$\alpha = \lambda^2/3A_0{}^{2\prime} \ \beta = \lambda^2/4C_0{}^2 \qquad (2)$$

where λ is the wavelength of the x-ray. Here, α and β were determined by using the least square method; from seven to eleven lines appeared on the film of x-ray diffraction.

In several runs, the composition was also determined by measuring the weight change. Ferric oxide was taken by weight as a starting material in these cases. It was reduced to metallic iron by hydrogen and then sulfurized by hydrogen sulfide. After equilibrium had been established, the weight of pyrrhotite was measured and the composition calculated. The accuracy of this method was considered to be ± 0.005 for $1 + x$ and the results were in good agreement with the x-ray results.

Materials

The pyrrhotite used was prepared from sulfur and electrolytic iron as described in a previous paper.[15] Ferric oxide was of a guaranteed reagent grade. Hydrogen sulfide was produced by Kipp's apparatus, purified by passing through a potassium hydroxide solution, calcium chloride, and phosphorus pentoxide tubes successively, and finally distilled twice in vacuum by liquid air. The hydrogen used was produced by electrolysis of sodium hydroxide solution and purified by passing through red-heated copper chips, calcium chloride, and phosphorus pentoxide successively.

RESULTS

The experimental results are shown in Figure 3, in which the logarithms of P_{H_2S}/P_{H_2} are plotted against the composition of solid phase. The values are very close to those obtained by Rosenqvist,[6] although the latter's were measured at higher temperatures. The results obtained by Sano and Okajima[5] tend to give lower pressures than those of the present work. It is observed that P_{H_2S}/P_{H_2} is almost independent of temperature.

The activity A'_S of sulfur in pyrrhotite, relative to the stoichiometric FeS as a standard state, is given as

$$A'_S = (P_{H_2S}/P_{H_2})/(P_{H_2S}/P_{H_2})_0 \tag{3}$$

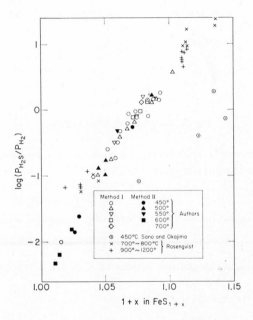

Fig. 3. Results of experiments.

where $(P_{H_2S}/P_{H_2})_0$ is the composition of gas in equilibrium with stoichiometric FeS, or equal to that in equilibrium with FeS–Fe coexisting phases. Alcock and Richardson's data[16] are adopted for $(P_{H_2S}/P_{H_2})_0$. This is one of the most reliable determinations and is in good agreement with those by Sudo,[17] Sano,[18] and Rosenqvist.[6] Values of A'_S are thus determined as shown in Figure 4.

From the Gibbs-Duhem equation

$$\eta_{Fe}d \ln A'_{Fe} = -\eta_S d \ln A'_S \tag{4}$$

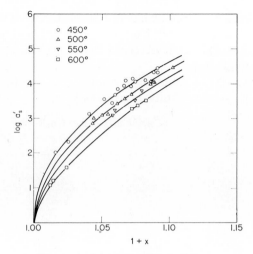

Fig. 4. Activities of sulfur in FeS_{1+x}.

where n_{Fe}, n_S are, respectively, the mole fractions of iron and sulfur. If pyrrhotite is represented as FeS_{1+x},

$$\eta_S/\eta_{Fe} = (1 + x) \qquad (5)$$

Rewriting Eq. (4) by an integral form of common logarithm,

$$\log A'_{Fe} = - \int_{x=0}^{x} (1 + x)d \log A'_S \qquad (6)$$

By the graphical integration, values of A'_{Fe} are determined as shown in Figure 5.

The total free energy $\bar{F}$ is defined as

$$\bar{F} = [1/(2 + x)]RT \ln A'_{Fe} + [(1 + x)/(2 + x)]RT \ln A'_S \qquad (7)$$

where $\bar{F}$ is the difference of energy between FeS_{1+x} and stoichiometric FeS, when the total number of atoms is fixed and is equal to Avogadro's number. Here, $\bar{F}$ is shown in Figure 6.

The free energy change $\Delta F^{(8)}$ in the following reaction:

$$FeS(\beta) + (x/2)S_2(g) = FeS_{1+x} \qquad (8)$$

is given as

$$\Delta F^{(8)} = (2 + x)\bar{F} - (x/2) \mu'_{S_2} \qquad (9)$$

where μ'_{S_2} is the chemical potential of S_2 gas with one atmospheric

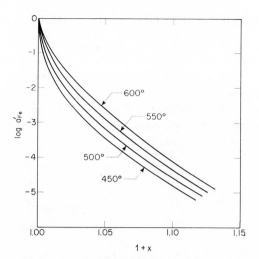

Fig. 5. Activities of iron in Fe_1S_{+x}.

pressure, the standard state being taken as stoichiometric FeS.   If the sulfur pressure in equilibrium with stoichiometric FeS is represented by $P_{S_2}{}^0$,

$$\mu'_{S_2} = -RT \ln P_{S_2}{}^0 \tag{10}$$

From $\bar{F}$ and Alcock and Richardson's value for $P_{S_2}{}^0$, values of $\Delta F^{(8)}$ are computed by Eq. (9) as shown in Figure 7.

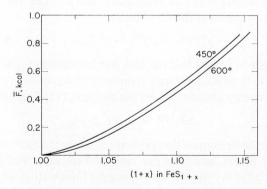

Fig. 6. The total free energy $\bar{F}$.

THERMAL DECOMPOSITION OF PYRITE

Anderson has discussed the phase separation in the nonstoichiometric compounds by a statistical theory.   Though its principle is qualitatively valid, difficulties may arise when it is applied, in order to obtain the quantitative values, to the system in which each phase does not have the same crystal structure.   In the present section, therefore, the decomposition equilibrium of pyrite is discussed on the basis of classical thermodynamics.

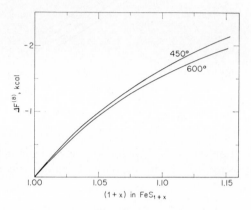

Fig. 7. The free energy change $\Delta F^{(8)}$ for the reaction $FeS(\beta) + x/2\ S_2(g) = FeS_{1+x}$.

The solid solution range existing in pyrite phase is so narrow, that it may be negligible for the thermodynamical calculations, the activity of pyrite being regarded as practically unity.   The reaction of decomposition of pyrite is then written as

$$2/(1-x)FeS_2 = 2/(1-x)FeS_{1+x} + S_2(g) \qquad (11)$$

It is incorrect to regard this reaction as that between pyrite and stoichiometric FeS, as Kelley[19] and Wunderlich[20] have done.

The free energy change $\Delta F_T^{(11)}$ for reaction (11) is given as

$$\Delta F_T^{(11)} = -RT \ln P_{S_2} \qquad (12)$$

where P_{S_2} is the decomposition pressure of pyrite; $\Delta F_T^{(11)}$ is the energy per mole of S_2 gas, and that per mole of FeS_2 or of FeS is given by $(1-x)/2\Delta F_T^{(11)}$.   If the free energy of formation of pyrrhotite saturated with cation vacancies from α-Fe and S_2 gas is represented by $\Delta F_T{}^{\text{pyrr.}}$, the free energy of formation of $\text{FeS}_2\Delta F_T{}^{(13)}$ from α-Fe and S_2 gas at temperature T is given as

$$\text{Fe}(\alpha) + S_2(g) = \text{FeS}_2 \tag{13}$$

$$\Delta F_T{}^{(13)} = -(1 - x)/2\Delta F_T{}^{(11)} + \Delta F_T{}^{\text{pyrr.}} \tag{14}$$

The $\Delta F_T{}^{\text{pyrr.}}$ can be separated into two terms, the free energy of formation $\Delta F_T{}^{\text{FeS}}$ of stoichiometric FeS and that of addition of excess sulfur $\Delta F^{(8)}$, viz.,

$$\Delta F_T{}^{\text{pyrr.}} = \Delta F_T{}^{\text{FeS}} + (\Delta F^{(8)})_{\text{S}} \tag{15}$$

The $(\Delta F^{(8)})_{\text{S}}$ is the $\Delta F^{(8)}$ for pyrrhotite saturated with cation vacancies.

Using standard enthalpy, entropy, and heat capacities, one may write $\Delta F_T{}^{(13)}$ as

$$\Delta F_T{}^{(13)} = \Delta H_{298}{}^{(13)} + \int_{298}^{T} \Delta Cp^{(13)} \, dT -$$
$$T \left\{ \Delta S_{298}{}^{(13)} + \int_{298}^{T} (\Delta Cp^{(13)}/T) dT \right\} \tag{16}$$

There are accurate values for entropies and heat capacities for $S_2(g)$, α-Fe, and FeS_2. From Kelley's new data,[21] entropies at 298°K of $S_2(g)$, α-Fe, and FeS_2 are, respectively, 54.40 ± 0.10, 6.49 ± 0.03, and 12.7 ± 0.2 e.u. and $\Delta S_{298}{}^{(13)}$ is then determined to be -48.2 ± 0.3 e.u. For heat capacities, the following values are taken:

$$\alpha\text{-Fe}^{21} : C_p = 3.37 + 7.10 \times 10^{-3}T + 0.43 \times 10^5 T^{-2}$$

$$S_2(g)^{21} : C_p = 8.54 + 0.28 \times 10^{-3}T - 0.79 \times 10^5 T^{-2}$$

$$\text{FeS}_2{}^{22} : C_p = 17.88 + 1.32 \times 10^{-3}T - 3.05 \times 10^5 T^{-2}$$

From these values $\Delta F_t{}^{13}$ at 798°K is calculated as

$$\Delta F_{798}{}^{(13)} = \Delta H_{298}{}^{(13)} + 760 + (48.2 - 1.51) T \text{ cal} \tag{17}$$

To calculate $(\Delta F^{(8)})_{\text{S}}$, it is necessary to determine the saturated limit of $1 + x$. Studies by Haraldsen,[1] Roberts,[2] and Lukes et al.[23] have shown that the saturated value of $1 + x$ remains up to 433°C at about 1.14. In the present calculation, it is assumed that Haraldsen's value, 53.4 atomic-% of S, or $1 + x = 1.148$ is maintained over the temperature range considered.

From Figure 6, $(\Delta F^{(8)})_{1.148}$ is determined as follows:

$$(\Delta F^{(8)})_{1.148} = -2890 + 1.07T \text{ cal} \tag{18}$$

As $\Delta F_T{}^{\text{FeS}}$, Alcock and Richardson's data are adopted, viz.,

$$\Delta F_T{}^{\text{FeS}} = -35,910 + 12.56T \qquad (19)$$

From Eqs. (14), (15), (17), (18), and (19), one obtains

$$\Delta F_{798}{}^{(11)} = -(\Delta H_{298}{}^{(13)}/0.426) - 92,860 - 77.7T \qquad (20)$$

The experimental measurements on the decomposition pressures of pyrite were ordinarily carried out at the temperature in the neighborhood of $928°\text{K}$. Using the data of heat capacities of FeS_2, $S_2(g)$ and regarding FeS_{1+x} as equal to that of FeS, viz.,

$$FeS^{22}: Cp = 12.20 + 2.38 \times 10^{-3}T \ (598 \sim 1468°\text{K})$$

$\Delta F^{(11)}$ at $928°\text{K}$ is obtained as

$$\Delta F_{928}{}^{(11)} = -(\Delta H_{298}{}^{(13)}/0.426) - 93,600 - 77.5T \qquad (21)$$

According to Eq. (12), this gives the decomposition pressure of pyrite as

$$\log_{10} P_{S_2} = (\Delta H_{298}{}^{(13)}/1.9485T) + (20,350/T) + 16.94 \qquad (22)$$

The value of P_{S_2} has been experimentally measured by many authors[24-28] as shown in Figure 8. It is found that $\Delta H_{298}{}^{(13)}$ of $-74,400$ cal/mole is best fit for the experimental values, as shown by the straight line in Figure 8. From this value

$$\Delta F_{928}{}^{(11)} = 74,500 - 77.5T \text{ cal} \qquad (23)$$

From Rossini's table,[29] the standard enthalpy change for the vaporization of sulfur is given as

$$2S(\lambda) = S_2(g) \qquad (24)$$

$$\Delta H_{298} = 29,860 \text{ cal/mole} \qquad (25)$$

Consequently, the standard enthalpy of formation of FeS_2 from $S(\lambda)$ and α-Fe is

$$\Delta H_{298}{}^{\text{FeS}_2} = -41,540 \text{ cal/mole} \qquad (26)$$

This value is smaller than Kelley's value[19] of $-38,770$ cal but near to Rossini's value,[29] of $-42,520$ cal.

The expression of Eq. (23) for the free energy change of the decomposition of pyrite may be valid over the temperature range of $650 \pm$

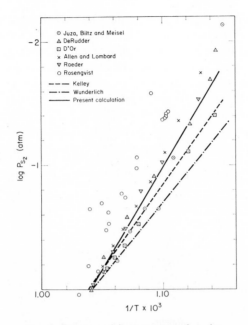

Fig. 8. Decomposition pressure of pyrite.

150°C, without correction of heat capacity terms. Decomposition pressures calculated by Kelley's[19] and Wunderlich's[20] formulas are also shown in Figure 8. The values of these reports, however, have a tendency to indicate lower dependence of P_{S_2} on temperature.

OXIDATION OF PYRRHOTITE

The mechanism of oxidation of ferrous sulfide was reported in the previous paper,[15] where it was observed that in the initial stage of oxidation, iron ions react with oxygen by migrating from the interior of FeS crystal to the surface, without evolution of SO_2, until the deficiency of iron attains a certain limiting value.

This fact is now discussed from a thermodynamical viewpoint. In the previous report,[15] it was observed that the major product of oxidation in the initial stage is magnetite. Therefore, the following two reactions are considered to occur:

$$\text{Fe (in pyrrhotite)} + {}^2/_3O_2 \longrightarrow {}^1/_3Fe_3O_4 \qquad (27)$$

$$\text{S (in pyrrhotite)} + O_2 \longrightarrow SO_2 \qquad (28)$$

As a qualitative interpretation, it may be said that if the activity of iron in pyrrhotite is sufficiently high, reaction (27) preferentially proceeds, whereas if the activity of sulfur is sufficiently high, (28) preferentially proceeds, and for a certain composition of pyrrhotite reactions (27) and (28) equally proceed.

As a thermodynamical consideration, the free energy change for the following reaction is of significance:

$$\tfrac{1}{3}Fe_3O_4 + \tfrac{2}{3}S \text{ (in pyrrhotite)} = Fe \text{ (in pyrrhotite)} + \tfrac{2}{3}SO_2 \qquad (29)$$

If the free energy change $\Delta F^{(29)}$ of the above reaction is positive, reaction (27) prevails, and if it is negative (28) prevails. The free

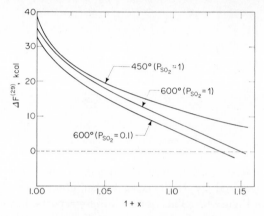

Fig. 9. The free energy change $\Delta F^{(29)}$ for the reaction $\tfrac{1}{3}Fe_3O_4 + \tfrac{2}{3}S$ (in pyrrhotite) = Fe (in pyrrhotite) + $\tfrac{2}{3}SO_2$.

energy change $\Delta F^{(29)}$ is given as

$$\Delta F^{(29)} = RT \ln A_{Fe} + \tfrac{2}{3}\Delta F_T^{SO_2} - \tfrac{1}{3}\Delta F_T^{Fe_3O_4} - \tfrac{2}{3}RT \ln A_S \qquad (30)$$

where $\Delta F_T^{SO_2}$ and $\Delta F_T^{Fe_3O_4}$ are the free energies of formation for SO_2 and Fe_3O_4, A_{Fe}, and A_S are the activities of iron and sulfur, respectively, the pure elements being taken as a standard state. From the definition of activity,

$$\ln A_{Fe} = \ln A_{Fe}^0 + \ln A'_{Fe} \qquad (31)$$

$$\ln A_S = \ln A_S^0 + \ln A'_S \qquad (32)$$

Here, A_{Fe}^0 and A_S^0 are, respectively, the activities of iron and sulfur in stoichiometric FeS, and

$$\ln A_{Fe}^0 + \ln A_S^0 = \ln A_{FeS} = \Delta F_T^{FeS}/RT \tag{33}$$

$$\ln A_S^0 = \ln P_{S_2}^0 \tag{34}$$

From the relations (31), (32), (33), and (34), Eq. (30) is rewritten as

$$\Delta F_T^{(29)} = {}^2/_3 \Delta F_T^{SO_2} - {}^1/_3 \Delta F_T^{Fe_3O_4} + \Delta F_T^{FeS} - {}^5/_3 RT \ln P_{S_2}^0$$
$$+ RT \ln A'_{Fe} - {}^2/_3 RT \ln A'_S \tag{35}$$

Using the values of $\Delta F_T^{SO_2}$ and $\Delta F_T^{Fe_3O_4}$ calculated according to Coughlin's table, and ΔF_T^{FeS} from Alcock and Richardson's data,[16] one computes $\Delta F_T^{(29)}$ as a function of the composition of pyrrhotite, as shown in Figure 9.

It is observed in Figure 9 that $\Delta F_T^{(29)}$ is positive over the whole measurable range at 450°C, whereas for 600°C it is zero at 1.146 and 1.123 of $1 + x$, respectively, for 1 and 0.1 atm of P_{SO_2}. The pyrrhotite containing less sulfur than these values is, therefore, oxidized initially by reaction (27), until the composition attains the above values. In the oxidation experiments,[15] the composition of pyrrhotite undergoing oxidation yielded 52.3 and 52.8 atomic-% sulfur or 1.09 and 1.12 of $1 + x$, respectively, at 500 and 600°C. These experimental values are slightly smaller than those calculated above. However, the differences may be permissible, because the process of oxidation is not strictly at equilibrium, and the pressure of SO_2 is actually not maintained at 1 atm but may be far less than that.

References

1. Haraldsen, H., *Z. anorg. u. allgem. Chem.*, **246,** 169 (1941).
2. Roberts, H. S., *J. Am. Chem. Soc.*, **57,** 1034 (1934).
3. Hägg, G., and I. Sucksdorff, *Z. physik. Chem. (Leipzig)*, **B22,** 444 (1933).
4. Ueda, R., T. Ichinokawa, and T. Mitsui, *Busseiron Kenkyu*, **33,** 55 (1950).
5. Sano, K., and K. Okajima, *Bull. Research Inst. Mineral Dressing and Met.*, **7,** 163 (1951).
6. Rosenqvist, T., *J. Iron and Steel Inst.*, **179,** 37 (1954).
7. Anderson, J. S., *Proc. Roy. Soc. (London)*, **A185,** 68 (1946).
8. Fowler, R. H., and E. A. Guggenheim, *Statistical Thermodynamics*, Cambridge Univ. Press, New York, 1939; R. H. Fowler, *Proc. Cambridge Phil. Soc.*, **32,** 144 (1936).
9. Libowitz, G. G., *J. Chem. Phys.*, **27,** 514 (1957).
10. Takeuchi, S., and K. Igaki, *J. Japan Inst. Metals*, **B14,** 23 (1950).

11. Sambongi, K., *Tetsu to Hagane*, **33**, 3 (1947); **34**, 2 (1948).

12. Wagner, C., *J. Chem. Phys.*, **21**, 1819 (1953).

13. Wagner, J. B., and C. Wagner, *J. Chem. Phys.*, **26**, 1602 (1957).

14. Lorenz, G., and C. Wagner, *J. Chem. Phys.*, **26**, 1607 (1957).

15. Niwa, K., T. Wada, and Y. Shiraishi, *J. Metals*, **9**, 269 (1957).

16. Alcock, C. B., and F. D. Richardson, *Nature*, **168**, 661 (1951).

17. Sudo, K., *Sci. Rept. Research Inst. Tôhoku Univ.*, **A2**, 321 (1950).

18. Sano, K., *Nippon Kagaku Zasshi*, **60**, 59 (1939).

19. Kelley, K. K., *Bureau of Mines*, Bull. 406 (1937).

20. Wunderlich, G., *Z. Elektrochem.*, **56**, 218 (1952).

21. Kelley, K. K., *Bureau of Mines*, Bull. 447 (1948).

22. Coughlin, J. P., *J. Am. Chem. Soc.*, **72**, 5445 (1950).

23. Lukes, J., C. F. Prutton, and D. Turnbull, *J. Am. Chem. Soc.*, **67**, 697 (1954).

24. Juza, R., W. Biltz, and K. Meisel, *Z. anorg. Chem.*, **25**, 273 (1932).

25. de Rudder, F., *Bull. soc. chim. Belges*, **47**, No. 4, 1225 (1930).

26. D'Or, L., *J. chim. Phys.*, **27**, 239 (1930).

27. Allen, E. T., and R. H. Lombard, *Am. J. Sci.*, **43**, No. 4, 175 (1917).

28. Raeder, M. G., *Kgl. Norske Videnskab. Selskabs Forh.*, **2**, 151 (1929).

29. Rossini, F. D., et al., "Selected Values of Chemical Thermodynamic Properties," Natl. Bureau of Standards, 1952.

Discussion

C. L. McCabe (*Carnegie Inst. of Technology*): Niwa and Wada have provided some essential experimental data for a more complete understanding of the thermodynamics of the oxidation of ferrous sulfide. Their calculations have enabled them to make some remarks about the mechanism of the oxidation of ferrous sulfide. This discussion contains a suggestion for a more detailed mechanism, which fits in with their calculations and statements, but goes into somewhat greater detail.

When a ferrous sulfide particle, initially stoichiometric, has reached the stage of oxidation when both iron and sulfur are being oxidized, two possibilities exist. One is that magnetite and sulfur dioxide form at different sites and the other that, at any spot, they form alternately. If one considers the two-site mechanism, one comes to the conclusion that the rise of iron activity at the edge of the solid magnetite, due to the increase of Fe/S caused by the formation of sulfur dioxide, will result in the lateral growth of the magnetite and eventual disappearance of the site where sulfur dioxide is being formed. The two-site mechanism is therefore internally unstable. On the other hand, the alternate or cyclic mechanism is internally stable and has a firm thermodynamic basis. This mechanism logically follows the view of Niwa and Wada's that, on roasting stoichiometric ferrous sulfide, Fe_3O_4 forms until ΔF[29] reaches zero. It is likely, however, that the formation of magnetite continues beyond this point until the SO_2 plus S_2 pressure, fixed by the sulfur potential in the sulfide and the oxygen potential in the oxide at sulfide-oxide interface, reaches a value high enough to rupture the magnetite layer allowing oxygen gas to diffuse through the gaseous phase to the sulfide surface

DISCUSSION TABLE I

Conditions	Approx S in FeS, %	P_{S_2}, atm	P_{SO_2}, atm
FeS in equil. with FeO–Fe$_3$O$_4$	36.8	3.8×10^{-7}	3.4×10^{-9}
FeS in equil. with Fe$_3$O$_4$ and 1 atm total of gas	39.2	2.0×10^{-2}	9.8×10^{-1}
FeS at edge of FeS field, FeS$_{1.1}$	42.0	11.2	3.7×10^3

[Evidence (Morgan, J. A., and C. L. McCabe, unpublished results) for rupture of the magnetite layer was found in experiments at Carnegie in which it was found that simultaneous oxidation of iron and sulfur occurred only at isolated areas where the ruptured magnetite layer was clearly visible on sectioning and observing a partially roasted particle.] Sulfur dioxide then will be formed from the reaction of oxygen gas and sulfur in the ferrous sulfide, until the decrease in S/Fe results in the iron activity becoming high enough to nucleate and grow Fe$_3$O$_4$ on the sulfide surface. Magnetite will then form until the increase in the S/Fe gives the conditions, as described above, for rupture of the magnetite film by the combined pressure of SO$_2$ and S$_2$. Discussion Table I gives the results of some thermodynamic calculations, using data from several authors [Darken, L. S., and R. W. Gurry, *J. Am. Chem. Soc.*, **67**, 1407 (1945); C. B. Alcock and F. D. Richardson, *Nature*, **168**, 661 (1951); F. D. Richardson and J. H. E. Jeffes, *J. Iron Steel Inst. (London)*, **160**, 267 (1948); T. Rosenqvist, *ibid.*, **176**, 42 (1954); F. D. Richardson and J. H. E. Jeffes, *ibid.*, **171**, 170 (1952); J. P. Coughlin, *Bureau of Mines Bull.* 542; L. Himmel, R. F. Mehl, and C. E. Birchenall, *J. Metals*, **4**, 147 (1952)] which show that at 1000°K there is a range of S$_2$ plus SO$_2$ pressures which could easily provide for the rupture of the Fe$_3$O$_4$. The pressures in Discussion Table I are calculated for various sulfide and magnetite compositions where the iron activity is the same in both phases. For this to be applicable to oxidation the assumption is made that the sulfur solubility is small in magnetite and the oxygen solubility is small in ferrous sulfide. The cyclic mechanism fits in with the observation [Niwa, K., T. Wada, and Y. Shiraishi, *Trans. Am. Inst. Mining Met. Petrol. Engrs.*, **209**, 269 (1957)] that simultaneous oxidation of iron and sulfur occurs at approximately the same time that the sulfur dioxide pressure reaches 1 atm (the fact that Niwa, Wada, and Shiraishi found that the Fe/S was slightly higher than for one atmosphere SO$_2$ could be due to experimental error or to there being concentration gradients in the ferrous sulfide phase), that a porous magnetite (Morgan, J. A., and C. L. McCabe, unpublished results) is formed during the stage when there is simultaneous oxidation of iron and sulfur, whereas dense magnetite is formed when only iron is oxidizing in the initial stage of the oxidation of ferrous sulfide, and that the cyclic mechanism is an extension of the well-founded mechanism for the reduction of oxides to metal proposed by C. Wagner [*Trans. Am. Inst. Mining Met. Engrs.*, **194**, 214 (1952)].

The Oxygen Content of Copper Mattes

MITSUO KAMEDA and AKIRA YAZAWA

Department of Metallurgy, Faculty of Engineering, Tôhoku University, Sendai, Japan

Abstract

The applicability of the hydrogen reduction method for determining the oxygen content of copper mattes was examined with satisfactory results. The oxygen content of some synthetic and commercial mattes ranged between 0.1 and 10%. The oxygen content of mattes is controlled by several factors; one of the major factors is the silica content in slags equilibrated with mattes. It was disclosed that the oxygen content increases with decreasing silica content in slag. The oxygen content of commercial mattes was briefly discussed based on the results of this series of study.

INTRODUCTION

For the purpose of obtaining a better understanding of copper smelting, an experimental investigation has been made, presenting partial liquidus diagrams for the systems $FeS-FeO-SiO_2$[1] and Cu_2S-$FeS-FeO$,[2] solubilities of constituents of matte in slag,[3] solubility of FeO in copper matte equilibrated with $FeO-SiO_2$ slag saturated with silica,[4] and mutual dissolution between matte and slag produced in the system $Cu_2S-FeS-FeO-SiO_2$.[5] It has been confirmed from these studies that there is an appreciable mutual dissolution between matte and slag; namely, the slag dissolves to some extent the cuprous and ferrous sulfides from matte, while the matte holds a considerable amount of ferrous oxide from slag in solution. Furthermore, it has also been disclosed that the FeO content of matte decreases with increasing matte grade. In the previous papers,[1-5] in order to minimize the magnetite content of the systems, experimental heats have been made mostly in iron crucibles in nitrogen flow over a relatively wide range of composition where the iron crucible is stable with respect to corrosion by the melt. Thus, the iron oxide in matte, as a first approximation, has been expressed as FeO, the amount of which was calculated from chemical analyses of iron, copper, and sulfur in the matte.

Since this estimation method is indirect, in the present paper the availability of a hydrogen reduction method was examined for determining the oxygen content of copper mattes, and the solubility of oxygen in the matte was reverified by the application of this method. Moreover, the oxygen content of commercial mattes in several Japanese smelters was determined, and the results obtained were compared with the results of the fundamental researches in our laboratory.

Furthermore, in equilibrium between synthetic matte and slag, the effect of FeO or SiO_2 content of slag on the oxygen content of matte was examined as one of the factors controlling oxygen.

Since no way of describing the structure of liquid matte has yet been found in the previous papers, matte constituents will be conventionally expressed by molecular form as Cu_2S, FeS, FeO, etc., in this paper.

DETERMINATION OF OXYGEN CONTENT OF COPPER MATTES

For estimating the oxygen content of matte the following methods have been hitherto available.

1. Acid method. This method was first applied by Hawley[6] and improved by Drummond,[7] Ellwood and Henderson,[8] Asano,[9] and others. Its outline is as follows: The matte is attacked with a strong solution of sodium chlorate in nitric acid, which dissolves the sulfides and leaves the iron oxides substantially unattacked. The residue is then analyzed for ferric and ferrous iron, and the amounts of FeO and Fe_3O_4 thus calculated. In the course of this study it was found that a portion of the iron oxides is readily soluble in the strongly oxidizing solution and that the results are lower than those of a hydrogen reduction method adopted in the present paper which will be discussed later.

2. Calculation method. A synthetic matte of the Cu_2S-FeS-FeO system will be taken as an example to explain this method. First, the sample is analyzed chemically for copper, iron, and sulfur,

secondly, the copper in matte is regarded to form into Cu_2S, thirdly, the remainder of sulfur and a portion of iron is considered to be present as FeS, and finally the rest of iron takes the form of FeO. As mentioned above, this procedure has been adopted in the preceding papers in this series.   However, commercial mattes are very complicated in composition and hence they would require more assumptions on the form of constituent compounds, as compared with the synthetic matte.

3. Hydrogen reduction method. This is one of the most conventional procedures available for determining the oxygen content in metal.   For copper matte, Pound, Derge, and Osuch[10] briefly stated that the matte was analyzed for oxygen by hydrogenation, and Lander and Schuhmann[11] analyzed the matte samples for oxygen by hydrogen reduction.   However, their brief descriptions did not give detailed information on the procedure.

Hydrogen Reduction Method Employed

Samples

As raw materials of synthetic mattes the cuprous and ferrous sulfides and ferrous oxide were used; these were prepared in the same manner as in the previous reports.[1,3]   Mixtures of powdered materials were melted in pure iron crucibles under a current of nitrogen to form mattes as samples for determination of oxygen.   Commercial mattes were also subjected to oxygen determination.

Apparatus and Procedure

A schematic diagram of the apparatus employed is shown in Figure 1, which is substantially the same as that used by Isawa and Kameda[12] for determining the oxygen content of blister copper. The assembly was of all glass construction, except for the short connections at a weighing tube.   Hydrogen generated by the electrolysis of potassium hydroxide solution was passed through calcium chloride and phosphorous pentoxide containers and a heated palladium asbestos tube in order to remove moisture and oxygen, and then conducted into a reaction tube, made of opaque quartz, 2 cm in inner diameter and 35 cm long.   The sample was held on a boat in the reaction tube.   The boat was 4.5 cm long, made of alumina

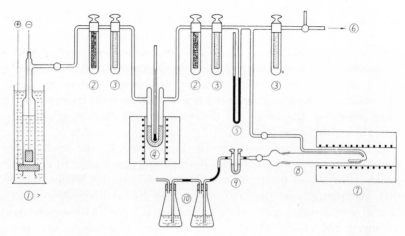

Fig. 1. Apparatus of the hydrogen reduction method. 1, Hydrogen generator; 2, calcium chloride container; 3, phosphorus pentoxide container; 4, heated palladium asbestos tube; 5, manometer; 6, to vacuum pump; 7, heating furnace; 8, reaction tube; 9, weighing tube; 10, container for hydrogen-sulfide absorbent.

above 95% in purity, and was substantially stable for attack of the sample due to high density and low content of silica. The oxygen in samples reacted with hydrogen to form water vapor that was caught in a small weighing tube containing phosphorus pentoxide. Since samples consisted mainly of sulfides, the outlet gas from the reaction tube contained hydrogen sulfide, which was passed through the weighing tube, and subsequently caught in an absorbent for hydrogen sulfide. A stock of absorbent was one liter of solution dissolving 40 g zinc acetate, 10 g cadmium acetate, and 30 cu cm glacial acetic acid.

The mattes were ground down to under 100 mesh by using an agate mortar. This was done as quickly as possible to avoid oxidation by air. The sample weight was large enough to get a weight increase of the weighing tube ranging from 10 to 20 mg caused by absorption of water vapor. (For medium grade mattes the weight of the sample was usually about 0.5 g.) The sample on the boat was placed in the reaction tube, in which the atmosphere was replaced by hydrogen after evacuation and this procedure was repeated three times for complete replacement by hydrogen. Subsequently, hydrogen was passed through the whole assembly for 30 min, a furnace was positioned so as to heat the sample in its center, and hydrogen reduction was carried on at a certain temperature. The flow rate of hydrogen was about 40 cu cm/min. After a definite time the furnace was removed and the hydrogen flow was continued for another hour in order to expel hydrogen sulfide entirely from the reaction and weighing tubes. A U-type weighing tube which weighed about 15 g was used. Since the weight change of the tube was very sensitive to temperature and moisture in the atmosphere, the correction was made by keeping the tube standing beside a balance overnight and by referring to the weight change of spare weighing tubes under the same conditions. The blank value of hydrogen flow was estimated to be +0.1 mg/2 hr. The content of hydrogen sulfide was determined by titrating the absorbent solution using standard solutions of iodine and sodium thiosulfate.

Preliminary Experiments

Effect of Sulfides on the Oxygen Content

The experiment was started with a sample of iron oxide composed of ferrous and ferric oxides. Chemical analysis showed the result of 73.62% total iron and 34.23% ferric iron. The calculation based on the above result indicated that the ferrous oxide was 44.04%, the ferric oxide 56.32%, and the total oxygen 26.74%. The samples,

TABLE I
Determination of Oxygen Content of Iron Oxides with or without Sulfides

No.	Sample	Sample wt, g	Reduction temp, °C	Reduction time, hr	Oxygen content of iron oxide, wt-%
1	Iron oxide	0.1008	900	3	26.8
2	Iron oxide	0.1060	950	2	26.6
3	Iron oxide	0.0916	1000	2	26.5
4	Iron oxide FeS	0.1099 0.1669	900–1000	8.5	26.8
5	Iron oxide FeS Cu₂S	0.1149 0.1314 0.1101	800–1000	21.5	26.4

TABLE II

Chemical Compositions of Synthetic Mattes

Sample	Chemical analysis, wt-%			Component of matte calculated, wt-%				Oxygen value, wt-%	
	Cu	Fe	S	Cu_2S	FeS	FeO	Total	$O_{calc.}$ [a]	$O_{obs.}$ [b]
EM1	—	68.57	23.41	—	64.17	35.78	99.95	7.97	7.78
EM2	—	68.43	25.07	—	68.72	31.88	100.60	7.10	7.02
EM3	5.18	64.25	22.82	6.49	58.96	34.48	99.93	7.68	7.51
EM4	10.71	58.11	25.73	13.41	63.13	23.17	99.71	5.16	5.02
EM5	22.18	48.62	25.52	27.77	54.63	17.71	100.31	3.99	3.91
EM6	37.80	34.97	24.76	47.33	41.75	10.87	99.95	2.42	2.25

[a] Oxygen content calculated.
[b] Oxygen content determined by the hydrogen reduction method.

each weighing 100 mg, were subjected to the oxygen determination, and the results are listed in Nos. 1, 2, and 3 in Table I. It can be seen from the table that both oxygen values are in a good agreement. To examine the effect of coexistence of sulfides on the oxygen content, mixtures of the iron oxide and ferrous and/or cuprous sulfides were also analyzed for oxygen. Preliminary experiments showed the oxygen contents of the ferrous and cuprous sulfides to be 0.23 and 0.15%, respectively; hence, the oxygen values corrected based on this blank are shown in Nos. 4 and 5 in Table I. These values are indicative of good accord with those of the iron oxide alone. Therefore, it may be safely said that the hydrogen reduction method will be available even to samples rich in sulfides. The expression of temperature in the table of t_1-t_2 means first holding the temperature at t_1 °C for about half the total heating time, then raising the temperature gradually up to t_2 °C, and finally holding the temperature at t_2 °C for half an hour.

Effect of Reduction Time on Oxygen Content

This study was aimed at finding an adequate time required for the oxygen determination. The compositions of the synthetic mattes used refer to Table II; the calculation method has already been mentioned. Table III provides the data of the effect of time on the oxygen content for samples EM1 and EM2 in Table II. For EM1,

TABLE III
Effect of Time on Oxygen and Sulfur Observed during Reduction of Matte

Sample	Sample wt, g	Temp., °C	Time, hr	$O_{obs.}$ wt-%	S, wt-%
EM1	0.1541	875	0.5	2.73	3.17
	0.1768	875	1	3.71	6.94
	0.1330	875	2	5.55	14.83
	0.1817	875	3	6.02	15.99
	0.1499	875	4	7.12	20.03
	0.1487	875	5	7.41	22.85
	0.1289	875	6	7.79	23.17
	0.1556	875	7	7.77	23.49
EM2	0.1519	890	4	6.03	13.44
	0.1519	820	6	6.91	16.45
	0.1519	895	8	7.02	23.95

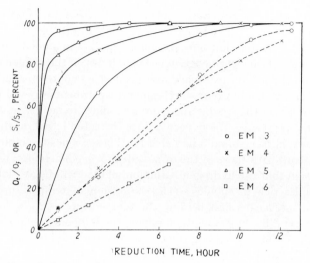

Fig. 2. Effect of time on the percentage of O_t/O_f of S_t/S_f during reduction of matte.

the sample was taken for each varying holding time, and for EM2 the same sample was used continuously. Samples EM1 and EM2 were mattes of the copper-free FeS-FeO system and it can be seen from Table III that rate of conversion from oxygen to water vapor is slow and the reaction is not completed until a substantial amount of sulfur is completely consumed in the hydrogen sulfide. However, when mattes contain cuprous sulfide, the reduction time can be reduced. For samples EM4 to EM6 the experiments were carried out at 820°C, and the relationship between reduction time and the percentage of O_t/O_f or S_t/S_f is shown in Figure 2, in which $\%O_t$ or $\%S_t$ denotes the oxygen or sulfur content observed at a given time during the reduction of matte, $\%O_f$ indicates a final constant value regarded as a true value, and $\%S_f$ is a chemical analytical value for sulfur. In Figure 2 it is clearly seen that the reaction of oxygen with hydrogen takes place more easily than the reaction between sulfur and hydrogen, and the release of oxygen becomes faster with increasing matte grade in spite of the increase in the amount of sample taken. Here, it must be noted that the reduction proceeds easily up to about 90% for oxygen, but the remaining oxygen takes a longer reduction time. The oxygen contents thus obtained are listed in the right-hand column of Table II and can be compared with the calculated values. Here, substantial agreement may be found. It is quite natural that the oxygen values obtained by the hydrogen reduction method are more reliable. Commercial mattes also followed the same general trend which indicates that a rise in matte grade makes the release of oxygen faster.

Effect of Reduction Temperature on Oxygen Content

Effect of temperature was examined for two hours of reduction time for sample EM1 weighing 0.15 g which is slow in the reduction rate for oxygen. Table IV shows the results; that is, the reduction

TABLE IV

Effect of Temperature on Oxygen and Sulfur Observed during Reduction of Mat

Sample	Sample wt, g	Temp., °C	$O_{obs.}$ wt-%	S, wt-%
EM1	0.1515	700	2.00	2.69
EM1	0.1535	800	2.95	7.21
EM1	0.1330	875	5.55	14.83
EM1	0.1528	900	6.87	15.66
EM1	0.1519	950	7.20	19.86
EM1	0.1481	1000	7.86	23.80

rate is considerably slow up to 800°C and becomes faster from about 900°C. These samples were expected to melt at about 920°C, and the experiments of 950 and 1000°C confirmed this expectation. It is quite certain that increasing temperature results in promoting the reaction rate; however, the following undesirable results could be expected at temperatures above 900°C at an initial stage: (1) Samples, when melted, would tend to react with the boats. (2) For commercial mattes containing some volatile zinc, lead compounds, and the like, a high temperature would cause such volatile elements to be carried into the weighing tube and to condense in it. (3) If such a reaction as $Zn(g) + H_2O(g) = ZnO(s) + H_2(g)$ could occur in a gas phase, a small portion of the oxygen would deposit as zinc oxide in a cooler part of the apparatus.

If lower temperature is applied at an initial stage of the reduction, the volume ratio of water vapor to volatile metal gas would become greater, and hence initial lower temperature would be effective in avoiding the above-mentioned difficulties. Therefore, a heating method such as 800–1000°, whose abbreviation has already been explained, was taken as the standard. For ordinary grade mattes of 30 to 50% copper, sufficient time required for oxygen determination was found to be from 4 to 5 hr in all.

Effect of Fineness of Sample on Oxygen Content

The above-mentioned experiments were carried out for samples of under 100 mesh. A comparison of experimental results for samples of under 100 mesh and of 14–20 mesh shows that the reduction rate for the coarse sample is markedly slow. Furthermore, it was confirmed that there is no possibility of increasing oxygen content due to natural oxidation of samples during grinding.

Oxygen Content of Commercial Mattes

By means of the method mentioned above, the mattes made at several Japanese smelters were analyzed for oxygen. It was concluded with reasonable certainty that silica, lime, alumina, and magnesia present in mattes in solution or in suspension are not reducible by this method, and the only determinable substances are iron oxides and, if present, base-metal oxides except for the above-mentioned ones. The measurement was repeated two or three times and the mean value was listed in the tables. The analytical values were reproduced within ±3% of the oxygen value.

The results of oxygen determination are given in Tables V to VIII. Oxygen contents estimated in a similar manner to that for synthetic matte are also given. Commercial mattes, as shown in Tables V to VIII, are very complicated in constitution and hence no precise calculation method is available at present. However, as a first approximation, the following method may be acceptable: Table V(a) indicates a complete chemical analysis of the blast-furnace matte at smelter S; however, as has been pointed out, the compositions do not total 100% and it is considered that the deficiency is attributed mainly to the existence of oxygen in matte. First, the copper, lead, and zinc are calculated as sulfides. The arsenic, antimony, tin, nickel, etc., are also assumed to be present as sulfides, however they are minute in amount, so that, for simplification, 1.4 times the sum of their percentages is computed as total sulfides.

TABLE V

(a) Complete Chemical Analysis of Matte Made in Blast Furnace at Smelter S, wt-%

Sample	Cu	Fe	S	Pb	Zn	SiO_2	Al_2O_3	MgO	CaO	As	Sb	Sn	Ni	Total
SBM1	34.20	31.33	23.86	2.52	3.28	0.19	0.18	0.03	0.01	0.16	0.27	0.48	0.28	96.79
SBM2	37.07	28.75	23.57	2.87	3.23	0.19	0.18	0.05	0.02	0.16	0.24	0.51	0.35	97.19
SBM3	39.37	26.78	23.71	3.03	2.94	0.19	0.15	0.04	0.01	0.22	0.27	0.57	0.36	97.64
SBM4	41.20	25.30	23.51	3.19	2.94	0.15	0.17	0.01	0.01	0.16	0.24	0.51	0.45	97.84
SBM5	45.06	21.92	22.80	3.25	2.56	0.14	0.11	0.01	0.01	0.20	0.24	0.54	0.46	97.30

(b) Component of Blast-Furnace Matte at Smelter S Calculated by Chemical Analysis

Matte component, wt-%

Sample	Cu_2S	PbS	ZnS	(As, Sb, Sn, Ni)-S	(SiO_2, Al_2O_3, MgO, CaO)	FeS	FeO	Total	Oxygen content, wt-%	
									$O_{calc.}$	$O_{obs.}$
SBM1	42.83	2.91	4.89	1.67	0.41	34.95	11.75	99.41	2.62	2.58
SBM2	46.42	3.32	4.81	1.76	0.44	32.04	10.81	99.60	2.41	2.25
SBM3	49.30	3.50	4.38	1.99	0.39	30.98	9.13	99.67	2.03	2.05
SBM4	51.59	3.68	4.38	1.90	0.34	29.19	8.70	99.78	1.94	2.09
SBM5	56.42	3.75	3.82	2.02	0.27	24.95	7.81	99.04	1.74	1.83

TABLE VI

(a) Complete Chemical Analysis of Matte from Smelter H, wt-%

Sample	Cu	Fe	S	Pb	Zn	SiO$_2$	Al$_2$O$_3$	MgO	CaO	As	Ni	Mn	Total
HBM1[a]	30.88	33.33	24.04	1.61	5.13	0.61	0.21	0.05	0.16	0.04	0.09	0.05	96.20
HBM2[a]	34.25	31.41	23.77	1.72	5.03	0.50	0.15	0.02	0.05	0.04	0.07	0.02	97.03
HCM3[b]	55.88	15.74	23.01	1.26	1.76	0.05	0.17	0.09	0.05	0.02	0.02	0.09	98.14
HCM4[b]	66.47	6.87	20.64	1.25	1.87	0.26	0.18	0.02	0.03	0.02	0.25	0.02	97.88
HCM5[b]	68.09	6.84	21.38	0.63	1.61	0.09	0.04	0.02	0.05	0.04	0.01	0.02	98.82
HCM6[b]	73.91	2.79	20.10	0.42	1.45	0.35	0.08	0.02	0.03	0.02	0.15	0.02	99.34

(b) Component of Matte at Smelter H Calculated by Chemical Analysis

Sample	Matte component, wt-%								Oxygen content, wt-%	
	Cu$_2$S	PbS	ZnS	(As, Ni, Mn)-S	(SiO$_2$, Al$_2$O$_3$, MgO, CaO)	FeS	Iron Oxide	Total	O$_{calc.}$	O$_{obs.}$
HBM1[a]	38.67	1.86	7.65	0.27	1.03	36.71	12.88	99.07	2.87	3.08
HBM2[a]	42.89	1.99	7.49	0.20	0.72	33.80	12.79	99.88	2.85	2.93
HCM3[b]	69.97	1.46	2.62	0.20	0.36	21.36	3.00	98.97	0.83	1.26
HCM4[b]	83.23	1.44	2.79	0.44	0.49	7.18	3.19	98.76	0.88	0.91
HCM5[b]	85.26	0.73	2.40	0.11	0.20	8.99	1.56	99.25	0.43	0.47
HCM6[b]	92.55	0.49	2.16	0.29	0.48	1.59	2.46	100.02	0.68	0.13

[a] Here, HBM indicates blast-furnace matte at smelter H.
[b] Here, HCM indicates converter matte at smelter H.

TABLE VII
Chemical Composition of Matte Made in Blast Furnace at Smelter K

Sample	Chemical analysis, wt-%					Component calculated, wt-%						Oxygen content, wt-%	
	Cu	Fe	S	Pb	Zn	Cu_2S	FeS	PbS	ZnS	FeO	Total	$O_{calc.}$	$O_{obs.}$
KBM1	36.63	29.14	23.39	2.84	4.99	45.87	30.87	3.28	7.44	12.26	99.72	2.73	2.75
KBM2	37.02	28.93	22.91	2.93	4.80	46.36	29.52	3.38	7.15	13.10	99.51	2.92	2.90
KBM1	36.26	30.05	22.58	2.82	4.89	45.40	29.06	3.26	7.29	14.91	99.92	3.32	3.03

TABLE VIII
Chemical Composition of Matte at Smelters N and A

Sample	Chemical analysis, wt-%					Component calculated, wt-%						Oxygen content, wt-%	
	Cu	Fe	S	Pb	Zn	Cu_2S	FeS	PbS	ZnS	Fe_3O_4	Total	$O_{calc.}$	$O_{obs.}$
NRM1[a]	41.74	22.49	24.16	3.33	5.65	52.27	28.34	3.85	8.42	6.21	99.09	1.72	2.40
NRM2[a]	43.38	19.65	23.85	4.04	6.20	54.32	25.33	4.67	9.24	4.92	98.48	1.36	2.11
NRM3[a]	46.94	18.08	23.69	3.31	5.43	58.78	23.79	3.82	8.09	4.10	98.58	1.13	1.76
AFM1[b]	43.47	27.14	25.14	0.25	1.34	54.43	36.95	0.29	2.00	5.07	98.74	1.40	2.13

[a] Here, NRM indicates reverberatory furnace matte at smelter N.
[b] Here, AFM indicates matte made in flash smelting at smelter A.

(The figure of 1.4 is the average conversion coefficient from the metals to the sulfides.) Secondly, the remainder of sulfur, i.e., the total sulfur minus the sulfide sulfur, is presumed to be present as ferrous sulfide, and then the remainder of iron is computed as iron oxide. As for the form of iron oxide, the ferrous oxide is assumed for mattes of blast furnace, while the magnetite is presumed to be for mattes of reverberatory furnace, converter, and flash smelting. Finally, the oxygen content is calculated from the amount of iron oxide. This method of calculation is based upon many assumptions, nevertheless it may be safely adopted as a reasonable first approximation. From Tables V to VIII it can be seen that for the blast-furnace mattes at smelters S, H, and K the oxygen contents determined are in a fairly good agreement with those calculated. In contrast, for converter matte at smelter H the difference between the two is appreciable to some extent and for reverberatory-furnace matte or for flash-smelting matte it is quite noticeable. A further study will be required to clearly explain the discrepancies in the latter cases.

A general view of the results mentioned above may lead to the fact that the oxygen content of matte decreases with increasing matte grade. A detailed explanation in this respect will be given later.

SOME FACTORS DETERMINING THE OXYGEN CONTENT OF COPPER MATTES

The oxygen content of mattes is affected by several factors; the major factors are as follows: (1) matte grade, or in other words, activity of Cu_2S or FeS in matte, (2) activity of SiO_2 or FeO in the slag equilibrated with matte, (3) activity of Fe_3O_4 in the slag above matte; that is, oxygen potential in slag, and (4) temperature.

The effects of factors (1) and (2) on the oxygen content have been referred to in the preceding papers[2,4] and will be briefly redescribed here.

The Cu_2S-FeS-FeO system is considered one of the most essential systems for clearly understanding the nature of the matte. The study of the solubility of FeO in the matte has been carried out, and the results are given in Figure 3. For the purpose of minimizing the magnetite content of melts, pure iron crucibles were used in most cases, and hence the experimental heats could not cover the whole

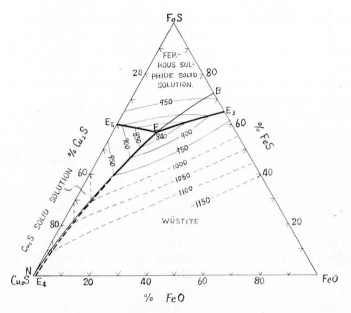

Fig. 3. Partial liquidus diagram for the Cu₂S-FeS-FeO system (curve *BN:* FeO solubility in the matte equilibrated with silica-saturated FeO-SiO₂ slag).

field of this ternary system and could not extend to higher temperatures because of the corrosive action of molten sulfides against iron crucibles. Moreover, the real meaning of the equilibrium in the binary Cu₂S-FeO system could not be realized. Therefore, the Cu₂-FeS-FeO system cannot be considered a true ternary equilibrium system in a strict sense, but one of the sectional liquidus diagrams included in the quaternary Cu-Fe-S-O system viewed as a tetrahedron, and the portion determined may be interpreted as the iron-saturated surface located extremely close to the triangular Cu₂S-FeS-FeO plane. Nevertheless, Figure 3 may give a fair concept of matte on the solubility of FeO. There exist three primary phase field boundaries and one ternary eutectic point, which, strictly speaking, might be a "piercing point."[13] Isotherms of the liquidus surface of FeO indicate that the matte is generally capable of dissolving an abundant amount of FeO when the activity of FeO is unity, and that the FeO content decreases rather sharply with increasing matte grade at a given temperature. However, mattes coexist with slags in industrial smelting, and hence, in this case, the activity of FeO is considered smaller than unity, and this is expected to result in decreasing the dissolved FeO content. When, for simplification, a slag is chosen as of the silica-saturated FeO-SiO$_2$ system, the solubility of FeO in mattes at 1200°C can be expressed by the curve BN superimposed on Figure 3.

From Figure 3 a concept of the effect of factors (1) and (2) on the oxygen content of copper mattes can be induced. Experiments on the effect of factor (2) will be described in detail later on in this section. The effect of factor (1) on the oxygen content of commercial mattes will be mentioned in the next section.

Factor (3) is considered to strongly affect the oxygen content of commercial mattes, especially of those made in reverberatory furnace, converter, and flash smelting, and a fundamental study of the Cu$_2$S-FeS-FeO-Fe$_3$O$_4$ system is of great importance. This study requires a troublesome experimental technique for controlling the partial pressures of both oxygen and sulfur in the matte-slag system, and it is now being carried on in our laboratory.

On the effect of temperature, it has been reported in a previous paper[4] that when mattes are in equilibrium with the silica-saturated slags, the oxygen content is practically insensitive to temperature. This insensitivity results from the relationship between the activity of SiO$_2$ or FeO in slag and the slag composition remains substantially constant over the matte-smelting temperature range. It might be expected with reasonable certainty that as long as slags contain little magnetite, the temperature produces only a second-order effect.

Effect of Ratio FeO/SiO$_2$ in Slag on Oxygen Content of Mattes

In a previous paper[5] in this series it has already been disclosed that mutual solubilities between matte and slag, as a general rule, can be greatly reduced by the addition of silica. Naturally, in slags, the variation of silica content affects the FeO content. Thus, experimental heats were made for a more detailed examination of the influence of the variation of SiO$_2$ or FeO content in slags on the oxygen content of mattes.

Experimental Procedure

The experimental procedure and apparatus were nearly the same as those used in previous papers.[2,4,5] Iron crucibles were used for the heats over the range of matte composition, for which they are stable. Corrosion of iron crucibles in these heats depended upon both Cu_2S and FeO contents of mattes; an increase in the copper content of mattes produced a bad effect on corrosion, whereas a rise in FeO content produced a beneficial influence. Generally speaking, for high-copper mattes the iron crucibles did not withstand corrosion, and this made it necessary to use sintered alumina crucibles instead of iron crucibles.

Synthetic matte and slag (about 4 g each) were melted together in purified nitrogen flow and held at 1200°C, long enough to approach equilibrium between two phases. After the melts were rapidly solidified, each product was analyzed chemically or electrophotocolorimetrically for individual common elements, and the oxygen content of the matte was determined by the hydrogen reduction method. It must be noted here that in the high-copper composition range of matte considerable solubility of alumina into slags from sintered alumina crucibles was observed (usually about 6%).

Experimental Results

The oxygen content of the mattes is plotted in Figure 4 against the percentage of cuprous sulfide in mattes. Curve $B'N'$ in the figure corresponds to curve BN in Figure 3. The points represented by crosses are the oxygen values determined by the hydrogen reduction method and are plotted to fit curve $B'N'$ within experimental errors. Curve $B'N'$ should indicate the minimum content of oxygen in mattes, as long as the simple $FeO-SiO_2$ slags are equilibrated with the mattes. When the slag contains less silica than in the case of silica saturation, or in other words, when the FeO-activity becomes larger, the content of oxygen dissolved in the matte is expected to increase. A study on the data of this experiment, as indicated in Figure 4, is made by drawing the curves of various constant weight ratios of FeO/SiO_2 in the slags, although it is more desirable theoretically to use iso-activity lines of FeO or SiO_2. In this experiment, a considerable amount of ferrous sulfide and simultaneously a little amount of cuprous sulfide were dissolved in the slags equilibrated with the mattes (ranging from several per cent to about 25% of ferrous sulfide). For that reason, the slags in this case are considered to be approximate to the $FeO-SiO_2-FeS$ system, but at present the relationship between the activity of FeO or SiO_2 and the composition

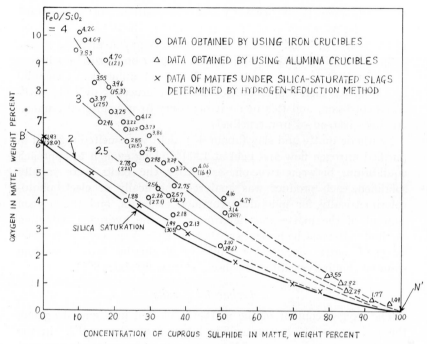

Fig. 4. Effect of Cu_2S concentration on the oxygen content of mattes at various weight ratios of FeO/SiO_2 in FeO-SiO_2 slags equilibrated with the mattes.

of such a slag is unknown. Therefore, in Figure 4 the curves of various constant weight ratios of FeO/SiO_2 are drawn from the location of the points plotted. The value of the ratio FeO/SiO_2 is given, and in some cases the weight-% of SiO_2 in the slag (shown in parentheses) is also given. The oxygen contents of high-copper mattes obtained by the heats using alumina crucibles are indicated by the points on the right in Figure 4. In this range, the slags are practically of the FeO-SiO_2-Al_2O_3 system, and hence these results cannot be connected satisfactorily with those obtained by using iron crucibles. However, the light solid curves representing the constant weight ratio FeO/SiO_2 are extended on the Cu_2S composition scale to 100%, on referring to the results obtained by using alumina crucibles, and the extension is indicated by broken curves.

From Figure 4 it is evident that the oxygen content of mattes decreases with increasing matte grade at a given constant ratio

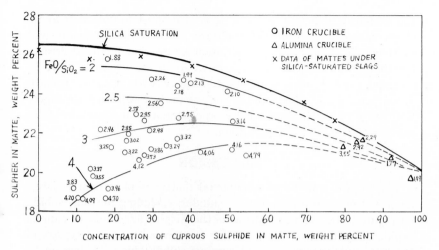

Fig. 5. Effect of Cu₂S concentration on the sulfur content of mattes at various weight ratios of FeO/SiO₂ in FeO-SiO₂ slags equilibrated with the mattes.

FeO/SiO₂ in slag and is supposed to be reduced substantially to zero at iron-free Cu₂S matte composition. In some cases, the variation of oxygen content covers the range from nearly 0 to 10% oxygen. These facts seem to support the suggestion of the authors that the solubility of oxygen in matte might be related to the ferrous-sulfide content of matte.

It can also be seen that at a given matte grade the oxygen content increases with the value of the weight ratio FeO/SiO₂ in slag, in other words, with increasing basicity of the slag. Also, the rate of increase in the oxygen content becomes larger as the ratio FeO/SiO₂ approaches that of the silica-saturated slag, that is, with decreasing basicity of the slag.

In addition, Figure 5 gives a plot of the sulfur content of the mattes versus the matte grade in this experiment. The value of the ratio FeO/SiO₂ is given to each point representing the experimental result, and constant-ratio curves similar to Figure 4, are also drawn. The upper heavy solid curve represents the sulfur content of the mattes in equilibrium with the FeO-SiO₂ slags saturated with silica, corresponding to curve $B'N'$ in Figure 4. It is apparent that at a definite matte grade the sulfur content decreases as the ratio FeO/SiO₂ in slag increases. This fact can be clearly explained by the solubility of FeO in matte. It is of interest to note that at the larger values of the ratio FeO/SiO_2 the sulfur content increases with matte grade, then shows a maximum value, and finally decreases. On the other hand, the sulfur content of the oxygen-free stoichiometric Cu_2S-FeS mattes increases linearly with decreasing matte grade (see Fig. 8). The repulsive effects in the lower copper composition range of matte result in the approximately flat portion of the curve in the case of silica saturation.

DISCUSSION

The oxygen content of commercial mattes is plotted in Figure 6 against the percentage of the sulfides excluding ferrous sulfide. In Figure 6 the abscissa represents the weight percentage of cuprous sulfide of synthetic mattes, and for commercial mattes it represents the total weight percentage of cuprous sulfide plus some base-metal sulfides excluding ferrous sulfide. Such expression of matte-grade scale is based on the above-mentioned suggestion that the solution of oxygen in matte might be closely related to the FeS in matte. The method of calculating matte components has already been mentioned and the scale of abscissa, if desired, can be easily replaced by the percentage of ferrous sulfide. Furthermore, the conversion scale from per cent oxygen to per cent FeO or per cent Fe_3O_4 is presented

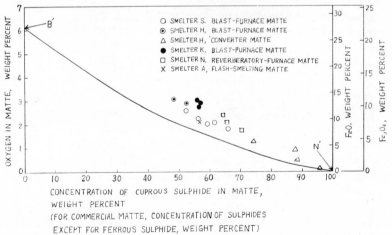

Fig. 6. The oxygen content of commercial mattes versus the matte composition.

for reference as the ordinate on the right-hand side.   It is apparent from Figure 6 that there is a general trend for the oxygen content to decrease as the sulfide content increases, however individual points are located somewhat above the basic curve $B'N'$; that is, the oxygen content of commercial mattes is higher to some extent than that of the mattes represented by curve $B'N'$.   Causes of the difference in the oxygen content between two kinds of mattes may be considered as follows: (1) the higher value of the activity of FeO in ordinary slags due to unsaturation with silica;   (2) unequilibrium state in industrial smelting, especially the existence of some iron oxide (perhaps magnetite) in mattes caused by mechanical suspension; and (3) difference in the form of iron oxide in mattes, in other words, the existence of ferric oxide or magnetite in actual slags instead of or in addition to FeO.

Factor (1) is believed to be most important, and in Figure 4 it was shown how the oxygen content of matte varies with cuprous-sulfide concentration at various weight ratios of FeO/SiO_2 in slag. This study, however, deals with the simple FeO-SiO_2 slags and cannot be connected directly with the results presented in Figure 6 because of the complexity of the component of actual slags.   Nevertheless, the general tendency of the increase in the oxygen content with the value of ratio FeO/SiO_2 in slag (as shown in Fig. 4) is believed to be of great help in explaining the results of Figure 6.   There are no precise data to confirm factor (2); however, the magnetite in suspension was not revealed by microscopic examinations for the commercial mattes employed.   Factor (3) raises an important question as to whether FeO or Fe_3O_4 is the iron oxide in mattes. Based on the observation in industrial operation it has been pointed out that commercial mattes contain an appreciable amount of magnetite in suspension or in solution, but the dissolution of FeO in matte has been disregarded.   The results (as shown in Figs. 3 and 4) give evidence of the dissolution of FeO in matte, and the complete figure of oxygen in the matte could not be disclosed without the results presented in this series of study.   It is believed that matte in general is capable of dissolving both FeO and Fe_3O_4, and the substantial iron oxide is FeO for the mattes made in Japanese blast furnaces, while the magnetite is a major form rather than FeO for the mattes in reverberatory furnace, converter, and flash smelting. Even though (as shown Fig. 6) no considerable difference in per cent oxygen can be found among the mattes produced from various smelting furnaces at a definite matte grade, more precise and basic data on this point are highly desirable. The assumption that the oxygen in blast-furnace mattes most often takes the form of FeO is due to the results of microscopic examinations; a representative example is shown in Figure 7. In Figure 7, wüstite is observed but magnetite is scarce. A good agreement between the oxygen content determined and that calculated in Tables V to VIII seems to strengthen the validity of the assumption mentioned above. In contrast, magnetite* is frequently observed in the mattes in reverberatory furnaces, as can be seen in Figure 8.

* The acid method by Hawley and others[6-9] seems to be useful in solving the question as to whether the dissolved oxygen comes from wüstite or magnetite. The procedure was as follows: An acid solution was prepared by dissolving 60 g sodium chlorate into 100 cu cm of distilled water and by adding 100 cu cm of nitric acid to this. Subsequently, samples were treated with the solution for 16 hr by cooling in running water. Experiments, however, showed some unsoundness of the method. The results obtained are listed in Table IX, indicating that oxygen values obtained by this method are lower than those by the hydrogen reduction method. Some suggestion, however, may be obtainable from the ratio FeO/Fe_2O_3 derived from the analytical values, even though the slight tendency was recognized in analysis of the residue that the oxidation from ferrous to ferric iron occurred to some extent due to inevitable exposure of the sample to a strongly oxidizing agent. Table IX indicates that the FeO content is much larger than the Fe_2O_3 content in blast-furnace mattes, while the Fe_2O_3 content is greater in the mattes of converters, reverberatory furnace, and flash smelting. These facts are in near agreement with the authors' assumption.

TABLE IX
Chemical Analysis of Iron Oxide in Copper Matte by Acid Method

| Sample | Matte grade, % Cu | Chemical analysis of the residue, wt-% | | | | | O_H[b] wt-% |
		Fe	Fe^{2+}	FeO	Fe_2O_3	O_A[a]	
SBM1	34.20	5.88	4.77	6.14	1.58	1.84	2.58
SBM4	41.20	4.48	3.49	4.49	1.42	1.43	2.09
HBM1	30.88	6.64	4.99	6.42	2.36	2.14	3.08
HBM2	34.25	7.41	5.30	6.82	3.02	2.43	2.93
HCM3	55.88	2.72	1.25	1.61	2.10	0.99	1.26
HCM4	66.47	2.20	1.19	1.53	1.44	0.77	0.91
KBM2	37.02	6.29	4.73	6.09	2.23	2.03	2.90
NRM1	41.74	4.31	1.77	2.28	3.63	1.60	2.40
NRM2	43.38	3.77	1.38	1.78	3.42	1.43	2.11
AFM1	43.47	4.48	1.67	2.15	4.02	1.69	2.13

[a] Here, O_A is determined by the acid method.
[b] Here, O_H is determined by the hydrogen reduction method.

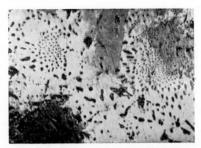

Fig. 7. Microphotograph of blast-furnace matte HM1 (etched with a solution of stannous chloride). Scattered black spots are wüstite. 470×.

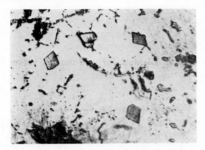

Fig. 8. Microphotograph of reverberatory-furnace matte NRM1 (etched with a solution of stannous chloride). Gray angular crystallites are magnetite. 470×.

Figure 9 shows a plot of the oxygen content of blast-furnace mattes versus the percentage of the sulfides excluding ferrous sulphide, similar to Figure 6. Plotted in Figure 9 is the monthly analytical data* of some Japanese blast furnaces. The oxygen content is not determined but calculated in the same manner as already mentioned. The points presented in Figure 9 follow the same general trend as that in Figure 6. It is noted that the points representing the oxygen content of mattes made in blast furnace at smelter K are in general below curve $B'N'$. This is due to the fact that the slags at smelter K are very high in silica content (about 40%) and are relatively low in FeO content (about 30%), and hence the values of FeO activity are expected to be somewhat smaller.

Next, the sulfur content of commercial mattes will be considered. It has been pointed out that the sulfur in commercial mattes is

* In one of the previous papers[4] these data were also adopted, but the method of plotting the data was somewhat different.

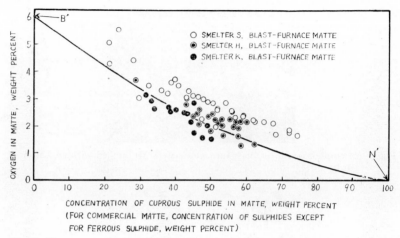

Fig. 9. The oxygen content of blast-furnace mattes versus the matte composition.

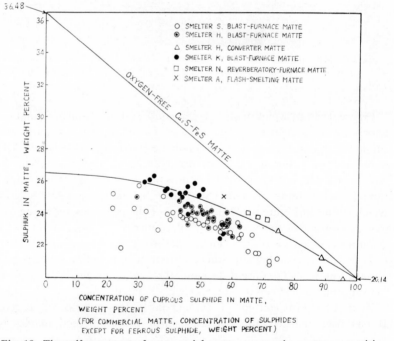

Fig. 10. The sulfur content of commercial mattes versus the matte composition.

generally less in content than in the mattes estimated as stoichio-metric mixtures of Cu_2S and FeS. The deficiency in sulfur has commonly been ascribed to the fact that mattes, when heated lose some portions of the sulfur by vaporization and become mattes of the Cu_2S-FeS-Cu-Fe system. However, the deficiency in sulfur is believed to be caused by the dissolution of oxygen in the matte, as mentioned in the preceding section. This idea is also supported by the results of microscopic examination of commercial mattes which reveals the existence of wüstite and/or magnetite instead of metallic iron or copper. Figure 10 shows the variation of sulfur content with composition of the matte, and the data plotted are the sulfur content of the commercial mattes employed in this experiment and the monthly analytical data of some Japanese blast furnaces. The oxygen contents in both cases were shown in Figures 6 and 9. Here, the solid curve represents the sulfur content of the synthetic mattes equilibrated with the FeO-SiO_2 slags saturated with silica. The upper solid line indicates the estimated sulfur content of the stoichiometric Cu_2S-FeS mattes. The points representing the sulfur content of commercial mattes are generally below the curve of the synthetic mattes equilibrated with the FeO-SiO_2 slags saturated with silica. This fact is attributed to the higher oxygen content of the commercial mattes, as shown in Figures 6 and 9. The results of the synthetic mattes, as shown in Figure 5, also help to explain this fact. It is noted that the sulfur contents of mattes made in blast furnace at smelter K, in reverberatory furnace at smelter N, and in flash smelting at smelter A are larger than those of mattes under the silica-saturated slags. High sulfur values of mattes at smelter K are considered to be reasonable as a result of lower oxygen content of the mattes as shown in Figure 9. However, in the cases of mattes in reverberatory furnace and in flash smelting, both oxygen and sulfur contents (as indicated in Figs. 6, 9 and 10) tend to be somewhat higher. This fact requires a further study and it is hoped that it can be clearly explained in a future paper.

SUMMARY

From the theoretical point of view of copper smelting, it is desirable to obtain the precise data on the solubility of oxygen in copper matte and to find out the factors which determine the oxygen content of matte. The present work is a part of a series of study along this line.

Applicability of a conventional hydrogen reduction method for determining the oxygen content of copper mattes was examined with satisfactory results. The solubility of iron oxide was reverified by determining the oxygen content of both synthetic and commercial mattes by means of this method.

Several factors affecting the oxygen content of mattes were cited, among them the effect of ratio FeO/SiO_2 in the simple FeO-SiO_2 slag equilibrated with matte. It is found that the oxygen content of mattes decreases with increasing matte grade at a constant ratio FeO/SiO_2 in slag and increases with the ratio FeO/SiO_2 at a given matte grade.

Factors controlling the oxygen content of commercial mattes were briefly discussed. In addition, the sulfur content of synthetic and commercial mattes was presented and also briefly discussed in relation to the oxygen content.

The authors wish to thank Mr. F. Ito, Mr. A. Miya, Mr. T. Kadowaki, Mr. Y. Yokota, and Miss S. Saito for their assistance. Their appreciation is also extended to Saganoseki, Hitachi, Kosaka, Naoshima, and Ashio Smelters for supplying samples of mattes.

The investigation was financed partly by a grant-in-aid for developmental scientific research by the Ministry of Education.

References

1. Yazawa, A., and K. Kameda, *Technol. Repts. Tôhoku Univ.*, **18**, 40 (1953), Part I.

2. Yazawa, A., and K. Kameda, *Technol. Repts. Tôhoku Univ.*, **19**, 239 (1955), Part III.

3. Yazawa, A., and K. Kameda, *Technol. Repts. Tôhoku Univ.*, **19**, 1 (1954), Part II.

4. Yazawa, A., and K. Kameda, *Technol. Repts. Tôhoku Univ.*, **19**, 251 (1955), Part IV.

5. Yazawa, A., *Technol. Repts. Tôhoku Univ.*, **21**, 31 (1956), Part V.

6. Hawley, F. G., *Eng. Mining J.*, **131**, 319 (1931).

7. Drummond, P. R., *Trans. Can. Inst. Mining Met.*, **43**, 627 (1940).

8. Ellwood, E. C., and T. A. Henderson, *Bull. Inst. Mining Met.*, **552**, 55 (1952).

9. Asano, N., and S. Nojima, *Mem. Ehime Univ., Sect. III*, **2**, 175 (1955), (in Japanese).

10. Pound, G. M., G. Derge, and G. Osuch, *J. Metals*, **7**, 481 (1955)

11. Lander, H. L., and R. Schuhmann, Jr., *J. Metals*, **7**, 568 (1955).

12. Isawa, M., and M. Kameda, *J. Mining Inst. Japan*, **56**, 400 (1940), (in Japanese).

13. Schairer, J. F., *J. Am. Ceram. Soc.*, **25**, 241 (1942).

SECTION X: INDUSTRIAL APPLICATIONS OF PRINCIPLES

. . . .

Equilibria between Lead, Lead Sulfide, and Cuprous Sulfide and the Decopperizing of Lead with Sulfur

R. F. BLANKS and G. M. WILLIS

Metallurgy Department, University of Melbourne, Melbourne, Australia

Abstract

The solubility of lead sulfide in lead has been measured from 427 to 923°C. The copper content of lead saturated with PbS and Cu_2S is much higher than that which can be obtained by sulfur treatment. Silver is necessary for successful decopperizing; it inhibits the reaction between sulfur and lead. The effect of sulfur can be explained if it is assumed to produce, at least temporarily, high sulfur potentials which cause the formation of a copper-deficient cuprous sulfide in which the activity of copper is substantially reduced.

INTRODUCTION

Although the removal of copper from lead bullion by stirring in sulfur is common practice in lead refining, nothing appears to be known about the fundamental basis of this process. The statement made in 1936 by Dice, Oldright, and Brighton[1] that "the function of sulphur is supposedly to combine with the copper to form Cu_2S" could still stand as a summary of what is known about decopperizing with sulfur. Many authors have maintained that successful decopperizing requires the presence of various other metals in the bullion, but there is very little agreement between authors. For these reasons, the process appeared to be worth closer investigation.

Since it would be necessary to establish the Pb-rich end of the Pb-S system, before undertaking any more detailed study of the Pb–Cu–S system, the solubility of lead sulfide in liquid lead has also been determined. This was also of interest in connection with the thermodynamic properties of dilute solutions of sulfur in liquid lead, since

991

comparatively little is known of the properties of sulfur dissolved in liquid metals.

Plant Practice in Drossing Lead Bullion

In many smelters, copper is removed from the bullion in two stages. In the first, the bullion is allowed to cool, and a considerable amount of dross rises to the surface. A drop in Cu and As contents accompanies this "hot drossing" stage. The dross contains large amounts of entrained lead, the quantity of which can be reduced by vigorous agitation which gives a "dry" dross. Some typical copper contents at the end of this stage are given in Table I.

It is generally desirable to lower the copper contents further, particularly if the bullion is to be desilverized with zinc. The advantages of low copper bullion in conventional refining have been discussed by Hall[2] and, for continuous refining, by Williams[3] and will not be considered further here.

Copper can be further removed by additions of, e.g., Al or Zn, but at smelters sulfur is generally preferred, as the sulfur or "cold" dross can be readily absorbed in the treatment of the "hot" dross. Sulfur additions of the order of 1–2 lb/ton of bullion are stirred into the lead at as low a temperature as possible. It is generally believed that the temperature, the skill of the operator in adding the sulfur, the efficiency of stirring, and the time of stirring after the sulfur additions all enter into the efficiency with which copper is removed. In Table I some values for final Cu contents are given with other operating information. The most recent detailed accounts of sulfur drossing appear to be those of Gallager[4] and Green,[5] describing practice at Broken Hill Associated Smelters, Port Pirie.

The Role of Sulfur in Decopperizing

It has been suggested that the effect of sulfur is a physical one, in that it somehow agglomerates and so removes finely dispersed particles from the lead, producing an effect similar to that sometimes obtained by stirring in finely divided inert solids, such as sawdust, sand, and powdered resin. However, as Dice, Oldright, and Brighton[1] have pointed out, sulfur produces much lower copper contents than any of these treatments alone.

In the literature, it is generally stated that sulfur removes copper as a sulfide. However, there is no agreement as to which sulfide is

TABLE I

Typical Operating Results for the Removal of Copper from Lead Bullion

Operation	Temp, °C	Composition of bullion				Remarks	Ref.
		wt-%			oz/ton		
		Cu	As	Sb	Ag		
From blast furnace		1.20	0.28	0.80	46	S = 0.12% in blast furnace bullion	
After drossing at	385	0.03	0.12	0.83	46		Gallager[4]
After S treatment at	315-20	0.004	0.12	0.83	46		Green[5]
From blast furnace		0.44	0.05-0.20	0.85-1.2		Ag content not given	Dice et al.[1]
After drossing at	427	0.15	0.05	1.2			
After S treatment at	330	0.01	0.04-0.16	1.25			
From blast furnace forehearth		ca. 1.5					
After drossing at	370	0.06			ca. 90		Buchanan et al.[11]
After S treatment at	327	0.02	0.01	0.25			
Before S treatment		0.1-0.4		0.4-0.6	50-70	As content not given	Tafel[10]
After S treatment		0.005		0.4	50-70		

formed and there appears to be no published account of any examination of sulfur drosses or identification of the substances in them.
Dice et al.[1] examined dross after it had been melted, and their identification of chalcocite and galena (and metallic lead) does not necessarily indicate that the copper is removed as Cu_2S.

George[6] states that the dross contains CuS, and Tafel[10] claims that
the sulfide is CuS since "it is not decomposed at the operating temperature." English and American authors seem to favor Cu_2S, e.g.,
Dennis[7] and Hayward.[8]

Gallager states that PbS will not extract Cu from bullion at 320°C.
This presumably refers to a bullion which has a Cu content of about
0.05% after hot drossing. Also, if after successful decopperizing,
bullion and dross are heated together, Cu reverts to the metal. This
may be an indication of a change of equilibrium with temperature, as
Gallager believed. At 340–360°C sulfur treatment leaves relatively
high Cu contents, e.g., 0.01 to 0.03%. Gallager, using Ellingham's
free energy curves[9] noted for the reaction

$$2Cu(c) + PbS(c) = Cu_2S(c) + Pb(l) \tag{1}$$

that $\Delta G° = 0$ at ca. 400°C, and $+1500$ cal at 330°C, so that for Cu
removal a substantial lowering of the activity of Cu_2S was necessary.
Since the solubility of Cu_2S in PbS is small, solution of Cu_2S in PbS
could not account for the required reduction of the activity of Cu_2S.
He drew the conclusion that "the success of sulphur treatment must
depend on some other factor," which he did not attempt to identify.

The Effect of Other Metals in Decopperizing with Sulfur

Various authors have given remarkably different accounts of the
effect of other metals in the bullion on the success of sulfur treatment.
Tafel[10] states that 0.12% Sn at least is necessary; this is confirmed by
Haig[12] who gives a Sn content of 0.15% as being necessary to bring Cu
to <0.04%. In reply to Haig, Haney[13] pointed out that at Port
Pirie, Cu could be lowered to 0.004%, or even as low as 0.002% in a
bullion which contained no tin.

Dennis[7] states that antimony is necessary in order to obtain 0.005
to 0.01% Cu, and this is supported by Blanderer[14] who gives 0.02%
as a practical limit in the absence of antimony; with antimony, he
claims, it should be possible to get as low as 0.002% Cu.

Gallager claims that Port Pirie plant results show that if the arsenic content of bullion is below about 0.07%, difficulty is experienced in obtaining low copper.

Tafel states that Sn is not removed and that its effects must be "catalytic"; "what cannot be explained must be catalysis." Blanderer states that a trace of zinc inhibits decopperizing completely. Zinc is not likely to be present in blast-furnace bullion which has already been drossed but could be of importance in secondary metal.

George[6] states that it is possible by repeated sulfur treatment to lower the Cu content of desilverized lead to 0.02%. Cunningham[15] has found that sulfur is not effective in decopperizing desilverized lead, and this has been confirmed in our work.

Few of these claims are accompanied by any details such as temperature of treatment and complete analysis of lead before and after treatment. Haig suggested that the arsenic and/or silver in Port Pirie bullion may behave similarly to tin in his bullion. It appears that decopperizing may be comparatively sensitive to the presence of other metals and that the composition of the bullion as a whole should be considered.

It is tempting to ascribe the reduction in Cu to precipitation of Cu_2S following an increase in the sulfur dissolved in the lead. However, this view does not seem tenable for the following reasons:

1. The lead is probably saturated with respect to lead sulfide, which is generally supposed to precipitate along with sulfide, arsenide, and perhaps antimonide of copper while the bullion is cooling in the first drossing. If the lead is saturated with PbS, further additions of sulfur can only form more.

2. The sulfur content of lead saturated with PbS is extremely small. As will be shown later, the sulfur content of lead at 327°C is found by extrapolation from results at higher temperatures to be 0.0003 wt-%. Since sulfur additions are of the order of 1 to 2 lb/ton, say, 0.05 to 0.1%, they are very much greater than required for saturation of the lead. The sulfur is also more than is required to combine with the copper, e.g., 0.05% Cu would require 0.025% S if CuS is formed and 0.0125% for Cu_2S. A large proportion of the sulfur is converted to PbS and the dross, with entrained metallic lead, contains only about 5% Cu.

3. Sulfur treatment may require only some ten minutes for 100 tons of lead. The rate of solution of PbS in liquid lead is com-

paratively slow; times of the order of a few hours are required to approach saturation at much higher temperatures, e.g., 600–700°C.

4. The thermodynamic data indicate that there is very little difference in the standard free energies of formation of Cu_2S and PbS near the melting point of lead. If $\Delta G° = 0$ for reaction (1), the copper content of lead in equilibrium with Cu_2S and PbS will be the same as that for saturation with metallic copper; i.e., 0.06 wt-% according to Kleppa and Weil.[16]

Equilibrium in the Pb–Cu–S System

If equilibrium is attained in decopperizing with sulfur, it should be possible to define the copper (and sulfur) contents of the lead, and the constitution of the dross in terms of the Pb–Cu–S system. In practical applications this may be modified by As, Sb, Sn, etc.

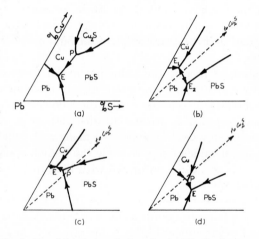

Fig. 1. Possible phase relations in the Pb-Cu-S system.

Although Meissner[17] and Guertler and Landau[18] have studied the system at high temperatures, there is no quantitative information about the equilibria near the freezing point of lead. Both agree for the equilibrium after complete solidification that there is a join Pb–Cu_2S. On the other hand, Jänecke[19] gives a peritectic point for which $l + Cu_2S \rightarrow Cu + PbS$. His diagram is shown schematically in Figure 1a. For clarity, the Pb–PbS eutectic which lies at practically pure Pb, has been moved to the right in all the diagrams of Figure 1. The essential relations are not changed by this. Here, P is the peritectic point, and E is a ternary eutectic. Jänecke apparently regarded this as the only way in which the four eutectics of the binary systems could be related to one another. His phase relations imply that at the temperature of P, Cu_2S is in equilibrium with solid Cu and PbS and liquid Pb, and at lower temperatures Cu_2S is no longer stable with respect to Cu and PbS. Sulfur treatment should then give PbS not Cu_2S.

However, there are other possibilities which Jänecke did not consider; these are shown in Figures 1b, 1c, and 1d. In Figure 1b the Pb–Cu_2S join is strictly binary, as is assumed by Guertler and Landau[20] in their discussion of the complex high temperature equilibria. There is a temperature maximum joining the two ternary eutectics E_1 and E_2, at which the liquids disappear respectively by

$$l_1 \longrightarrow Cu, Cu_2S, Pb$$

$$l_2 \longrightarrow Cu_2S, PbS, Pb$$

The diagram indicates that equilibrium between Cu_2S and liquid lead containing Cu and S can be maintained down to the temperature at which solid lead starts to freeze out.

A third possibility is that shown in Figure 1c where at the peritectic point P, $l + PbS = Pb + Cu_2S$. Under equilibrium conditions, the liquid would freeze finally at E to give Cu, Cu_2S, and PbS.

The fourth possibility when P lies below the Pb–Cu_2S join is shown in Figure 1d and leads to $l \rightarrow$ Pb, PbS, and Cu_2S at the ternary eutectic.

Most collections of thermodynamic data show Cu_2S to be more stable than PbS at higher temperatures with their free energy-temperature curves crossing. There is little agreement however as to the temperature at which this occurs. Thus, Ellingham's curves give about 400°C, those of Richardson and Jeffes[21] 234°C. Small errors in the data have a comparatively large effect on the temperature for which $\Delta G° = 0$ for the reaction

$$2Cu + PbS = Cu_2S + Pb \qquad (2)$$

If this temperature lies above the final freezing temperature, then Jänecke's diagram is correct. If it is lower, then Figures 1b, 1c, and 1d are all consistent with the greater stability of Cu_2S. If a tempera-

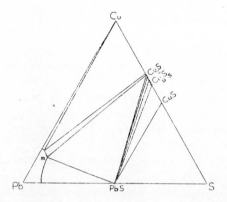

Fig. 2. Phase diagram for the Pb-Cu-S system, schematic.

ture of, e.g., 400°C be accepted as that which $\Delta G° = 0$, decopperizing at, say, 327°C could not be due to sulfur reacting with Cu to form Cu_2S, since PbS is the stable phase. The small change in free energy of liquid lead due to its dissolved Cu and S will mean that the temperature of P in Figure 1a is not exactly that for which $\Delta G° = 0$, but the difference will be extremely small.

The diagrams of Figure 1 do not include the other sulfides of copper: covellite (CuS) and digenite, a copper-deficient phase with a range of composition around Cu_9S_5 according to Buerger.[22] At the temperatures of interest here, little is known of the sulfur potentials, e.g., of the Cu_2S and Cu_9S_5 phases. The range of composition of the high chalcocite phase is much narrower than that of the digenite, for which Rahlfs[23] has shown there is considerable disorder in the copper atoms at 170°C. As might be expected, preliminary experiments have shown that the sulfur pressure varies slowly with the sulfur percentage in digenite. If it is assumed that a slightly sulfur-rich Cu_2S may have a sulfur potential high enough to bring about precipitation of PbS from liquid lead, the phase relations just before freezing are those shown schematically in Figure 2. The scale of the lead corner has been increased for clarity. The minimum copper content obtainable under equilibrium conditions with sulfur additions is that at the point m where lead is saturated with both Cu_2S and PbS.

The copper content of lead saturated with both Cu_2S and PbS can be calculated from the standard free energy charge for reaction

(1), combined with Kleppa and Weil's data for the solubility of Cu in Pb. The detailed calculation is given in the Appendix; it includes the direct comparison of the standard free energies of Cu$_2$S and PbS made by J. B. Wagner and C. Wagner,[24] which appeared during the course of this work. As the calculated copper contents are about ten times greater than those obtained by sulfur treatment, the copper in lead in equilibrium with Cu$_2$S and PbS was determined, as well as the sulfur in lead saturated with PbS.

EXPERIMENTAL

Two grades of lead have been used; their analyses are given in Table II. The high purity lead is that described by Green.[5] For some work, the lead was melted under caustic soda to reduce the Sb even further; this gave a lead in which Sb could not be detected spectrographically. No difference in results has been observed with leads of different purity.

TABLE II
Lead Analyses (in wt-%)

	Refined Pb, oz/ton	High purity Pb, oz/ton	Silver	Copper	Tin
Ag	0.03	0.03	99.98	0.001	—
Pb	99.99	99.999	0.003	0.002	0.01
Fe	0.0004	0.0001	0.007	0.01	0.002
Cu	0.00014	0.0003	0.006	99.98	0.0025
As	0.0001	—	—	0.0002[a]	0.0001[a]
Sn	—	—	—	0.001	99.96
Sb	0.0037	0.0001	—	—	0.025
Bi	0.003	0.0001	—	0.0006	0.002
Zn	0.0006	0.0001	—	—	—

[a] As As$_2$O$_3$.

Sulfur was purified by recrystallization from redistilled carbon disulfide, followed by sublimation in a stream of N$_2$.

The producers' analyses of the copper, tin, and silver are included in Table II.

The H$_2$ and N$_2$ were purified by conventional methods. The H$_2$S in H$_2$ for preparative purposes was prepared by passing S vapor in H$_2$ over a catalyst of Ni strip.

The Cu_2S and PbS were prepared by heating the elements in evacuated sealed tubes at about $500°C$; for Cu_2S, the final heating was carried out in contact with an excess of Cu foil, to ensure the sulfide was in equilibrium with metallic Cu.

Temperature Measurement and Control

Temperatures were measured with a deflection potentiometer and Chromel-Alumel thermocouples regularly calibrated at the freezing points of Sn, Pb, Zn, Al, and Ag and at the Cu-Al eutectic temperature.

By locating the controlling thermocouple close to the furnace windings and arranging the controller to switch on or off only a small portion of the total furnace current, it was found possible to reduce temperature fluctuations to $0.2°C$ at about $900°C$ and $0.1°C$ at around $400°C$.

Temperature variations over the central zone of the furnace with the empty crucible assembly were of the same order; the crucible containing the lead was located in the center of the zone of practically uniform temperature. No temperature variation within the liquid lead could be detected; the temperature of the lead was measured by a thermocouple sheathed in thin-walled silica tubing immersed in the lead.

Analytical: Determination of Sulfur in Lead

Analysis of lead containing small amounts of sulfur presents a problem, since co-precipitation of Pb with $BaSO_4$ was found to occur when $BaSO_4$ was precipitated after extraction of the sulfur from the lead by fused NaOH. A radiochemical method using ^{35}S was tried in the hope that the lead contamination would not interfere unduly or could be allowed for. It was found, however, that the presence of 1–2% of $Pb^{35}SO_4$ considerably lowered the activity for a given weight of ^{35}S in the sulfate and it appeared desirable to remove lead completely before precipitation of $BaSO_4$.

A cation exchange resin (Zeocarb 225) was used to remove lead. The complete sample of Pb-S alloy was melted under fused caustic soda in a nickel crucible and heating continued until the caustic was clear. It was essential to cover the sample completely with NaOH to avoid atmospheric oxidation. After cooling, the caustic layer was extracted with hot water, and excess Br$_2$ water added. The solution was then boiled for 30 min, and after cooling slightly, was neutralized with 1:1 hydrochloric acid and 2–5 ml excess HCl were added, and the solution boiled to ensure removal of excess Br$_2$.

After filtration, the solution was passed down the ion-exchange column in which the resin was in the hydrogen form; the first 30–40 ml of solution passing through were discarded as they contained no sulfate. The column was finally washed with $2^1/_2$ column volumes of water.

The combined effluent and washings were heated to near boiling, and BaSO$_4$ was precipitated with a slight excess of hot 5% BaCl$_2$ solution. The precipitate was allowed to settle overnight. Precipitation was not complete if the solution was held just below boiling for an hour. The precipitate was ignited and weighed in the usual way.

Blank analyses using high purity lead were run on each set of sulfur determinations, to check on sulfur from reagents, etc. Usually, no weighable precipitate was obtained; if there were a precipitate, the results for the batch were discarded. The main source of extraneous sulfur appeared to be the caustic soda; it was desirable to use freshly opened bottles.

"Radio" sulfur was used to check that there was no loss of sulfur (1) to the nickel crucible, (2) in the residue from the filtration before the removal of lead, and (3) in the resin itself.

Synthetic lead-sulfur alloys of ca. 0.09 to 0.7 wt-% sulfur were prepared in evacuated sealed tubes and analyzed by the method outlined above. The maximum variation was 2% of the sulfur content, which in view of the small sulfur percentage, and the well-known difficulties associated with BaSO$_4$ precipitates, appeared to be satisfactory. Copper was determined colorimetrically using the A.S.T.M. standard method.[25] Silver was determined by cupellation, using Guerin's method.[26]

Preparation of Saturated Pb–S Alloys

For preliminary work at the lower temperatures, Pb-S alloys were prepared in Pyrex; for higher temperatures a graphite crucible was used. The graphite was "washed" free of possible contaminations by melting several fresh batches of lead in it.

Lead was melted under hydrogen, so surface oxide would be reduced. A clean surface was generally obtained, and the lead behaved very like mercury.

Sulfur was added by bubbling H_2S through the lead, until it was detected in the exit gases. The H_2S reacts rapidly at first, and none escapes from the metal until it approaches saturation with PbS. This was generally done at a temperature some 50°C above that for which the first measurement was to be taken. The alloy was cooled to the required temperature and maintained at temperature for periods of five to fifteen hours and the sample taken. The temperature was then lowered, and the process repeated. The majority of the measurements were thus taken with equilibrium approached from the high sulfur side. A few runs were made with lead and lead sulfide maintained at constant temperature, thus approaching equilibrium from the low sulfur side. These have been noted as "prepared at temperature" in Table III.

For the alloys at higher temperatures solid PbS was added, and if necessary to ensure rapid addition of S to the melt, H_2S passed through as before. The melt was agitated by a slow stream of N_2 passing through two holes in the silica stopper rod while the melt was cooling to the required temperature. The flow of N_2 was cut off while the alloy was held at constant temperature under a slight positive pressure of N_2. Although PbS rises very rapidly to the surface of the lead, it was thought desirable to allow a considerable time for any finely dispersed sulfide to rise to the surface.

Sampling

It is essential to ensure that the liquid lead sample is not contaminated with suspended PbS. At high temperatures, a long period at constant temperature seems to enable a satisfactory separation by gravity of PbS from the metal. For preliminary work at lower temperatures, the device shown in Figure 3a was used to filter the liquid through a Pyrex glass-wool plug. It is also important to ensure that there is no drop in temperature while solid and liquid are being separated. The portion of the sampling tube shown was heated by a small resistance winding to about 50°C above the metal temperature. The lead was sucked through the glass-wool and ran up and over into the sample tube. When the pressure

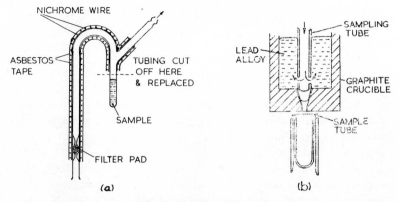

Fig. 3. Sampling devices.

was restored, the excess ran back, so there was a clear separation of the sample from the rest of the liquid.

For the graphite crucible, a small hole tapering to $1/8$ in. was drilled in the bottom of the crucible. This was closed by a ground silica tube, which could be raised to allow the sample to run into a small silica test tube located immediately beneath the crucible. This sample tube could then be lowered and removed from the bottom of the furnace tube. The arrangement is shown schematically in Figure 3b. A good stream of N_2 was maintained during the removal to prevent any air entering the furnace tube. In each method, the whole of the sample was taken for analysis.

The same method was used for the determination of the copper content of lead saturated with Cu_2S, or with Cu_2S and PbS. The sulfides were added to the lead and held at ca. 650°C before cooling to the temperature at which the sample was taken, generally after five hours at constant temperature.

Sulfur treatment was carried out in graphite crucibles in a pot furnace. The crucible was fitted with a graphite lid, a laboratory type stirrer with silica shaft and blades, and a device for adding sulfur. Copper additions were made as metal or Cu_2S, the temperature raised to ensure complete solution, and the crucible was then cooled to the temperature at which the sulfur treatment was to be carried out. Melting was carried out under hydrogen and a N_2 atmosphere was then maintained. Samples were taken by means of a pre-heated silica spoon.

RESULTS

Relative Stability of Cu_2S and PbS

Preliminary experiments to roughly locate the temperature at which the standard free energies of formation of Cu_2S and PbS became equal were carried out by sealing Cu and a mixture of Pb and PbS in Pyrex tubes with hydrogen to act as a sulfur carrier from the Pb/PbS mixture to the Cu located some distance away. This method was chosen in preference to direct contact between metal and sulfide, in order to eliminate any effects due to the solution, e.g., of Cu in PbS which might cause a disproportionately large effect on the sulfur potential. The tubes were evacuated and heated, then filled with H_2, re-evacuated and finally sealed with a small partial pressure of H_2, and maintained at a constant temperature. At 280°C no tarnishing of the Cu was observed; at 305°C, the next highest temperature studied, the copper was slowly tarnished giving a thin bluish film, which was identified as Cu_2S by its powder pattern. Similar experiments with metallic Pb and Cu_2S with excess copper showed no change in the surface of the lead.

During the course of the work, a direct comparison of the free energies was made by J. B. Wagner and C. Wagner.[24] They found $\Delta G° = 0$ at 279 ± 4°C and no attempt was made to locate the temperature more accurately by sulfur transfer experiments.

Solubility of PbS in Lead

The results obtained with samples taken through the bottom of a graphite crucible are given in Table III. For comparison, some values obtained using filtration in preliminary experiments are included. The agreement obtained with the two sampling techniques is satisfactory and indicates that the sampling is reliable. It may be noted that the two methods give samples drawn from the upper and lower portions of the liquid.

The results of 720.8 and 550.1°C show the reproducibility which could be obtained. The value at 693.3°C appears to be too high; it was obtained when the level of the lead was much lower than usual and in this sample it is possible that some PbS was carried out by the stream of lead. For the equilibrium

$$PbS(c) = Pb(l) + S \text{ in Pb}$$
$$K = a_{Pb} \cdot a_s$$

TABLE III
The Solubility of Lead Sulfide in Lead

Temp, °C	S, wt-%	S, atomic-%	Remarks[a]
923.4	1.12	7.41	H.P.
912.1	1.16	7.04	C.T.
892.0	1.01	6.19	H.P., prepared at temp.
861.2	0.737	4.57	C.T.
808.5	0.486	6.06	H.P., prepared at temp.
770.4	0.344	2.18	C.T.
720.8	0.215	1.37_3	H.P., sampled after 3 hr
	0.214	1.37_0	H.P., sampled after 15 hr
693.3	0.174	1.11	C.T. metal low in crucible, possibly some PbS included
677.0	0.127	0.818	C.T.
663.1	0.101	0.647	C.T.
627.3	0.066_5	0.428	C.T.
616.5	0.0568	0.356	C.T.
609.6	0.052_2	0.33_6	H.P.
590.1	0.0467	0.300	C.T.
580.4	0.0370	0.240	C.T.
$(580)^b$	$(0.037)^b$		
550.1	0.0226	0.146	C.T.
	0.0229	0.148	
$(550)^b$	$(0.024)^b$		
487.2	0.0085	0.055	H.P., prepared at temp.
$(483)^b$	$(0.0085)^b$		
460.1	0.0059_5	0.038_4	C.T.
$(436)^b$	$(0.0037)^b$		
434.7	0.0036	0.023	C.T., prepared at temp.
427.2	0.0026	0.017	H.P.

[a] Here, H.P. indicates high purity lead and C.T. indicates caustic treated refined lead.

[b] Results for samples taken by filtration are given in parentheses.

and if S in Pb obeys Henry's law, its activity can be taken as equal to its atomic percentage, while that of the lead is equal to its atomic fraction.

Then $K = N_{Pb}$[atomic-% S], and $\log_{10} K$ is plotted against $1/T$ in Figure 4. The points lie close to a straight line showing that the assumption that S in lead obeys Henry's law is valid up to about 7 atomic-% S. No differences between the two grades of lead can be detected, showing the activity is not noticeably affected by the

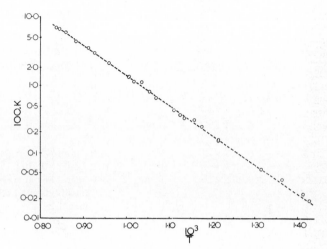

Fig. 4. Log K vs. $1/T$ for lead saturated with lead sulfide.

small concentrations of impurities in the leads used here. However, the solubility of PbS in lead bullion with relatively high concentrations of impurities may be different from the values reported here.

Equilibrium between Pb, Cu₂S, and PbS

Figure 5 gives the copper in lead saturated with Cu_2S and PbS. The values are in fair agreement with those calculated in the Appendix. Both experimental and calculated values are considerably higher than those obtained by stirring in sulfur thus, at 330°C,

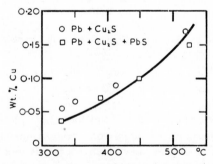

Fig. 5. Copper in lead: O, lead to which Cu_2S was added; □, Cu_2S and PbS added; and ——, calculated.

0.047% Cu was found in the lead, while S treatment at temperatures only a few degrees lower can give 0.005% Cu or less.

Lead to which only Cu₂S was added gave rather higher results (see Fig. 5). The solid phase left on top of the lead was found by x-ray powder pattern to be chalcocite, as expected, but small amounts of PbS could not be detected in this way.

Sulfur Treatment of Pure Pb–Cu Alloys

It was suspected that the function of the sulfur in decopperizing was, by maintaining a high sulfur potential, to produce a sulfur-rich copper sulfide in which the activity of Cu would be lowered. Such a S-rich sulfide would be in equilibrium with a low % Cu in Pb. Under conditions of equilibrium, the sulfur potential could be kept to a low value by the Pb/PbS equilibrium, but if high sulfur potentials were maintained where liquid sulfur and copper sulfide were in contact, it should be possible to achieve a low Cu in the lead. This hypothesis is consistent with Gallager's observation that it is not possible to decopperize lead with PbS, since PbS in contact with Pb could only maintain a very low sulfur potential.

Attempts at decopperizing pure Pb-Cu alloys were unsuccessful, although a number of techniques with different conditions of stirring in sulfur, etc., and also the use of sulfur vapor were tried. The lowest copper content obtained was 0.02% from lead with initially 0.045% Cu. The dross contained large amounts of metallic lead, and there was a tendency for thick crusts of galena to form, sometimes almost completely enclosing large globules of molten sulfur. It was also noted that the temperature of the lead rose 3–5°C while the sulfur was being added. These results confirm the observations of Cunningham.[15]

Following Cunningham's indication that the presence of Ag was necessary for successful decopperizing, this was attempted with alloys of 0.18% Ag. It was noticed immediately that there was no longer any temperature rise, and that the dross was a fine black powder with a slightly dark-blue tinge. Copper contents of 0.002% and 0.001% were obtained with no difficulty, confirming Cunningham's conclusions. The Ag contents were unchanged; in one experiment, a slight rise in silver was observed, which was probably not more than the error in determining Ag in the presence of copper by cupellation. Similar results were obtained with 0.094% Ag.

X-ray powder patterns of the dross showed PbS and Pb, but definite identification of the copper sulfides was not possible, as the few lines unaccounted for were faint and diffuse, and common to Cu_2S and digenite.

The Rate of Reaction of Sulfur with Lead

It has already been mentioned that when sulfur was stirred into lead free of silver, the temperature rose by as much as $3-5°C$; when Ag was present, the rise in temperature under otherwise identical conditions was no more than 0.1 to $0.2°C$. This indicates that the rate of reaction of sulfur with lead is very much less in the presence of Ag. This was confirmed by passing sulfur vapor in N_2 over high purity lead and a 0.094% Ag alloy in alumina boats side by side in a horizontal tube furnace, or by heating the metal in sealed evacuated tubes containing S.

Two typical results are shown in Table IV.

TABLE IV

			Gain in wt, mg	
Wt of metal, g	Time, hr	Temp, °C	Lead	Lead + 0.094% Ag
6.959	3	330	78.8	2.4
8.855	1	335	351.3	3.3

The appearance of the two specimens was strikingly different The Ag-lead alloy was covered with a thin light-gray film, the pure lead with a thick cauliflower-like dark-gray crust projecting well above the level of the boat.

Preliminary experiments have shown that 0.15% Sn, if anything, tends to increase slightly the rate of reaction with sulfur vapor.

It perhaps should be mentioned that the appearance of the PbS seems to vary greatly even with apparently similar conditions of preparation. This was also noticed in decopperizing with sulfur where fine black powder formed in the presence of Ag was characteristic and very different from the thick lighter colored crusts formed in the absence of Ag. Under our conditions, successful decopperizing could always be predicted from the appearance of the dross.

DISCUSSION

The PbS Liquidus

The lead sulfide liquidus obtained here may be compared with other values in the literature. Guertler and Landau[18] find lower sulfur percentages, but their results are very scattered. Those of Friedrich and Leroux[27] around 10 atomic-% S are rather higher than those found in this work. However, their liquidus temperatures around 10 atomic-% S seem low in comparison with their values at higher sulfur percentages. The results obtained here lie on a smooth curve with their higher sulfur points and it appears likely that their thermal analysis has given rather low liquidus temperatures for the more dilute alloys.

The eutectic concentration from Eq. (2) is 0.0017 atomic-% or 0.0003 wt-% S. This is higher than the value of 0.0001 wt-% S (0.0006 atomic-%) given as the upper limit for the eutectic concentration by Greenwood and Worner.[28] At 0.0001 wt-% S they found PbS to be the primary phase by micro-examination. However, identification of the primary crystals in such a dilute alloy is difficult and a slight curvature in the line of Figure 4 or a small change in its slope would reconcile these values. The calculated eutectic concentration is best regarded as giving the order of magnitude. It is consistent with the solid solubility limits of less than 0.0006 atomic-% S at 300°C given by Greenwood and Worner.

The method of least squares gives the following equation for the straight line of Figure 4.

$$\log {}_{10}K = -4,385/T + 4.523$$

or for $PbS(c) = Pb(l) + [S]$ atomic-% in Pb

$$\Delta G^\circ = 20,100 - 20.69T$$

If this is combined with the free energy of formation of PbS from the Appendix; viz.,

$$Pb + {}^1/_2S_2 = PbS \quad \Delta G^\circ = -39,400\ 21.25T$$

Then,

$$^1/_2S_2 = [S] \text{ atomic-\% in Pb}$$

$$\Delta G^\circ = -19,300 + 0.6T$$

This may be compared with Sudo's results[29] which give, with 1 atomic-% as the standard state of S in Pb, $\Delta G° = -27,820 + 5.65T$.

Sudo's equation gives $\Delta G°$ some 3 kg cal more negative at 1000°K, and hence would predict higher S contents in Pb than those found experimentally. There seems to be no obvious explanation of the disagreement unless Sudo's sampling of the S-Pb alloy gave consistently high sulfurs.

Sudo's results show that S in Pb follows Henry's law up to at least 0.3 to 0.4 wt-%, i.e., approximately 2 atomic-%.

The fact that S in lead apparently obeys Henry's law up to around 7 atomic-% is rather unexpected. This suggests that the S-S interaction which Rosenqvist[30] has shown to occur in Ag-S melts is less marked in Pb-S melts. In silver, sulfur follows Henry's law up to 3 atomic-%. As a comparative measure of the attractive forces between dissolved S atoms in various metals, the temperature required for complete miscibility may be tentatively used. In the Ag-S system, miscibility is not complete until 1125°C, while in the Pb-S system, complete miscibility is found, although with an extremely flat liquidus surface showing that at about 1050°C the melt is close to separation into two liquids. For S in Cu at 1200°C, Henry's law holds to 0.87 or 1 wt-% according to Sudo[31] and Rosenqvist,[32] respectively; the limit is thus not more than 2 atomic-% S, and the wide miscibility gap can be attributed to strong S-S interaction. The behavior of sulfur in iron at 1600°C is not consistent with that in the other metallic solvents, as there is no separation into two liquid phases, and the results of Sherman, Elvander, and Chipman[33] would place the limit of Henry's law at definitely less than 2 atomic-% S. It appears that interaction between dissolved S atoms may set in comparatively rapidly once a certain concentration has been reached; this is shown in Rosenqvist's results where the partial molar heat of solution of S in liquid silver shows a sharp break at 3 atomic-% S. Similar behavior must be shown by S in Pb at concentrations not much greater than those studied here, in order to produce the extremely flat liquidus around 1050°C. If this is the case, it is difficult to see how the sulfur atoms distributed at random in a dilute solution undergo a comparatively rapid "clustering" as their concentration is increased.

Equilibrium between Pb, Cu₂S, and PbS

When a substance such as Cu_2S which has a range of stable composition is added to lead, it is not necessary that the Cu and S enter the lead in the atomic ratio of 2. The copper content is *much* greater than the sulfur content for saturation of pure Pb with PbS. Although it is possible that interaction between dissolved Cu and S could lead to higher S contents in solutions containing Cu than those found with pure lead, such an effect would be expected to be small.

The system $Pb + Cu_2S$ is not binary but will consist of liquid lead containing Cu and a small amount of S, and a Cu-deficient sulfide. If the deficiency is substantial, the sulfur potential may be high enough for PbS to be precipitated. On cooling, Cu and S will be taken up by the "Cu_2S." The sulfur will be provided from PbS or from dissolved sulfur. If this sulfur is not the equilibrium amount, i.e., if the reaction $l + PbS \rightarrow$ "Cu_2S" does not take place readily, the Cu_2S and liquid will tend to be higher in copper than if equilibrium were maintained. Since in the runs with only Cu_2S added initially, the amount of PbS formed would be small, and as it dissolves rather slowly in lead, it is possible that nonattainment of equilibrium may be responsible for the higher copper content found. It will be shown in the next section that the sulfur not taken up on cooling must be an extremely small amount.

In Figure 6, the lead corner of the system has been shown. The sulfur contents were not determined but were taken from the results on the Pb-S system, and the relation $a^2Cu \cdot a_s$ = constant has been

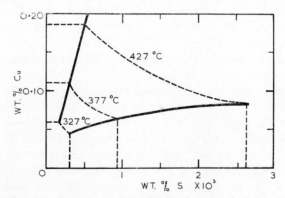

Fig. 6. The lead corner of the Pb-Cu-S system (calculated).

approximated by (wt-% Cu)^2(wt-% S) = constant; i.e., interaction between dissolved Cu and S has been neglected.

The Activity of Copper in Cu-Deficient Cuprous Sulfide

If the function of sulfur in decopperizing lead is to form a copper deficient Cu$_2$S, in which the activity of Cu is lowered, it is necessary to show that this reduction is sufficient to account for the observed decopperizing. By emf measurements, J. B. Wagner and C. Wagner[34] have shown the activity of copper in Cu$_2$S to vary rapidly with small changes in composition; e.g., at 435°C, a_{Cu} = 0.007 for Cu$_{1.93}$S; at 400°C from their Figure 1, a_{Cu} = 0.1 for Cu$_{1.995}$S. From the emf quoted[24] for Cu$_{1.98}$S at 300°C, a_{Cu} = 0.017.

For the relation between the deficiency in Cu per atom of S, δ (their δ^*) and chemical potential of Cu they give

$$\delta = 2x° \sinh \left[(\mu_{Cu}° - \mu_{Cu})/RT \right] \qquad (3)$$

$$\delta = 2x° \sinh (-\ln a_{Cu})$$

where $x°$ is the concentration per atom of S of free electrons (or of electron holes) in ideal Cu$_2$S, in which $\mu_{Cu}°$ is the chemical potential of Cu. The standard state is that of Cu in ideal Cu$_2$S, not pure metallic Cu. For Cu$_2$S in equilibrium with copper, $\delta°$ = 4($\pm$2) $\times$ 10^{-4} at 400°C, and increases slightly with increasing temperature. They do not give values of $x°$ for temperatures around the melting point of lead but $x°$ = 3.5 $\times$ 10^{-4} at 400°C. It will be assumed that $\delta°$ is unchanged by the change in temperature. The relatively high value of $x°$ shows the energy gap between valence and conduction bands must be comparatively small, so $x°$ will have a rather low temperature coefficient. Log ($\delta/x°$) against log a_{Cu} gives a straight line for log a_{Cu} < −1, and the effect of changes in $x°$ is to move the curve along the log $\delta/x°$ axis. At the same time, the value of the activity for equilibrium with copper, i.e., at the composition δ = 4 $\times$ 10^{-4} alters. However, if the standard state is taken to be the familiar one of pure Cu the value of the activity on this scale remains unchanged once $\delta/x°$ is large enough. Thus, if $2x°$ is taken arbitrarily as 10^{-4} or 10^{-5}, the curve shown in Figure 7 is obtained; if the value of 7 $\times$ 10^{-4} is used, the activity of copper, with pure solid copper as the standard state lies at the most about 0.2 log units above this. The relation between activity and copper de-

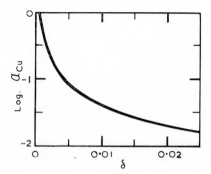

Fig. 7. Change in activity of copper with copper deficiency in Cu_2S.   Standard state for copper is the pure metal.

ficiency is fairly closely defined even in the absence of a direct experimental value of $x°$.   Thus, to lower the copper activity by a factor of 10 or 20 below that for equilibrium with Cu_2S + PbS which is about what occurs in practice, δ must be about 5×10^{-3}.

For Cu_2S in equilibrium with PbS, the copper activity is approximately 0.8, for which δ is about 5×10^{-4}.

Since the activity of copper is so sensitive to the Cu/S ratio near the stoichiometric compositon, it is not surprising that the results in Figure 5 are scattered.   The difference between the two results at 330°C corresponds to a difference of the order of 1 in 10^4 in Cu deficiency, or a few milligrams of S in 10 g Cu_2S.

The results show the possibility of using a liquid alloy for determining the metal activity in a phase which behaves like Cu_2S, although well-defined values must be difficult to determine near the stoichiometric composition.

The "effective" sulfur pressure can be obtained by a Gibbs-Duhem integration using Eq. (3).   Since the Cu/S ratio is very close to 2, this can be approximated by

$$2d \log a_{Cu} \sim - d \log p_{S_2}^{1/2}$$

or

$$4d \log a_{Cu} \sim - d \log p_{S_2}$$

If the Cu activity is depressed below the equilibrium value by a factor of ten as a result of sulfur treatment, the effective p_{S_2} is about 10^4 times that for equilibrium between Pb and PbS.   Some of the sulfur potentials in the system at 327°C are as follows: liquid sulfur, −8.6 kg cal; CuS-"Cu$_2$S" (or digenite) = −12.8 kg cal (from Richardson and Jeffes[21]) Pb/PbS = −52.9 kg cal; Pb containing 0.005% Cu and "Cu$_2$S" with δ ∼5 × 10^{-3}, −44 kg cal.

Only a small fraction of the total sulfur potential is effective in decopperizing. This is because the reaction of lead with sulfur and with higher copper sulfides is tending to lower it continually.

There is no need to assume the formation of digenite or covellite to explain the observed decopperizing. They may be formed where high sulfur potentials are maintained, e.g., by liquid sulfur trapped in a crust of sulfides. The formation of CuS could also be expected if sulfur were added to dross floating on the top of the kettle of lead, so that only limited contact between metal and CuS is possible.

Mechanism of Decopperizing

J. B. Wagner and C. Wagner[34] found that for Cu$_2$S discs of 1–2 mm thickness, uniformity of composition was achieved in about 10 min at temperatures comparable with those of interest here. This shows the high mobility of Cu$^+$ ions in Cu$_2$S, which must be necessary to account for the rapid decopperizing. A small Cu$_2$S particle, partly converted to digenite or covellite, will have a very low copper activity, and reaction will not be hindered by diffusion of Cu ions away from the lead/Cu$_2$S interface. Diffusion of copper in dilute solution in the liquid may be slow, and one of the functions of agitation is to bring fresh solution and copper sulfide particles into contact. Since 100 tons of lead may be decopperized in about 10 min, the overall reaction is fast, and it is unlikely that there is an appreciable activation energy for passage of Cu from the metal to the sulfide phase. The addition of Cu to the Cu$_2$S is probably analogous to the tarnishing of silver by sulfur by the migration of Ag$^+$ ions through Ag$_2$S, as described by Wagner.[35]

Successful decopperizing of lead with sulfur depends on inhibiting the reaction of sulfur with lead. This occurs if silver is present, and the production of a sulfur-rich copper sulfide is then possible, at least where a high sulfur potential is maintained, e.g., where the copper sulfide is in contact with droplets of molten sulfur. The sulfur potential of liquid sulfur is high enough to form CuS. However, this is rapidly reduced by liquid lead, and the final copper content is a compromise between the tendency of sulfur to increase the sulfur content and so lower the copper activity in the copper sulfide, and that of lead to remove sulfur from sulfur-rich copper sulfides. If stirring is unduly prolonged, the latter reaction will continue, and a slow rise in the copper in the bullion as found in practice can be expected. Similarly, an increase in temperature will tend to facilitate the approach to complete equilibrium with a high copper content. During the treatment, direct reaction of sulfur with lead is producing PbS since this is only slowed down by the presence of silver, and not completely prevented.

It is interesting to consider the mechanism by means of which sulfur reacts with the dilute copper solution. In view of the very low solubility of sulfur in lead, and the low rate of solution of PbS in lead, homogeneous reaction between dissolved Cu and S is not possible. The reaction presumably occurs at the interface between liquid lead and liquid sulfur. The importance of adequate stirring in practice is in breaking up the sulfur into small droplets, thus increasing the interfacial area. Nevertheless, in a solution containing only about, say, 0.05 wt-% or about 0.2 atomic-% Cu, it is surprising that the copper reacts so readily with the sulfur. Even if Ag is present, and the Pb-S reaction is inhibited, it is not stopped, and dross always contains large amounts of PbS. It would be expected that the rate of reaction of Pb with S would still be greater than that of copper, simply because of the low copper concentration.

In plant practice, it is possible for the lead to have Cu₂S and PbS already present since it is common to separate dross and bullion in the hot drossing at higher temperatures, e.g., 400°C. The separation is never complete, and so Cu₂S may be present from the hot drossing. While the bullion is cooling to just about freezing point, more Cu₂S (and PbS) may be precipitated. In contact with droplets of sulfur, as it is swept through the lead, it will tend to pick up Cu, and the reaction may be regarded as the addition of Cu to a Cu-deficient Cu₂S.

The Cu₂S left from hot drossing, or precipitated from bullion while cooling to the temperature for sulfur treatment, could thus provide a S-rich phase which could be expected to remove copper by a "tarnishing" reaction. This may be reasonable for plant operations, but it does not lend itself as readily to explaining why successful decopperizing can be obtained when only Cu and Ag are present initially; i.e., no Cu_2S could be present until the sulfur was added. Possibly, excess sulfur reacts to form both Cu_2S and PbS at the interface, and once some solid Cu_2S is formed, the same mechanism can account for the growth of Cu_2S crystals.

A second possibility is presented by the work of Bloem and Kröger[36] who showed that at quite low temperatures, 100–400°C, copper can diffuse into PbS crystals. The rate of penetration depends on the previous history of the PbS; crystals which have been heated in high partial pressures of sulfur show very limited penetration of copper, which is attributed to formation of Cu_2S on internal surfaces, dislocations or similar imperfections which contain excess sulfur. The PbS crystals grown from melt under a sulfur pressure of one atmosphere were found to contain about 15% S instead of the stoichiometric 13.4%.[36] This is much greater than the S excess in well-annealed PbS crystals.[37]

The maximum Cu content taken up by PbS crystals was found by Bloem and Kröger to correspond to about 0.15 wt-% Cu. It appears unlikely that incorporation of copper in this way within imperfect PbS crystals could account for the removal of Cu on sulfur treatment, where the dross contains around 5% Cu, which is of course even less than the per cent in Cu_2S + PbS because of the presence of entrained lead. However, it is possible that a sulfur-rich surface is produced by the liquid sulfur and this could react effectively with dissolved copper. Imperfect PbS crystals are to be expected at low temperatures, since the diffusion of Pb in PbS is negligible below 500°C.[36]

If this excess S reacted only slowly with metallic lead, or rather, with lead containing silver, it could perhaps react effectively with dissolved Cu.

Effect of Other Elements in Decopperizing

Claims that Sb or Sn are essential for successful decopperizing are not borne out by success of decopperizing here with only silver present. However, these elements may affect the copper content before sulfur treatment. It is generally assumed that Cu is removed by precipitation as sulfide, arsenide, or antimonide during "hot" drossing. Complex sulfides may also be precipitated on cooling.

Arsenic if present in comparatively high concentrations may result in lower Cu contents, since if Cu_3As is being precipitated, then at a given temperature $a^3_{Cu} \cdot a_{As}$ is constant; similar relations will hold for complex sulfides such as Cu_3AsS_4 and Cu_3Sb. On the whole, high concentrations of As or Sb in the bullion should tend to produce low copper after cooling to around 400°C. With low copper to start with, better results on S treatment may be expected. If this were the only function of the impurities, the success of sulfur treatment could be forecast from the copper present before the sulfur addition. However, there are a number of possibilities which may be mentioned.

1. Impurities, or combinations of impurities, may behave like silver in pure Ag-Pb alloys. This is not true of tin, which seems to increase the rate of reaction of lead with sulfur slightly.

2. Impurities may lead to the formation of complex sulfides, e.g., Cu_3AsS_4, which should have lower copper activities than Cu_2S phases. Ross[38] has shown that As, Sb, and Fe enter into solid solution in chalcocite and digenite at low temperatures. Even if complex sulfides are not formed, the relation between copper activity and sulfur pressure may be affected by, e.g., a Cu_2S phase in the presence of comparatively small amounts of other elements. The Cu_2S produced by sulfur treatment of bullion which contains appreciable amounts of As, Sb, Bi, etc., cannot be identified with that produced from materials of much higher purity in the laboratory.

It is perhaps worth considering the effect of some other elements in more detail.

Silver

It is not possible to suggest the way in which Ag inhibits the reaction of sulfur with lead. Although Ag is not removed by sulfur treatment, it may be incorporated in the lead sulfide at the same Ag/Pb ratio as in the bullion, the composition of which then remains unchanged. If Ag^+ were accommodated in PbS at the expense of vacant cation sites, it could reduce the rate of diffusion of the Pb^{2+} in PbS, and so lower the reaction rate. However, it is doubtful if diffusion of Pb through the PbS lattice is involved in the growth of the PbS at temperatures near the melting point of lead since this is extremely slow below 500°C.[36]

Antimony

Schrader and Hanemann[39] have investigated the system Pb-Cu-Sb and have shown that for the eutectic trough along which the various phases of the Cu-Sb system are in equilibrium with liquid lead, comparatively high copper and antimony contents can be present, e.g., 0.9% Sb and 0.2% Cu; 0.13% Cu and 0.33% Sb. It is unlikely therefore that precipitation of *pure* Cu-Sb phases during the first drossing assists in removing Cu. This agrees with the general tendency for the antimony to remain unchanged in this stage.

Arsenic

The Pb-rich corner of the Pb-Cu-As system is not known. The heat of formation of Cu_3As is much greater than that of Cu_3Sb; $\Delta H°_{298} = -25.6 \pm 5$ and -2.5 ± 1.0 kg cal, respectively, according to Kubaschewski and Evans.[40] If these are taken as rough measures of the free energies of formation at higher temperatures, the equilibrium $Cu_3As = 3[Cu]_{in\ Pb} + [As]_{in\ Pb}$ will give much lower Cu contents than that with antimony. Precipitation of Cu_3As on cooling bullion can be expected, and Table I shows such a decrease in both Cu and As. Arsenic can indirectly assist final decopperizing in removing copper by precipitation of Cu_3As before sulfur treatment. Antimony is not likely to be effective in the same way, and the claims that it is necessary for successful decopperizing by sulfur need experimental justification.

Tin

Like As and Sb, Sn is not essential for removal of copper to low values. It may be of assistance when other conditions are not favorable. Haig's figure of 0.15% Sn being necessary to bring Cu down to <0.04% does not indicate very satisfactory removal of Cu, possibly because the lead was secondary metal, and thus free of silver. If the effect of Sn is real, it behaves differently from silver, which is to be expected from the lack of any chemical similarity between Sn and Ag.

From Richards' data,[41] the free energy of formation of SnS at 600°K is very close to that of PbS and Cu_2S at the same temperature. The tendency to form SnS from a dilute solution of Sn in Pb is thus small, in agreement with Tafel's statement that Sn is not normally removed unless excess sulfur is used.

Tentatively it may be suggested that SnS_2 acts as a sulfur carrier. If locally, small portions of Sn-Pb alloy react completely with excess sulfur, SnS_2 rather than SnS could be formed, and this may serve as a source of sulfur at a high potential for reaction with dissolved Cu.

$$Sn_2 + 2[Cu] \rightarrow SnS + Cu_2S$$

In this way, if all the Sn and Pb in this portion of alloy are finally converted to their sulfides, there will be no change in the % Sn in the metal.

Applications to Other Systems

Decopperizing Tin with Sulfur

According to Jones[42] sulfur at 240–50°C can reduce the copper in tin "to almost any percentage desired"; SnS alone is not very effective. This is similar to sulfur and PbS in decopperizing lead, and the effectiveness of sulfur must be due to the formation of a copper-deficient Cu_2S. At 250°C, the standard free energies of formation are $Cu_2S = -27.8$ and $SnS = -29$ kg cal so, if anything, SnS is slightly more stable than Cu_2S, and removal of Cu from dilute solutions in tin on the basis of the equilibrium

$$2[Cu]_{in\ Sn} + SnS = Cu_2S + Sn(l)$$

should not give very low copper, even allowing for the partial molar heat of solution of solid Cu in liquid Sn.

It is suggested that the sulfur lowers the copper activity by forming a copper sulfide of low copper activity just as with lead.

Decopperizing Bismuth with Sulfur

Metals such as bismuth, which form sulfides considerably less stable than Cu_2S may be decopperized effectively by sulfur since the equilibrium

$$6[Cu]_{in\ Bi} + Bi_2S_3 \rightarrow 3Cu_2S + 2Bi(l)$$

should result in low [Cu] even without the formation of a sulfur-rich Cu_2S.

General

The decopperizing of lead (and probably of tin) gives copper percentages which are lower than the values when equilibrium is established. Equilibrium is apparently "overshot" only for copper in lead but not for the copper sulfide which has a sulfur potential higher than that for Pb/PbS.

It is possible that in other refining operations similar conditions may be met with and, in fact, complete equilibrium may not prevail, not because of overall kinetic limitations but because of sluggish reactions on the part of one element. Behavior similar to that found here with sulfur may also occur with oxidation or chlorination, where the products of reaction are nonstoichiometric or where compounds of higher valency are stable in the presence of high partial pressures of the nonmetal. If a phase of higher nonmetal to metal ratio exists it will have a lower metal activity than, e.g., the phase stable in contact with metal. At high temperatures, and with liquid phases, it is unlikely that differences in rates of reaction would lead to the formation of a nonequilibrium *phase*. However, variations in *composition* due to the gradient in oxygen potential between slag-gas ahd slag-metal interfaces are familiar in basic open-hearth slags.

At comparatively low temperatures, and where solid phases are produced, differences in, e.g., diffusion rates may allow the formation of substantial amounts of a nonequilibrium phase. If this is more or less removed from contact with the bulk of the material, e.g., by floating to the top of a bath of metal, it may then react only slowly, and the steady state will not be one of complete equilibrium.

These conditions are often found in practical refining operations where the nonmetal is stirred in, like sulfur, or as with air or chlorine, blown through liquid metal.

If a dross rather than a liquid slag is formed, then the properties of the solids constituting the dross may determine the course of the reaction. Complete understanding of processes of this type requires a detailed knowledge of the properties of the solids. It will be obvious that the present investigation has raised many more queries about the properties of the sulfides of lead and copper than it has answered. The decopperizing of lead with sulfur appears to be the first example recognized where a practical refining operation has in effect taken advantage of the thermodynamic properties of a nonstoichiometric solid.

Financial assistance to one of us (R. F. B.) has been generously provided by Consolidated Zinc Pty. Ltd., and by the Australian Atomic Energy Commission, who also assisted with the cost of equipment. Discussions with the staff of the Broken Hill Associated Smelters have been of great help, and we are indebted to the Research Manager, Mr. R. J. Hopkins, for making available to us Mr. D. A. Cunningham's results on the effect of silver.

APPENDIX

Thermodynamic Data for Cu₂S and PbS

Because of the uncertainty as to the temperature at which the standard free energies of formation of Cu_2S and PbS become equal, it seemed worth attempting to define their thermodynamic properties as closely as possible. Even if no more definite conclusions were reached, a critical survey could, it was thought, help in assessing the possible errors in the data.

The measurements of Sudo[43] on the equilibrium

$$PbS + H_2 = Pb(l) + H_2S \tag{A1}$$

appear to be the most reliable. The equation of Richardson and Jeffes[21] is that given by Sudo and was apparently obtained from a $\log K - 1/T$ plot by the method of least squares. Although it fits the experimental results well, it is not suitable for extrapolation to lower temperatures. Sudo gives another equation based on a Σ plot of his results, which should be more reliable for calculating values at lower temperatures. However, for the reaction (A1) he obtains

$$\Delta G^\circ_{298} = 14,469 \text{ cal}, \ \Delta H^\circ_{298} = 17,484 \text{ cal}$$

from which

$$\Delta S^\circ_{298} = 10.1 \text{ cal}/^\circ C$$

Kelley's entropies[44] of Pb, PbS, and H_2 and that of Evans and Wagman[45] for H_2S give

$$\Delta S^\circ_{298} = 11.6 \text{ cal}/^\circ C$$

The greatest single source of error is ± 0.5 in the entropy of PbS. Although part of the disparity may be due to errors in high temperature heat capacities, it appears possible that the experimental errors "drift" slightly with temperature.

Using data from Kelley[44,46] and from Evans and Wagman[45] for H_2S in the form

$$\Delta G_T = \Delta_{298} + \Delta(H_T - H_{298}) - T[\Delta S_{298} + \Delta(S_T - S_{298})]$$

ΔH_{98} was calculated from Sudo's results. It was found advantageous to rearrange the data in the form of the free energy function $(G - H_{298})/T$, which permits of graphical interpolation and extrapolation since it changes only slowly with temperature. The advantages of the free energy function have been pointed out by Margrave[47] and here, constancy in ΔH_{298} shows the data to be consistent with the entropies. The results are collected in Table V.

TABLE V

$T°K$	$\Delta G°$(Sudo)	$-\Delta(G°-H°_{298})/T$	$\Delta H°_{298}/T$	$\Delta H°_{298}$
855	9.63	10.64	21.91	18.73
904	9.52	10.59	21.13	19.10
952	9.04	10.52	20.02	19.06
1000	8.60	10.46	19.06	19.06
1048	8.32	10.42	18.36	19.24

The values of $\Delta H°_{298}$ lie within 0.3 kg cal of the average of 19.04 kg cal with a slight tendency to increase with increasing temperature. At the melting point of lead, the present calculation gives $\Delta G° = 12.53$ kg cal while Sudo's equation gives 11.9 kg cal. The value of $\Delta H°_{298}$ when combined with that for

$$H_2 + {}^1/_2S_2(g) = H_2S$$

$\Delta H°_{298} = -20.24$ kg cal gives

$$Pb + {}^1/_2S(g) = PbS, \Delta H°_{298} = -39.28 \text{ kg cal}$$

or for

$$Pb + S(rh) = PbS, \Delta H°_{298} = -23.86 \text{ kg cal}$$

The latter may be compared with Zeumer and Roth's value of -23.12 kg cal.[48]

A similar treatment of the results of Kiukkola and Wagner[49] for the reaction

$$Pb(c,l) + S(l) = PbS$$

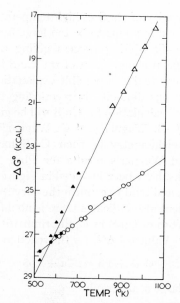

Fig. 8. Standard free energy of formation per mole of PbS and Cu₂S (from metal and $1/2S_2(g)$). PbS, △ Sudo; ▲, Kiukkola and Wagner. Cu₂S, ● J. B. and C. Wagner; O, Brooks. ——— from recalculation of Sudo's results.

gives for $\Delta H°_{298}$ for Pb + Srh = PbS as -23.29, with $\Delta H°_{298}$ ranging from -23.45 to -23.19. For Pb + $1/2S_2$ =. PbS, $\Delta H°_{298}$ is then -38.71 kg cal. The mean of the two sets of results is $\Delta H°_{298}$ = -39.0 ± 0.5 kg cal.

The two sets of experimental results may be compared with one another in Figure 8 where the values have been calculated for the reaction Pb + $1/2S_2(g)$ = PbS. The difference in the $\Delta H°$ values is obvious; the solid line is that calculated using the new value of $\Delta H°_{298}$ from Sudo's results. It is clear that a small change in slope, i.e., in $\Delta S°_{298}$ would close the gap in the $\Delta H°_{298}$ values. A more exact determination of the entropy of PbS seems desirable.

The measurements of Brooks[50] for the equilibrium Cu₂S + H₂ = 2Cu + H₂S which extend down to 342°C, when plotted as $\Delta G°$ against T show an unusual change in slope near 800°K. His results at higher temperatures and those of Richardson and Antill[51] are in good agreement. They noted that experimental and calculated values of $\Delta S°$ were in poor agreement and were inclined to attribute this to the heat capacity of Cu_2S at high temperatures. The change in slope of Brooks' curve seems to be too large for a phase change in the Cu_2S or some disordering process giving an anomalous heat capacity. A change in composition of the Cu_2S in equilibrium with solid Cu may be suggested as a possible explanation of the disparity. Because of the obvious difficulty in reconciling the thermodynamic data, no "third law" calculation for Cu_2S will be given here.

The results of J. B. Wagner and C. Wagner[24] corrected for the departure from stoichiometry of their Cu_2S have been combined with Kiukkola and Wagner's results for PbS. These, as well as the results of Brooks, have been included in Figure 8. The values are in good agreement, and tend to confirm the curvature in the $\Delta G° - T$ plot. The agreement also indicates there is no difference in the thermodynamic properties of Cu_2S in equilibrium with Cu, and Cu_2S in contact with PbS. Values of $\Delta G°$ for the reaction

$$Cu_2S + Pb = 2Cu + PbS \qquad (A2)$$

were read from a large scale graph.

Calculation of Copper in Lead in Equilibrium with Cu_2S and PbS

From the results of Kleppa and Weil[16] for the solubility of copper in liquid lead, for dilute solutions (<2 atomic-%), if 1 wt-% Cu is taken as the standard state, then for

$$Cu(c) = [Cu] \text{ wt-\% in } Pb(l) \qquad (A3)$$
$$\Delta G° = 9700 - 10.55T$$

Combining these, $\Delta G°$ for the reaction

$$Cu_2S(c) + Pb(l) = 2[Cu] \text{ in } Pb + PbS(c) \qquad (A4)$$

for round temperatures is shown in Table VI; the activity of the lead is assumed to be 1.

TABLE VI

$T°K$	$\Delta G°_2$	$2 \times \Delta G°_3$	$\Delta G°_4$	wt-% Cu in $Pb(l)$
600	630	6840	7470	0.044
700	2200	4630	6830	0.086
800	3000	2520	5520	0.176

It should be noted that a formal thermodynamic calculation of this type is not self-consistent. The thermodynamic properties of Cu$_2$S are those for Cu$_2$S saturated with respect to pure Cu. The result obtained indicates the Cu$_2$S to be in equilibrium with a solution with a lower copper content, i.e., with an activity <1 relative to solid Cu as a standard state. The Cu$_2$S phase must also have a copper activity <1, and therefore a lower Cu content than that of Cu$_2$S in equilibrium with pure solid Cu. Although the integral free energy of formation of the Cu$_2$S phase may change very slightly with composition, the change in activity of Cu and of S may be much greater. Complete thermodynamic description of equilibria like this requires a knowledge of both activities over the complete range of composition. The equilibria would be better regarded as

$$[Cu] \text{ in Pb} = Cu \ (\text{in } Cu_{2-\delta}S)$$

and

$$[S] \text{ in Pb} = S \ (\text{in } Cu_{2-\delta}S)$$

Increasing the S/Cu ratio in the Cu$_2$S lowers the copper activity in both phases, until the liquid lead becomes saturated with respect to PbS when the minimum copper content in lead is reached. It may also be emphasized that measurements of H$_2$S/H$_2$ equilibria do not give integral free energies but partial molar free energies of sulfur for the metal + sulfide two phase region. Calculation of integral free energies from such equilibria is generally based on the implicit assumption that the sulfide in equilibrium with the metal is stoichiometric.

References

1. Dice, C. M., G. L. Oldright, and T. B. Brighton, *Trans. Am. Inst. Mining Met. Engrs.*, **121**, 127 (1936).

2. Hall, A. E., *Trans. Am. Inst. Mining Met. Engrs.*, **121**, 194 (1936).

3. Williams, G. K., *Trans. Am. Inst. Mining Met. Engrs.*, **121**, 226 (1936).

4. Gallager, D., *Proc. Australasian Inst. Mining & Met.*, **No. 162–163**, 31 (1951).

5. Green, F. A., *The Refining of Non-ferrous Metals*, Institute of Mining and Metallurgy, London, 1950, p. 281.

6. George, W., *Metall u. Erz.*, **27**, 605 (1930).

7. Dennis, W. H., *Metallurgy of the Non-ferrous Metals*, Pitman, London, 1954, p. 244.

8. Hayward, C. R., *An Outline of Metallurgical Practice*, 3rd. ed., Van Nostrand, New York, 1952, p. 195.

1026   PROCESS METALLURGY

9. Ellingham, H. J. T., *J. Soc. Chem. Ind.*, **63**, 125 (1944).

10. Tafel, V., *Lehrbuch der Metallhüttenkunde*, 2nd ed., Vol. II, Hirzel, Leipzig, 1953, p. 141.

11. Buchanan, D. T., A. J. Perry, H. K. Wellington, and B. V. Börgelt, *Proc. Australasian Inst. Mining & Met.*, **No. 171**, 229 (1953).

12. Haig, K. V., *Refining of Non-Ferrous Metals*, Institute of Mining and Metallurgy, London, 1950, p. 316.

13. Haney, L. B., *Refining of Non-Ferrous Metals*, Institute of Mining and Metallurgy, London, 1950, p. 321.

14. Blanderer, J., *Metall*, **11**, 662 (1957).

15. Cunningham, D. A., private communication from Broken Hill Associated Smelters, Pt. Pirie.

16. Kleppa, O. J., and J. A. Weil, *J. Am. Chem. Soc.*, **73**, 4848 (1951).

17. Meissner, K. L., *Metall u. Erz*, **18**, 145 (1921).

18. Guertler, W., and G. Landau, *Metall u. Erz*, **31**, 169 (1934).

19. Jänecke, E., *Z. Elektrochem.*, **42**, 373 (1936).

20. Guertler, W., and G. Landau, *Z. anorg. u. allgem. Chem.*, **218**, 321 (1934).

21. Richardson, F. D., and J. H. E. Jeffes, *J. Iron Steel Inst. (London)*, **171**, 165 (1952).

22. Buerger, N. W., *Econ. Geol.*, **36**, 19 (1941).

23. Rahlfs, P., *Z. physik. Chem.*, **B31**, 157 (1936).

24. Wagner, J. B., and C. Wagner, *J. Electrochem. Soc.*, **104**, 509 (1957).

25. A.S.T.M. *Methods for Chemical Analysis of Metals*, Am. Soc. Testing Materials, Philadelphia, 1950, p. 402.

26. Guerin, B. D., *Proc. Australasian Inst. Mining & Met.*, **No. 182**, 67 (1954).

27. Friedrich, K., and A. Leroux, *Metallurgie*, **2**, 536 (1905).

28. Greenwood, J. N., and H. W. Worner, *J. Inst. Metals*, **65**, 435 (1939).

29. Sudo, K., *Sci. Repts. Research Inst. Tôhoku Univ.*, **A3**, 631 (1951).

30. Rosenqvist, T., *J. Metals*, **1**, 451 (1949).

31. Sudo, K., *Sci. Repts. Research Inst. Tôhoku Univ.*, **A2**, 519 (1950).

32. Rosenqvist, T., *J. Metals*, **3**, 535 (1951).

33. Sherman, C. W., H. I. Elvander, and J. Chipman, *J. Metals*, **2**, 334 (1950).

34. Wagner, J. B., and C. Wagner, *J. Chem. Phys.*, **26**, 1602 (1957).

35. Wagner, C., *Z. physik. Chem.*, **B21**, 25, 42 (1933).

36. Bloem, J., and F. A. Kröger, *Philips Research Repts.*, **12**, 281 (1957).

37. Bloem, J., and F. A. Kröger, *Z. physik. Chem. N. F.*, **7**, 1 (1956).

38. Ross, V., *Econ. Geol.*, **49**, 734 (1954).

39. Schrader, A., and H. Hanemann, *Z. Metallk.*, **33**, 49 (1941).

40. Kubaschewski, O., and E. Ll. Evans, *Metallurgical Thermochemistry*, 2nd. ed., Pergamon Press, London, 1956.

41. Richards, A. W., *Trans. Faraday Soc.*, **51**, 1193 (1955).

42. Jones, E. H., *The Refining of Non-Ferrous Metals*, Institute of Mining and Metallurgy, London 1950, p. 347.

43. Sudo, K., *Sci. Repts. Research Inst. Tôhoku Univ.*, **A2**, 325 (1950).

44. Kelley, K. K., *U. S. Bur. Mines, Bull.*, **No. 477** (1950).

45. Evans, W. H., and D. D. Wagman, *J. Research Natl. Bur. Standards, U. S.*, **49**, 141 (1952).

46. Kelley, K. K., *U. S. Bur. Mines, Bull.*, **No. 476** (1949).
47. Margrave, J. L., *J. Chem. Educ.*, **32**, 520 (1955).
48. Zeumer, H., and W. A. Roth, *Z. physik. Chem.*, **A173**, 365 (1935).
49. Kiukkola, K., and C. Wagner, *J. Electrochem. Soc.*, **104**, 379 (1957).
50. Brooks, A. A., *J. Am. Chem. Soc.*, **75**, 2464 (1953).
51. Richardson, F. D., and J. E. Antill, *Trans. Faraday Soc.*, **51**, 22 (1955).

Discussion

C. B. Alcock (*Imperial College, London*): We have recently measured the equilibrium constant for the process

$$[S \text{ in } Pb]_c + H_2 = H_2S$$

in the temperature range 500–680°C. By combining these results, which disagreed with the previously published work, with data for the equilibrium

$$PbS + H_2 = Pb + H_2S$$

one can derive the saturation solubility of sulfur in liquid lead in equilibrium with solid lead sulfide. Our results for this solubility agree within 10% with those reported in this paper, and thus would appear to eliminate any doubts as to the accuracy of these two researches.

Incidentally, we made use of radioactive sulfur, and determined the sulfur content of our lead samples by counting barium radio-sulfate. We encountered no difficulties such as those reported in Blanks and Willis' paper.

B. C. H. Steele, K. Murden, and **F. D. Richardson** (*Imperial College, London*): We have found this a most interesting paper for one of us (F.D.R.) has always cited the decopperization of lead by sulfur as a fine example of what would not be predicted by application of thermodynamics alone. He used to suggest that the lead reacts with the sulfur much more slowly than does copper, so that the sulfur potential prevailing during decopperization is higher than that for the system Pb + PbS [N.P.L. London Symposium, No. 9 (1959), p. 6A 18]. The authors' conclusion that small concentrations of dissolved silver inhibit the reaction between sulfur and lead is most interesting but would seem to be extraordinarily difficult to explain.

Recently, we have attempted the decopperization of high purity lead and of lead containing small amounts of antimony, sulfur, and arsenic, both separately and together. Surprisingly enough, we have not been able, in preliminary experiments, to get below 0.015% copper either with or without these additions. It was observed, however, in agreement with Blanks and Willis that the temperature rise following the addition of sulfur was markedly less in the presence of silver than in the other cases, and that the dross was finer. We wonder, therefore, whether it is really certain from the experiments quoted in the paper that silver is the essential agent. In any event the kinetics of this remarkable reaction would seem well worth further study.

R. F. Blanks and **G. M. Willis:** In reply to Dr. Alcock's statement that he used a counting technique for the determination of sulfur in lead, our experience is that the barium sulfate precipitated from the caustic extraction contains lead. Separate experiments showed that small percentages of $Pb^{35}SO_4$ affected the self-absorption curve for $Ba^{35}SO_4$, so that a prerequisite for the counting technique is the elimination of lead from the barium sulfate precipitate.

The agreement of our results with those of Alcock seems to remove the inconsistencies remaining in the data on the lead-sulfur system.

The results of Steele, Murden, and Richardson on decopperizing in the presence of small amounts of antimony, sulfur, and arsenic are as expected, since Cunningham found no effect with arsenic and antimony in the absence of silver. Silver is the only element we have investigated in the decopperizing reaction, and there is no doubt as to its efficiency. We have not claimed that other elements or combinations of elements may not behave similarly.

Analysis of Factors Affecting Temperature Drop between Tapping and Teeming in Steelmaking

N. L. SAMWAYS, T. E. DANCY, K. LI, and J. HALAPATZ

Research Division, Jones & Laughlin Steel Corporation, Youngstown, Ohio

Abstract

As part of a study of process variability in steelmaking, bath and teeming stream temperatures have been measured with calibrated thermocouples on 73 open hearth and 25 basic oxygen heats covering a range of grades. The validity of the teeming temperature measurements is examined and reference is made to the pattern of temperature changes during teeming. Theoretical calculations of temperature drop in 285T and 84T ladles have been made covering a range of ladle refractory temperature and tapping holding and teeming times. Estimates have also been made of the temperature effect of ladle additions using available thermodynamic data.

The theoretical values have been compared with temperature coefficients derived from a least squares solution of linear equations relating the variables between tapping and teeming. From these results an attempt has been made to evaluate the relative importance of the different variables.

INTRODUCTION

The control of furnace tapping temperature in steelmaking is not sufficient to define the ingot teeming temperature. In this paper the factors affecting temperature drop between furnace tapping and ingot teeming have been examined as a first step in estimating quantitatively the process variability associated with tapping and ladle practice.

A statistical analysis of data from open hearth and basic oxygen shops have been made incorporating thermodynamic calculations of ladle addition heat effects. This analysis has been supplemented by an independent theoretical treatment of heat transfer by conduction and radiation.

1029

The main variables associated with the process for one plant may be listed as follows:

1. Steel bath temperature at end of refining.
2. Steel bath oxygen level.
3. Slag iron oxide content.
4. Blocking additions in medium and high carbon heats.
5. Character of tapping stream.
6. Tapping time.
7. Ladle refractory temperature.
8. Ladle additions.
9. Holding time.
10. Teeming time.
11. Teeming temperature.

In this initial work the importance of bath temperature, tapping time, ladle additions, ladle refractory temperature, holding time, teeming time, and teeming temperature has been examined and certain assumptions made concerning the other factors.

It is difficult to estimate the heat effects associated with ladle additions due to the uncertain behavior of the various components during tapping. Therefore, alternative assumptions have been made and the resulting heat effects have been incorporated into the statistical analysis. From an examination of the statistical solutions an indication of the probable magnitude of these heat effects has been obtained.

From a comparison of the best statistical solution with the theoretical treatment, which deals solely with conduction and radiation losses in the ladle, an estimate has been made of temperature drop in the tapping stream.

Although the results obtained indicate the probable effects of the variables, they also show that much more attention should be paid in the future to such factors as the effect of tapping stream turbulence on the level of oxidation in the steel and the mechanism of deoxidation. Only when these mechanisms are fully understood can effective control be established.

PREVIOUS WORK

Sosman[1] and later Winkler[2] have examined aspects of temperature drop between tapping and teeming, but it is difficult to apply their results in a general manner to widely different practice. Also the temperature effect of deoxidizing additions is not considered in any detail in these papers.

Later work by Brower, Bain, and Larsen[3] deals with oxygen pickup during tapping, and this is of considerable significance in attempting to define the mechanism existing in the recovery and temperature effects of ladle additions. This work receives special attention in the present study.

The temperature drop between furnace tapping and teeming in an electric furnace shop has been discussed by Buchovecky, Langenberg, and Kollman.[4]

PLANT MEASUREMENTS

Data have been collected during normal operations of nominal 285T open hearth and nominal 84T basic oxygen furnaces, and includes measurements on rim, semi-killed, and killed steels.

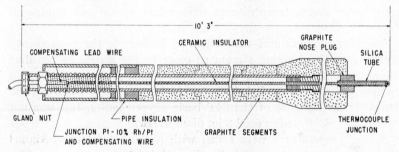

Fig. 1. Thermocouple assembly.

All steel temperature measurements were taken with slightly modified plant Pt-Pt 10% Rh thermocouples (Fig. 1), which were calibrated against the liquidus temperatures of ingot iron (2795°F). The units employed for bath temperatures had 2 in. long silica sheaths, and those used for immersion in the teeming stream had $1^1/_2$ in. long sheaths. The recorders used were checked with a standard potentiometer emf before and after each series of measurements. Both bath and teeming stream measurements are believed consistent to ±10°F.

In taking tap temperatures of blocked open hearth heats, measurements were made before block and also immediately before tap. In

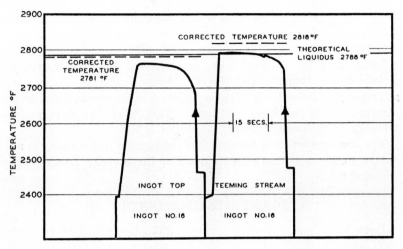

Fig. 2. Recorder traces of teeming stream and ingot top temperatures—rim heat.

most other cases, temperatures were taken within one minute of tap.

Teeming temperatures were taken by immersing the silica sheath slowly into the teeming stream as close to the nozzle as possible. In measurements on 285T open hearth ladles, it was necessary to reduce the steel flow slightly to avoid breaking the silica sheath. However, in the case of the 84T basic oxygen ladles, this was not necessary.   Both ladles used 2 in. diam nozzles.

Ladle temperatures were taken with a contact Chromel-Alumel thermocouple to give an indication of brick temperature.   The temperatures of the 285T open hearth ladles were within a range of 100–200°F so that ladle refractory temperature was not considered as a variable in the subsequent study.   The 84T ladle refractory temperature varied between 100 and 1000°F; and, therefore, this factor was included among the variables.   Ladle additions, tapping times, holding times, and teeming times were all recorded.

Before considering an analysis of data obtained, it is necessary to examine the validity of the temperature measurements.   The bath temperature measurements have been accepted as reliable, successive readings having shown a variability no greater than ±10°F.

The measured teeming stream temperatures are also believed to be close to the true steel temperatures for the following reasons.   The

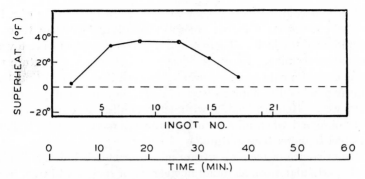

Fig. 3. Variation in superheat during teeming—hot heat.

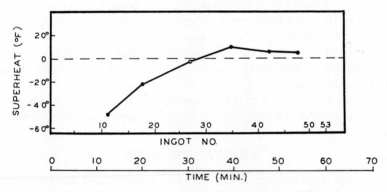

Fig. 4. Variation in superheat during teeming—cold heat.

recorder traces made during stream measurements on individual ingots rose to a maximum and leveled off in a consistent manner. The change in slope of these curves was similar to measurements made in ingot tops as shown in Figure 2. The whole silica sheath, which was $1/2$ in. shorter than the stream diameter was immersed in the stream, and care was taken not to immerse the graphite head of the thermocouple unit. A separate observer was employed to check immersion. Smooth recorder traces were taken as a sensitive indication of a good reading. In addition to these indications of accuracy, the consistency of the method was confirmed by the fact that a clearly defined pattern of stream temperature showed up within any one heat using different thermocouples on succeeding measurements. This same pattern was evident whether the heats were hot or cold.   Figure 3 shows this pattern in the case of a hot heat where the early ingots are substantially colder than those in the middle of the heat.   There is also a fall off in temperature toward the end of teeming.   Figure 4 illustrates a similar temperature rise in the case of a cold heat.   During this work it was noted that temperatures below the liquidus were obtained in some heats, and these heats were often associated with ladle skulls.   A ladle skull was never observed when all measurements were more than 10°F above the steel liquidus temperature.

The existence of teeming stream measurements below the liquidus of the particular steel, as found in the case of some cold heats, needs some explanation.   It is thought that this is indicative of steel being teemed as a liquid with some solid.   It was found that measurements taken in the ingot top immediately after teeming gave a temperature higher than the teeming temperature and close to the liquidus.   This seems to indicate that the solid material present in the stream during teeming had settled to the bottom of the ingot leaving liquid at the liquidus temperature.

Figure 2 also shows that the temperature in the ingot top is close to steel liquidus temperature.   This is typical of both killed and rim ingots.

ANALYSIS OF DATA

Overall temperature drops between tapping and teeming were measured on 73 open hearth heats varying between 280 and 310 tons. Of these 47 were rim, 8 semi-killed, and 18 killed grades.   Similar measurements were made on 25 basic oxygen heats, all of which were rim grades.

The hottest teeming stream temperature of the series within a heat was chosen as being most representative of the average temperature of the steel in the ladle.   The first few ingots teemed had a lower temperature and cannot be considered representative due to temperature stratification within the ladle.

In the following treatment a net temperature drop is used, which is defined as the difference between the measured drop and the calculated ladle addition effect.

Ladle Additions

The ladle addition heat effects include the change in sensible heat of the components and the heat of reactions which occur.

TABLE I

Ladle Addition-Temperature Effects—Open Hearth Rim Heat

1	Heat wt (in ladle):		594,000 lb
2	Ladle additions:		
	Regular manganese (75% Mn)		2,800 lb
	Electrolytic manganese		500 lb
	Aluminum		25 lb

3. Steel analysis:	% C	% Mn	% O
At tap	0.06	0.08	0.057ᵃ
At teeming	0.07	0.31	—

4. Materials balance (lb atoms):	C	Mn	Si	Al	Fe	O
Steel—at tap	29.7	8.6	—	—	Bal.	21.2ᵇ
Steel—at teeming	34.7	33.5	—	—	Bal.	—
Ladle additions:						
Regular manganese	15.2	38.2	1.3	—	8.6	—
Electrolytic manganese	—	9.1	—	—	—	—
Aluminum	—	—	—	0.9	—	—
	15.2	47.3	1.3	0.9	8.6	—
Addition recovery	5.0	24.9	—	0.9	—	—
Addition loss	10.2	22.4	1.3	0.9	8.6	—

(continued)

TABLE I (continued)

5. Heat effect of components:

1	2	3	4	5
Reaction	ΔH, Btu/lb atom of components	Component lb atoms	ΣH, Btu	TA
Aluminum[c,d]				
50% with (O) slag; 50% with O metal:				
$Al(s)_{77} \rightarrow Al(l)_{2900}$	24,000	0.45	11,000	1,3
$Al(s)_{77} + 1\frac{1}{2} O_{2900} \rightarrow \frac{1}{2}Al_2O_3(s)_{2900}$	−267,000	0.45	−120,000	1,2,3
$Al(s)_{77} + 1\frac{1}{2}FeO(l)_{2900} \rightarrow \frac{1}{2}Al_2O_3(s)_{2900} + 1\frac{1}{2}Fe(l)_{2900}$	−192,000	0.45	−86,000	2
Silicon[c-f]				
100% with O metal:				
$Si(s)_{77} + 2O_{2900} \rightarrow SiO_2(s)_{2900}$	−219,000	1.3	−285,000	1,2,3
Manganese[c,d]				
Manganese recovered:				
$Mn(s)_{77} \rightarrow Mn(l)_{2900}$	34,800	24.9	867,000	1,2,3
Manganese lost:				
$Mn(s)_{77} \rightarrow Mn(l)_{2900}$	34,800	22.4	780,000	1
$Mn(s)_{77} + FeO(l)_{2900} \rightarrow MnO(s)_{2900} + Fe(l)_{2900}$	−35,000	22.4	−784,000	2
$Mn(s)_{77} + O_{2900} \rightarrow MnO(s)_{2900}$	−91,000	22.4	−2,038,000	3
$\frac{1}{2}O_2(g)_{77} \rightarrow O_{2900}$	39,000	22.4	−874,000	3

Carbon[c,d,g]

In regular manganese:				
$Mn_3C(s)_{77} \rightarrow 3Mn(s)_{77} + C(s)_{77}$	-6,000	15.2	-91,000	1,2,3
All carbon:				
$C(s)_{77} \rightarrow C(s)_{2900}$	13,700	15.2	208,000	1,2,3
Carbon recovered:				
$C(s)_{2900} \rightarrow \underline{C}_{2900}$	11,500	5.0	58,000	1,2,3
Carbon lost:				
$C(s)_{2900} + FeO(l)_{2900} \rightarrow$				
$\quad CO(g)_{2900} + Fe(l)_{2900}$	56,000	10.2	571,000	2
$C(s)_{2900} + \underline{O}_{2900} \rightarrow CO(g)_{2900}$	0	10.2	0	3
$\tfrac{1}{2}O_2(g)_{77} \rightarrow \underline{O}_{2900}$	-39,000	10.2	-398,000	3
Heating:				
$Fe(s)_{77} \rightarrow Fe(l)_{2900}$	33,300	8.6	286,000	1,2,3

Iron[d]

6. Temperature effects:

Total heat effect (TA_1) = 1,714,000 Btu ≡ 16.1°F drop

Total heat effect (TA_2) = 624,000 Btu ≡ 5.9°F drop

Total heat effect (TA_3) = -2,376,000 Btu ≡ 22.4°F rise

[a] See ref. 5.
[b] Sufficient O for reaction with A and S.
[c] Kubaschewski, O., and E. L. Evans, *Metallurgical Thermochemistry*, Pergamon Press, London, 1955.
[d] Kelley, K. K., *U. S. Bur. Mines, Bull.* 476 (1949).
[e] Chipman, J., and N. J. Grant, *Trans. Am. Soc. Metals*, **28**, 361 (1943).
[f] Körber, F., and W. Oelsen, *Mitte., Kaiser-Wilhelm-Inst. Eisenforsch. Düsseldorf*, **18**, 109 (1936).
[g] Richardson, F. D., *J. Iron Steel Inst.* (London), **175**, 33 (1953).

The calculated effects are, however, dependent on the assumptions regarding the state of oxidation of steel when the ladle additions are made. Furthermore, the heat effects also depend upon whether, if there is a reaction with slag, some of the heat is transferred to the steel rather than to the slag and, if so, in what proportion. Due to lack of knowledge on this point, it has been assumed that temperature changes associated with these heat effects can be bracketed between two extremes, Ta_1 and Ta_3, which are defined below, together with an intermediate stage, Ta_2.

Ta_1: All manganese and carbon losses result from reaction with slag iron oxide, and any heat effects transfer themselves to the slag. Aluminum and silicon are considered to react with oxygen in the steel, and therefore, affect steel temperature. If sufficient aluminum is present to deoxidize the steel completely, assuming oxygen levels given for normal open hearth heats[5] to be correct, then any excess aluminum and silicon are taken to react with slag. This will be called "complete oxidation outside steel."

Ta_3: Immediately after tapping, it has been indicated[3] that steel can be saturated with oxygen. If this is so, then all losses of carbon and alloy additions can be attributed to reactions in the steel with dissolved oxygen. In this case all the heats of oxidation reactions will be transferred to the steel. This will be called "complete oxidation within steel."

Ta_2: All losses of alloys react with slag iron oxide and the heat is transferred to the steel by agitation in the course of tapping.

The temperature effect of ladle additions was calculated for each heat on the basis of the three assumptions outlined.

Examples for rim and killed heats are given in Tables I and II.

In the tables the first column gives the ladle reactions, the second column the heats of reaction, the third the lb atoms of components involved, and the fourth the total heat effect. The fifth column designates by 1, 2, and 3, the appropriate Ta term. The equations are given in the form which will permit application to different combinations of ladle additions. For example, the carbon in ferro-manganese, assumed to be Mn_3C, is decomposed at 77°F, and the carbon then treated separately. Thus, any elemental carbon addition can be added to the combined carbon in estimating the heat effect.

In rim heats (Table I) losses of manganese and carbon are treated according to the assumptions Ta_1, Ta_2, and Ta_3 and are designated in the Ta column.

TABLE II

Ladle Addition Temperature Effects—Open Hearth Killed Steel

1. Heat-wt (in ladle): 561,000 lb
2. Ladle additions:
   - Carbo-coke: 300 lb
   - Regular manganese (75% Mn): 5,500 lb
   - Ferro-silicon (48% Si): 2,500 lb
3. Steel analysis:

	% C	% Mn	% Si	% O
At tap	0.34	0.13	—[a]	0.018[b]
At teeming	0.45	0.77	0.23	—

4. Materials balance (lb atoms):

	C	Mn	Si	Fe	O
Steel—at tap	158.9	13.3	—[a]	Bal.	6.1
Steel—at teeming	210.3	78.5	46.1	Bal.	—
Ladle additions:					
Carbo-coke	24.9	—	—	—	—
Regular manganese	29.8	75.0	2.4	16.9	—
Ferro-silicon	—	—	42.9	23.2	—
	54.7	75.0	45.3	40.1	—
Addition recovery	51.4	65.2	45.3	40.1	—
Addition loss	3.4	9.8	-0.8[a]	—	—

(continued)

TABLE II (continued)

5. Heat effect of components:

	1	2	3	4	5
	Reaction	ΔH, Btu/lb atom of components	Component, lb atoms	ΣH, Btu	TA
Silicon[e-f]	Oxidation, excess Si alloying with steel				
	Decomposition of ferro-silicon:				
	$Fe_{0.54}$ $Si(s)_{77} \rightarrow 0.54Fe(s)_{77} + Si(s)_{77}$	19,000	42.9	815,000	1,2
	Decomposition of regular manganese:				
	$Si(s)_{77} \rightarrow Si(s)_{77}$	35,000	2.4	84,000	1,2
	Oxidation:				
	$Si(s)_{77} + 2O_{2900} \rightarrow SiO_2(s)_{2900}$	-254,000	3.1	-787,000	1,2
	Si alloying with steel:				
	$Si(s)_{77} \rightarrow \underline{Si}_{2900}$	-13,000	42.2	-549,000	1,2
Manganese[e,d]	Manganese recovered:				
	$Mn(s)_{77} \rightarrow Mn(l)_{2900}$	34,800	65.2	2,269,000	1,2
	Manganese lost:				
	$Mn(s)_{77} \rightarrow Mn(l)_{2900}$	34,800	9.8	341,000	1
	$Mn(s)_{77} + FeO(l)_{2900} \rightarrow MnO(s)_{2900} + Fe(l)_{2900}$	-35,000	9.8	-343,000	2

Carbon[c,d,g]

Decomposition of Mn_3C:

$Mn_3\underline{C}(s)_{77} \rightarrow 3Mn(s)_{77} + C(s)_{77}$ .... $-6,000$ ...... 29.8 ...... $-179,000$ 1,2

All carbon:

$C(s)_{77} \rightarrow C(s)_{2900}$ .... $13,700$ ...... 54.7 ...... $749,000$ 1,2

Carbon alloying with steel:

$C(s)_{2900} \rightarrow \underline{C}_{2900}$ .... $11,500$ ...... 51.4 ...... $591,000$ 1,2

Carbon lost:

$C(s)_{2900} + FeO(l)_{2900} \rightarrow CO(g)_{2900} + Fe(l)_{2900}$ .... $56,000$ ...... 3.4 ...... $190,000$ 2

Iron[d]

Heating:

$Fe(s)_{77} \rightarrow Fe(l)_{2900}$ .... $33,300$ ...... 40.1 ...... $1,335,000$ 1,2

6. Temperature effects:

Total heat effect $(TA_1) = 4{,}669{,}000$ Btu $\equiv 46.7°F$ drop

Total heat effect $(TA_2) = 4{,}175{,}000$ Btu $\equiv 41.7°F$ drop

[a] Deficiency of silicon equivalent to 0.07% Si at tap.
[b] See ref. 5.
[c] Kubaschewski, O., and E. L. Evans, *Metallurgical Thermochemistry*, Pergamon Press, London, 1955.
[d] Kelley, K. K., *U. S. Bur. Mines, Bull.*, 476 (1949).
[e] Chipman, J., and N. J. Grant, *Trans. Am. Soc. Metals*, **28**, 361 (1943).
[f] Körber, F., and W. Oelsen, *Mitt., Kaiser-Wilhelm-Inst. Eisenforsch. Düsseldorf*, **18**, 109 (1936).
[g] Richardson, F. D., *J. Iron Steel Inst. (London)*, **175**, 33 (1953).

The example of a killed heat (Table II) has been deliberately chosen to illustrate the uncertainty of the state of oxidation during and after tap and the consequent ladle reactions following a furnace block. The calculation is based on normal operating data and also illustrates the need of a more detailed study of the system before a satisfactory solution can be obtained. In this example the oxygen level at tap was obtained from published data,[5] and the silicon content at tap was assumed to be zero for the Ta_1 and Ta_2 calculations. Subsequent calculation shows that there was an insufficient silicon ladle addition to account for the final silicon residual in the steel. This indicates that there was a silicon residual at tap, and hence it is unlikely that the oxygen level was as high as that assumed. Furthermore, the silicon loss in the tapping stream and from the ladle addition is unknown since the silicon at tap was not determined. (A study to clarify the situation is currently in progress.) Losses of carbon and manganese are treated in the same way as outlined for the Ta_1 and Ta_2 assumption. Without a knowledge of silicon at tap, it is not possible to calculate the heat effect in terms of the Ta_3 assumption. Due to the uncertainty of the mechanism, the calculation of the Ta_3 effect for this blocked heat and other killed heats was not considered justified.

Statistical Analysis

In order to determine the independent effects of tapping, holding and teeming on heat losses from steel in the ladle, the net temperature drop $(\Delta T - Ta)$, where ΔT is the measured overall temperature drop, was equated with linear functions relating tapping time, holding time, and teeming time with their respective unknown coefficients. Where applicable, the time between measuring the tap temperature and tapping the furnace was included.

The linear functions were chosen for simplicity and subsequent usefulness in the mill. This is consistent with the theoretical treatment over the ranges considered.

The equations for each experimental heat may then be written:

$$(\Delta T - Ta_1) = K + k_b t_b + k_t t_t + k_h t_h + k_p t_p \qquad (1)$$

where Ta_1 can be replaced by Ta_2 or Ta_3 and t_b, t_t, t_h, t_p are the time before tap, tapping time, holding time, and teeming time, respectively. The factors k_b, k_t, k_h, and k_p are the coefficients.

For the basic oxygen data a term for initial ladle refractory temperature is included in the equation and can be written:

$$(\Delta T - Ta_1) = K + k_b t_b + k_t t_t (T_s - T_0)$$
$$+ k_h t_h (T_s - T_0) + k_p t_p (T_s - T_0) \quad (2)$$

or

$$(\Delta T - Ta_1) = K + k_b t_b + k_t t'_t + k_h t'_h + k_p t'_p \quad (3)$$

where T_s is the initial steel temperature and T_0 the initial ladle refractory temperature. It is seen that for small charges in T_s or T_0, the factors k_t, k_h, and k_p will alter very little.

A program was set up on a digital computer to solve equations in this form for groups of experimental data from both open hearth and basic oxygen furnace shops to give the least squares solution for values of k_b, k_t, k_h, k_p, and the constant K.

From a consideration of the best statistical equation obtained and a theoretical treatment described in the next section, it should be possible to indicate: (1) The most likely heat effect of ladle additions and, consequently, the nature of ladle deoxidation. (2) The effect of tapping time, holding time, and teeming time. (3) The validity of the theoretical treatment.

The statistical solutions obtained for the data using the different ladle additions effects, in which temperature is expressed in °F and time in minutes, are as follows:

Open Hearth Data

Number of heats, $N = 73$ (rim, semi-killed, and killed):

$$\Delta T - Ta_1 = +47.80 - 0.88t_b + 1.13t_t + 1.36t_h - 0.12t_p \quad (4)$$

Standard error $= 16.3°$

$$\Delta T - Ta_2 = +42.59 - 0.24t_b + 2.35t_t + 1.64t_h + 0.16t_p \quad (5)$$

Standard error $= 18.9°$

Number of heats, $N = 47$ (rim heats only):

$$\Delta T - Ta_1 = +43.84 - 0.62t_b + 1.68t_t + 1.28t_h - 0.19t_p \quad (6)$$

Standard error $= 16.9°$

$$\Delta T - Ta_2 = +34.56 - 0.41t_b + 2.35t_t + 1.88t_h + 0.21t_p \quad (7)$$

$$\text{Standard error} = 18.2°$$

$$\Delta T - Ta_3 = +85.03 - 0.90t_b + \underline{1.61t_t} + 0.67t_h + 0.10t_p \quad (8)$$

$$\text{Standard error} = 18.2°$$

Since the Ta_3 effect was not determined for killed heats, Eq. (8) is considered together with Eqs. (4) and (5) in the subsequent discussion.

Statistical expressions have also been derived for 25 basic oxygen heats:

Basic Oxygen Data

$N = 25$ (all rim heats):

$$\Delta T - Ta_1 = -41.78 + \underline{1.76t_b} + 5.46 \times 10^{-3}t'_t$$
$$+ 1.47 \times 10^{-3}t'_h + 1.13 \times 10^{-3}t'_p \quad (9)$$

$$\text{Standard error} = 24.2°$$

$$\Delta T - Ta_2 = +6.55 + 0.97t_b + 3.52 \times 10^{-3}t'_t$$
$$+ 0.93 \times 10^{-3}t'_h + 0.54 \times 10^{-3}t'_p \quad (10)$$

$$\text{Standard error} = 25.7°$$

$$\Delta T - Ta_3 = -65.18 + \underline{2.74t_b} + 7.88 \times 10^{-3}t'_t$$
$$+ 1.87 \times 10^{-3}t'_h + 1.83 \times 10^{-3}t'_p \quad (11)$$

$$\text{Standard error} = 24.6°$$

The underlined coefficients have been found statistically significant.

THEORETICAL TREATMENT

The theoretical calculation of heat losses between furnace tapping and the teeming of an ingot is limited to a consideration of heat losses by conduction to the ladle brickwork, during the tapping, holding, and teeming periods and by radiation from the exposed steel surface in the ladle during tapping.

The discussion given below will deal with (1) conduction loss through ladle walls, (2) conduction loss through ladle bottom, and (3) radiation and convection losses from surface during tapping.

Heat losses from the tapping stream, which are not as yet amenable to mathematical treatment, will be discussed in an overall analysis of results.

Heat Loss by Conduction through Ladle Walls

Assumptions to be made are as follows:

1. Since the brick lining is relatively thick (in excess of 7 in.) heat will only penetrate a short distance in the time intervals involved. Thus the problem is considered as one of a semi-infinite solid body of refractory material with a cavity filled with steel. This assumption is substantiated by the calculations by Sosman[1] of temperature distribution in the $7^{1}/_{2}$-in. brick lining containing steel initially at 1585°C (2885°F).

2. Steel in the ladle is well mixed so that temperature of steel is uniform throughout and does not change sufficiently to affect the calculation of heat loss.

3. The brick lining of an actual ladle is generally tapered and terraced, but it will be assumed to be of cylindrical shape with an effective radius such that

$$A_w = 2\pi r_e L \tag{12}$$

where A_w is the contact area between steel and lining, r_e the effective radius, and L the depth of steel.

4. Physical and thermal properties of the ladle lining are independent of temperature.

With the above assumptions, the differential equation to be solved for the lining is

$$\partial T/\partial t = \alpha(\partial^2 T/\partial r^2 + (1/r)\partial T/\partial r) \tag{13}$$

with the initial and boundary conditions:

$$T = T_0 \text{ at } r > r_e \text{ and } t = 0$$
$$T = T_s \text{ at } r = r_e \text{ and } t > 0$$
$$T = T_0 \text{ at } r = \infty \text{ and } t > 0$$
$$\partial T/\partial r = 0 \text{ at } r = \infty \text{ and } t > 0$$

where T is the temperature, T_s is the initial steel temperature, T_0 is the initial ladle refractory temperature, r is the radius measured from the axis of cylinder, r_e is the effective radius of lining, t is the time, and α is the thermal diffusivity of refractory material.

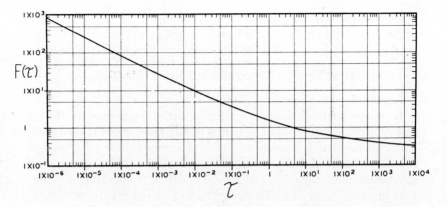

Fig. 5. $F(\tau)\left(= \int_0^{4/\sqrt{\tau}} \exp\{\tau\mu^2\} \cdot \dfrac{J_2(u)\,Y_0(u) - J_0(u)\,Y_2(u)}{J_0^2(u) + Y_0^2(u)} \cdot du\right)$ vs τ.

The solution of Eq. (13), satisfying the initial and boundary conditions, obtained by the method of Laplace transform is

$$\frac{T - T_0}{T_s - T_0} = 1 + \frac{1}{\pi} \int_0^\infty e^{-\eta t}$$

$$\frac{J_0(\sqrt{\eta/\alpha}\,r)\,Y_0(\sqrt{\eta/\alpha}\,r_e) - J_0(\sqrt{\eta/\alpha}\,r_e)\,Y_0(\sqrt{\eta/\alpha}\,r)}{J_0^2(\sqrt{\eta/\alpha}\,r_e) + Y_0^2(\sqrt{\eta/\alpha}\,r_e)} \cdot d\eta/\eta \quad (14)$$

where $J_0(x)$ and $Y_0(x)$ are Bessel functions of the first and the second kind, respectively, both of zero order. Using dimensionless groups $\theta = (T - T_0)/(T_s - T_0)$, $\tau = \alpha t/r_e^2$, $R = r/r_e$, and $u = (\sqrt{\eta/\alpha})r_e$, Eq. (14) becomes

$$\theta = 1 + \frac{2}{\pi} \int_0^\infty \exp\{-\tau u^2\} \frac{J_0(uR)\,Y_0(u) - J_0(u)\,Y_0(uR)}{J_0^2(u) + Y_0^2(u)} \cdot \frac{du}{u} \quad (15)$$

The heat flow per unit time at any r is given by

$$q_1 = -2\pi r Lk(\partial T/\partial r) = -2\pi R Lk(T_s - T_0) \cdot \partial\theta/\partial R \quad (16)$$

where q_1 is the heat transferred per unit time and k the thermal conductivity of refractory material.

We then have for $R = 1$ (i.e., $r = r_e$)

$$\frac{q_1}{L(T_s - T_0)k} = 4 \int_0^\infty \exp\{-\tau u^2\} \cdot \frac{J_1(u)\,Y_0(u) - J_0(u)\,Y_1(u)}{J_0^2(u) + Y_0^2(u)} \cdot du \quad (17)$$

where $J_1(x)$ and $Y_1(x)$ are Bessel functions of the first and second kind, respectively, both of first order.

Integration of the right-hand side of Eq. (17) may be simplified by dividing the integral into two parts

$$\int_0^\infty = \int_0^{u_1} + \int_{u_1}^\infty \qquad (18)$$

It can be shown that for u_1 larger than a certain limit, the second integral on the right becomes negligibly small. This limit is found to be $4/\sqrt{\tau}$. Evaluation of the integral $\int_0^{4/\sqrt{\tau}}$ was carried out numerically on a digital computer, and results are given in Figure 5.

The total heat loss for any length of time can now be calculated by

$$Q_1 = \int_0^t q_1 . dt \qquad (19)$$

It will be noted that Eq. (17), being expressed in terms of dimensionless quantities, will be applicable for any initial and boundary conditions and even problems other than the one treated here provided the conditions are comparable. Furthermore, the geometry of the ladle lining can be more closely represented by dividing the ladle into a finite number of cylindrical sections of varying radius; the total heat loss will be the sum of heat losses through individual sections calculated by Eq. (17).

Another advantage of dividing the ladle into sections is that Eq. (17) can also be used to calculate heat losses during tapping and teeming.* The procedure to be followed is to subject each section to an initial condition at different times. In other words, the time lapse during which heat is conducted away from the steel will be different for each section, being shorter for sections near the top and longer for sections near the bottom when filling and emptying. In the present calculation the ladle is divided into 10 sections. It is apparent that the accuracy of calculation increases with increasing number of sections.

Heat Loss by Conduction through Ladle Bottom

The bottom of a ladle is often lined with over 10 in. of brick and may, therefore, be considered as a semi-infinite solid of refractory material. In addition, assumptions 2 and 4 made in the preceding

---

* Paschkis[6] used an analog computer to study heat loss from ladles during holding only.

treatment will be applied here.   The differential equation for this case is

$$\partial T/\partial t = \alpha(\partial^2 T/\partial x^2) \tag{20}$$

with the conditions

$$T = T_0 \text{ at } x > 0 \text{ and } t = 0$$
$$T = T_s \text{ at } x > 0 \text{ and } t > 0$$
$$T = T_0 \text{ at } x = \infty \text{ and } t > 0 \Big\}$$
$$\partial T/\partial x = 0 \text{ at } x = \infty \text{ and } t > 0 \Big\}$$

where x is the distance measured from the steel-bottom interface into the lining.   The solution[7] of Eq. (20) is

$$(T - T_0)/(T_s - T_0) = 2/\sqrt{\pi}.\int_x^\infty / \sqrt[2]{\alpha t} \exp\{-\lambda^2\}.d\lambda \tag{21}$$

The heat flow per unit time is given by

$$q_2 = -Ak(\partial T/\partial x) = [Ak(T_s - T_0)]/\sqrt{\pi \alpha t}.$$
$$\exp\{-(x/2\sqrt{\alpha t})^2\} \tag{22}$$

At $x = 0$

$$q_2 = [Ak(T_s - T_0)]/\sqrt{\pi \alpha t} \tag{23}$$

where A is the area of contact between steel and bottom.

Integration of Eq. (23) with respect to t gives the total heat loss

$$Q_2 = \int_0^t q_2 dt = [2Ak (T_s - T_0)]/\sqrt{\pi \alpha}.\sqrt{t} \tag{24}$$

Heat Loss by Radiation and Convection from the Surface

Heat loss by radiation and convection from the exposed steel surface in the ladle will be considered only for the period of tapping.   At completion of tapping, the steel is covered by a layer of slag and heat is dissipated from the slag surface by radiation and convection principally at the expense of the sensible heat and/or heat of fusion of the slag.   Thus, the temperature of the steel will not be affected by these losses.

The radiant heat loss per unit time is considered both for the case where the bottom of the ladle is just covered with steel, and the case where the ladle is full.   The mean of these two values is taken to be the rate of heat loss attributable to surface radiation for any tapping time.   The method of calculation is similar to that outlined by Schuh-mann.[8]

Calculation of heat loss due to convection during the tapping period has been made.   It was found, however, that the loss involved was very small and can be neglected.

Numerical Results

Temperature drops due to various heat losses discussed here were calculated using the following numerical data.

1. Properties of ladle lining (clay fire brick)

Composition: spot analysis—65% SiO_2, 27% Al_2O_3

Density: $\rho = 125$ lb/cu ft

Heat capacity: $C = 0.20$ Btu/lb°F

Thermal conductivity: $k = 0.0081$ Btu/min ft °F

Thermal diffusivity: $\alpha = k/C_p = 0.00032$ ft²/min

These values were not actually measured but estimated from data[9] on a refractory brick of similar composition.

2. Properties of liquid steel

Density: $\rho_s = 449.5$ lb/cu ft

Heat capacity: $C_s = 0.18$ Btu/lb °F

3. Temperature conditions

Initial steel temperature: $T_s = 2800, 2900, 3000$°F

Initial ladle refractory temperature: $T_0 = 100–1000$°F

4. Dimensions of ladle

	Open hearth ("285T" ladle)	Basic oxygen ("84T" ladle)
Top diam	12 ft 7 in	8 ft 8 in
Bottom diam	10 ft 5 in	6 ft 9 in
Height	13 ft 0 in	9 ft 9 in
Steel mass	600,000 lb	176,000 lb

The results of the numerical calculations for the open hearth and basic oxygen ladles are shown in Figures 6 to 11.

Figures 6 and 9 show the temperature drop of steel against total tapping time due to conduction, radiation, and conduction and radiation combined for the 285T open hearth and 84T basic oxygen ladles. In the case of the open hearth ladle, the initial ladle refractory temperature is considered constant at 100°F; the effect of heat loss due to

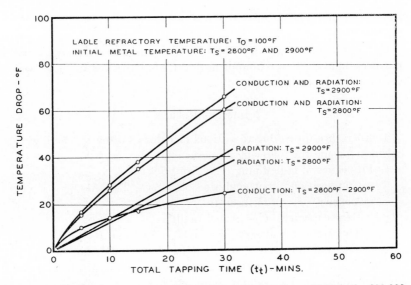

Fig. 6. Theoretical temperature drop vs total tapping time—285T ladle, 600,000 lb steel.

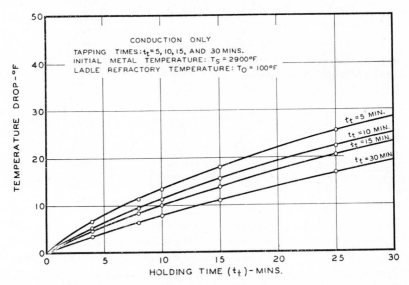

Fig. 7. Theoretical temperature drop vs holding time—285T ladle, 600,000 lb steel.

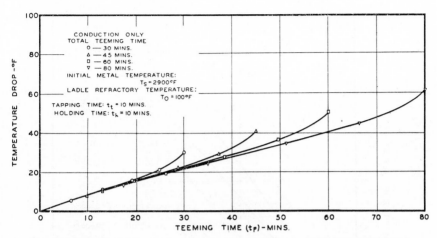

Fig. 8. Theoretical temperature drop vs teeming time—285T ladle, 600,000 lb steel.

radiation is shown for initial steel temperatures of 2800 and 2900°F. In the case of the basic oxygen ladle, the effect of the ladle refractory temperature is indicated for 100 and 1000°F, together with radiation losses at initial steel temperatures of 2800, 2900, and 3000°F.

In Figures 7 and 10 the temperature drop is shown against holding time for various tapping times for the 285T and 84T ladles, respectively. In both cases the initial steel temperature is 2900°F and the initial refractory temperature 100°F.

Examples of temperature drop during teeming are shown in Figures 8 and 11 for the 285T and 84T ladles, respectively, for specific tapping and holding times. The curves shown illustrate the temperature drop associated with different total teeming times. It can be seen that during the last stages of teeming, the rate of temperature drop becomes greater in all cases as the volume of steel in the ladle decreases.

Equation (17) shows that the heat loss for a particular ladle is proportional to $(T_s - T_0)$, therefore a small change in either initial steel temperature or initial refractory temperature will have only a minor effect on the temperature drop. However, if $(T_s - T_0)$ is appreciably different from those shown, the heat loss can be calculated by direct proportion to the change in $(T_s - T_0)$.

It will also be noted from Figure 6 that the heat loss due to radiation is more sensitive to steel temperature than the conduction loss.

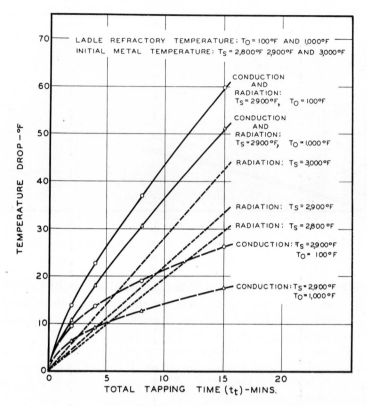

Fig. 9. Theoretical temperature drop vs total tapping time—84T ladle, 176,000 lb steel.

DISCUSSION OF RESULTS

The statistical analysis of the data obtained from the open hearth shop indicates that the temperature drop between tapping and teeming can be predicted for 67% of all heats to within $\pm 19°F$ with prior knowledge of the tapping temperature, the time between measurement of the tapping temperature and tapping, the quantities and composition of the ladle additions, tapping time, holding time, and teeming time.   This is a small error in view of: (1) possible errors in the two temperature measurements, which are each considered to be reliable to within $\pm 10°F$; (2) variations in the character of the tapping

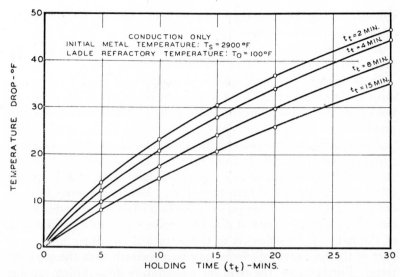

Fig. 10. Theoretical temperature drop vs holding time—84T ladle, 176,000 lb steel.

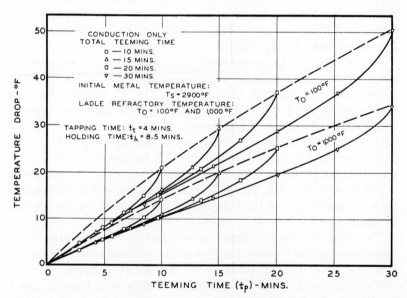

Fig. 11. Theoretical temperature drop vs teeming time—84T ladle, 176,000 lb steel.

streams having the same total tapping time; and (3) lack of precise knowledge of ladle addition heat effects.

It is further noted from Eqs. (4)–(7) that the exclusion of semi-killed and killed heats does not reduce the standard error.

In the case of the basic oxygen data, the calculated temperature drop has an error of $\pm 26°F$ for 67% of the heats, but this is nevertheless considered satisfactory in view of the combined errors outlined previously.

A comparison on the basis of standard error of the three statistical equations (4), (5), and (6) from the open hearth data, or Eqs. (9), (10), and (11) from the basic oxygen data, fails to show that any one solution is clearly better than the others. Hence, it cannot be indicated directly which assumption of the heat effect of ladle additions is most satisfactory. Nor is it possible to give a detailed interpretation of the individual coefficients in the statistical equations since some part of the temperature effects may be associated with the constant term. Furthermore, the term for temperature drop during tapping may include heat losses from the steel in the ladle and from the tapping stream which may be of a complex nature. However, by making use of the theoretical results it is possible to obtain indications of the most likely heat effect of ladle additions and an estimate of the heat losses from the tapping stream.

For this purpose the theoretical values for individual temperature drops will be assumed reliable and this assumption is substantiated by comparison with Eq. (10), involving Ta_2. In this equation the constant term is small, and consequently a direct comparison between theoretical and statistical treatments should be valid. It is found that the average differences between the statistical and theoretical values are only 3°F for holding and 1°F for teeming. This comparison includes widely varying initial ladle refractory temperatures.

The assumptions Ta_1, Ta_2, and Ta_3 can be examined in conjunction with a consideration of the independent effect of the tapping stream, designated by Tf.

The effect Tf was calculated by subtracting the theoretical temperature drop due to heat losses in the ladle (conduction and radiation only) from $(\Delta T\text{-}Ta)$ given by the statistical equations.

The values of Tf were then correlated linearly with tapping time t_t resulting in the following equations:

Open Hearth Data

$$Tf_1 = 12.9 - 0.5t_t \quad \text{[from Eq. (4) and Figs. 6, 7, 8]} \quad (25)$$
$$\text{Standard error} = 8.0°$$

$$Tf_2 = 24.9 + 0.2t_t \quad \text{[from Eq. (5) and Figs. 6, 7, 8]} \quad (26)$$
$$\text{Standard error} = 6.5°$$

$$Tf_3 = 46.3 - 0.2t_t \quad \text{[from Eq. (8) and Figs. 6, 7, 8]} \quad (27)$$
$$\text{Standard error} = 8.0°$$

Basic Oxygen Data

$$Tf_1 = -10.8 + 8.4t_t \quad \text{[from Eq. (9) and Figs. 9, 10, 11]} \quad (28)$$
$$\text{Standard error} = 6.9°$$

$$Tf_2 = 3.4 + 6.0t_t \quad \text{[from Eq. (10) and Figs. 9, 10, 11]} \quad (29)$$
$$\text{Standard error} = 4.5°$$

$$Tf_3 = 3.3 + 11.5t_t \quad \text{[from Eq. (11) and Figs. 9, 10, 11]} \quad (30)$$
$$\text{Standard error} = 11.6°$$

Comparison of the standard errors in these two sets of equations indicates that Eqs. (26) and (29) are marginally better. This im-

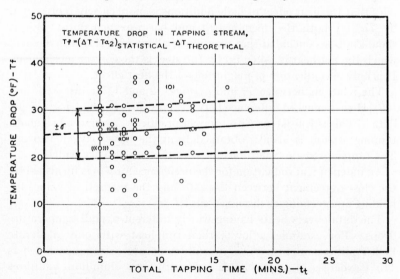

Fig. 12. Tapping stream temperature drop vs total tapping time. Open hearth furnace.

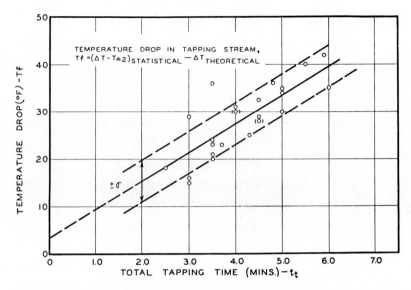

Fig. 13. Tapping stream temperature drop vs total tapping time.   Basic oxygen
furnace.

plies that the heat effect of ladle additions is more closely represented
by Ta_2 for both the open hearth and basic oxygen data.   But it
should not be concluded that reaction of alloys with slag iron oxide in
which the net heat is taken up by the steel is the correct mechanism.
It is only an indication of magnitude of the heat effect.

The relations between Tf and t_1 [Figs. 12 and 13 or Eqs. (26) and
(29)] show a marked difference between open hearth and basic oxygen
data.   This is consistent with tapping practice.   A relatively smooth
tapping stream is always obtained from the basic oxygen furnace.
The tapping stream conditions for the open hearth vary widely.

An independent indication for the preference for Ta_2 is furnished by
the close agreement between Eq. (10) and the theoretical values for
holding and teeming as discussed earlier.

The data covers heats having widely different overall temperature
drops.   For example, a low carbon rim heat with only moderate
ladle additions might have an overall temperature drop of as much as
115°F whereas in a fully killed heat with large aluminum additions
it may be as small as 31°F.   The treatment discussed here is equally
applicable to those extremes.

The relative magnitude of the individual temperature effects are shown in Table III.

TABLE III

	Open hearth, °Fa	Basic oxygen, °Fa
Ladle additions (Ta_2)	$-52-+45$	$+9-+20$
Tapping		
from tapping stream	$+20-+30$	$+15-+40$
in the ladle	$+15-+45$	$+10-+30$
Holding	$+5-+20$	$+10-+35$
Teeming	$+5-+40$	$+5-+35$

a Here, the + sign indicates a temperature drop, and − sign indicates a temperature rise.

It can be seen from the above that the major temperature effects are due to the ladle additions and tapping. For this reason stress has been placed upon the heat effects of ladle additions and of the tapping stream in this work. The elucidation of the mechanisms involved forms the subject of another study which is currently in progress.

CONCLUSIONS

1. It is possible to represent by a statistical equation [Eq. (5) for open hearth heats and Eq. (10) for basic oxygen heats] the temperature drop of steel between the furnace and teeming stream in terms of tapping time, ladle additions, holding time, and teeming time, despite lack of precise knowledge of the overall system. The standard errors of the statistical equations are comparable with experimental accuracy.

2. The comparative effects of ladle heat losses due to conduction and radiation during tapping, holding, and teeming can best be studied theoretically. A general theoretical expression [Eq. (17)] has been derived for the heat loss due to conduction to a cylindrical container in terms of dimensionless quantities. This expression is applicable to problems for any initial and boundary conditions as well as the one treated here provided the conditions are comparable.

3. An estimate of the effect of tapping stream from the open hearth and basic oxygen furnace has been obtained by considering both statistical and theoretical results. It is indicated that the major

part of the overall temperature drop occurs during tapping and can be attributed to the effect of ladle additions and tapping stream.

4. The study suggests that the heat effects of ladle additions are of similar magnitude to that obtained if any alloy losses are reacted with slag iron oxide contributing the net heat to the steel. This has been represented by Ta_2.

The authors wish to express their thanks to Research, Metallurgical and Operating Personnel of Jones & Laughlin Steel Corporation without whose help and cooperation this work would not have been possible. In particular, the contributions of D. C. McCune, senior staff statistician, and W. J. Howard, technician, are gratefully acknowledged.

References

1. Sosman, R. E., *Trans. Am. Inst. Mining Met. Engrs.*, **176**, 15 (1948).

2. Winkler, T. B., *Open Hearth Proc.*, *Am. Inst. Mining Met. Engrs.*, **32**, 11 (1949).

3. Brower, T. E., J. W. Bain, and B. M. Larsen, *Trans. Am. Inst. Mining Met. Engrs.*, **188**, 851 (1950).

4. Buchovecky, W. A., F. C. Langenberg, and W. C. Kollmann, *Electric Furnace Conference*, Am. Inst. Mining, Metallurgical, and Petroleum Engrs., Detroit, 1958.

5. *Basic Open Hearth Steelmaking*, Am. Inst. Mining and Metallurgical Engrs., New York, 1951, p. 652.

6. Paschkis, V., *Trans. Am. Foundrymen's Soc.*, **64**, 565 (1956).

7. Ingersoll, L. S., O. J. Zobel, and A. C. Ingersoll, *Heat Conduction*, Univ. of Wisconsin Press, Madison, 1954.

8. Schuhmann, R., Jr., *Metallurgical Engineering*, Vol. I, Addison-Wesley Press, Cambridge, Mass., 1952, pp. 232–234.

9. Ruddle, R. W., "The Solidification of Castings," Monogr. and Rept. Ser. No. 7, Inst. of Metals, London, 1950.

Discussion

C. M. Adams (*MIT*): I have read the paper with much interest, and feel a real contribution has been made to rationalization of the complex thermal bookkeeping which arises in trying to assess temperature changes during handling of liquid steel between the furnace and the ingot. However, the heat conduction relationships have made the paper seem unduly complicated and can be replaced by very accurate algebraic expressions, or at least handled by references to standard works on the subject.

Equation (15) and the equivalent of Eq. (17) are given by H. S. Carslaw and J. C. Jaeger (*Conduction of Heat in Solids*, Oxford Univ. Press, London, 1947), who also present a log-log graph of the integral in Eq. (17), similar to that presented by the authors in Figure 5. For more precise numerical work, tabulation of values for the integral in Eq. (17) has been presented by Jaeger and Clarke [*Proc. Roy. Soc. (Edinburgh)*, **61**, 229 (1942)].

Whenever the depth of heat penetration into a cylindrical surface is small compared to the radius of that surface, the heat flux may be very closely approximated by

$$q_1/(2\pi r_e L) = K(T_s - T_0)[(1/2r_e) + (1/\sqrt{\pi \alpha t})] \tag{D1}$$

where the terminology is that used by the authors. In other words, the integral in Figure 5 is given by

$$F(\tau) = \sqrt{\pi}/2[(\sqrt{\pi}/2) + (1/\sqrt{\tau})] \tag{D2}$$

with good accuracy for values of τ less than 1.0. The value τ never exceeds 0.05 for any of the situations reflected in Figures 6 through 11, and large values of τ would never obtain in this kind of work; if such were not the case, the assumption that ladle walls are, in effect, infinitely thick, would be invalid. Equation (D1) has been used in studies of heat flow from sand castings [Adams, C. M., Jr., and H. F. Taylor, *Trans., Am. Foundrymen's Soc.*, **60**, (1952); *ibid.*, **61**, (1953); *ibid.*, **65** (1957)] and, of course, is easily integrated to give an expression for Q_1.

"The existence of teeming stream measurements below the liquidus of the particular steel," is strongly questioned. Liquid steel which has been cooled to the point where it becomes partly solid, will, in general, only be a few degrees below the liquidus temperature. For example, a steel having the theoretical liquidus temperature, 2788°F, quoted in Figure 2, will be half solid at a bulk temperature 5° below the liquidus. The temperature (but not the heat content) of a liquid-solid steel mixture is a simple function of the liquid composition. Thus, a teeming stream which gives an apparent temperature 30°F below the liquidus would have to involve a liquid composition containing 0.20% carbon higher than the nominal composition of the alloy, and this seems quite impossible. It has been the writer's experience when a sheathed thermocouple is introduced into low carbon steel at its liquidus temperature (i.e., with no superheat), an additional sheath of solid steel immediately forms on the thermocouple, which remelts very slowly, if at all. The metallic sheath so formed has a much higher thermal conductivity than silica, and low readings inevitably result. While it is felt teeming stream temperatures below the liquidus must somehow be explained in terms of temperature measurement, since no such difficulty is experienced at higher temperatures, there is no reason to question temperatures measured well above the liquidus. With respect to comparison of ingot top and teeming temperatures for "cold" heats, it should be pointed out the abstraction of solid from a liquid-solid mixture will not have the effect of heating the liquid. Furthermore, if one were to measure temperature in the center of the ingot when the ingot was half solid, the liquid zone would still be virtually at its liquidus temperature [Bishop, H. F., F. A. Brandt, and W. S. Pellini, *Trans. Am. Foundrymen's Soc.*, **59**, 435 (1951)]; in sum, liquid steel simply does not "cool off" much during solidification.

Finally, the importance of radiation as a heat loss mechanism during tapping is emphasized in Figures 6 and 9, which show more than half the total heat loss to be radiative. That such a huge effect can be completely inhibited by a slag cover during teeming and holding is hard to accept.

I hope these remarks may be of some use; this is certainly an ambitious undertaking and the best job of its kind yet.

N. L. Samways, T. E. Dancy, K. Li, and **J. Halapatz:** The authors thank Professor Adams for the interesting points he has raised in his discussion. Regarding the theoretical calculations of heat loss, we appreciate his calling to our attention the pertinent literature references. However, it will be noted that in Figure 5 the curve covers a range of τ, wider than either the tabulation of Jaeger and Clark or the suggested approximate equation. Although the values of τ involved in the present work are small, we have in mind other problems where large values of τ would be required. Discussion Table I compares the calculated results for $F(\tau)$.

DISCUSSION TABLE I

	$F(\tau)$		
τ	Present work	Adams & Taylor	Jaeger & Clark
1.0×10^{-4}	89.42	89.3	
1.0×10^{-2}	9.63	9.65	9.48
1.0	1.55	1.67	1.57
10.0	0.81	1.06	0.83

We believe that we were justified in discussing our method of treatment in some detail in order to provide a mathematical background on which the derivation is based. We agree, however, that the approximations given by Professor Adams would be quite adequate for this particular study.

We ourselves questioned the validity of teeming stream temperatures below the liquidus of a particular steel when the results became available, and it is possible, as Professor Adams suggests, that there may have been heat conduction along solid material in contact with the silica sheath. However, on further examination, we have concluded that this may not be the complete explanation.

The teeming stream measurements shown in Figure 4 were taken during the pouring of a heat of steel containing 0.25% C. This carbon content corresponds to a freezing range of approximately 78°F. Following the reasoning of H. F. Bishop, F. A. Brandt, and W. S. Pellini [*Trans. Am. Foundrymen's Soc.*, **59**, 435 (1951)] a temperature measurement 49°F below the liquidus would correspond to a system containing approximately 54% solid and 46% liquid. The heat in question also had a skull in the ladle, which can be detected when the ladle is first opened up. We believe that the pouring stream, during the teeming of the first few ingots, consisted of a mixture of solid and liquid from the bottom of the ladle together with liquid drawn from the central portion of the ladle. It is possible for the bulk temperature of the material from the ladle bottom to be well below the liquidus temperature of the steel; whereas, the temperature of the liquid from the central portion of the ladle probably was near the liquidus temperature. Under this condition, if a thermocouple were introduced into the stream some solidification might take place around the silica sheath, as Professor Adams suggests, together with some of the solid material from the ladle bottom.   This would result in a temperature below the liquidus.   We do not believe that the percentage of solid present in the pouring stream approached 54%, but we do believe that a certain amount of solid material was present.

During teeming, the liquid from the upper portion of the ladle will mix with the small amount of segregated liquid from the bottom resulting in a liquid which has a composition and liquidus temperature close to that of original steel.

When the mould is full, the solid material settles to that bottom of the ingot, possibly giving rise to a zone of negative segregation, leaving a solid free liquid at the top close to the liquidus temperature as reported.

We, therefore, agree that the abstraction of solid from a liquid-solid mixture will not have the effect of heating the liquid since under these circumstances, it may be possible for the liquid to be close to the liquidus temperature of the original steel while the solid material is purer and at a temperature below the original liquidus.   One of the authors (Samways, N. L., "Mechanism of Solidification of Metals," thesis, Imperial College, London, 1953) has carried out experiments similar to those of Bishop, Brandt, and Pellini and has also found that the liquid at the center of a casting reached the liquidus within a very short time after pouring and remained at that temperature until solidification started at the center.

We realize that the mechanism outlined above is open to conjecture, but we feel that it is a satisfactory explanation of the observed data at the present time.

It may be of interest to add that in the case of lower carbon heats, not quoted in the paper, teeming stream measurements below the liquidus were also obtained, but it was observed that the amount below the liquidus was much less than the example quoted.   It was also found that when measurements below the liquidus were obtained they were found to be associated with ladle skulling.

Referring to the question of radiation heat loss being negligible after the ladle is filled, R. E. Sosman [*Trans. Am. Inst. Mining Met. Engrs.*, **176,** 15 (1948)] offers support to our assumption.

J. K. McCauley (*Crucible Steel Co.*): The observed error in temperature drop for 2 out of 3 heats is given as $\pm 19°F$ or $\pm 26°F$.   Would you estimate the error for the 2σ limits or 95% confidence level, which may be more suitable to the needs of the operating personnel?

The theoretical equations are derived with the assumption of constant k, C_p, and ρ values.   These assumptions are not valid for ladle brick because over the temperature range 100 to 2900°F, k varies about 50%, ρ changes as is characteristic of ladle brick, and C_p varies about 60%.   The diffusivity, $\alpha = k/\rho\,C_p$ varies also but less markedly.   For this case of variable properties, I would like to know if some numerical method such as described by Dusinberre might be more accurate.

The objection to using the theoretical equations shown is important even when α is constant because Eq. (13) cannot be derived without the assumption that k = constant.   Further the assumption of constant k results in a direct error of up to 50% in Eqs. (16), (17), (19), (22), (23), and (24) where k appears without $\rho\,C_p$ in the denominator.

The observation of temperatures in the hot top which were *higher* than the temperature in the teeming stream from which the hot top was filled is interesting

The authors explain that liquid and solids are in the stream which then separate by gravity in the mold to produce a measurably hotter liquid steel temperature.

This does not seem probable since the solids, if present, would have to be small to flow through a nozzle and would therefore be very close to temperature equilibrium with the liquid steel. No amount of separation will make the liquid steel hotter than it used to be (excluding a temperature inversion due to an unstable state).

Does it seem plausible that the best explanation of the observed facts is that the silica sheath, thermocouple, and the steel achieved a steady state at a thermocouple temperature lower than the actual stream temperature are due to heat losses through the short silica tube and the imperfect fluid continuum around the sheath with voids and/or solid present?

N. L. Samways, T. E. Dancy, K. Li, and **J. Halapatz:** In reply to the discussor's question regarding the 2σ limits or the 95% confidence level, our errors are as follows:

$$\text{Open hearth shop: } 2\sigma = \pm 35°F$$
$$\text{Basic oxygen shop: } 2\sigma = \pm 37°F$$

The discussor brings up an interesting point on the assumption of constant R, C_p, and ρ values, which was not discussed in the paper. While it is true that variation in thermal conductivity with temperature would alter the temperature distribution given by Eq. (15), the effect may be accounted for by replacing T in Eq. (13) by a new variable, if the variation of thermal conductivity with temperature were known,

$$\overline{V} = 1/k_0 \int_0^T R.dT \tag{D3}$$

where k_0 is the thermal conductivity at $T = 0$, and R is the value at T. Thus, the form of the solution will remain the same as Eq. (15). The validity of this substitution depends only on the constancy in the thermal diffusivity, α.

In the present work our prime interest was to estimate the heat loss, not the temperature distribution. It follows from Eq. (D3) that

$$\partial v/\partial r = R/R_0 . \partial I/\partial r \tag{D4}$$

and hence by our treatment

$$q_1 = 2\pi r L k_1 (\partial v/\partial r)$$
$$= -2\pi r L R_1 (R/R_0) . \partial I/\partial r \tag{D5}$$

where k_1 is the chosen value for thermal conductivity. If this value is equal to k_0, then the heat loss calculated by Eq. (16) would be true.

Similar arguments may be applied to the treatment of the heat loss through the ladle bottom.

By this argument, it is seen that the accuracy of the theoretical heat losses depends on the choice of k_1. In our calculations, a value of k_1 close to that of k_0 was used; and, therefore, the calculated results should be reasonably accurate.

Until more accurate thermal data become available, a more rigorous theoretical analysis is perhaps not justified.

Where the assumption of constant α does not hold or cannot be tolerated in a particular case, numerical methods may prove to be less complicated and more convenient.

With regard to the latter question, we should like to refer to our reply to Professor Adams, where we have given our views in greater detail than in the paper.

Vacuum Distillation of Minor Elements from Liquid Ferrous Alloys

MICHEL OLETTE

Physical Chemistry Department, Institut de Recherches de la Sidérurgie, Saint-Germain-en-Laye, France

Abstract

The elimination of residual elements from iron melts by means of vacuum fusion has been studied. The main features of the method used were the following: (*1*) Gas pressure (argon) varied from one run to another between 10^{-5} and 20 mm of mercury. (*2*) Quantity of distilled iron was determined for each experiment. (*3*) In many cases, metal samples were taken during the run every 15 min. For arsenic, it was found that its elimination may be reasonably considered as an example of fractional distillation. Phosphorus was found to remain nearly constant and As, S, Sn, Cu, Mn, and Pb showed increasing elimination in the order given. Manganese evaporates at such velocity that its elimination can be considered as a degassing process. For Si and Al, the oxygen content of the melt and the crucible material seem to have a serious influence. The possibility of formation of volatile suboxides is discussed.

INTRODUCTION

The early basic ideas on vacuum melting of metals appeared in the last century, but although the first U.S. patent for a complete vacuum furnace is dated 1867, it is only during the last 15 years that vacuum melted or vacuum poured metal was produced on a significant industrial scale.[1,2]

There is at present growing interest in vacuum processes for steelmaking, and research is undertaken almost everywhere to study their beneficial effects on the quality of steels thus obtained. But while a lot of work has been reported on the elimination of gaseous components or products, attention has been drawn only recently to the composition of vacuum-treated steels.[3-6]

1065

However, elements such as As, Sn, Cu, and Pb, when present in steels as impurities, can have detrimental influence on their physical or mechanical properties. Vacuum treatments could be, for some of those elements which have a high vapor pressure in the 1500–1600°C range of temperature, one of the best processes, or even the only technique to remove them from the melt.

The case of arsenic is of particular interest since there are many iron ores which contain As and no good method in steelmaking has been able to lower its content to a suitable level.

On the other hand, it is important to know how the steel content in alloying elements varies under vacuum conditions with respect to Si, Al, Mn, Cr, Ni, and Co.

The present work is the first step of an experimental study of the composition changes which take place during vacuum processing of ferrous metals.

THERMODYNAMICAL SURVEY

During vacuum processing of metals, it is usually desired to prevent returning of the evaporated elements to the original surface of the melt. In these nonequilibrium conditions, the metal constituents will continue to evaporate at a rate which depends on their vapor pressures, the residual gas pressure, and the concentration gradient of the gas phase between the melt and the condenser surfaces.

If the residual gas pressure is maintained to a low value and the distance between evaporating and condensing surfaces is rather short, the concentration gradient in the gas is almost insignificant and the rate of distillation may be important. These conditions can be attained in practice under vacuum.

Therefore, in order to solve problems of vacuum distillation in steel industry, consideration of the vapor pressure of the constituents above the melt is of considerable interest. Unfortunately, very few data are available with respect to vapor pressure of elements above their dilute solutions in iron. However, vapor pressures of pure elements are more or less precisely known and a plot of those data versus temperature (see Fig. 1) may be used in certain cases as a rough guide in determining which elements may be evaporated out.

Similar graphs have been previously published, but according to the last vapor pressure measurements on some pure metals, it appeared

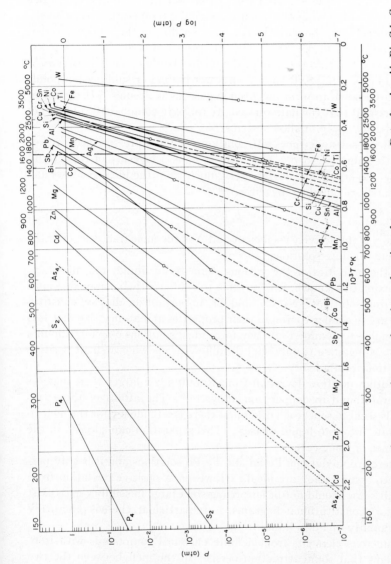

Fig. 1. The vapor pressure of some pure elements plotted as a function of temperature. Data for Ag, Al, Bi, Cd, Cr, Cu, Fe, Mg, Mn, Pb, Si, Sn, Ti, W, and Zn taken from Hultgren.[7] Data for As, Ca, P, and Si taken from Brewer.[8] Data for S taken from Kubaschewski and Evans.[9]

necessary to make corrections. The very recent compilation of Hultgren[7] has been mainly used for that purpose. At 1600°C, which may be considered as the mean steelmaking temperature, the elments under consideration show increasing volatility in the following order: W, Ti, Co, Ni, Fe, Cr, Si, Cu, Sn, Al, Ag, Mn, Pb, Sb, Bi, Ca, Mg, Zn, Cd, As, S, P-Ca, Mg, Zn, and Cd have low boiling points, between 750 and 1450°C; As, S, P have even lower boiling or sublimation points and are known to form polyatomic gaseous molecules. It should be emphasized that the data quoted are for pure components and do not necessarily apply in alloy systems.

When a substance goes into solution, its vapor pressure is depressed from a value $p°$ to p. The ratio $p/p°$ is a measure of its activity (metal vapors do not deviate very much from the ideal gas laws and pressures are equal to fugacities):

$$a = p/p° = \gamma N \tag{1}$$

where γ is the activity coefficient and N is the mole fraction. For the solvent in dilute solutions, $\gamma = 1$.

If the activities of the various elements in liquid iron alloys are approximately known, it is possible to evaluate their vapor pressures over iron solutions; Ni, Co, and Cr, important as alloying constituents, are so similar to iron in their properties and atomic size that it is reasonable to assume that they form ideal solutions obeying Raoult's law. Manganese is only slightly different, showing a small positive deviation from ideality.[10]

Another positive deviation from Raoult's law larger than that for Mn was found in copper-iron alloys.[11,12] The atoms of these two metals seem to repel each other and there is a tendency for the melt to separate into two liquid phases. This separation can succeed in the presence of some carbon.

There are no data on Fe-Sn and Fe-Pb solutions and it is only possible to assume they are ideal. However, a positive deviation from Raoult's law should not be surprising since large miscibility gaps exist in binary constitutional diagrams.[13] In particular, there is practically no solubility of Pb in liquid iron.

Numerous elements from definite chemical compounds with iron. It seems that some attraction persists in the melt between the two varieties of atoms, and consequently these solutions present a negative deviation from Raoult's law. Systems of this type can be de-

TABLE I

Thermodynamic Data for Some Metallic Elements

Elements	Atomic wt, A_y	Vapor pressure for pure elements at 1600°C[a] mm Hg, $P°_y$	Activity coefficient in dilute Fe solutions, $\gamma°$ at 1600°C	Source of data for $\gamma°$	Vapor pressure over dilute Fe solutions at 1600°C[a] mm Hg			Evaporation coefficient $\alpha = \gamma°(P°_y/P_{Fe})\sqrt{M_{Fe}/M_y}$
					0.050%	0.2%	1%	
Pb	207.21	340	1	Assuming ideality	0.046	(two liquids)		(3000)
Mn	54.94	42	1.3	Sanbongi and Masayasu[10]	0.028	0.11	0.55	900
Al	26.98	1.9	0.031	Chipman and Floridis[14]	0.00006	0.00024	0.0012	1.4
Cu	63.54	1.0	8.0	Morris and Zellars,[11] Koros and Chipman[12]	0.0035	0.014	0.070	125
Sn	118.70	0.8	1	Assuming ideality	0.00019	0.00076	0.0038	9.1
Si	28.09	0.42	0.0072	Chipman et al.[15]	0.000003	0.000012	0.00006	0.07
Cr	52.01	0.19	1	Assuming ideality	0.0010	0.004	0.020	3.3
Fe	55.85	0.060[b]	1			0.060		1
Ni	58.71	0.043	1	Assuming ideality	0.00002	0.00008	0.00041	0.7
Co	58.94	0.031	1	Assuming ideality	0.000015	0.00006	0.0003	0.5

[a] Approximate values.
[b] After Rist.[16]

tected by their phase diagrams and include such familiar elements as silicon, aluminum, and titanium.

When calculating vapor pressures of the elements above their solutions in iron, it is important to consider these deviations from Raoult's law for the effect can be very large, especially in complex alloys.

Thermodynamic data, including vapor pressures calculated in accordance with known or assumed activities, have been listed in Table I. The vapor pressure of iron at 1600°C was taken from recent experiments by Rist.[16]

It is clear from Table I that the classification of the elements after their reduced vapor pressure in dilute solution is different from that after their vapor pressure in the pure state.

A Tentative Theory of Distillation of Minor Elements out of Iron Melts

The above considerations do not permit any quantitative treatment of the distillation of constituents out of iron baths in vacuum. This requires the ratio of volatilization rates. It has been shown[17,18] that the evaporation rate W of a substance in vacuum, in terms of weight, is related to the molecular weight and the partial vapor pressure of the substance and temperature by the function

$$W = 0.05833 \, p \, \sqrt{M/T} \qquad (2)$$

Here, W is in g cm^{-2} sec^{-1} when p is in mm of mercury and T is in °K. Thus, p can be reduced from Eq. (1) as follows:

$$p = \gamma N p^\circ$$

Relation (2) becomes

$$W = 0.05833 \, \gamma N p^\circ \sqrt{M/T} \qquad (3)$$

in which p° and M are physical constants for the substance and γ and N characteristics of the solution.

Let us now consider an iron melt containing A grams of iron and B grams of element Y, heated to a temperature T°K. At time 0, vacuum is applied; at this moment there is no distillate; t seconds later, there is a distillate composed of xg of iron and yg of element Y. The melt contains $(A - x)g$ of iron and $(B - y)g$ of Y.

At time $t + dt$, there is $(x + dx)g$ of iron and $(y + dy)g$ of Y in the distillate.

The rate of evaporation for iron is given by [relation (3)]:

$$dx/dt = 0.05833\ \gamma_{Fe}\cdot[(A - x)/M_{Fe}]/[(A - x)/M_{Fe}$$
$$+ (B - Y)/M_Y]\ p^\circ\ \sqrt{M_{Fe}/T}$$

or

$$dx/dt\ /\ 0.05833\ \gamma_{Fe}\cdot p^\circ{}_{Fe}(TM_{Fe})^{-1/2}\cdot(A - x)/$$
$$[(A - x)/M_{Fe} + (B - y)/M_Y]\quad(4)$$

Similarly, the rate of evaporation of element Y is

$$dy/dt = 0.05833\ \gamma_Y\ p^\circ{}_Y(TM_Y)^{-1/2}\ (B - y)/$$
$$[(A - x)/M_{Fe} + (B - y)/M_Y]$$

We may choose as a distillation criterion, the ratio of evaporation rates which is an algebraic formulation of elimination possibility of element Y under consideration:

$$dy/dx = (\gamma_Y/\gamma_{Fe})(p^\circ{}_Y/p^\circ{}_{Fe})\sqrt{(M_{Fe}/M_Y)(B - y)/(A - x)}\quad(5)$$

If we call evaporation coefficient α the quantity:

$$\alpha = (\gamma_Y/\gamma_{Fe})(p^\circ{}_Y/p^\circ{}_{Fe})\sqrt{M_{Fe}/M_Y}$$

it follows that

$$dy/dx = \alpha(B - y)/(A - x)$$

or

$$dy/(B - y) = \alpha\ dx/(A - x)$$

By integration $\qquad y = -\ k\ (A - x)^\alpha + B$

When $x = 0$, y must be 0 then

$$k = B/A^\alpha$$

The final function is

$$y = -\ B/A^\alpha\ (A - x)^\alpha + B\quad(6)$$

with

$$\alpha = (\gamma_Y/\gamma_{Fe})(p^\circ{}_y/p^\circ{}_{Fe})\sqrt{M_{Fe}/M_Y}$$

In fact, we study distillation of minor components from iron melts; in such solutions, iron obeys Raoult's law and γ_{Fe} is very close to unity; the solute Y at low concentrations obeys Henry's law and γ_Y is nearly constant and equal to $\gamma^\circ{}_Y$. It would be equal to 1 if the solution were ideal.

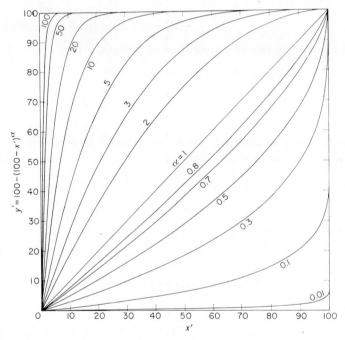

Fig. 2. Family of curves of the function: $y' = 100 - (100 - x')^\alpha$ for different values of α.

Under such conditions

$$\alpha = \gamma^\circ{}_Y(p^\circ{}_y/p^\circ{}_{Fe})\sqrt{55.85/M_Y} \tag{7}$$

The function (6) expresses the relation between the weight y of constituent Y and the weight x of iron in the distillate. It is a useful formulation of the distillation process since, when comparing results of different experimental runs, it considerably reduces the influence of experimental factors such as temperature, pumping speed, importance, and structure of the evaporating surface of the distilland.

Equation (6) may be written

$$100y/B = - [100 - (100\ x/A)]^{\alpha} + 100$$

in which $100y/B = y'$ and $100x/A = x'$ are percentages of constituent Y and of iron, respectively, which have been evaporated from the distilland.

The function under consideration is then simplified:

$$y' = 100 - (100 - x')^{\alpha} \qquad (8)$$

It is easy to see that the slope at the origin is α. On this graph, the function for iron is evidently represented by the diagonal $\alpha = 1$.

With that representation, it is easier to obtain for each element in iron a typical curve which permits predicting the conditions of its removal.

If, for a given element, α is greater than 1, its removal should be possible, the quicker the greater the value α; if α is smaller than 1, its elimination by vacuum distillation is impossible and it concentrates in iron melts the faster the smaller the value of α.

Figure 2 gives the family of curves drawn from Eq. (8) for different values of α.

EXPERIMENTAL PROCEDURE

The experiments reported have been performed in a laboratory vacuum fusion apparatus of a maximum capacity of 2 kg[19] in which the metal was heated by induction. The lowest pressure obtainable was 5.10^{-6} mm of mercury. The crucibles used were made of pure alumina or magnesia.

A few preliminary runs consisted in maintaining liquid pure binary iron alloys or steels for a known time (from a few minutes to 4 hr) under a known low pressure of argon (10^{-5} to 10 mm of mercury). Samples of 70 to 150 g of metal were melted in cylindrical pure alumina crucibles about 3 cm in diameter and 3–5 cm in height, the depth of the melt being from 1.5 to 3 cm and its surface area about 6 cm². The distilled products were condensed on a cylindrical tube of silica surrounding the top of the crucible and on the wall of the silica glass enclosure which is water cooled.

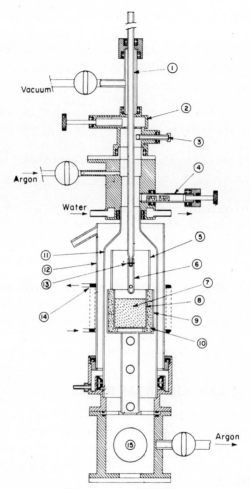

Fig. 3. Vacuum furnace arrangement: 1, silica glass tube; 2, isolating valve; 3, sighting device; 4, additions storage; 5, silica condenser; 6, sampling silica test tube; 7, liquid metal; 8, crucible; 9, outer crucible; 10, insulating material (alumina); 11, silica glass furnace tube; 12, Plexiglas tube (waterjacket); 13, molybdenum pin; 14, induction coil; and 15, vacuum outlet.

The disadvantage of this technique is the heterogeneity of the metal before and after vacuum treatment, even on a 100-g scale.

Segregation of elements at low concentrations cannot be avoided completely in ingots which are solidified rather slowly, and it is important to sample and analyze with care to obtain representative results.

Therefore, further experiments were made in an improved fusion apparatus (see Fig. 3) in which it was possible to draw off a sample of metal of 5 to 10 g from the melt every 10 or 15 min. For that purpose a special arrangement was made including an intermediate vacuum chamber which permits the introduction under vacuum, of a silica testtube in the melt, which fills through a hole on the side with about 1 cm^3 of liquid metal. This operation is performed without any air entering. By use of commercial Wilson seals,[20] the simplicity of mounting was improved. In that technique, batches of 600 to 1200 g were melted in cylindrical crucibles of about 5 cm in inside diameter and 10 cm in height, the depth of the liquid metal being from 3 to 7 cm.

The temperature of the melt was not measured in the research presently reported, because of the complexity of the furnace head. But, by comparison with similar vacuum melting operations in that

TABLE II

Effect of Vacuum Melting on the As Content of Pure Binary Alloys and Commercial Steels (in Alumina Crucibles)

	Heat No.	Pressure of argon, mm Hg	Time, min	Weight of ingot, g		As content, %	
				Initial	Final	Initial	Final
Pure iron-arsenic	G0.12	10	30	81	79	0.200	0.190
alloys	G0.13	10	120	85	72	0.205	0.167
	G0.17	10^{-5}	60	95	85	0.210	0.165
Total impurities	G0.16	$<10^{-5}$	90	102	50	0.205	0.046
(as excepted)	G0.11	2.10^{-5}	120	102	71	0.205	0.090
less than	G0.58	10	30	128	125	0.065	0.064
0.050%	G0.53	10	120	70	52	0.062	0.026
	G0.56	$<10^{-5}$	60	85	32	0.060	<0.005
	G0.52	$<10^{-5}$	120	90	22	0.069	<0.005
Thomas steel							
0.035% C	ZI1	10	60	120	94	0.060	0.052
0.38% Mn	ZI3	10	120	152	127	0.073	0.063
0.02% S							
0.04% P	ZI2	$<10^{-5}$	60	145	85	0.053	0.12_5
0.04% O$_2$	ZI4	$<10^{-5}$	90	151	71	0.075	0.023

furnace, it can be assumed that the temperature was not much different from 1600°C.   The quantity of evaporated iron was measured by difference between initial and final weights of melt, correction being made for addition elements and for sampling.

EXPERIMENTAL RESULTS

First, arsenic was removed, and a series of pure As alloys containing up to 0.2% were prepared and vacuum treated.   The results of these experiments are shown in Table II.

Two pressures were used: a very low one (10^{-5} mm of Hg) able to give the very limit of the distillation process and a much higher one, 10 mm of mercury of argon, similar to an industrial vacuum obtained at low cost.   The times of vacuum treatment were much longer than those which could be used in practice, but the aim of the present work was mainly to follow the process to the lowest measurable concentrations.

It is easy to see from Table II that the elimination of arsenic can be almost complete (run G052) only at the cost of very high iron losses (68 g out of 90 g in the same run).   Under such conditions, practical removal of arsenic by vacuum processes seems to be hopeless.

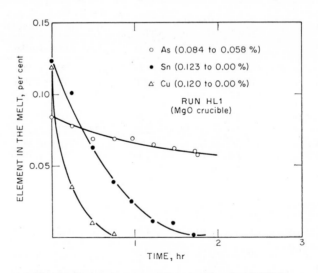

Fig. 4. Change in composition vs time of melt HL1.

TABLE III

Effect of Vacuum Melting on the Composition of Complex Iron Alloys

Heat No., crucible material	Pressure of argon, mm Hg	Time, min	Weight of ingot, g	Composition, %							
				As	Cu	Sn	Al	Si	Mn	S	P
HCl (Al₂O₃)	5.10^{-5}–2.10^{-5}	0	1040	0.210							
		180	880	0.152							
HL1 (MgO)	8.10^{-5}–2.10^{-5}	0	645	0.084	0.120	0.123	0.028				
		105	532	0.058	0.00	0.00	0.00				
HL3 (MgO)	2.10^{-4}–10^{-5}	0	902	0.142	0.190	0.165	0.152				
		141	773	0.098	0.00	0.013	0.00				
HL4 (Al₂O₃)	10^{-4}–2.10^{-5}	0	906	0.094	0.215	0.203	0.195				
		240	674	0.051	0.00	0.003	0.012				
HL2 (MgO)	10^{-5}–8.10^{-6}	0	645	0.075				0.110	0.257		
		240	257	0.005				0.00	0.00		
Steel ZK4 (Al₂O₃)	10^{-5}	0	1230	0.055					0.088	0.019	0.038
		240	1000	0.035					0.00	0.006_5	0.040

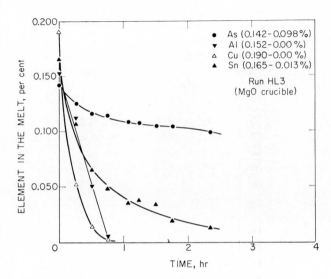

Fig. 5. Change in composition vs time of melt HL3.

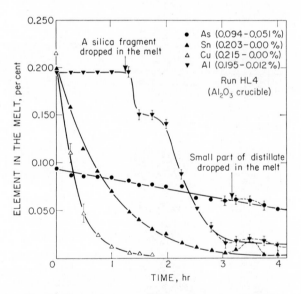

Fig. 6. Change in composition vs time of melt HL4.

Using the distillation characteristics of As-Fe binary system as a standard, experiments were performed on more complex alloys to study vaporization of such elements as Mn, Cu, Sn, Al, and Si.   It is

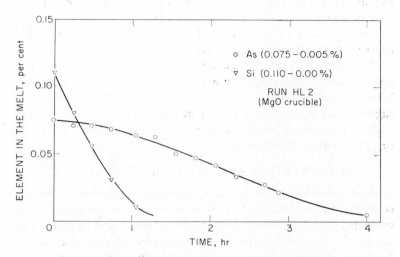

Fig. 7.   Change in composition vs time of melt HL2.

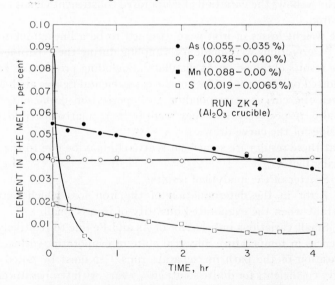

Fig. 8. Change in composition vs time of melt ZK4.

interesting to study the influence of these elements on the elimination of As. Results of that second series are reported in Table III.

Analyses of successive samples are not given in Table III, but for the runs HL1, HL3, JL4, HL2, and ZK4 they have been plotted against time in Figures 4, 5, 6, 7, and 8, respectively.

The ZK4 was a Thomas steel and it was used to see how S, P, and Mn contents varied during vacuum melting.

The curves in Table III show that Mn, Cu, Al, Si, Sn, and S decrease quicker than arsenic in a melt under vacuum. On the other hand, phosphorus does not move; its content seems to increase very slightly, that is to say, iron is evaporating quicker than phosphorus.

Rather surprising results obtained on Si and particularly on Al in run HL4 will be discussed later.

PRESENTATION AND DISCUSSION OF RESULTS

When considering all the data collected, it was found that they could not be compared on a time basis because of variations in temperature, effective surface area, pumping speed, and pressure above the melt. It is much better to use the graphical representation which has been discussed in the section entitled "Thermodynamical Survey" and which shows the variation of evaporated constituent versus evaporated iron.

The weight losses of iron were assumed to be a linear function of time. Corrections were made for sampling during the experiment.

The results obtained on As distillation including progressive values are plotted on Figure 9. Most of the experimental figures are located between the curves corresponding to vaporization coefficients α of 1.6 and 6, respectively, and they seem to be regularly distributed on both sides of the curve drawn for $\alpha = 3$.

That these results are somewhat scattered, may be due to the following factors:

1. Scatter of the analytical results.

2. Error in the determination of the iron loss which may be important when the evaporated quantity of iron is small.

3. Small variations in behavior of As and Fe due to relatively big differences in temperature, physical state of evaporating surface, and composition of the bath for separate runs. It must be noted that activity coefficients for dilute solutions γ° vary with temperature, this variation being possibly slightly different for various elements.

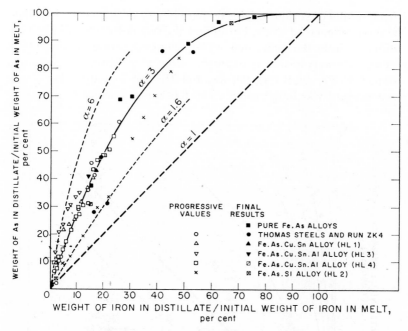

Fig. 9. Results of vacuum distillation of As.

4.   In complex alloys and steels, influence of third elements on As distillation.

Without reducing the importance of the three first factors of scatter, it is believed that the fourth one is predominant and could explain most of the low figures.

The results of runs HL1 and HL3 suggest that the evaporation rate of As is increased by the presence of Cu or Sn; however, the evaporation rate seems to be decreased by the presence of Si (run HL2) and possibly Al.   As these third elements are in small quantity (0.1 to 0.2%), a physical explanation must be found, and further verification is required, especially on pure ternary iron alloys.   One of the possible explanations could be the existence of bonding between the added elements and As.   In certain cases the product might be more volatile, in other cases, less volatile than As itself.

In order to classify the elements after the evaporation parameter, the data have been plotted on a graph similar to that used for As (see Fig. 10).   It is not a very accurate classification since it is deduced from results of various origins on pure binary or more complex alloys and on commercial steels, but in fact the real order must not be very different from the found one.   The evaporation rate of elements in dilute solutions in iron is increasing from P to Mn in the following order: P, Fe, As, S (Si), Sn, Cu, and Mn (see Fig. 10).   For P, the α-coefficient was found to be about 0.6, a consequence of the strong

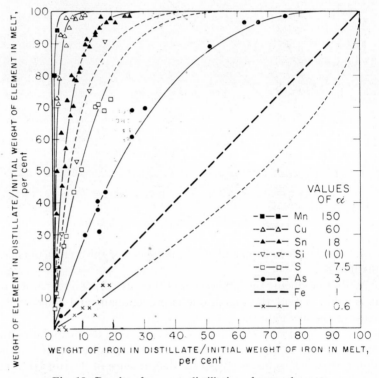

Fig. 10. Results of vacuum distillation of some elements.

binding forces between Fe and P atoms.   Phosphorous cannot be removed by vacuum melting.

For As, Figure 10 presents only the curve previously drawn ($\alpha = 3$) and the results for pure alloys without intermediate values.   As mentioned above, when arsenic is effectively distilled from iron, iron losses are important: for example, to eliminate 50% of As contained in a steel, an eventual loss of iron of about 20% ought to be tolerated.

In such conditions, vacuum melting alone is not sufficient for industrial removal of As.

Removal of S seems to be limited for industrial applications: α for S was found to be about 7.5, which means that to reduce the sulfur content by roughly 50% a loss of iron of 10% has to be accepted. The presence of C, which increases the evaporation rate of S,[5] improves the process.

In general, iron losses of 5 to 10% could be tolerated if the evaporated metal could be used as raw material in other refining processes.

The position of the Si curve ($\alpha = 10$) is surprising since calculation of α yielded a particularly low value (0.07). This case will be discussed later.

The Sn, Cu, and Mn can be eliminated by vacuum melting since for a loss of iron of 5%, more than 50% of these elements are evaporated. Experimental α-values for Cu vary from 40 to 100 with a mean value of about 60. It is only slightly smaller than the α found theoretically (125).

In fact the Fe-Cu system is one of the best known, particularly after the published results of Morris and Zellars[11] and Koros and Chipman.[12]

The differences between computed and experimentally found α are more important for Sn (9, 1–18) and Mn (900–150). Some experiments have been performed with Pb but under our conditions, its evaporation seemed so rapid that no quantitative results could be obtained.

However, the classification is the same on the whole for calculated and experimental values of α, except for Si and Al. Aluminum results have not been plotted on Figure 10 because of their surprising nature: in some cases, Al was quickly removed (runs HL1 and HL3, see Table III) in others, Al content decreased only slowly or in steps (run HL4).

A Tentative Explanation of Al and Si Behavior

The evaporation of Al and Si from iron dilute solutions cannot be explained thermodynamically by a simple distillation process only.

It was noticed in run HL4 (see Fig. 6) that the Al content did not vary very much until a piece of silica was accidentally added to the melt; from then on the evaporation of Al became much quicker.

This fact suggested the importance of reactions of elements in solution in the melt with crucible material.

First, considering the reaction between dissolved Al and silica, it will be assumed that volatile suboxides of Si and Al are formed:

$$(SiO_2)_S + 2[Al]_{Fe} = (SiO)_g + (Al_2O)_g$$

(Calculations will be done for 1600°C.)

The reaction constant is

$$K = p_{SiO} \cdot p_{Al_2O}/a^2_{Al}$$

where a_{Al} is the activity of Al in iron solution, taking as standard state liquid aluminum at 1600°C.

Free energies of formation for SiO_2 ($-130,440$ cal/mole), SiO_g ($-57,700$ cal/mole), and Al_2O ($-71,600$ cal/mole) were taken from Coughlin.[21] Free energy of solution of one atom of Al in iron was deduced from activity measurements of Chipman and Floridis[14] (who proposed 0.031 at 1600°C for activity coefficient of Al in dilute iron solutions).

$$\Delta F°_{sol} = 4,574T \log \gamma° = -13,000 \text{ cal}$$

When one molecule of SiO is formed by the above reaction, it is required that one molecule of Al_2O appears at the same time, then

$$p_{SiO} = p_{Al_2O}$$

and

$$K = (p_{SiO})^2/a^2_{Al}$$

it follows that

$$p_{SiO} = p_{Al_2O} = a_{Al}\sqrt{K}$$
$$= 0.0026 \text{ mm Hg}$$

This is roughly ten times more than the vapor pressure of Al over Al solution in iron containing 0.2% Al (0.00024 mm Hg). It is therefore reasonable to think that removal of Al from iron solution and vacuum may be accelerated by the presence of silica and formation of an Al suboxide as Al_2O.

In runs HL1 and HL3, the alloy was melted in a magnesia crucible (see Table III). The possibility of reaction between Al in iron solution and MgO may be thermodynamically evaluated according to the following reaction:

$$(MgO)_S + 2[Al]_{Fe} = (Al_2O)_g + (Mg)_g$$

The free energies of formation of MgO at 1600°C ($-82,700$ cal/mole) are also given by Coughlin[21] and as above, a similar calculation yields the vapor pressure of Al_2O:

$$p_{Al_2O} = p_{Mg} = a\sqrt{K}$$
$$= 0.0007 \text{ mm Hg}$$

The pressure of Al_2O formed is about equal to 3 times the vapor pressure of Al above an iron solution at 0.2% Al.   It is interesting to compare these results to pressures of suboxides species which could be formed in an alumina crucible.   The reaction involved is the following:

$$(Al_2O_3)_S + 4[Al]_{Fe} = 3(Al_2O)_g$$

Using a method and data similar to those explained above:

$$p_{Al_2O} = a_{Al}^{4/3}\sqrt{K}$$

$$p_{Al_2O} = 0.000001 \text{ mm Hg}$$

That pressure is much lower than p_{Al} over 0.2% Al solution in iron and it is evident that in an alumina crucible vaporization of Al as Al_2O volatile compound is rather a negligible effect.   This result explains the stability of Al at the beginning of run HL4.

In run HL2, silicon was quickly evaporated.   This fact is in contradiction with the α-value computed from thermodynamic data (0.07).   We may imagine, as for Al, a similar reaction involving gaseous silicon monoxide by the following reaction:

$$(MgO)_S + [Si]_{Fe} = (SiO)_g + (Mg)_g$$

with the same assumptions and data, we obtain:

$$p_{SiO} = p_{Mg} = \sqrt{a_{Si}K}$$

where K is the equilibrium constant of the above reaction.

The free energy of solution of Si in iron was computed from equilibrium results of Chipman et al.,[15] using the following equation:

$$\Delta F^\circ = 4574T \log \gamma^\circ$$

According to these authors, $\gamma°$ was equal to 0.00725 (at 1600°C). It was obtained finally (for 0.2% Si in iron alloy):

$$p_{SiO} = p_{Mg} = 0.008 \text{ mm Hg}$$

which is considerably more than vapor pressure of Si over 0.2% Si iron solution (0.000012 mm Hg).

A comparison can be made between vapor pressures and α-coefficients. For Al in contact with SiO_2 at 1600°C, it was found that

$$p_{Al_2O}/p_{Al} = 10$$

and the ratio between computed α for pure Al (1.4) and experimental α from run HL4 (roughly 40) is about 28. Similarly, for the Al-Fe alloy in a MgO crucible, $p_{Al_2O} = 3$ and $\alpha_{exp.}/\alpha_{calc.} = 10$ to 15.

Silicon in solution in iron reacts with a MgO crucible:

$$p_{SiO}/p_{Si} = 0.008/0.000012 = 650 \text{ and } \alpha_{exp.}/\alpha_{calc.} = 150$$

Differences between these pairs of values are important, but considering the uncertainty of the data used it is possible to think that the order of magnitude is about the same.

In general, it can be concluded that, in vacuum, reactions occurring between oxides contained in the crucible or in the melt and some elements which may form volatile suboxides must not be neglected.

Surprising results on Si behavior have also been detected by Gill et al.[6] Severe unexpected losses during vacuum melting have been recently demonstrated for Si[3] and Al.[2]

The author is indebted to Professor C. Crussard for valuable advice. He also wishes to thank Professor P. P. Kozakevitch for continuous interest and friendly discussions throughout this work, Dr. A. Rist for helpful suggestions, Mr. A. Chaillou for assistance in the experimental work, and Dr. J. Coulombeau and Mr. R. Boulin for analytical determinations.

References

1. Darmara, F. N., J. S. Huntington, and E. S. Machlin, "Vacuum Induction Melting," to be published in *J. Iron Steel Inst. (London)*.

2. Child, M. C., and G. T. Harris, *J. Iron Steel Inst. (London)*, **190**, 414 (1958).

3. Bungardt, K., and H. Sychrovsky, *Stahl u. Eisen*, **76**, 1040 (1956).

4. Jäniche, W., and H. Beck, *Tech. Mitt. Rheinhausen*, No. 5, 281 (Dec., 1957).

5. Fischer, W. A., and A. Hoffmann, *Arch. Eisenhüttenw.*, No. 6, 339 (June, 1958).

6. Gill, G. M., E. Ineson, and G. N. Austin, *J. Iron Steel Inst. (London)*, **191**, 172 (1959).

7. Hultgren, Ralph, "Thermodynamic Properties of Metals and Alloys," private communication.

8. Brewer, L., "The Thermodynamic and Physical Properties of the Elements," in Z. *Quill's Chemistry and Metallurgy of Miscellaneous Materials*, McGraw-Hill, New York, 1950, Ch. 8.

9. Kubaschewski, O., and E. L. Evans, *Metallurgical Thermochemistry*, Pergamon Press, London, 1956.

10. Sanbongi, K., and O. Masaya su, *Sci. Repts. Inst. Tôhoku Univ.*, **A7**, 204 (1955).

11. Morris, J. P., and G. R. Zellars, *J. Metals*, **8**, 1086 (1956).

12. Koros, P. J., and J. Chipman, *J. Metals*, **206**, 1102 (1956).

13. Hansen, M., *Constitution of Binary Alloys*, 2nd ed., McGraw-Hill, New York, 1958.

14. Chipman, J., and T. P. Floridis, *Acta Met.*, **3**, 456 (1955).

15. Chipman, J., J. C. Fulton, N. Gokcen, and G. R. Caskey, *Acta Met.*, **2**, 439 (1954).

16. Rist, A., unpublished data, private communication.

17. Dushman, S., *Scientific Foundations of Vacuum Technique*, Wiley, New York, 1949.

18. Martin, A. J., *Metal Ind.*, **88**, No. 23, 473, 495 (1956).

19. Olette, M., and A. Chaillou, *Vide*, No. 76, 177 (July–Aug., 1958).

20. Chaillou, A., and M. Olette, *Vide*, No. 71, 383 (Sept.–Oct., 1957).

21. Coughlin, J. P., *U. S. Bur. Mines*, Bull. 542 (1954).

22. Brewer, L., and A. W. Searcy, *J. Am. Chem. Soc.*, **73**, 5308 (1951).

Discussion

J. P. Morris (*U.S. Bureau of Mines, Pa.*): I wish to call attention to the large discrepancy between the calculated evaporation coefficient for manganese in iron and the observed value. The calculated coefficient is 6 times greater than the observed coefficient.

At the Bureau of Mines we have measured the vapor pressures of liquid manganese and liquid iron and the activity coefficient of manganese dissolved in liquid iron. Our results give a theoretical evaporation coefficient of about 900, the same value as used by the author.

The discrepancy is too large to be explained by a lowering of the activity coefficient of manganese by the presence of small quantities of other elements.

P. P. Turillon (*Kelsey-Hayes Co., New Hartford, N.Y.*): This paper is a very valuable contribution to the study of vacuum induction melting. The evaporation of such volatile elements as manganese is a constant problem in melts of industrial size.

A recent study in our laboratories ("Deoxidation of Pure Iron by Vacuum Induction Melting," New York Univ. Vacuum Metallurgy Conference, June 1–3, 1959) showed that under certain conditions an iron bath of low carbon and low oxygen contents would react readily with an alumina or magnesia crucible. Under these circumstances, an alumina crucible could bring aluminum into the melt and prevent aluminum evaporation until silica is added to the melt, thus raising the oxygen level and stopping the contamination from the crucible.

Application of Physical Chemistry to the Basic Oxygen Steelmaking Process

A. DECKER and P. METZ

Centre National de Recherches Métallurgiques, Liège, Belgium

Abstract

After a brief description of the operational procedure of the basic oxygen steelmaking process with injection of powdered lime (LD-AC process), the authors give some relations between elements of the metallic bath and the slag: carbon-oxygen, phosphorus of the metal and iron of the slag, and desulfurization and residual manganese content.

INTRODUCTION

Since the LD-AC process has been recently described[1,2] in English language publications, it will only be briefly recalled at this time.

The LD process consists in blowing, by means of a lance, pure oxygen into a converter. This is done without the addition of solid, pulverized material. The early development of this process was the work of several people.[3-8] Important industrial plants, several of which are to be found on the North American continent,[9,10,11] have been or are now employing this method.

The development was mainly applied to low phosphorus pig irons. Investigation was also conducted[12-17] with the aim to also treat pig irons containing higher phosphorus contents. It is also necessary at this point to mention that two processes, employing rotating furnaces—Kaldo[18] and Rotor[19]—are being utilized.

The results of research conducted during the last ten years at the C.N.R.M. led us to believe, in 1956,[20] that a simultaneous blowing of pulverized lime and commercially pure oxygen could also be successfully employed. The high temperatures produced by the injection

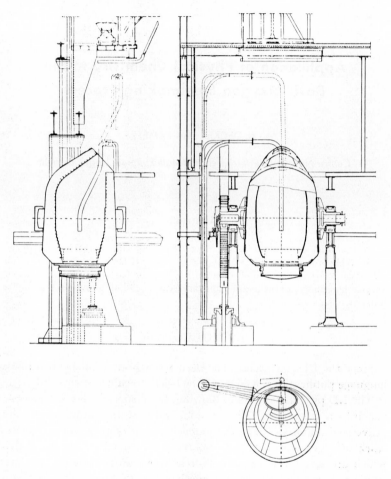

Fig. 1.

of the CaO-O_2 mixture and the possible use of an intermediate de-slagging operation were thought to be of considerable importance.

The construction of the actual industrial installation began in June 1956. The 26 metric ton lance-equipped converter at ARBED/Dudelange is shown in Figure 1. The shape of the lance was imposed by local conditions.

The pig iron used for these tests was of the normal basic Bessemer type supplied by the steel plant mixer. Its composition varied between the following limits:

	C, %	Si, %	Mn, %	P, %	S, %
Min	3.35	0.10	0.31	1.72	0.032
Max	4.12	0.75	0.65	2.15	0.085

OPERATIONAL PROCEDURE

The technique consists in first placing all the necessary pig iron in the converter, most of the scrap, about one third of the total quantity of lime and, since we aim for a high scrap charge, only a limited amount of ore (1100 lb). If the silicon content of the pig iron is too low, it is useful to add either sand or some other siliceous compound so as to facilitate foaming and to produce a slag better suited for agricultural purposes.

The lance is then placed in a high position, and oxygen is blown through at a high rate. During this period, which lasts for about five minutes, no lime is added. This is to prevent the slopping of metal droplets from the converter. This procedure is also beneficial since it facilitates rapid foaming of the liquid slag. This foaming action takes place rapidly as a result of the initial lime and oxygen additions. At the end of the first five minutes of the pure oxygen blast, lime powder is simultaneously added to the jet. The lance is then, depending upon the intensity of the flame, slowly lowered.

If the lance is kept too high the foaming action becomes too violent and there is danger of overflow. On the other hand, too sudden lowering of the lance may result in a liquid or solid slag and an increase of projections and brown fumes. Thanks to our flame radiation recorder, the adjustment of the lance height is not difficult.

This second phase of the first part of the procedure can be stopped at a carbon content above 1% in case we want to employ two intermediate deslagging operations. Usually, however, we continue the blowing until a carbon content of about 0.7% is attained. At this point we perform a single intermediate deslagging.

The total time of blowing before tilting the converter is about 14 min. The temperatures reached are approximately 1570 to 1650°C. At these temperatures the foamy slag is easily removed by tilting the converter. Lime consumption during the first phase varies depending upon the silicon and phosphorus content of the pig iron and lies between 132 and 177 lb/ton of pig iron.   The characteristics of the pig iron employed do not, so far as we could detect, influence in any way the course of the operation.   It is to be noticed that the relatively high silicon levels (0.75%) combined with the depth of the bath (49 in.) did not produce either an overflow of the foam or a decrease of the yield.

The slag removed contains more than 20% P_2O_5 and 4 to 9% iron. Citric solubility of the slag is excellent.   The phosphorus content of the metal is usually below 0.2%.

We chose the rather late tilting of the converter (at a carbon content of 0.7%) since it is possible at that point to determine with reasonable accuracy the remaining length of blowing and the thermal corrections necessary to attain the desired final temperature.   This rather low carbon level is of no disadvantage with our method of combined oxygen-lime powder injection.   This is especially true concerning the formation of a suitable slag at a later stage since it is continually formed upon the arrival of the lime with the oxygen jet at its contact on the metallic bath.

After slag removal and the addition of scraps (or iron ore) required for the thermal control of the process, the second and last blowing period begins.   According to the quality of the pig iron and the degree of elimination of the first intermediate slag, it may be advan-

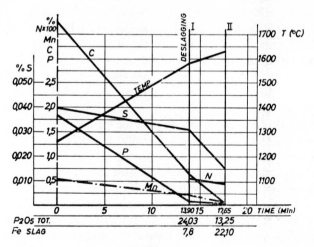

Fig. 2.

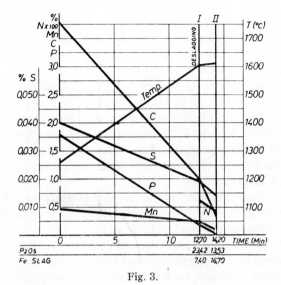

Fig. 3.

tageous to add, after this deslagging operation, a small quantity of fluxing agents (bauxite or sand).

The procedure employed during the second period consists in the simultaneous injection of oxygen and powdered lime up to the end of conversion. This operation is timed with a stopwatch or with the quantity of oxygen when making hard steels. It is stopped after a period which depends upon the carbon content determined at the end of the first period. In the production of mild steels, the operation is timed with the aid of the flame recorder.

Since this second period lasts for between three and five minutes, the total blowing time for 26–28 metric tons of steel varies between 16 and 20 min. This corresponds to a total blowing time of between 35 and 45 sec/ton of steel. It is probable that, working on an industrial scale with a well-equipped converter, we can be able to arrive at a tap-to-tap time of 40–45 min. Lime consumption during the second period is about 80 lb per net ton of pig iron. The total lime consumption is thus between 180 and 240 lb per net ton of pig iron for the total conversion operation.

When the last blowing period is finished, the slag is removed. The lime dam is constructed and the steel is poured into a ladle containing the required additions of solid or liquid ferromanganese.

Figure 2 shows the evolution of a typical cast, performed with one intermediate deslagging operation and achieved according to the procedure described above. The history of a heat containing a high carbon content is shown in Figure 3.

It is also possible to realize some heats without an intermediate deslagging operation. In this case, however, the lime consumption is higher and a low phosphorus content is more difficult to attain.

At the end of March, 1959, more than 700 casts have been produced using this new process. This corresponds to more than 20,000 metric tons of steel. The converter operates 24 hr/day when production conditions permit.

The procedure described above is very extensively used since it seems to give extremely favorable metallurgical and economical results in addition to very good metallic yield.

It is not possible, of course, to describe all the metallurgical aspects of this process in one relatively short report. The open hearth and basic Bessemer processes, both about one hundred years old, are still not completely understood. We would, however, like to discuss briefly some points which are particularly important: (1) elimination of carbon, phosphorus, and sulfur, (2) consumption of lime, (3) oxidation degree, and (4) loss of iron.

In order to give a better idea of the possibilities of this process, we have intentionally selected some heats possessing the greatest possible variations.

The simultaneous injection of powdered lime and oxygen in the

TABLE I

C, %	P, %	Temp., °C
0.190	0.016	1610
0.200	0.020	1595
0.200	0.020	—
0.260	0.029	1600
0.280	0.020	1555
0.290	0.018	1645
0.330	0.021	1610
0.360	0.021	1625
0.390	0.018	1580
0.400	0.028	1600
0.420	0.024	1600
0.430	0.028	1610

iron bath provokes a very rapid and vigorous decarburization and dephosphorization reaction.   Our operating method permits us to operate on and control the relative rates of dephosphorization and decarburization.   In this manner, we can obtain, with a high carbon content, a final metallic bath sufficiently low in phosphorus and which also possesses a suitable casting temperature.

Table I gives some examples of the carbon content corresponding to low phosphorus values in 12 representative heats.

RELATION BETWEEN CARBON AND OXYGEN

The carbon and oxygen contents are interrelated.   This fact is well known in the open hearth and electric furnace[21] processes.   Similar relationships are to be found in the new procedures of refining pig irons, such as the Kaldo[21] and Rotor[22] processes which finish the conversion on the carbon content.

The Vacher and Hamilton carbon-oxygen relationships, for P_{CO} = 1 atm, is shown in Figure 4.   Two other curves, situated slightly above the former, are also indicated.   Curve II refers to the American open hearth process and is taken from Chipman.[23]   The second curve, indicated I in the diagram, refers to the tests of Speith and vom

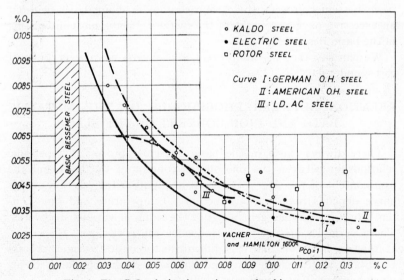

Fig. 4. The C-O relation in various steelmaking processes.

Ende[24] in Germany.   This curve has been drawn in free-hand through the experimental points reported by these authors.   Curve III in Figure 4 was obtained from a series of 200 successive LD-AC heats. This curve is located slightly under that of the open hearth.   When the carbon content is less than 0.05%, the LD-AC curve eventually intersects that of the Vacher and Hamilton.   We have not, as yet, fully investigated this behavior.

Based on these results, the LD-AC process produces, at the end of the refining process, a product which is at least equal to the open hearth steel insofar as the carbon and oxygen contents are concerned. It thus follows that all physical and mechanical properties, which are dependent upon the concentration of these two elements, should be the same in both types of steel.

As Pottgiesser[25] has shown, a relationship between carbon and oxygen contents also exists in the basic Bessemer process.   In this particular case, however, the partial pressure of gaseous CO is diluted by nitrogen and, as a result, becomes definitely lower than in the open hearth process.   Pottgiesser found that the final carbon content attained was an exponential function of the nitrogen volume blow through the bath which decreased gradually as the amount of nitrogen increased.   This explains why, at the end of the refining in the basic Bessemer process, the carbon content is about 0.01% without an excessive oxygen content in the metal.   This is most interesting in the basic Bessemer process.

We can say that in this process, the oxygen content is, in most cases, under 0.08%.

RELATION BETWEEN PHOSPHORUS OF THE METALLIC BATH AND IRON CONTENT OF THE SLAG

There always exists in the basic Bessemer process a hyperbolic relationship between the phosphorus content of the bath and the iron content of the slag.   As shown in Figure 5 the position of this curve depends upon various factors.   Temperature and lime content are, for example, generally not the same in various steelworks. These variables are known to influence the position of the curve. It appears, however, that it is difficult in the basic Bessemer process to obtain, with a single slag and lime as a dephosphorizing agent, phosphorus contents inferior to 0.02%.

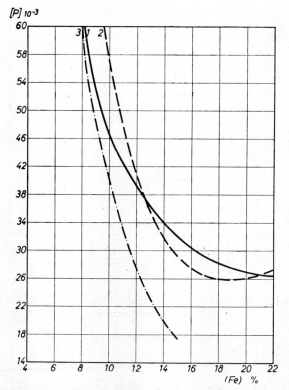

Fig. 5. The [P]-(Fe) relation in the basic Bessemer process. (*1*) Kosmider, H., and H. Schenk, *Stahl u. Eisen*, **77,** 918 (1957); (*2*) Weber, F., T. Kootz, and K. H. Obst, *Stahl u. Eisen*, **78,** 1735 (1958); (*3*) Geller and Wilms, *Stahl u. Eisen*, **61,** 337 (1941).

It is also normal in the case of the LD-AC process, starting from phosphorus-containing pig irons, to find a relationship between the phosphorus content of the metallic bath and the iron content of the slag. This can be seen even in the first or intermediate slag (Fig. 6). The position of the curve, as indicated, depends strongly upon the lime input during the first period of conversion.

Nevertheless, there is an optimum in the lime consumption during this phase compatible with the best final yield.

We can also observe, at the end of the second conversion period, a definite relationship between the two above-mentioned parameters. This dependence is shown in Figure 7.

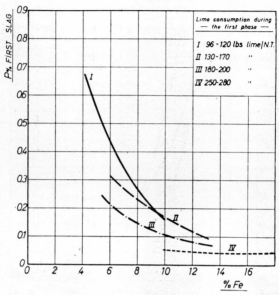

Fig. 6. The [P]-(Fe) relation in the LD-AC process at the end of the first period
for different line consumptions.

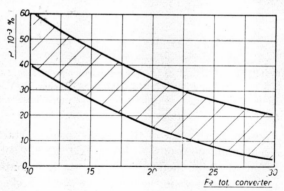

Fig. 7. The [P]-(Fe) relation in the LD-AC process at the end of the last period.

We thus confirm the well-known observations made in the basic
Bessemer process.

Three questions may arise from the examination of Figure 7:

1. Does the high iron content of the slag represent an excessive
loss of iron?

2. Does this high content indicate an increased oxidation of the metallic bath?

3. Are there any other factors which have an influence on the phosphorus content when the iron of the slag exceeds 20%?

Iron in the Slag and Metallic Yield

If we assume an identical lime consumption for a given pig iron analysis and if, with our LD-AC process or any other steelmaking method, we merely consider a process without an intermediate de-slagging operation, it is certain that the iron loss will be proportional to the iron content of the slag.

If we consider phosphorus content in the metal to be around 0.04% it is normal to find 10% iron in the slag. This represents a moderate loss. Should we desire to operate on lower phosphorus content, the study of the metallic yield from an economic stand-point suggests that an intermediate deslagging operation is neces-sary. (This is valuable, of course, in the case of basic Bessemer pig iron containing up to 1.8 or 2.0% phosphorus. The conversion con-ditions would change and become easier when the phosphorus con-tent of the pig iron decreases.)

The amount of slag removed at the end of the first conversion period is large since it contains all the silicon and a large part of the phosphorus of the pig iron. The physical condition of this slag is of great importance. Thanks to the high degree of foaming which takes place, the mean percentage of slag removed is about 78%. It is thus evident that the second slag, formed during the second stage of conversion, will be less abundant. For this reason it can contain a relatively high iron content without inducing a corresponding de-crease in the metallic yield. The presence of a slag tapping hole would further decrease this iron loss.

From the beginning of our tests we were convinced that the quan-tity of lime injected per unit volume of oxygen smaller in the first than in the second period, would permit us to obtain the required results with a very low lime consumption. We developed an op-erating procedure to test this belief. Results revealed, as expected, that excellent results were obtained when aiming for very mild steels containing less than 0.02% phosphorus. The lime consumption varied between 180 and 240 lb per metric ton of iron in the normal

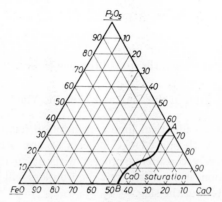

Fig. 8. The CaO saturation curve for the P₂O₅-CaO-FeO system.

case involving one intermediate deslagging operation. The lime consumption would be further reduced by the use of a tapping hole.

Using the same grade of pig iron and no intermediate deslagging operation, a lime consumption of 240 to 280 lb per metric ton is generally necessary if a final phosphorus content less than 0.03% is desired.

A priori, it can be said that as the lime consumption per ton of pig iron is increased, the lower will be the iron content of the slag for the same final phosphorus content. There are, however, other considerations to be taken into account.

In order to obtain an easy dephosphorization, it is, of course, desirable to attain lime saturation in the slag. The ternary phase diagram CaO-P₂O₅-FeO permits us to estimate this saturation limit. This saturation level is shown in Figure 8 due to Oelsen. Under ideal conditions, the lime injection should follow this saturation level. If the iron content of the slag is progressively increased along the line AB, the lime content will consequently vary. The phosphorus content will continually increase.

If we exceed by 10% the lime concentration necessary for saturation, neither dissolution and, therefore, dephosphorization, would be possible if we do not burn more iron. This dilutes the system.

If we have, for example, a lime-saturated slag containing 20% iron and 0.015% phosphorus, we could obtain the same phosphorus content with an excess of 10% lime. The iron content, as a result of dilution, is now 18%. The total iron loss is, therefore, not decreased.

Iron in the Slag and Metal Oxidation

Since one might believe that the degree of oxidation of the metal is a function of the iron content of the slag, the phosphorus/iron relationship previously mentioned could seem misleading.

This is because it would seem to indicate that low phosphorus contents cannot be obtained without a simultaneous high iron content in the slag. This, in turn, would necessitate a high oxygen content in the metal.

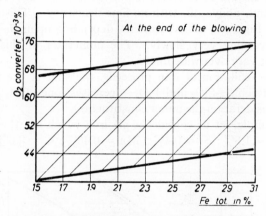

Fig. 9. The (Fe)-(O) relation at the end of the heats.

This oxygen/iron relationship is shown in Figure 9. There seems to be a slight tendency for the oxygen and iron contents to simultaneously increase. The dispersion in the experimental points is so high, however, that the relation is statistically not quite significant. It is possible to predict the above tendency since we found a carbon/oxygen relationship, and for a given carbon content, one can obtain the entire scale of phosphorus or iron contents.

In addition, there also exists, in the basic Bessemer process, a relation between the iron content of the slag and oxygen content[26] of the metal. There, again, the relationship is not well defined.

We may conclude from what we have written above that there is no real danger, as far as our pig iron is concerned, to excessively increase metal oxidation by a high iron content in the slag if we keep the carbon content under control.

Another observation in the field of the iron content of the slag is the extremely characteristic relationship between this content and the slag basicity represented by

$$CaO\% / (1.866\ SiO_2 + 1.577\ P_2O_5)$$

Similar relationships again exist in the open hearth and electric furnace[27,28] processes.

Let us examine the two parameters which govern the shape of this curve:

1. One attempts to establish a lime-saturated slag with neither too much, and, above all, with no lime deficiency. This means, as indicated in Figure 9, a CaO content, depending upon the iron concentration, varying very slowly. The numerator of this equation thus does not vary over wide limits.

2. As the oxidation of iron proceeds, the sum of the two other major constituents—SiO_2 and P_2O_5—decreases (one must, of course, take into consideration the minor constituents).

As an example, let us consider a pig iron which has the following analysis: P = 1.8%; Si = 0.4%; Mn = 0.45%; C = 3.6%. Let us

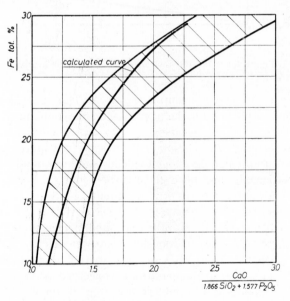

Fig. 10. Relation between the iron content of the slag and the basicity ratio.

also consider that we add lime to the slag so that it is exactly saturated and calculate then the shape of the curve as indicated by Decker.[29]

$$Fe = f[CaO/(1.866\ SiO_2 + 1.577\ P_2O_5)]$$

The calculation gives the curve shown in Figure 10. The shaded band corresponds to the area occupied by the experimental points. One can see that the agreement is very satisfactory.

Other Dephosphorization Factors

The following equation expresses the dephosphorization reaction:

$$2\underline{P} + 5\underline{O} + 4CaO = 4CaO \cdot P_2O_5$$

If we assume as do Fischer and vom Ende[30] that the heats are saturated with lime and phosphate, the oxygen will depend only upon the phosphorus, at a given temperature, according to

$$\log K'_P = 1/\underline{P}^2 \cdot \underline{O}^5 = 50.700/T - 17.87$$

This equation is valid in the basic Bessemer process.

We shall, assuming that this relationship is also true in the present case, compare the phosphorus contents, from a series of heats we have studied, calculated from T and O, with those actually found. It is revealed that these calculated values are much higher than the real phosphorus contents.

In the LD-AC process, we often find relatively low P_2O_5 contents in the slag. It thus seems probable that, since these slags are not saturated with P_2O_5, the activity of this anhydride must enter into equilibrium formula, if this equilibrium exists. This equation must, therefore, be of the following form:

$$K_P = a_{4CaO \cdot P_2O_5}/\underline{P}^2 \cdot \underline{O}^5$$

Upon multiplying both sides by $\underline{P}^2 \cdot \underline{O}^5$, we obtain

$$a_{4CaO \cdot P_2O_5} = K_P \cdot \underline{P}^2 \cdot \underline{O}^5$$

A knowledge of K_P, $\underline{P}$ and $\underline{O}$ permits us to determine the right side of the above equation and to write $a_{4CaO \cdot P_2O_5}$ in terms of several variables.

Figure 11 shows the logarithm of this term plotted as a function of the P_2O_5 content of the slag for a series of heats. In spite of the high dispersion due to various factors, it appears that the mean value of

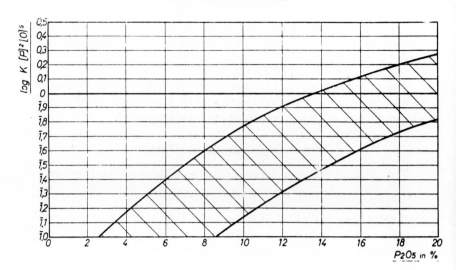

Fig. 11. Relation between log $K \cdot [P]^2 \cdot [O]^5$ and the $P_2O_5\%$ content of the slag for a series of heats.

the activity approaches 1 when the P_2O_5 concentration exceeds 18%. This is often realized in the basic Bessemer process. The influence of P_2O_5 becomes important only at concentrations less than 15%. In the series of LD-AC casts which we have chosen, about one-half had P_2O_5 contents less than 10%.

Using different blowing conditions, for another series of heats, we observed that this area or band was displaced either to the left or to the right.

We thus draw the conclusion that there is not necessarily an equilibrium established between the slag and metal. The iron content of the slag has, in fact, considerable influence and it is difficult to separate the effect of the iron content from the effect of the P_2O_5.

In the case of nonsaturated slags, the lack of lime results in a higher phosphorus content in the metal.

The previous description permits us to state the conditions responsible for the very good dephosphorization realized with the LD-AC process.

1. It is necessary to provide a sufficient lime content in order to ensure complete lime saturation of the slag.

2. The P_2O_5 content of the final slag must be as low as possible.

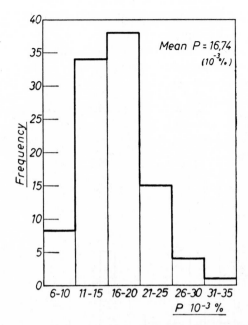

Fig. 12. Frequency curve of the P content of one-hundred heats.

3.   The slag must also contain a sufficient amount of iron oxide.

4.   All other conditions being equal, a low final temperature is obviously favorable to ensure the elimination of phosphorus.

The mean value—0.0167%—of the phosphorus content in heats No. 500 to No. 599 is shown in the frequency curve, Figure 12.

STUDY OF DESULFURIZATION

The elimination of sulfur in the LD-AC process is excellent.   The average desulfurization level approaches 67% with an average final sulfur content in the steel equal to 0.017% (Fig. 13).

In two heats, where the original sulfur content of the pig iron was in the range 0.081 to 0.085%, the final sulfur content in the steel was in the range 0.031 to 0.035%.   In five other heats these two sulfur contents were 0.076 to 0.080% and 0.026 to 0.030%, respectively. In ninety-three other heats the final sulfur contents were below 0.025%.

In the first conversion period, with our lime consumption, we already realize a mean desulfurization of 40%. At the end of this period, a deslagging operation which removes approximately 78% of the slag, also eliminates a large part of the sulfur.

The basicity and the temperature play a very important part during the first conversion period.

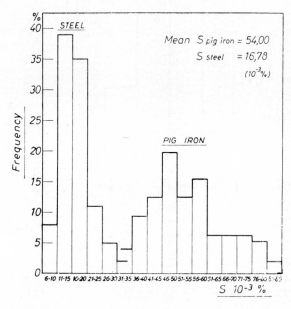

Fig. 13. Frequency curve of the sulfur content of the pig iron and of the steel.

We have also examined the influence of the iron content of the slag on desulfurization. The diagram showing the desulfurization level in the first period versus the iron content in the slag usually fails to show any relationship. If we consider the desulfurization level versus the sulfur content in the pig iron for two different iron contents in the slag, a favorable influence of this last element is revealed (Fig. 14).

At the end of the second period of conversion, the desulfurization level increases with the iron content of the slag as is shown in Figure 15. The correlation coefficient r of the relationship is equal to 0.30.

It is not certain, however, that the iron content of the slag is in itself favorable for a good desulfurization. It could be an indirect result which involves the relationship previously referred to—that

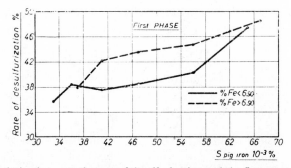

Fig. 14. Relation between the rate of desulfurization and the S content of the iron
for two (Fe) levels at the end of the first period.

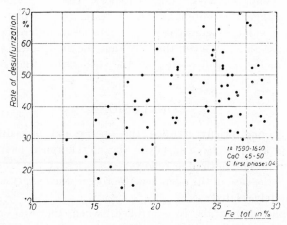

Fig. 15. Relation between the rate of desulfurization and the iron content of the
slag.

existing between the iron content of the slag and the basicity index
(for which $r = 0.85$).

$$CaO/(1.866\ SiO_2 + 1.577\ P_2O_5)$$

We have calculated the relationship between the desulfurization
rate and this basicity ratio.   The correlation coefficient—higher than
in the case for iron content in the slag—is equal to 0.43.

This aspect of desulfurization is still being studied.

It is obvious that, if we operate with a lime consumption higher in
the first and second periods, we could obtain desulfurization levels

still higher than those actually obtained. This would, however, have a detrimental influence on the metallic yield.

STUDY OF MANGANESE

The equilibrium constant of manganese is given by the well-known equation

$$K_{Mn} = a_{MnO}/Mn \cdot a_{FeO}$$

If we consider that $a_{FeO} = O_{anal.}/O_{sat.}$ and that

$$a_{MnO} = \{n_{MnO}/[N - (CaO\ comb + CaO\ excess)]\}$$

as has been previously done,[29] one can, upon the insertion of the K_{Mn} value of Chipman, Gero, and Winkler,[32] calculate values of the residual manganese content. For 50 heats, the calculated residual manganese values averaged 0.07%. The mean difference is 0.02% in absolute value. We can thus say that the manganese content is a function of the oxygen content of the steel rather than of the FeO content of the slag.

CONCLUSIONS

After having briefly recalled the operational procedure of the LD-AC process, we have surveyed the metallurgical characteristics which can be summarized as follows:

1. As is the case in the open hearth process, the oxygen and carbon are intimately related.

2. Dephosphorization is controlled, when the lime content is sufficient, by the iron and P_2O_5 contents of the slag and the temperature of the bath.

3. A high iron content in the slag does not involve a significantly higher oxidation of the metallic bath.

4. The desulfurization level is controlled by the well-known factors: basicity, temperature, and iron content of the slag.

5. The distribution of manganese depends, at a given temperature. on the oxygen content of the metal.

References

1. Metz, P., *Blast Furnace Steel Plant*, **46,** 1065 (1958); *ibid.,* 1187 (1958).
2. Metz, P., *Iron & Steel*, **31,** No. 10, 455 (1958).
3. Schwarz, K. V., *Stahl u. Eisen*, **72,** 1642 (1952).

4. Durrer, R., and H. Hellbrugge, *Stahl u. Eisen*, **70**, 1208 (1950).

5. Trenkler, H., *Rev. universelle mines*, **9**, 644 (1953).

6. Rosner, K., *Stahl u. Eisen*, **72**, 997 (1952).

7. Cuscoleca, O., *Stahl u. Eisen*, **72**, 899 (1952).

8. Drei Jahre LD, Voest, 1956.

9. McMulkin, F. J., *J. Metals*, **7**, 530 (1955).

10. *Iron Steel Engr.*, 191 (1958); D. R. Loughrey, "The Basic Oxygen Process," Am. Inst. Mining Met. Engrs. Meeting, Feb., 1959.

11. Austin, C. R., *Iron Steel Engr.*, **33**, 64 (1956).

12. Springorum, F., K. G. Speith, O. Darmann, and H. vom Ende, *Stahl u. Eisen*, **77**, 1284 (1957).

13. Kosmider, H., N. Neuhaus, and H. Schenk, *Stahl u. Eisen*, **77**, 1277 (1957).

14. Rellermeyer, H., H. Knuppel, and J. Sittard, *Stahl u. Eisen*, **77**, 1296 (1957).

15. Rellermeyer, H., and T. Kootz, *Stahl u. Eisen*, **77**, 381 (1954).

16. Trenkler, H., *Eisenhüttentag*, Dusseldorf, 1957.

17. Lambert and Messin, C. I. T., No. 4, 819 (1958).

18. Kalling, B., *Rev. universelle mines*, **9**, 612 (1953).

19. Graef, R., *Stahl u. Eisen*, **77**, 10 (1957).

20. Metz, P., Brevet belge, No. 551946 (Oct. 19, 1956), Publ. Feb. 14, 1957.

21. Kalling, B., and F. Johansson, *Rev. universelle mines*, **14**, 455 (1958).

22. Graef, R., and L. von Bogdandy, *Rev. universelle mines*, **14**, 467 (1958).

23. Chipman, J., *Basic Open Hearth Steelmaking*, AIME, 1951, p. 652. Figs. 16–17.

24. Speith, K. G., and H. vom Ende, *Stahl u. Eisen*, **76**, 1164 (1956).

25. Pottgiesser, *Stahl u. Eisen*, **78**, 291 (1958).

26. *Stahl u. Eisen*, **78**, 1734 (1958).

27. *Basic Open Hearth Steelmaking*, AIME, 1951, p. 226.

28. *Met. Italiana*, **49**, No. 12, 805 (1957).

29. Decker, A., *Arch. Eisenhüttenw.*, **28**, 57 (1957).

30. Fischer, W. A., and H. vom Ende, *Stahl u. Eisen*, **72**, 1398 (1952).

31. *Stahl u. Eisen*, **74**, 509 (1954).

32. Chipman, J., J. B. Gero, and P. B. Winkler, *J. Metals*, **2**, 341 (1950).

A Study of the Physical Chemistry of Titanium in the Blast Furnace

F. D. DELVE, H. W. MEYER, and H. N. LANDER

Jones & Laughlin Steel Corporation, Pittsburgh, Pennsylvania

Abstract

The solubility of titanium in carbon-saturated iron has been measured at 150C and 1600°C under neutral and nitrogen atmospheres. The precipitated phases of TiC and Ti(C,N) have been examined. The rate and manner of reduction of TiO_2 into carbon-saturated iron from several silicate slags have been investigated with particular reference to the formation of TiC. It has been found that the reduction of TiO_2 and SiO_2 from blast furnace slags proceeds on an interdependent basis. The fundamental studies are discussed together with results taken from blast furnace operation, and an attempt is made to draw conclusions regarding the use of titaniferous ores in the conventional blast furnace.

INTRODUCTION

The fact that titanium-bearing burdens can cause poor operation in blast furnaces producing basic pig iron is well known, but the underlying mechanism by which titanium causes trouble has not been fully understood.

The experiments reported in this paper are divided into two categories. First, determination of the titanium solubility in carbon and carbon-nitrogen-saturated iron and an examination of the precipitated solid phase of TiC or Ti(C,N); secondly, experiments in which titanium was reduced into carbon-saturated iron from silicate slags. An attempt has also been made to correlate the laboratory work with the results of blast furnace operating tests. Previous experimental work connected with titanium in the blast furnace has been carried out almost exclusively by Russian or German investigators, and, in most cases, their results have not been directly applicable to American practice. From experience, operation of titanium burdens is usually

1111

successful for a period of 2–4 weeks before any signs of trouble appear. There are no reported data on extended blast furnace operation with titaniferous burdens, the furnace trials which have been reported[1,2] appear to have been of less than three weeks' duration.

Titanium is a strong carbide and nitride former, and the formation of titanium carbide and/or nitride is of particular importance in any investigation of the behavior of titanium in the blast furnace. Work by Tofaute and Buttinghaus,[3] on the Fe-Ti-C system, using x-ray and metallographic techniques, has been used by Wentrup et al.[4] to supply evidence that in carbon-saturated iron, at smelting temperatures, titanium carbide will not separate out until the titanium content of the iron reaches about 1%. Tofaute and Buttinghaus' work[3] did not extend beyond 3% carbon, but a liquidus line has been extrapolated up to 7% carbon. This line, for which there are no data, is immediately a suspect since it implies that the addition of only 0.3% Ti lowers the melting point of carbon-saturated iron by 300°C. Some of the results which were inexplicable to Wentrup et al.[4] were due to carbide precipitation at less than 1% Ti in the metal.

The discussion in this paper is centered around conventional blast furnace operation to produce iron for basic steelmaking and not specialized types of operation such as the production of vanadium pig iron[1] or cupola-type operations[5] in which the FeO content of the slag is above 1%.

The thermodynamics of titanium solution in carbon-saturated iron, and the effect of various alloying elements, have not been pursued in this paper, but it is planned to examine such aspects at a later date.

EXPERIMENTAL METHODS

Materials

The iron used in laboratory tests was electrolytic iron analyzing 99.83% Fe, 0.015% C, 0.004% Mn, 0.008% Si, 0.007% Ni, 0.009% S, and 0.027% all other trace elements. The titanium metal used in the solubility studies was crushed titanium sponge of 98.5% purity. The slags were prefused and produced by melting reagent grade CaO, MgO, SiO_2, Al_2O_3, and TiO_2 in a graphite crucible and chill casting the resultant liquid slag on an iron plate. The slags were crushed to −65 mesh, thoroughly mixed, and sampled for chemical analysis. The argon, carbon monoxide, and nitrogen used were of 99.99%,

99.5%, and 99.7% purity, respectively.   All gases were dried before entering the apparatus by passing them through a column of Drie-rite.

Apparatus

The apparatus used (Fig. 1) consisted of a solid graphite cylinder 6 in. long and 3 in. in diameter, having six $3/4$-in. holes drilled to a depth of $3^1/_4$ in., spaced equidistantly on the circumference of a 2-in. diam circle.   Graphite crucibles, $1/_8$ in. wall thickness and $3^3/_4$ in. long, fitted snugly into these holes.   A $1/_2$-in. diam hole, $3^1/_4$ in. deep,

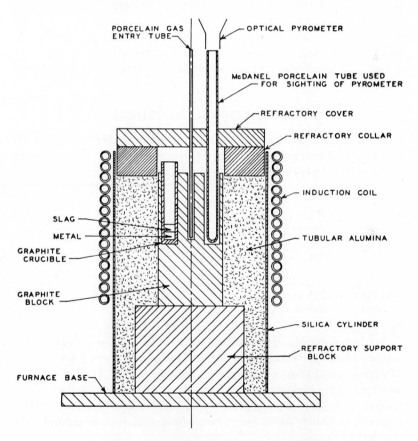

Fig. 1. Schematic drawing of apparatus.

drilled through the center of the graphite block, served to preheat the carbon monoxide, nitrogen, or argon used as a protective atmosphere.

Temperature Measurements

Temperature measurements were made by sighting an optical pyrometer down a $^3/_8$-in. diam McDanel high temperature porcelain protection tube located in one of the circumferential holes in the graphite block. The optical pyrometer employed was calibrated against a National Bureau of Standards platinum-platinum 10% rhodium standard thermocouple. The bottom of the porcelain tube was set at a height which corresponded to the level of the metal surface in each crucible. The graphite block was centered in an induction coil such that each of the circumferential holes was the same distance from the induction coil. It was confirmed that there was no measurable temperature variation between crucibles.

EXPERIMENTAL PROCEDURE

In order to check the apparatus and technique, blanks were run at two temperatures using only electrolytic iron in the graphite crucibles. After the melt had been held at temperature for 1 hr, samples

TABLE I
Solubility of Carbon in Liquid Iron

Temp, °F	C, %[a]	C, %[b]
2732	5.15	5.14
2912	5.40	5.42

[a] Chipman et al.[6]
[b] This investigation.

for carbon determination were aspirated into a glass capillary tube. Table I shows the excellent agreement between the results of this investigation and those obtained by Chipman et al.[6] During the titanium solubility experiments, each small crucible was charged with electrolytic iron and varying percentages of titanium powder. It was established that 1 hr at temperature was sufficient to saturate the iron with titanium.

Experiments were also carried out to study the relative rates of reduction of TiO_2 from silicate slags, and in these experiments the metal and slag were charged to the crucibles before inserting them into the holes. The apparatus was purged with nitrogen for about 20 min while the crucibles were heating up. The gas was then changed to carbon monoxide or argon. The crucibles were brought to the desired temperature and samples were taken at various time intervals up to a maximum of 6 hr.

In the titanium solubility experiments, metal samples were aspirated into a glass capillary tube, the metal and glass were subsequently separated, and the metal sample was crushed to -20 mesh. In the TiO_2 reduction experiments, however, since the metal was covered by slag, samples were obtained by withdrawing a graphite crucible at the desired time and quenching it in water, making sure that no water entered the crucible. Subsequent to quenching, the crucible was broken and the slag and metal portions separated. Good physical separation of the two phases was possible. The metal samples were cleaned on an abrasive wheel until all surface impurities had been removed. The metal button was then fractured to insure that no slag was trapped in the metal during solidification. It was then crushed to approximately -20 mesh. The slag sample was crushed to -65 mesh and a magnetic separation carried out.

In addition to the laboratory work, a large number of tests were taken at the blast furnace under actual operating conditions in order to compare the results with those obtained in the laboratory. Blast furnace metal and slag samples were taken over a period of seven days. The metal samples were aspirated from a sampling spoon into a glass capillary tube to obtain a chilled iron sample. Three metal samples per cast were taken at the following intervals:

1. Within 5 min after start of cast.
2. Between 10 to 15 min after start of cast.
3. Between 20 and 25 min after start of cast.

This sampling technique was used to determine if there was any abnormal variation in the titanium content between the start, middle, and end of a cast.

Flush slag samples were taken near the middle of the flush, and cast slag samples were taken as soon as possible after the slag began to flow from the furnace.

TABLE II

Titanium Solubility in Carbon- and Carbon-Nitrogen-Saturated Iron

Experiment and sample no	Temp, °C	Time at temp, hr	Atm	Metal analysis, wt-%			PPTD phase analysis, mole-%		
				Ti, soluble	Ti, total	Si	TiC	TiN	TiN/TiC
2-1	1500	$1\,^1/_4$	N_2	0.16	0.24	0.05	—	—	—
2-1A	1500	$1\,^2/_3$	N_2	0.15	0.27	0.01	—	—	—
2-2	1500	$1\,^1/_3$	N_2	0.16	0.26	0.03	—	—	—
2-2A	1500	$1\,^2/_3$	N_2	0.15	0.27	0.01	—	—	—
2-3	1500	$1\,^1/_3$	N_2	0.15	0.40	0.01	—	—	—
2-3A	1500	$1\,^2/_3$	N_2	0.14	0.36	0.02	—	—	—
2-4A	1500	$1\,^2/_3$	N_2	0.14	0.27	0.01	—	—	—
2-5A	1500	$1\,^2/_3$	N_2	0.18	0.83	0.01	—	—	—
3-1	1500	$1\,^1/_4$	A	0.25	0.44	0.08	—	—	—
3-2	1500	$1\,^1/_3$	A	0.27	0.56	0.18	—	—	—
3-3	1500	$1\,^1/_3$	A	0.29	0.60	0.06	—	—	—
3-4	1500	$1\,^1/_2$	A	0.28	0.91	—	—	—	—
3-5	1500	$1\,^1/_2$	A	0.30	1.10	0.05	—	—	—
5-1	1600	1	A	0.26	0.91	—	—	—	—
5-2	1600	$1\,^1/_4$	A	0.32	0.86	—	—	—	—
5-5	1600	$1\,^1/_2$	A	0.32	0.90	—	—	—	—

6-1	1500	1	A	0.26	0.46	—	—	—	—
6-2	1500	1	A	0.26	0.40	—	—	—	—
6-3	1500	$1\frac{1}{4}$	A	0.24	0.40	—	—	—	—
6-4	1500	$1\frac{1}{4}$	A	0.25	0.38	—	—	—	—
6-5	1500	$1\frac{1}{8}$	A	0.26	0.38	—	—	—	—
7-3	1600	6	CO	0.28	3.00	—	90–100	—	—
8-1	1600	$1\frac{1}{2}$	N_2	0.22	0.50	—	69	31	0.449
8-2	1600	$2\frac{1}{2}$	N_2	0.19	0.52	—	67	33	0.492
8-3	1600	$3\frac{1}{2}$	N_2	0.19	0.46	0.90	65	35	0.538
8-4	1600	$3\frac{1}{2}$	N_2	0.13	0.50	1.95	54	46	0.852
8-5	1600	$3\frac{1}{2}$	N_2	0.18	0.47	—	59	41	0.694
9-1	1500	$3\frac{1}{4}$	N_2	0.16	0.32	—	59	41	0.694
9-2	1500	6	N_2	0.14	0.39	—	52	48	0.923
9-3	1500	7	N_2	0.17	0.38	1.02	53	47	0.886
9-4	1500	7	N_2	0.08	0.26	1.96	66	34	0.515
9-5	1500	7	N_2	0.08	0.37	—	44	56	1.272
10-1	1600	$3\frac{1}{2}$	N_2	0.21	0.42	—	71	29	0.408
10-2	1600	6	N_2	0.20	0.51	—	69	31	0.449
10-3	1600	7	N_2	0.20	0.39	1.71	61	39	0.639
10-4	1600	7	N_2	0.11	0.53	0.02	81	19	0.235
10-5[a]	1600	7	N_2	0.19	0.62	—	—	—	—

[a] 0.16 wt-% S in the metal.

TABLE III

Results of Experiments with Silicate Slags

Experiment and sample no	Atm	Temp, °C	Time at temp, hr	Slag classification[a]	Metal analysis, wt%			TiO$_2$ in slag, wt%
					Ti, soluble	Ti, total	Si	
T-14-1	CO	1500	1	AL	0.06	0.04	0.16	1.10
T-14-2	CO	1500	2	AL	0.08	0.07	0.28	1.06
T-14-3	CO	1500	3	AL	0.11	0.12	0.42	1.07
T-14-4	CO	1500	4	AL	0.10	0.13	0.47	1.14
T-16-1	CO	1500	1	BL	0.05	0.06	0.14	1.20
T-16-2	CO	1500	2	BL	0.07	0.09	0.11	1.15
T-16-3	CO	1500	3	BL	0.08	0.12	0.21	1.13
T-16-4	CO	1500	4	BL	0.09	0.14	0.27	1.08
T-17-1	CO	1500	1	DL	0.07	0.08	0.10	1.38
T-17-2	CO	1500	2	DL	0.09	0.10	0.13	1.31
T-17-3	CO	1500	3	DL	0.10	0.13	0.24	1.30
T-17-4	CO	1500	4	DL	0.10	0.14	0.24	1.25
T-18-1	CO	1500	1	AH	0.15	0.34	0.18	5.97
T-18-2	CO	1500	2	AH	0.21	0.48	0.24	5.74
T-18-3	CO	1500	3	AH	0.25	0.52	0.30	5.64
T-18-4	CO	1500	4	AH	0.28[b]	0.56	0.32	5.34
T-19-1	CO	1500	1	CH	0.20	0.38	0.11	6.29
T-19-2	CO	1500	2	CH	0.26	0.45	0.12	5.99
T-19-4	CO	1500	4	CH	0.29[b]	0.60	0.18	5.52
T-19-5	CO	1500	5	CH	0.30[b]	0.60	0.19	5.80
T-19-6	CO	1500	6	CH	0.29[b]	0.54	0.20	5.67
T-20-1	CO	1500	1	BH	0.25	0.55	0.23	6.26
T-20-2	CO	1500	2	BH	0.25	0.55	0.31	5.92
T-20-4	CO	1500	4	BH	0.24[b]	0.60	0.35	5.75
T-20-5	CO	1500	5	BH	0.24[b]	0.46	0.34	5.42
T-20-6	CO	1500	6	BH	0.25[b]	0.50	0.40	5.20

T-21-1	CO	1500	1	DH	0.21	0.34	0.08	3.74
T-21-2	CO	1500	2	DH	0.23	0.54	0.12	3.74
T-21-4	CO	1500	4	DH	0.27b	0.58	0.14	3.42
T-21-5	CO	1500	5	DH	0.28b	0.57	0.21	3.54
T-21-5	CO	1500	6	DH	0.26b	0.60	0.20	3.38
T-23-1	CO	1600	1	AL	0.15	0.18	0.65	1.14
T-23-2	CO	1600	2	AL	0.17	0.26	1.02	1.02
T-23-4	CO	1600	4	AL	0.18	0.37	1.61	0.84
T-23-6	CO	1600	6	AL	0.21	0.48	2.26	0.78
T-25-1	CO	1600	1	CL	0.10	0.12	0.20	1.21
T-25-2	CO	1600	2	CL	0.12	0.19	0.37	1.09
T-25-4	CO	1600	4	CL	0.16	0.28	0.71	1.00
T-25-6	CO	1600	6	CL	0.20	0.30	0.87	0.88
T-26-1	CO	1600	1	BL	0.13	0.19	0.29	1.15
T-26-2	CO	1600	2	BL	0.15	0.26	0.82	1.03
T-26-4	CO	1600	4	BL	0.14	0.34	1.06	0.84
T-26-6	CO	1600	6	BL	0.12	0.39	1.68	0.78
T-27-1	CO	1600	1	DL	0.15	0.20	0.28	1.05
T-27-2	CO	1600	2	DL	0.16	0.29	0.42	1.08
T-27-4	CO	1600	4	DL	0.20	0.45	0.91	0.88
T-27-6	CO	1600	6	DL	0.22	0.47	1.27	0.78
T-28-1	CO	1600	1	AH	0.29	0.50	0.30	5.35
T-28-2	CO	1600	2	AH	0.30b	0.60	0.32	4.97
T-28-4	CO	1600	4	AH	0.30b	0.90	0.45	4.42
T-28-5	CO	1600	5	AH	0.30b	1.01	0.90	4.45
T-28-6	CO	1600	6	AH	0.26b	0.81	0.90	3.97
T-29-1	CO	1600	1	CH	0.29	0.65	0.20	5.65
T-29-2	CO	1600	2	CH	0.28b	0.75	0.20	5.24
T-29-3	CO	1600	3	CH	0.30b	0.90	0.33	5.00
T-29-5	CO	1600	5	CH	0.28b	0.75	0.35	4.79
T-29-6	CO	1600	6	CH	0.28b	1.00	0.60	4.59

(continued)

TABLE III (*continued*)

Experiment and sample no	Atm	Temp, °C	Time at temp, hr	Slag classification[a]	Metal analysis, wt-%			TiO$_2$ in slag, wt-%
					Ti, soluble	Ti, total	Si	
T-30-2	CO	1600	2	BH	0.29[b]	0.90	0.30	4.54
T-30-3	CO	1600	3	BH	0.29[b]	0.90	0.30	4.32
T-30-5	CO	1600	5	BH	0.30[b]	0.90	0.35	3.67
T-30-6	CO	1600	6	BH	0.28[b]	1.15	0.55	3.22
T-31-1	CO	1600	1	DH	0.32	0.70	0.20	6.77
T-31-2	CO	1600	2	DH	0.31[b]	0.80	0.25	6.32
T-31-3	CO	1600	3	DH	0.33[b]	0.90	0.35	6.15
T-31-5	CO	1600	5	DH	0.38[b]	1.08	0.50	5.74
T-31-6	CO	1600	6	DH	0.32[b]	0.95	0.45	5.55
T-32-1	CO	1500	1	AL	0.09	0.14	0.30	2.13
T-32-2	CO	1500	2	AL	0.11	0.15	0.23	2.10
T-32-4	CO	1500	4	AL	0.16	0.25	0.31	2.05
T-32-5	CO	1500	5	AL	0.14	0.26	0.33	1.98
T-32-6	CO	1500	6	AL	0.17	0.29	0.36	1.87
T-33-1	CO	1500	1	BL	0.09	0.13	0.08	1.78
T-33-2	CO	1500	2	BL	0.10	0.15	0.13	1.77
T-33-4	CO	1500	4	BL	0.14	0.18	0.18	1.73
T-33-5	CO	1500	5	BL	0.14	0.20	0.36	1.72
T-33-6	CO	1500	6	BL	0.14	0.23	0.48	1.73
T-34-1	CO	1500	1	DL	0.10	0.17	0.20	1.23
T-34-2	CO	1500	2	DL	0.13	0.20	0.20	1.26
T-34-4	CO	1500	4	DL	0.16	0.26	0.20	1.20
T-34-5	CO	1500	5	DL	0.17	0.28	0.20	1.20
T-34-6	CO	1500	6	DL	0.18	0.32	0.34	1.12
T-35-1	CO	1500	1	AH	0.21	0.37	0.30	8.41
T-35-2	CO	1500	2	AH	0.22	0.37	0.16	8.32

T-35-4	1500	CO	4	AH	0.23[b]	0.42	0.19	7.97
T-35-5	1500	CO	5	AH	0.24[b]	0.48	0.22	7.39
T-35-6	1500	CO	6	AH	0.24[b]	0.48	0.30	7.67
T-36-1	1500	CO	1	CH	0.25	0.25	0.18	8.76
T-36-2	1500	CO	2	CH	0.27	0.58	0.16	8.56
T-36-3	1500	CO	3	CH	0.27	0.44	0.16	8.61
T-36-5	1500	CO	5	CH	0.27[b]	0.37	0.12	8.46
T-36-6	1500	CO	6	CH	0.27[b]	0.44	0.16	8.24
T-37-1	1500	CO	1	BH	0.23	0.40	0.24	8.01
T-37-2	1500	CO	2	BH	0.27	0.52	0.24	8.04
T-37-3	1500	CO	3	BH	0.26	0.40	0.20	8.04
T-37-5	1500	CO	5	BH	0.26[b]	0.54	0.28	7.82
T-37-6	1500	CO	6	BH	0.27[b]	0.44	0.28	7.29
T-38-1	1500	CO	1	DH	0.17	0.44	0.24	8.74
T-38-2	1500	CO	2	DH	0.23	0.42	0.10	8.46
T-38-3	1500	CO	3	DH	0.25	0.40	0.12	8.57
T-38-5	1500	CO	5	DH	0.25[b]	0.48	0.14	8.31
T-38-6	1500	CO	6	DH	0.25[b]	0.40	0.16	8.24

[a] Classification of slags:

Classification	wt-% (CaO + MgO)/(0.6 Al_2O_3 + SiO_2)	Approx Al_2O_3 (wt-%)
AL	1.31 ± 0.02	9.0
AH	1.27 ± 0.06	9.7
BL	1.08 ± 0.04	21.9
BH	1.04 ± 0.01	21.8
CL	1.63 ± 0.02	9.5
CH	1.57 ± 0.04	9.5
DL	1.27 ± 0.04	21.5
DH	1.28 ± 0.06	22.0

[b] These results were included in the calculation of the mean titanium solubility in carbon-saturated iron.

Analysis

Analytical tests were conducted to show that the acid-soluble titanium content of the metal (that portion of the sample which is soluble in $1:9$ H_2SO_4 after digestion at $95°C$ for 1 hr) represents the titanium originally in solution in the liquid iron.

The acid-insoluble portion was examined by x-ray diffraction methods using a Debye-Scherrer camera. In heats made under argon or carbon monoxide, the precipitated phase was identified as titanium carbide, but under a nitrogen atmosphere the precipitated phase had a lattice parameter between that of titanium carbide and titanium nitride.

The analyses of the metal samples for other common elements and the slag analyses were conducted using standard analytical techniques.

RESULTS

Laboratory experiments have been carried out at $1500 \pm 10°C$ and $1600 \pm 10°C$ under one atmosphere of carbon monoxide, argon, or nitrogen. The results of experiments conducted to determine the solubility of titanium in carbon-saturated and carbon-nitrogen-saturated iron are given in Table II, which includes the results of the x-ray analyses on the precipitated phase. A few heats were run under a nitrogen atmosphere for times up to 7 hr, and to some of these heats silicon or sulfur was added. These results are also given in Table II.

Studies on the rate of reduction of TiO_2 from silicate slags also yielded titanium solubility figures, and these are marked with a superscript b in Table III which contains the results of experiments carried out under various silicate slags. It was established that the metal became saturated with titanium, when in contact with slags containing more than 4% TiO_2, in 3–4 hr at $1500°C$ and in less than 1 hr at $1600°C$. The slags used all contained about 7.5% magnesia and a key to their classification is given as a footnote to Table III.

Table IV contains a summary of the results from the blast furnace tests. Table V summarizes the results of titanium solubility measurements in carbon- and carbon-nitrogen-saturated iron.

TABLE IV. Data on Blast Furnace Tests

Cast and sample no.	Metal analysis, %			Slag analysis, %	
	Si	Acid sol. Ti	Total Ti	SiO$_2$	TiO$_2$
8921-1	—	0.08	0.16	—	1.58
8921-2	0.92	0.06	0.14	35.10	1.58
7304-1	—	0.10	0.18	—	1.35
7304-2	—	0.10	0.17	—	—
7304-3	0.82	0.10	0.18	33.56	1.32
8926-1	—	0.09	0.14	—	—
8926-2	0.79	0.08	0.10	34.10	1.02
8268-1	—	0.09	0.17	—	1.05
8268-2	—	0.10	0.19	—	—
8268-3	1.02	0.08	0.16	32.74	.93
13729-1	—	0.10	0.15	—	1.92
13729-2	—	0.10	0.15	—	—
13729-3	0.79	0.11	0.13	35.65	1.84
8176-1	1.15	0.07	0.14	—	0.72
8176-2	—	—	—	36.02	0.85
8941-1	—	0.08	0.15	—	0.88
8941-2	—	0.10	0.15	—	—
8941-3	1.10	0.08	0.16	35.64	0.97
7322-1	—	0.07	0.14	—	0.97
7322-2	—	0.07	0.14	—	—
7322-3	1.07	0.07	0.14	35.68	1.05
13744-1	—	0.07	0.13	—	1.28
13744-2	1.11	0.07	0.13	36.34	1.28
8181-1	—	0.07	0.22	—	0.75
8181-2	1.48	0.07	0.20	34.94	0.64
8946-1	—	0.08	0.15	—	1.08
8946-2	—	0.08	0.14	—	—
8946-3	0.79	0.08	0.15	32.48	0.88
13749-1	—	0.08	0.13	—	0.75
13749-2	—	0.07	0.14	—	—
13749-3	1.09	0.07	0.15	35.28	0.74
8186-1	—	0.10	0.20	—	0.97
8186-2	1.26	0.08	0.21	36.42	1.07
8951-1	—	0.10	0.24	—	0.88
8951-2	1.24	0.11	0.20	32.28	0.67
8955-1	—	0.05	0.13	—	0.97
8955-2	—	0.08	0.14	—	—
8955-3	1.08	0.06	0.13	36.68	0.90
8298-1	—	0.08	0.09	—	0.78
8298-2	0.85	0.05	0.08	37.44	1.52
8195-1	—	0.09	0.12	—	1.02
8195-2	0.86	0.09	0.14	35.64	0.90
8960-1	—	0.09	0.14	—	0.90
8960-2	—	0.08	0.15	—	—
8960-3	1.25	0.08	0.13	36.71	0.78
8302-1	—	0.08	0.20	—	1.02
8302-2	1.25	0.08	0.18	35.42	1.05

TABLE V
Solubility of Titanium in Carbon- and Carbon-Nitrogen-Saturated Iron

Temp, °C	Atmosphere	Number of Results	mean solubility Wt-%	Standard deviation, %
1500 ± 10	CO and A	30	0.263 ± 0.006	2.3
1500 ± 10	N₂	10	0.152 ± 0.010	6.4
1602 ± 10	CO and A	24	0.299 ± 0.008	2.7
1602 ± 10	N₂	6	0.202 ± 0.011	5.4

EXPERIMENTAL ERRORS

When the errors in temperature measurement and chemical analysis for the solubility experiments are compounded, the resulting error is in good agreement with the calculated standard deviation of the results. Titanium balances on the rate of reduction experiments were accurate to within the range ±3 to ±10%.

DISCUSSION

Titanium Solubility

The titanium solubility in carbon-saturated iron, which is limited by the precipitation of solid titanium carbide, has been measured as 0.299 and 0.263 wt-%* at 1600 and 1500°C, respectively. These values are considerably lower than those suggested by Tofaute and Buttinghaus[3] and Wentrup et al.[4] The metal samples were quenched almost instantaneously and microscopic examination revealed large particles of titanium carbide. There was no evidence of precipitation during cooling.

Some of the results used to calculate the mean titanium solubility in carbon-saturated iron, under CO and argon atmospheres, were taken from experiments in which the iron contained small amounts of silicon. No correlation whatsoever was found between the silicon content and the titanium solubility, and the difference between the mean solubilities in iron containing no silicon (0.266) and that containing less than 1% silicon (0.262) is well within the limits of experimental error. It is concluded, therefore that silicon, up to 1%,

---

* These values are slightly different from those given by Delve,[7] and are based on his data, plus additional data which has since become available.

has no measurable effect of the solubility of titanium in carbon saturated iron.

The standard free energy of formation of solid titanium carbide has been calculated by Richardson[8] from the data of Humphrey.[9]

$$\text{Ti }(s) + \text{C }(gr) \longrightarrow \text{TiC }(s) \tag{1}$$

$$\Delta F^\circ{}_1 = -41{,}600 + 3.16T + 3 \text{ kcal}$$

In the experiments carried out, the activities of carbon and titanium carbide were unity. Therefore, in Eq. (1):

$$RT \ln a_{\text{Ti}} = F^\circ{}_1 \tag{1a}$$

where a_{Ti} is the activity of titanium, in solution in carbon-saturated iron, with respect to pure solid titanium. From measurements of the titanium solubility (expressed as mole fraction) at 1500 and 1600°C, the corresponding activity coefficients may also be calculated. Thus at 1500°C, $a_{\text{Ti}} = 1.6 \times 10^{-5}$, $\gamma_{\text{Ti}} = 6.3 \times 10^{-3}$, and at 1600°C, $a_{\text{Ti}} = 3.1 \times 10^{-5}$, $\gamma_{\text{Ti}} = 1.1 \times 10^{-2}$.

When iron is saturated with nitrogen in addition to carbon, the solubility of titanium drops still further. This is to be expected since titanium is also a strong nitride former. Kootz[10] has shown that carbon-saturated iron becomes saturated with nitrogen in about 15 min at 1600°C when the nitrogen is bubbled through the melt. Experiments carried out under 1 atm of nitrogen showed no change in titanium solubility after $1^1/_2$ hr, the maximum experimental time being 7 hr. It has therefore been assumed that in all cases the iron was saturated with nitrogen. Under these conditions, we may consider reaction (1) as being accompanied by reactions (2) and (3).

$$\text{Ti}(s) + {}^1/_2\text{N}_2(g) \longrightarrow \text{TiN}(s) \tag{2}$$

$$\Delta F^\circ{}_2 = -80{,}930 + 22.79T \pm 3 \text{ kcal}^{7,8}$$

$$x\text{TiN}(s) + (1 - x)\text{TiC}(s) \longrightarrow \text{TiN}_x\text{C}_{1-x} \tag{3}$$

and

$$\Delta F^\circ{}_3 = (1 - x)\,\Delta F^\circ{}_1 + x\Delta F^\circ{}_2$$

On the assumption that TiC and TiN form an ideal solid solution,[11] the equilibrium ratios of TiC and TiN for $a_{[\text{C}]} = 1$ and various nitrogen pressures can be calculated. Considering reactions (1) and (2):

$$K_2/K_1 = [a_{\text{TiN}}/(a_{\text{Ti}} \cdot p^{1/_2}{}_{\text{N}_2})] \cdot [(a_{\text{Ti}} \cdot a_{\text{C}})/a_{\text{TiC}}] = (a_{\text{TiN}}/a_{\text{TiC}})/(1/p^{1/_2}{}_{\text{N}_2})$$

$$= N_{\text{TiN}}/N_{\text{TiC}} \cdot 1/p^{1/_2}{}_{\text{N}_2} \tag{4}$$

From the free energy equations the N_{TiN}/N_{TiC} ratio can be calculated.

$$\ln (K_2/K_1) = (18{,}280/T) - 9.88$$

Figure 2 shows a plot of N_{TiN}/N_{TiC} versus temperature in °C for 1.6, 1, and 0.8 atm. of nitrogen. Examining the TiN/TiC ratios reported in Table II, it is seen that, even allowing for the fact that these ratios are deduced from x-ray data which may be subject to an error $\pm 10\%$, the ratios are not in agreement with those for one atmosphere of nitrogen given by Figure 2, and are still moving toward

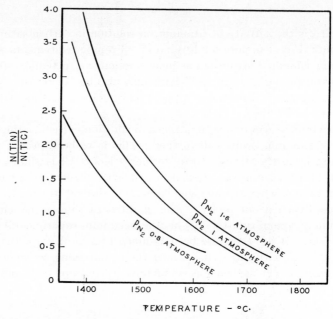

Fig. 2. Variation of composition of TiC-TiN solid solution in contact with graphite as a function of nitrogen partial pressure and temperature (calculated from thermal data[8,9]).

the equilibrium ratios after 7 hr. This lack of equilibrium is due to the experimental procedure used, since the iron would become saturated with carbon before it was saturated with nitrogen. We might, therefore, regard the carbide as having a "head start" on the nitride, and even though the melt was saturated with nitrogen, it would take some time for true equilibrium to be established in the carbonitride solid solution. It is, therefore, impossible to calculate a rigorous activity coefficient for titanium in carbon- and nitrogen-saturated iron. However, the free energies of formation of the carbide and nitride[8,9] at 1600°C are 38.7 ± 3 kcal and 38.3 ± 3 kcal, respectively, and at 1500°C, 39.0 ± 3 kcal and 40.50 ± 3 kcal, respectively. The difference between these values is within their accuracy limits, and the assumption $\Delta F°_1 = \Delta F°_2$ is a reasonable one. By making such an assumption, it follows that provided the iron is saturated with carbon and nitrogen (at 1 atm) the composition of the ideal solid solution will not affect the solubility of titanium. This is in agreement with the observed results, in that although the TiN/TiC ratio is changing with time, there is no detectable change in the titanium solubility. The assumption that $\Delta F°_1 = \Delta F°_2$ leads to titanium activity coefficients in carbon-nitrogen-saturated iron, which are essentially the same as those in carbon-saturated iron, but the titanium activities, at titanium saturation, are 8.7×10^{-6} and 2.3×10^{-5} and 1500 and 1600°C, respectively.

Considering the TiN/TiC ratios calculated from thermal data (Fig. 2), it is to be expected that the conditions prevailing in a blast furnace hearth are much more favorable toward the establishment of equilibrium between precipitated TiC and TiN. The acid-insoluble residues of hot metal samples taken from a blast furnace were subjected to x-ray analysis and the average TiN/TiC ratio was found to be 1.77:1. Assuming a nitrogen pressure of 1.6 atm this corresponds to an equilibrium temperature of about 1505°C which is a good average casting temperature. A sample of massive Ti(C,N) taken from a blast furnace salamander yielded a TiN/TiC ratio of 1.67, which corresponds to a temperature of 1527°C. This is perhaps a little high for salamander iron, but in view of the accuracy of the thermal data and the assumption of ideality for Ti(C,N) the agreement between the calculated and observed ratios is remarkably good.

The mean titanium solubility in hot metal was 0.082 ± 0.014 wt-%. This is considerably lower than that measured in carbon-nitrogen-saturated iron. However, blast furnace iron contains silicon (1.0%), sulfur (0.04%), manganese (0.80%), and phosphorus (0.20%) in addition to being saturated with carbon and nitrogen.

There are indications from the laboratory experiments (Table II) that silicon, in the presence of nitrogen, decreases the solubility of titanium. Vaughan and Chipman[12] found that up to 2% silicon increased the solubility of nitrogen in iron, and this could result in a decrease in titanium solubility.   Recent work by Pehlke and Elliott[13] suggests that Si_3N_4 may be formed at quite low Si concentrations in nitrogen-saturated iron.   If this is so, silicon nitride may go into solid solution with titanium carbonitride.   The x-ray diffraction patterns on the solid residues from titanium solubility experiments in which silicon and nitrogen were present were quite different from those in which silicon was absent, but the presence of Si_3N_4 *per se* could not be established.   It is not yet possible to deduce the mechanism by which silicon, in the presence of nitrogen, affects the titanium solubility.

It is known that titanium is an avid sulfide former.[14]   The one experiment carried out in this work (%S = 0.16) is not sufficient to deduce anything positive about the effect of sulfur on the titanium solubility in carbon-nitrogen-saturated iron.

Reduction of TiO_2 from Silicate Slags

The dependence of titania reduction, under smelting conditions, on the slow rate of silica reduction was first reported by Faust.[2]   This dependence was confirmed in the present work and shown to be substantially unaffected by temperature.   Figure 3 shows a plot of $Ti/(TiO_2)$ versus $Si/(SiO_2)$ for type A slags and for the mean blast furnace slag used in the blast furnace tests.   The slope of these lines is k', and the Ti term in the $Ti/(TiO_2)$ ratio is the total titanium reduced from the slag including that present as TiC.   The constant k' is not an equilibrium constant, but its constancy indicates that the reduction of titania and silica is proceeding interdependently.   Any variation of k' with slag composition reflects relative changes in the activities of silica and titania in the slags.   The oxide diagram of Richardson and Jeffes[15] shows that the $Ti-TiO_2$ and $Si-SiO_2$ lines are essentially parallel so that the insensitivity of k' to small temperature changes is to be expected.   Wentrup et al.[4] thought that TiC did not precipitate from carbon-saturated iron below 1% Ti, and their curves for k' show a decreasing slope with time and eventually a reversal from positive to negative slope.   If the titanium present as TiC is ignored, the results of the present studies indicate that this reversal is to be expected.

From similar plots to those given in Figure 3, the values of k' for B, C, and D type slags have been deduced; thus $k_A' = 9.5$, $k'_B =$

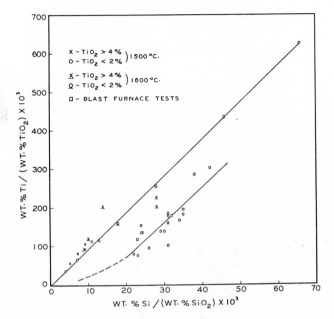

Fig. 3. Distribution factor k' for laboratory and blast furnace slags (k' = slope of line).

11.2, k'_C = 12.4, and k'_D = 13.4. Consideration of these k' values leads to the conclusion that the best slag for minimizing titania reduction is that containing the most silica and having the lowest CaO/SiO_2 ratio. This is in line with the conclusions reached by Ross[16] and other authors.[1,4]

The value of k' calculated from blast furnace data is 9.1. This is closest to the k' for A-type slags which are of similar composition and basicity. Figure 3 shows that the best straight line drawn through the blast furnace data, if extrapolated, does not pass through the origin by a large margin. From laboratory data, it would be expected that the line would pass through the origin, and therefore would curve sharply at its lower extremity as is shown (dotted). Such extrapolation of the curve, therefore, suggests that when only small amounts of titania have been reduced, relatively larger amounts of silica have been reduced. This may be explained by consideration of the conditions of reduction existing in a blast furnace. Reduction takes place over a range of temperature and slag compositions. Ini-

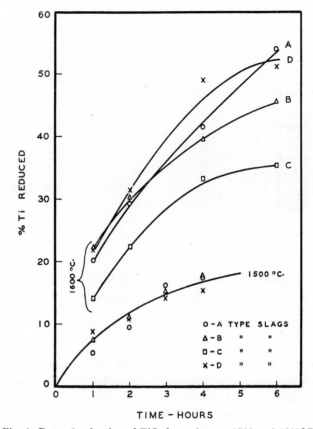

Fig. 4. Rate of reduction of TiO₂ from slags at 1500 and 1600°C.

tially the first liquid slag phase consists largely of calcium-magnesium-iron-silicates. This type of slag has a lower CaO/SiO_2 ratio than the final slag.[17] From consideration of the results on laboratory slags, therefore, silica will be reduced more easily and rapidly from the bosh slags. The dotted portion of the curve is, therefore, consistent with conditions existing in the blast furnace.

In addition to the above discussion on the co-reduction of SiO_2 and TiO_2, it is also important to examine the effect of slag composition on the rate of reduction. Figure 4 shows the rate of TiO_2 reduction expressed as per cent of total TiO_2 reduced versus time at 1500 and 1600°C. The curves consider only those slags containing less than

4% TiO_2, in which a good titanium balance was maintained. It will be seen that at 1500°C there is very little difference between the rates of TiO_2 reduction from the slags. At 1600°C there appear to be marked differences in that the rate of reduction of TiO_2 in slags B, C, and D has fallen off considerably after 4 hr, whereas in A-type slags, after this period of time, it is only just beginning to fall off.

In relating the results shown in Figure 4 to blast furnace practice, it must be remembered that the usual time interval between casts is about $4^1/_2$–5 hr and slag temperatures are normally in the 1530–1570°C range. Hence, from a rate of reduction point of view, the preferential order of slags is C, B, D, and lastly, A. The k' factors indicate which slag will have the lower $Ti/(TiO_2)$ ratio for a given $Si/(SiO_2)$ ratio, and the order of preference from this standpoint is A, B, C, and D. On balance therefore, B-type slags would seem the best choice, since C-type slags would be unsatisfactory in a blast furnace. The A-type slag, which appears good from a k' point of view, is higher in silica than other slags. It is reasonable to expect, therefore, that silica and consequently titania will be reduced faster from it than from the other slags. The addition of alumina to the A slag produces a B-type slag in which the silica activity is lowered by the addition of alumina.

The general conclusion is that for titaniferous burdens it is best to use a slag which is on the acid side, with respect to the CaO/SiO_2 ratio, and which contains a fairly high proportion of alumina. This is in agreement with the suggestions made by Russian authors[1,18] who, although they make no mention of the significance of alumina, have used slags containing at least 14% alumina. Ross[16] also arrived at the conclusion that acid slags were best for treating titaniferous ores but again did not comment on the importance of alumina. The authors are in general agreement with Ross so far as the deleterious effect of acid slags on desulfurization is concerned, and the possible need for considering some form of external desulfurization of the hot metal when operating with titaniferous ores.

There is one further point arising from the experimental results which is of some significance so far as the blast furnace is concerned. In the reaction

$$TiO_2(s) + 3C(gr) \longrightarrow TiC(s) + 2CO$$

$$\Delta F°_{1573} = -25,267 \text{ cal}[16] \tag{6}$$

it can be calculated that, in the presence of pure carbon and TiC and with $P_{(CO)} = 1$ atm, the equilibrium activity of (TiO_2) is 1.1×10^{-3}. Referring to Table III, it is seen that in experiments at 1600°C (T23–T27) the "total" titanium percentages are greater than those for the soluble titanium, even though titanium solubility was not exceeded. This means that titanium carbide must also have been present and can only have been formed by direct reaction between the titania in the slag and graphite walls of the crucible. It is reasonable to conceive that some of this titanium carbide finds its way into the metal. The titania content of the slags in question was only about 1%. It is therefore concluded that in all the slags used $a_{(TiO_2)}$ at 1 wt-% is greater than 10^{-3} and that the activity coefficient of (TiO_2) must be less than 10^{-1} (with respect to pure solid TiO_2). In the blast furnace, the CO pressure over the slag is about 0.7 atm and for TiC formation, $a_{(TiO_2)} = 5.5 \times 10^{-4}$. Although in the blast furnace some of the slag constituents may affect $a_{(TiO_2)}$ it seems certain that TiC can separate at quite low levels of TiO_2. This is only true in the hearth area since in the bosh the slag contains 2–3% FeO and the oxygen potential of the bosh slag would prevent the TiC from existing as an equilibrium phase. This point is further discussed below.

Effect of TiO_2 on Blast Furnace Operations

It is known that blast furnace operation on burdens containing significant amounts of TiO_2 has been successful for a short time. In Jones & Laughlin experience with unscreened burdens, levels corresponding to about 20 lb TiO_2/NTHM have presented no problems, but if the level was raised to 40–50 lb TiO_2/NTHM operation was satisfactory for a period of 2–4 weeks, and then hanging and rough operation occurred. Operators, in general, agree that titanium is at the root of these troubles, but opinions are somewhat divided between whether the cause is due to thickening of the slag or accretion "buildups." In either case, the mechanism by which the troubles are brought about is in considerable doubt.

As a result of the work described in this paper, it is felt that some light has been thrown on this subject, but further work will be necessary before titanium behavior in the blast furnace is completely understood.

Dealing first with the possibility of troubles originating from an increase in slag viscosity, the work of Semik[18] on blast furnace slags is of considerable importance. This work showed that the effect of TiO_2 on slag viscosity was qualitatively similar to that of CaO, but quantitatively very much less. This suggests that at least part of the titanium may be present as oxides lower than TiO_2, but no real confirmation of the existence of TiO can be obtained. Semik[18] showed that under atmospheres of CO, and in the presence of graphite, the viscosity of slags was initially slightly decreased by the addition of TiO_2. After holding at temperature for times up to and above 6 hr, he found a small increase in viscosity in slags containing as much as 20% TiO_2, but that with 30% TiO_2 the increase in viscosity was severe. These increases were undoubtedly due to the formation of solid TiC, which would form particularly at the slag graphite interface. The introduction of a number of small solid particles would not be expected to cause a great increase in viscosity, but as Semik found, eventually enough TiC would be formed to cause trouble when the TiO_2 content was high. At the TiO_2 levels of interest in this paper, therefore, Semik's work suggests that slag viscosity should be no problem. Furthermore, it is difficult to conceive the existence of TiC or TiN in the stack or bosh of a blast furnace, because the oxygen potential in the slag is too high.

While considering the possibility of sticky slags forming above the tuyere line in the blast furnace, it is also pertinent to examine the general course of reduction of titanium-bearing ores with specific reference to the formation of spinels. (Semik's work was concerned entirely with premelted slags.) A recent paper by Walsh et al.[14] describes the results of investigations into the reduction of ilmenites at temperatures below 1200°C; i.e., temperatures existing from the lower bosh upward in a blast furnace. These authors found that the main titaniferous phases produced during the reduction of the iron consisted of some rutile (TiO_2) at low temperatures, and a psuedo brookite type solid solution ($Fe_2O_3 \cdot TiO_2$-$FeO \cdot 2TiO_2$) at higher temperatures. Spinel-type phases were rarely observed and then only in some types of ilmenite. The spinels were thought to be present as an intermediate phase formed during the earlier stages of reduction of ilmenite-hematite intergrowths.

Walsh et al.[14] also suggest that some preoxidation of the ore should minimize formation of spinels. These points are pertinent to the blast furnace because a preponderance of high melting point spinels would be harmful in the slag. From this work on ilmenite reduction, spinels are not likely to be present in appreciable quantities in the blast furnace, particularly in the case of a sinter burden. It is also interesting to note that only indirect evidence of the presence of sub-oxides of titanium, in very small quantities, was found in the gangue phases formed at 1200°C.[7]

It has been concluded in the preceding section that low CaO/SiO_2 ratios do not favor titania reduction. Since bosh slags in general have a low CaO/SiO_2 ratio, it seems difficult to postulate any mechanism whereby titanium can cause trouble in the bosh of a blast furnace.

Considering the above factors, evidence is against titanium causing slag difficulties above the tuyere line. Furthermore, the time lapse which usually ensues before an increase in the titania content of the burden makes itself apparent, suggests that factors of slag viscosity are not of primary significance. The most important facts borne out by the present work are that titanium carbide/nitride solid solutions are precipitated from iron at much lower titanium levels than had previously been accepted. These solid solutions can also be formed from direct reaction between the coke and slag at comparatively low TiO_2 levels (1–3%), and under the conditions existing in the hearth zone they should have no difficulty existing as a nonequilibrium phase. Examination of a blast furnace, after it had been blown out, showed that massive titanium carbonitride had been formed and was found to be growing out from the brickwork. This furnace had been run on burdens which were low in titania content.

The blast furnace functions satisfactorily on low titania burdens because most of the Ti(C,N), which is undoubtedly formed, is swept out with the iron or slag. Taking a furnace which is operating smoothly, consider now a sudden and appreciable increase in the titania content of the burden. The amount of Ti(C,N) formed will increase and the iron and slag may not flush it all out of the furnace. Accretions may, therefore, build up on the floor and side walls of the hearth, and in time, could grow outward and upward into the slag layer. The resulting constriction of the hearth area could cause the slag layer to be higher than normal if standard casting times and production rates are maintained. A rising slag level can cause carry-up of slag or interfere with the lower edge of the raceway. Neither of these phenomena is unknown in a "full" furnace. Effects, such as described, would be cumulative and would eventually lead to rough operation and interruption of the flow of materials at levels above the tuyere line.

The hypothesis put forward above is purely speculative, but it does agree with the observations made so far. From the standpoint of TiO_2 and SiO_2 reduction, a faster moving furnace operating on self-fluxing sinter with high blast temperatures might allow greater TiO_2 tolerance because the decreased retention time of the materials in the furnace would aid in minimizing reduction. In addition to the above, a faster moving furnace would provide increased scouring action in the hearth and this would tend to keep the formation of accretions to a minimum. A blast furnace trial conducted at Jones & Laughlin to compare screened and regular burden operations brought some interesting facts to light. When using an unscreened burden 33.7% of the TiO_2 charged was reduced, but this figure decreased to 27.3% when a screened burden was charged to the furnace. When one considers the rate of reduction, however, the situation is reversed; the titanium was reduced more rapidly when the furnace was on screened burden operation (0.2975 lb Ti reduced/ft^2 hearth-hr-% TiO_2 in slag) than on a regular burden (0.2352 lb Ti reduced/ft^2 hearth-hr-% TiO_2 in slag). Thus, in a fast moving furnace, although the TiO_2 may be reduced more rapidly with respect to time, less TiO_2 is reduced per ton of hot metal produced. The net effect is, therefore, to increase the TiO_2 tolerance.

For the moment, the TiO_2 limits in a furnace using high blast temperature and a self-fluxing sinter burden with a suitable slag practice are not known. Future plans include the running of furnace trials which will increase our knowledge of the effect of such operation on TiO_2 tolerance.

CONCLUSIONS

1. The measured titanium solubility in carbon-saturated iron is considerably lower than previous estimates.

2. The solubility of titanium in carbon-saturated iron is markedly decreased by the presence of nitrogen.

3. The results indicate that silicon decreases the solubility of titanium in carbon-nitrogen-saturated iron, but has little effect in the absence of nitrogen.

4. Titanium carbonitride can be precipitated in the blast furnace from iron which contains as little as 0.1% titanium.

5. Experimental results confirm that TiC and TiN form a series of solid solutions, which do not deviate substantially from ideality.

6. The reduction of silica and titania proceeds interdependently.

7. In laboratory experiments, titanium carbide was precipitated from silicate slags containing as little as 1% TiO_2.

8. Operation of a blast furnace on titaniferous burdens is most likely to succeed using an acid slag which contains more than 10% alumina.

9. There are indications that a fast moving blast furnace will have a higher tolerance for titania in the burden.

The authors wish to express their sincere thanks to W. O. Philbrook of Carnegie Institute of Technology for his assistance and encouragement. The cooperation of W. F. Huntley, director of Blast Furnace Operations, and J. R. Lowe, superintendent, Eliza Blast Furnaces, Jones & Laughlin Steel Corporation, is gratefully acknowledged. The work of J. E. Paterson, in connection with the chemical and x-ray analyses, is much appreciated.

References

1. Shmanenkov and Tagirov, *Bull. Acad. Sci.*, No. 4, 391 (1947).

2. Faust, E., *Arch. Eisenhtütenw.*, **12**, 361 (1939).

3. Tofaute, W., and A. Buttinghaus, *Arch. Eisenhüttenw.*, **12**, 33 (1939).

4. Wentrup, H., H. Maetz, and P. Heller, *Arch. Eisenhüttenw.*, **20**, 139 (1949).

5. Halverson, R. A., U. S. Pat. 2,792,299 (May, 1957).

6. Chipman, J., R. M. Alfred, L. W. Gott, R. B. Small, D. M. Wilson, C. N. Thomson, D. L. Guernsey, and J. C. Fulton, *Trans. Am. Soc. Metals*, **44**, 1215 (1952).

7. Delve, F. D., *Trans. Am. Inst. Mining, Met. Petrol. Engrs.*, **212**, 183 (1958).

8. Richardson, F. D., *J. Iron Steel Inst.* (*London*), **175**, 33 (1953).

9. Humphrey, G. L., *J. Am. Chem. Soc.*, **73**, 226 (1951).

10. Kootz, Th., *Arch. Eisenhüttenw.*, **15** (1941).

11. Duwez, P., and F. Odell, *J. Electrochem. Soc.*, **97**, 229 (1950).

12. Vaughan, J. C., and J. Chipman, *Trans. Am. Inst. Mining, Met. Engrs.*, **140**, 224 (1940).

13. Pehlke, R., and J. F. Elliott, *Trans. Am. Inst. Mining, Met. Petrol. Engrs.*, to be published.

14. Walsh, R. H., H. W. Hockin, D. R. Brandt, and P. R. Giradot, *Trans. Am. Inst. Mining, Met. Petrol. Engrs.*, to be published.

15. Richardson, F. D., and J. H. E. Jeffes, *J. Iron Steel Inst.* (*London*), **163**, 397 (1949).

16. Ross, H. W., AIME Blast Furnace, Coke Oven and Raw Material Conference, 1958, p. 47.

17. Babarykin, N. N., and F. A. Yushin, *Stal*, **17**, No. 1, 7 (1957).

18. Semik, I. P., *Bull. acad. sci. URSS*, **4**, 55 (1941).

19. Kubaschewski, O., and Evans, E., *Metallurgical Thermochemistry*, Wiley, New York, 1956.

20. Abendroth, R. P., and A. W. Schlechter, *Trans. Am. Inst. Mining, Met. Petrol. Engrs.*, **215**, 145 (1959).

Discussion

H. U. Ross (*Univ. of Toronto, Canada*): The smelting of titanium-bearing iron ores has baffled ironmakers for many years, and there have been many theories propounded in an attempt to explain the problem. However, there are few scientific facts from which reliable conclusions may be drawn. The authors of this paper are to be complimented, therefore, on their fine efforts in carrying out a piece of fundamental research on the physical chemistry of titanium in the blast furnace. It forms a beginning from which more extensive research on the behavior of titanium in the blast furnace may be initiated and through which a solution to the satisfactory smelting of titaniferous ores may eventually be found.

In attempting to analyze the results obtained by the authors in their studies on the reduction of titanium dioxide from silicate slags, the reader of their paper is handicapped by the absence of any slag analyses. The only data available are the various slag classifications given in Table III, footnote a. These data alone are not sufficient to form a complete picture; in fact, they could be misleading. From the ratios of lime plus magnesia to silica plus alumina, the reader might assume that the four types of slags could be arranged in order of increasing basicity as follows: B, D, A, and C, and might expect the rate of reduction of titanium from the B-type slag to be the slowest and from the C-type slag to be the fastest. However, the order as indicated by the k' values is A, B, C, and D, and from Figure 4 after 5 hr is C, B, A, and D. Apparently there are other important factors which are not apparent to the reader. This trouble would likely be cleared up if the slag analyses were given, and it is hoped that the authors will include these when the paper is published.

For good reasons, the authors have restricted their studies to the conventional blast furnace operation to produce iron for basic steelmaking. However, if a general solution to the problem of smelting titaniferous ores is to be found, it will be necessary to work with furnace burdens and slags carrying higher titanium contents than those considered in this paper. The authors reached the conclusion that the best slag for minimizing titania reduction is that containing the most silica and having the lowest CaO/SiO_2 ratio. This is in keeping with my own conclusion, but I would suggest a CaO/SiO_2 ratio in the range of 0.8:1 to 1:1. This would be a departure from conventional blast furnace practice, but such a departure is likely necessary if higher titanium burdens are to be used. Research in the range of acidic slags is in order.

The reference to the importance of alumina is very interesting. It is worthy of further study because it deals with a point which is still not well understood.

J. Chipman (*MIT*): This paper is a fine example of the application of physical chemistry to the solution of a very practical blast furnace problem.

The titanium on the slag is referred to as TiO_2. I should like to ask the authors if this formula is based on an actual knowledge of the state of oxidation of titanium in the slag or if there is a possibility that it may be present as Ti_2O_3 or some lower oxide.

F. D. Delve, H. W. Meyer, and **H. N. Lander:** The authors wish to express their appreciation to Professor Ross and Professor Chipman for their interesting comments on the paper. In compliance with Professor Ross' request for additional slag data, the pertinent information is contained in Discussion Table I and is a supplement to the slag classification details contained in the Table III footnote in the paper. In point of fact the slag compositions can be calculated from the data given in the paper, but Discussion Table I removes the need for such calculation.

DISCUSSION TABLE I
Classification of Slags

Classi-fication	Analysis, wt-%				CaO, % + MgO, % / 0.6 Al$_2$O$_3$ + SiO$_2$, %
	CaO, %	SiO$_2$, %	Al$_2$O$_3$, %	MgO, %	
AL	45.63	36.24	8.34	7.84	1.30
AH	42.63	33.34	9.91	7.84	1.28
BL	39.42	30.19	21.98	7.47	1.08
BH	36.37	28.77	21.71	7.32	1.05
CL	51.94	30.72	9.44	7.09	1.62
CH	47.49	29.51	9.50	7.58	1.56
DL	43.06	26.54	21.83	7.63	1.28
DH	40.80	24.86	21.22	7.39	1.28

In reply to Professor Ross' suggestion that some of our data could be misleading, the k' values do not refer to rates of reduction, but rather to the relationship between silica and titania reduction as affected by their relative activity coefficients in the slag. The term k' is so defined in the paper, and it was pointed out that in addition to the k' values, the actual rates of reduction must be considered (Fig. 4). Professor Ross has also assumed that the rate of reduction of titanium is a straightforward function of slag basicity as defined by the ratio CaO + MgO/SiO$_2$ + 0.6Al$_2$O$_3$. This is not stated in the paper and in fact this has not been found to be the case.

In answer to Professor Chipman's point, we have purposely chosen to express the titanium content of the slag as TiO_2. It seems quite likely that the reduction of TiO_2 under these conditions may proceed in a step-wise manner through suboxides to the metal, but clear evidence on this point is somewhat scanty [Semik, I. P., *Bull. acad. sci. URSS*, **4**, 55 (1941); R. H. Walsh, H. W. Hockin, D. R. Brandt, and P. R. Giradot, *Trans. Am. Inst. Mining, Met. Petrol. Engrs.*, to be published]. We have chosen, therefore, to take pure solid TiO_2 as our standard state for titanium in the slag because the thermodynamics of this oxide are most accurately known.

Interpreting the data in terms of $a(\text{TiO}_2)$, etc., is therefore a matter of thermo-dynamic accuracy and convenience. From the blast furnace point of view, it was not considered necessary to know the precise valency state of the titanium in the slag. Should such information later become available, it may assist in a better interpretation of our results from a theoretical point of view.

Some Mechanisms in the Refining of Steel

B. M. LARSEN and L. O. SORDAHL

Edgar C. Bain Laboratory For Fundamental Research, United States Steel Corporation Research Center, Monroeville, Pennsylvania

Abstract

Experimental data from 100 lb melts in a laboratory indirect arc furnace and a gas-oxygen-fired furnace are shown to parallel or to accentuate certain effects involved in larger scale furnaces, especially the commercial open hearth. The low steady state boil rate in this process is shown to be transport controlled by diffusion rates in the gas boundary film just above the top surface of the slag. Simply displacing this (normally nitrogen-rich) film by an oxygen spray on the slag surface can increase overall boil rates by at least ten times the steady state level and 2 to 3 times the rate in heavy ore feeding; no direct contact of oxygen jet and liquid metal is involved. The resulting steep oxygen-pressure gradient in the slag layer can substantially increase the escaping tendency of SO_2; as much as 60 to 70% of the bath sulfur content has been volatilized under most favorable conditions. Nucleation and growth of CO bubbles increases with boil rate over the observed range; slag-metal interface area increases with boil rate, due mainly to the mechanism of bubble bursting at a phase boundary; thus neither of these factors appears as a limiting effect. These results give further support to the view that heat flow in slag boundary films limits boil rate under heavy ore feeding.

INTRODUCTION

It has been taken for granted for many years that a steel refining process such as that in the open hearth is operable and rather closely reproducible, although conducted under an atmosphere extremely oxidizing to the liquid metal. Indeed, with the great industrial importance of this process, the voluminous literature about it may itself have tended to obscure the fact that we do not yet understand precisely why it is operable. One simple way to regard the metal bath in this furnace is as a great sink for oxygen, with its oxygen activity, or pressure, at around 10^{-9} atm. With a gas atmosphere above the slag at an oxygen pressure probably averaging about 10^{-2}

atm, and the bath normally well stirred by the carbon boil, oxygen must flow downward continually. But this rate tends to drop quite rapidly to a very low level after cessation of such accelerating effects as a lime boil, ore feed, or oxygen injection; no satisfactory explanation has been given for the slow rate of this "steady-state" boil.

In normal commercial furnaces, with a slag-metal area of around 4 ft²/ton of liquid steel, this rate, in terms of "carbon drop," is around 12-18 points (0.12-0.18%) per hour. Since, at steady state the storage of oxygen in the bath is negligible (except at quite low carbon levels) the average rate may be expressed in terms of oxygen flux, as 0.133 lb mole/ft² hr or in cgs units as 0.045×10^{-6} g mole/cm² sec.

This flux of oxygen, entering the bath by oxidation reactions at the slag surface and coming out as CO bubbles, appears to involve a series of many steps, which may be postulated as follows (for clarity, we include each possible step; the circled numbers in Figure 1 may help to indicate the physical meanings involved).

1. A flow by diffusion of oxidizing gas molecules in a relatively quiescent film or boundary layer of gas just above the slag surface.

2. Absorption by gas-liquid reaction at the slag surface. The simplest probable reaction would be

$$2Fe^{2+} + (O) \text{ (from } O_2, CO_2, \text{ or } H_2O) \longrightarrow 2Fe^{3+} + O^{2-} \qquad (1)$$

3. Diffusion transfer of these ions (this may be complicated by a movement of electrons) through a similar boundary layer just below the slag surface).

4. Transfer by *diffusion + convection* down through the bulk slag to a similar thin boundary layer just above the slag-metal interface.

5. Diffusion transfer through this film to the actual slag-metal interface.

6. Oxygen transfer across the interface presumably by the reverse of the reaction above (at the slag-gas interface); that is

$$2Fe^{3+} + O^{2-} \longrightarrow 2Fe^{2+} + (O) \qquad (2)$$

7. Diffusion transfer of the dissolved oxygen atoms through a thin liquid-metal boundary layer just below the slag-metal interface.

8. Transfer by diffusion + convection through the bulk metal to the vicinity of the surfaces of CO bubbles either nucleating on the hearth surface or rising through the metal.

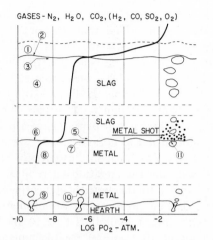

Fig. 1. Schematic diagram showing hearth-metal, slag-metal, and slag-gas interface zones in an open hearth refining bath at normal steady state including probable oxygen pressure gradients.

9.   Nucleation and initial growth of bubbles, mainly on small holes or crevices in the hearth surface.

10.   Diffusion transfer of oxygen and carbon atoms through a boundary layer at bubble surfaces, wherever they happen to be, in the metal phase.

11.   Combination of C and O atoms at bubble surfaces to form CO, perhaps through an intermediate FeCO complex, causing growth of the bubbles before they rise out through the slag.

Assuming this series as a working picture, one might conclude that since any slow step in such a series could limit the overall rate, the low level at steady state is not so surprising.   A closer look makes this appear less satisfying.   The actual chemical interchanges involved in steps 2, 6, and 11 are not likely to be slow at temperatures nearly always in the 1500–1650°C range, both from theoretical considerations and partly confirmed by the 150-fold multiplication of the rate of step 11 occurring in the Bessemer converter.   The diffusion + convection processes of steps 4 and 8 are also rapid and can be increased automatically by the increased stirring produced by the reaction itself.   Thus the probable limiting rates are in bubble nucleation or growth, or in some film diffusion process at a phase boundary, and the *most* probable step is one affecting the rate of entry of oxygen to the system, which would be 1 or 2.

There has been some tendency to regard the "blanketing" of much of the bath area by a flame zone and the combustion gases spreading out from it as an inhibitor of oxygen supply. This is all rather vague, but it is also rather neatly disposed of by an observation reported by Gibson[1,*] on a commercial furnace which, being accidentally deprived of fuel for a 2-hr period, gave a boil rate of 15–17 points/hr, in the middle of the normal steady state range for operating furnaces. There was no flame, essentially no water vapor, and only some CO_2 diluting the air atmosphere above the bath, yet the influx rate of oxygen to the bath held nearly constant at the normal level. The oxygen pressure (in atmospheres) in the bulk gas phase here was no higher than 10^{-1} to 2×10^{-1}, relative to a probable average between 10^{-2} and 10^{-3} with flame and combustion gases present. Compared to the level of 10^{-9} in the liquid metal, these differences are seen to be relatively small.

If we should arbitrarily assume that step 1 above was rapid, oxygen entry into the bath could be limited by steps 2 or 3. That is, either a rate of the oxidation reactions (in terms of molecular species)

$$(\tfrac{1}{2}O_2, CO_2, \text{ or } H_2O) + 3FeO \longrightarrow Fe_3O_4 + (CO \text{ or } H_2) \qquad (3)$$

probably at the slag surface, or a rate of movement of ferric ions through a thin diffusion film below the top slag surface could be the slow step in the overall process. Empirical evidence is given below to show that both of the latter assumptions appear untrue. This evidence also indicates that neither a rate of bubble nucleation or growth nor diffusion rates in the slag-metal interface films necessarily limit the influx of oxygen or the boil rate. This leaves us with step 1 above as the probable limiting factor. We will attempt to prove that in any steel furnace with a nitrogen-rich atmosphere (from fuel-air combustion or air in-leakage), the essential control factor is a rate of diffusion of H_2O, CO_2, or O_2 from the bulk gas phase through nitrogen in a relatively quiescent film just above the slag surface; that is, step 1 in our postulated series.

Approximate calculations† for the effective thickness of this film

* See Appendix, Section 1 for some details. The argument in this paper, being based on the fitting together of somewhat empirical or circumstantial evidence, can be presented more simply by detailing some of the evidence in the Appendix.

† See Appendix, Section 2.

indicate values of around 2 to 6 mm with normal fuel firing, up to a possible 16 mm with the relatively lower turbulence in bulk gas phase for the case reported by Gibson.[1]   It is essentially the high kinematic viscosity of the hot combustion gases which causes such relatively thick layers in which movement approaches a laminar or non-turbulent condition.

It is not meant to be implied here that this is yet a precise and well-proved concept.   High temperature data for the gases are relatively inadequate, and the complexity of the real system may be appreciated if we remember that even at the low boil rate in steady state, the system is disturbed by a volume of CO bubbles coming up through this slag-gas interface zone of about 0.7 cm^3/sec for each cm^2 of slag surface area.   This complexity, in fact, is the reason that we used an essentially empirical method of study, based on actual refining tests in small 100 lb melts in a laboratory furnace.   Such tests merely tend to prove that an open hearth bath *acts as though* a gas diffusion film layer of the order of a centimeter in thickness, above its surface, limits the rate of entry of oxygen to the system.

It seems simplest, in presenting the evidence, to start out with the schematic picture finally arrived at for the bath system.   This is shown in Figure 1, where the hearth-metal-slag-combustion gas system is simplified to the three interface zones, hearth surface-metal, metal-slag, and slag-gases, respectively.   This permits the vertical scale to be roughly actual size.   Bubbles are shown as nucleating at the hearth surface, and small metal shot as carried into the lower slag layer by the bursting of these bubbles across the slag-metal boundary. Not shown are tiny slag droplets projected into the gas phase by a similar bursting mechanism at the slag-gas boundary (these effects are discussed later).   It is assumed that in spite of these disturbances, we can draw, as shown, an approximate average oxygen pressure curve through gas-slag-metal zones.   Certain points on this curve are more or less known; the level in the bulk metal at about 10^{-9} atm and that in the bulk gas phase at around 10^{-2} atm are well established as typical values; that in the bulk slag at about 10^{-7} atm is estimated, in part from the data of Larson and Chipman.[2]   The level at the slag-gas interface at about 10^{-6} atm is not known, except indirectly from evidence given below. The implication here is that the largest drop in oxygen pressure normally occurs in a zone just above the slag surface, as implied above.

THE 100-LB LABORATORY FURNACE

This small furnace is shown in cross sections in Figure 2. For certain reasons of convenience, most of the earlier heats (total of 16) made to establish simulation of open hearth conditions in this very small bath were made, not with the steady state minimum boil condition of Figure 1 but with repeated iron oxide additions to the bath to imitate the ore feeding periods in the open hearth. We must therefore digress a little to indicate certain differences here. Heavy lumps of scale were fed, which sink through the slag to the metal-slag boundary, melt, and spread out to dissociate and react, delivering oxygen into the liquid iron-carbon melt. In effect, this eliminates steps 1 to 5 in the step-wise series described above. But a new factor is introduced, namely, a larger heat absorption near this slag-metal boundary to melt and dissociate the iron oxide. The overall enthalpy change is close to that given for reaction (9) in Table I.

TABLE I

Reaction	Q, 2900°F Btu/1/2 mole O_2
(1) $3FeO + {}^1/_2O_2 \longrightarrow Fe_3O_4$	115,000
(2) $3FeO + H_2O \longrightarrow Fe_3O_4 + H_2$	6,400
(3) $3FeO + CO_2 \longrightarrow Fe_3O_4 + CO$	−5,100
(4) $Fe_3O_4 + \underline{C} \longrightarrow 3FeO + CO$	−50,000
(5) $H_2 + {}^1/_2O_2 \longrightarrow H_2O$	108,000
(6) $CO + {}^1/_2O_2 \longrightarrow CO_2$	120,000
(7) Cold oxygen + $\underline{C} \longrightarrow CO$	48,000
(8) Cold ore + $\underline{C} \longrightarrow (Fe_x) + CO$	−88,000
(9) Cold scale + $\underline{C} \longrightarrow (Fe_x) + CO$	−93,000

Since an excess of potential oxygen supply can be supplied at the discretion of the furnace operator directly to the liquid metal surface, it is a reasonable assumption that a rate of heat flow through the stirred slag layer to this interface zone might be the limiting rate factor in such ore feed periods. Open hearth operating experience tends to support this assumption. A vigorous reaction to ore feeds demands some superheat in the bath and the rates of carbon drop obtained rarely go beyond the range of about 0.35 to 0.60% decrease in carbon/hr.

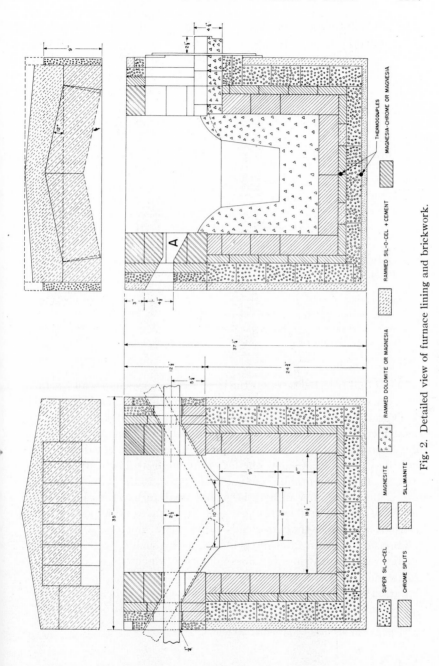

Fig. 2. Detailed view of furnace lining and brickwork.

Of course, other factors such as diffusion flow of oxygen through a liquid metal boundary layer, or a rate of nucleation or growth of CO bubbles (steps 7 and 9 above) could also limit this rate. Thus these scale-fed heats in the small furnace served a double purpose; namely, (a) to supply some additional evidence for heat flow as the critical limiting factor, and (b) to indicate that open hearth boil conditions and refining conditions, in general, can be simulated in this small furnace. Some comparative measured and calculated results* are shown in Table II.

TABLE II

Values for ore-feed periods	Commercial open hearth	100 lb laboratory furnace
Range of carbon drop/hr	0.35–0.60%	0.75–1.25%
Slag-metal or reaction surface area per ton of metal	4.0	9.0
Calculated carbon drop by metal transport film theory[a]	0.49%	0.90%
Heat supply required for enthalpy change only in reaction at slag-metal zone, Btu/hr, ft² bath area	17,600	16,700

[a] See Larsen,[3] p. 16.

The actual reaction rates for the large vs the very small scale operations are closely proportional to bath area per ton of metal, as would be expected. The rough agreement with calculated rates in both cases merely indicates that a diffusion rate in a metal transport-film boundary layer *may be one step* in the series-connected chain of limiting factors. Similarly, the fact that the heat flow rate per unit area to offset the enthalpy change in reaction at the maximum boil rate is about the same in both large and small furnaces is also *merely consistent with* heat flow being one limiting factor. A point often overlooked here is that at steady state there must be a constant relationship between rates in each step in any such series; ability to predict rates in any one step does not prove which one is controlling the overall rate.

Larsen[3] has given calculations to indicate a range of heat flow in the open hearth of 10,000–30,000 Btu/hr ft². During fast oreing, heavy

* Additional details in Appendix, Section 3.

boil periods the values would be in the range of 20,000–30,000 Btu/ hr ft^2 of bath area. Since some heat goes to raise bath and hearth surface temperatures in such periods of rapid carbon drop (due to the increase in liquidus temperature), these values are quite consistent with the 17,000 Btu values above for enthalpy change in reaction only. The scale-feeding tests on a dozen or more heats in the small laboratory furnace also showed that the oxide additions accounted for an average of 80% of the total carbon drop, with 20% due to air oxidation. This is also in qualitative agreement with open hearth experience, where air oxidation is normally an appreciable fraction of the whole. In summary, we have here good evidence that the laboratory furnace tends to simulate the much larger open hearth refining bath. The data above do not prove that heat flow is the decisive rate control factor in ore feeding, but the oxygen-spray heats described below to confirm this assumption.

LABORATORY MELTS WITH OXYGEN-SPRAY ON SLAG SURFACE

If we accept the conclusion above as to simulation of open hearth refining in the small furnace, the controlling effect of gaseous diffusion (step 1 in Fig. 1) may be tested quite simply, as indicated in the diagram of Figure 3. We have here a low angle jet of fluid "wiping" the slag surface. If we make the angle and jet velocity such as to

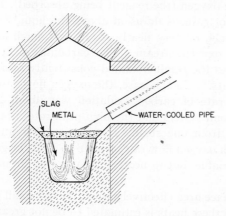

Fig. 3. Arrangement of oxygen spray on slag surface in small steel-refining furnace.

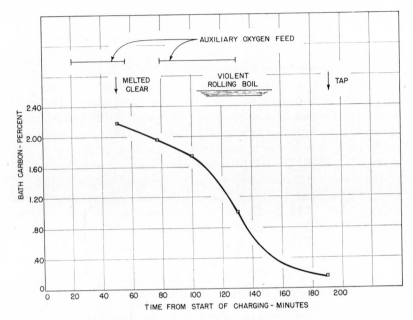

Fig. 4. Carbon drop curve, representative of heats with oxygen spray on melting charge and on slag surface during refining.

merely ruffle the liquid slag surface with no penetration, and if the jet fluid is pure oxygen (the reagent being absorbed), then any rate-limiting effect of gaseous diffusion above the liquid surface is eliminated completely, or very nearly so, in that small area effectively wiped by the oxygen stream. The carbon-drop curve shown in Figure 4 typifies the result obtained consistently in a long series of such experiments.* In this case, the oxygen flow rate was 6 lb/hr, and the peak rate of carbon oxidation was about 200 points/hr. With such a small system and the high peak rates obtained this is a transient shift from one steady state to another and back again. Other runs with oxygen flow rates from 6 to 15 lb/hr gave peak rates which were variable, but in nearly all cases were from 200 to above 300 points/hr.

The slag surface area effectively wiped by the small oxygen stream in a number of these heats is estimated to be not greater than about

* See Appendix, Section 3.

50 cm². Total oxygen feed in the 6–10-lb/hr range would correspond to $0.10-0.16 \times 10^{-4}$ g mole/sec/cm² of slag surface. Oxygen balances indicated that about 40 to 50% of the oxygen feed was actually absorbed by the bath over the cycle of an oxygen-spray period. This indicates a specific oxygen absorption rate of not less than 0.044 to 0.072×10^{-4} g mole/sec/cm². Compared to the average steady state boil of Figure 1, where oxygen flux averages around 0.045×10^{-6} g mole/sec/cm², this is a multiplication of approximately 100 to 150, due to the elimination of the diffusion factor (step 1) which is believed to determine, essentially, the minimum boil rate.

This high rate of oxygen absorption, with resulting boil rates up to 6 or 7 times those obtained in commercial open hearths and about 3 times as fast as those in the same small furnace by iron oxide additions, points to the following conclusions:

1. Heat flow really does control overall boil rate when oxygen is fed by ore feeds. The latter condition involves only steps 6–11, inclusive, in our series above. The boil with oxygen spray involves all these, plus steps 2 to 5. The only difference favoring speed with oxygen spray is the large enthalpy difference between reactions (1) + (4), and (9) in Table I.

2. Evidently, all the steps involved were speeded up when oxygen was supplied faster to the slag surface. Any convection or film diffusion transport rate would naturally be favored by the increased stirring of a faster boil and would be limited mainly by a viscosity factor. At the slag surface, the rate for reaction (1) (step 2) can evidently be very high, but it might be finite and affected by slag composition; other experimental techniques would be needed to answer this question. Steps 5 and 7 above could be limiting due to a limited slag-metal interface area, and steps 9 and 10 due to a rate of bubble nucleation or growth. Some evidence as to why these are not seriously limiting is given in a later section.

Changes in slag and metal composition over a heat with two successive cycles of oxygen spray on slag surface are indicated by Table III; (oxygen was also sprayed on the charge for 45 min during melt-down).

Data in Table III show how (1) oxygen stores up in the slag layer to a degree limited by the tendency for an increased boil rate, and how (2) when oxygen spray is cut off, the system returns to steady

TABLE III

Time from start of heat, min	Treatment		Slag, wt-%									Metal, wt-%		
	Oxygen heat		SiO$_2$	CaO	MnO	MgO	FeO	FeO	Fe$_2$O$_3$	Al$_2$O$_3$	P$_2$O$_5$	C	Mn	S
0														
46														
85			20.2	38.3	11.2	8.9	7.7	6.3	0.16	4.4	2.8	1.47	0.33	0.046
100			15.4	30.0	10.6	5.1	24.2	8.3	0.09	3.1	3.5	1.09	0.26	0.035
120			17.7	37.9	11.8	8.7	9.8	6.3	0.14	3.2	3.4	0.85	0.26	0.024
135			13.6	31.4	11.2	5.0	24.4	8.6	0.09	3.3	3.0	0.46	0.21	0.023
158			17.0	37.8	10.2	9.9	12.1	6.6	0.08	3.2	3.1	0.11	0.32	0.021

TABLE IV

	Slag, %									Metal, %			
	SiO_2	CaO	MnO	MgO	FeO	Fe_2O_3	S	Al_2O_3	P_2O_5	C	Mn	S	P
Scale-fed, avg of 8 heats	13.1	38.2	9.9	13.0	6.4	6.4	0.08	6.5	3.0	0.49	0.31	0.014	0.042
Oxygen spray, avg of 9 heats	13.4	41.1	9.9	8.9	11.7	8.3	0.06	3.4	2.6	0.40	0.28	0.014	0.031

state in a matter of minutes. Effect (1) is presumably caused by the predominance of the reaction

$$2Fe^{3+} + [Fe] \longrightarrow 3Fe^{2+} \tag{4}$$

over reaction (2) above until iron oxide levels in slag reach new steady state values. Effect (2) is illustrated by the average tap slag analyses in Table IV, where all samples were taken about 20 min after stopping scale additions or oxygen spray. Both averages compare well with open hearth practice.

LABORATORY MELTS IN A FUEL-OXYGEN FIRED FURNACE

Reiterating our basic assumption, one may regard a slag-metal steel bath on a boil as an "open system" with a steep oxygen gradient. Although oxygen must flow in continually, the large drop in oxygen pressure at the entrance point just above the slag surface (Fig. 1) plus the stirring and oxygen-consuming effect of the carbon boil is what maintains the oxygen pressure in the bulk slag at a low level only moderately above that in the steel. Thus, Figure 1 helps to explain why a condition of apparent equilibrium between slag and steel tends to exist in such a bath. But are we sure about the precise mechanism?

We have been postulating the cause of this large drop in oxygen pressure as a limited rate of diffusion due to the large percentage of inert nitrogen in an air-based atmosphere furnace. However, one could also postulate a "self-protecting" oxygen gradient caused by CO from the boil itself. There seemed no way to definitely disprove this by calculation or direct observation, though it appears improbable because the bursting of larger bubbles at the slag surface ought to disrupt the gas film layer and *promote* oxygen transfer. But suppose the CO issues in large part as very small invisible bubbles at low velocity which collect just above the slag as a low oxygen pressure layer so that, in effect, the bath *automatically shields itself* against rapid influx of oxygen. This would, for example, make it practicable to make steel in a one-way-fired fuel-oxygen furnace, eliminating regenerators and the conventional reversals of gas and fuel flow. On the other hand, if the concept in Figure 1 is valid, refining should be *inherently unstable* in such a furnace.

To answer these questions, there seemed no conclusive alternative but to actually try out an oxygen-fuel fired furnace. This was done, making it very similar to the small arc furnace of Figure 1, to be closely comparable.   It was fired with natural gas plus pure oxygen and fully instrumented with flow meters, draft control, and oxygen recording on exit gases.   Insulation was maximized to offset the tendency for heat loss to be excessive in such a small furnace.   Simply regarded as a high temperature furnace, it performs very well.   Flame development is very rapid, regardless of how the fuel and oxygen are introduced.   The flame is of course very hot but has a tendency to be low in luminosity.   No special study was made of heat transmission, since the objective was to determine the effect of the absence of nitrogen on the mechanisms in refining.

As was feared might happen, however, this furnace "behaved very badly" as a steelmaking furnace.   Its great instability and the difficulties in control made it not only very hard to operate but also difficult to describe here because it was so nearly impossible to keep under control and at the same time get adequate data.   However it did give some interesting qualitative results in various ways and strongly suggested again that the presence of the nitrogen-rich atmosphere in the open hearth is essential to its stability in operation. First, attempts were made to melt and refine a normal 60-40 pig iron-scrap charge in this oxygen-gas fired furnace.   The result was an almost complete conversion of the charge into a slag containing 77% of $FeO + Fe_2O_3$.   About 5% of the metal charged was recovered as a small ingot which still contained 0.07% carbon.   That is, the highly oxidizing gas phase over the bath created such a highly oxidizing slag that by the time the carbon in the metal was down to around 0.1%, iron was apparently being oxidized faster than carbon.

In later heats, the furnace was charged with 100% pig iron containing from 0.04 to 1% of silicon.   This iron could be melted fairly rapidly and tapped out without much loss of carbon and silicon, although the "essential trick" was usually to add small amounts of ferrosilicon to the bath at some stage.   For example, in one case a charge of 112 lb of basic iron was charged and melted in about 60 min to a bath analysis of

$$4.0\% \text{ C, } 0.47 \text{ Mn, } 0.137 \text{ P, } 0.53 \text{ Si}$$

Twenty minutes later the bath was already boiling and foaming heavily and was tapped out at the composition

$$3.85\% \text{ C, } 0.10 \text{ Mn, } 0.123 \text{ P, } 0.11 \text{ Si}$$

with no ferrosilicon addition in this case.   Apparently, in such cases a thin layer of rather high silica slag acts as a fairly protective barrier layer, slowing down oxygen transfer to the metal, at least as long as some silicon remains in the metal.   When silicon is gone and especially when the slag is made more basic, we encounter a condition which is unstable *because of two effects* acting simultaneously.

The first effect is the rapid oxygen supply to the whole bath surface, with no nitrogen-rich gas-diffusion barrier present; thus, in the extreme case, the only protective effect against oxygen feed to the liquid metal might come from a limited rate due to the chemical nature of the slag.   The second effect present in the small furnace is due to the fact that heat losses require the burning of some fuel which produces H_2O and CO_2 in the combustion space.   With no nitrogen present these molecules diffuse rapidly to the bath surface regardless of flame location.   Referring to Table I, a large part of the oxygen is now delivered to the slag, not by reaction (1) which is highly exothermic, but by reaction (3) which is slightly endothermic, and especially (due to more rapid diffusion of lighter H_2O molecules) by reaction (2) which is only slightly exothermic.   The Fe_3O_4 produced now reacts with carbon in solution by reaction (4) *at and below the slag-metal interface underneath the slag layer* with a large heat absorption.

The effects may be illustrated by one heat in which a charge of 115 lb pig iron + 0.66 lb lime was melted to a bath composition as follows:

Slag: 8.3% SiO_2, 3.3 CaO, 2.5 MnO, 3.1 MgO, 64.8 FeO, 14.0 Fe_2O_3, 0.5 P_2O_5

Metal: 2.57% C, 0.28 Mn, 0.049 P, 0.01 Si

in about 65 min.   After addition of another 0.66 lb of lime, a heavy boil began, with some foaming.   Carbon drop *averaged 760 points/hr* and after 15 min the bath analysis was

Slag: 5.0% SiO_2, 6.3 CaO, 2.0 MnO, 4.0 MgO, 65.1 FeO, 14.3 Fe_2O_3, 0.4 P_2O_5

Metal: 0.65% C, 0.03 Mn, Si − <0.01

About this time, the bath started to freeze, but carbon continued to drop at about 430 points/hr to about 0.07% C in 8 min.   The remaining liquid steel was tapped, leaving some 40% of the metal as a skull in the furnace.   In other heats, maximum rates of carbon drop were quite variable, probably due to variable bath temperature, but in many heats rates of 300 to 450 points/hr were observed.

We see from these results that along with the unstable runaway boil condition in this melting chamber with no nitrogen in the gas phase, there was an effect related to the *spatial distribution* of enthalpy changes in the bath system.   This effect is also important in the open hearth and is merely accentuated in this furnace.   With an intense oxygen-fuel flame above it, the boiling bath would suddenly start to freeze.   With a rolling boil present, the skull would often be on the hearth, as mentioned above, and a quick tap would be in order to avoid leaving 40–60% of the metal in the furnace.   But in several heats the boil appeared to occur mainly at the slag-metal interface, quickly producing a surface freezing effect as illustrated in the diagram of Figure 5.

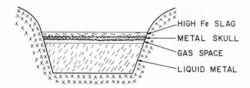

HIGH Fe SLAG

METAL SKULL

GAS SPACE

LIQUID METAL

Fig. 5. Sketch illustrating mode of surface freezing of bath in gas-oxygen furnace.

Referring to Table I, one may picture a liquid slag absorbing oxygen mostly from H_2O and CO_2 by reactions (2) and (3), with essentially no heat evolution.   Below, at the slag-metal interface, reaction (4) is removing carbon with a large heat absorption.   The decreasing carbon raises the liquidus temperature, but the shallow surface boil does not effectively mix this low carbon metal downward.   A solid surface layer forms and moves in from the perimeter.   Suddenly, as this thin skull covers the whole bath, the boil stops and the liquid drops about a half inch, presumably due to pressure rise and collapse of some bubbles in the liquid.   By punching through this $1/4$–$3/8$-in. layer of frozen metal, the liquid below could be tapped out.   In two heats, the thin skull remaining in the furnace analyzed between 0.04 and 0.07% C, with the liquid tapped out at a mixed composition of 0.50 to 0.55% C.

In dramatic contrast to this condition, we have the commercial open hearth heat mentioned above which was described by Gibson;[1] here was a furnace without fuel for two hours, with carbon drop at about 0.17%/hr after which fuel input was resumed and the heat tapped 45 min later. If we assume that this furnace was perfectly dampered so that no cold air in-leakage occurred, all the carbon + slag oxidation derived from preheated oxygen in air from regenerators. Calculations indicate that the net heat evolution from carbon oxidation to CO under these conditions was more than sufficient to maintain metal superheat and heat absorbed by the hearth, and that the available heat above the bath from burning the CO to CO_2 should have sufficed to offset about 50–60% of the probable heat losses above floor level.

In general, with a carbon drop rate of 30–50 points/hr or higher, *exclusively from oxygen in highly preheated air or by pure oxygen injection*, and with all cold air leakage eliminated, no fuel energy should be needed during refining in the average open hearth, in spite of conduction and water cooling losses. When cold ore feeds supply most of the oxygen, this condition is completely reversed and the *large heat absorption underneath the slag layer* dominates the refining process. When most of the oxygen comes from CO_2 and H_2O *in combustion gases*, the net heat which must come from combustion over the bath and *flow through the slag layer* is still some 50–60% as much as with ore feeding. Briefly, these factors explain why the use of cold 95–100% oxygen in spray or lances so greatly changes the thermal picture of refining in the open hearth. Cold air leakage and masses of limestone and ore underneath the charge normally complicate the picture of open hearth heat requirement, but in essence these factors merely accentuate the slowness of open hearth rates caused by the *"upside-down" spatial distribution* of enthalpy changes.

Summarizing the results from the fuel-oxygen furnace with nitrogen essentially eliminated: It demonstrated rather conclusively that the CO bubbles from the boil do not effectively shield a refining bath from rapid influx of oxygen. Therefore it seems almost certain that it is the diffusion rate-limiting effect of inert nitrogen in the gas phase above the slag surface that stabilizes the boil at a steady state oxygen influx rate of around 0.05×10^{-6} g mole/sec cm^2. The oxygen gradient picture of Figure 1 seems thus to approximate the real system in any air-atmosphere furnace such as the open hearth or the electric arc furnace.   Also, the effects of spatial distribution of enthalpy changes are more clearly demonstrated by being exaggerated in this fuel-oxygen fired furnace.

SULFUR TRANSFER FROM BATH TO GAS PHASE

One may postulate the presence of both sulfide (S^{2-}) and sulfate ($SO_4{}^{2-}$) ions in the slag at the slag-gas interface.   The following heterogeneous exchange reactions probably occur at this interface:

$$S^{2-} + {}^3/_2O_2 \longrightarrow O^{2-} + SO_2 \tag{5}$$

$$SO_4{}^{2-} \longrightarrow O^{2-} + SO_2 + {}^1/_2O_2 \tag{6}$$

Reaction (5) permits sulfide ion in the slag with *decreasing* stability as oxygen pressure rises.   Reaction (6) favors sulfate ion, with *increasing* stability as oxygen pressure rises.   This permits a minimum total sulfur in the slag surface layer (for any given p_{SO_2} in the gases) *at some optimum oxygen pressure*.   Earlier calculations by Darken[4] at this laboratory agree well with more recent data by St. Pierre and Chipman[5] in placing this optimum oxygen pressure for SO_2 evolution from slag surface to gases at between 10^{-4} and 10^{-5} atm.

These data form part of the basis for placing, in Figure 1, the oxygen pressure at the slag surface at about 1 to 5 $\times$ 10^{-6} atm for the steady state boil condition.   When pure oxygen is sprayed on this surface, its oxygen pressure should increase, but not by a very large factor simply because the violet resulting boil opposes such a large increase.   This is confirmed by the very moderate increase in Fe_2O_3 in the bulk slag shown in Table III for oxygen-spray periods. (The extreme top surface layer must contain more Fe_2O_3, but it cannot be sampled.)

This reasoning has the consequence that oxygen spray should cause some slag surface area to be in the optimum oxygen pressure range of 10^{-5} to 10^{-4} atm with resultant SO_2 evolution.   This effect did occur with complete consistency in all the heats* in the small furnace of Figure 2 (a total of 21 heats made with oxygen spray).   A brief summary of these results follows.

First, the small furnace behaved very much like the open hearth under similar conditions.   In heats without oxygen-spray injection,

* See Appendix, Section 5.

sulfur balances from the charge to the bath of slag + metal at tap normally checked very closely, indicating no loss into gases; when SO_2 was present in the furnace atmosphere, it was partly absorbed into the bath. On the other hand, even when SO_2 was injected *in the pure oxygen spray* (in amounts somewhat larger than those resulting from combustion of S-bearing open hearth fuels), some net loss of sulfur from the bath always occurred.

Oxygen was sprayed on the melting charge of basic pig iron and steel scrap in most of these heats. When nearly all the sulfur in metallic charge was contained *in the pig iron* portion of the metal charge, not more than a very few per cent of its sulfur was vaporized. When 40–80% of the sulfur in metal charge was contained *in the steel scrap*, an appreciable elimination of sulfur into gases always occurred during melting. For example, one heat with a high sulfur content in the 40% of steel scrap was sprayed with oxygen containing 0.75 wt-% of SO_2. Sixty-five per cent of the sulfur charged was eliminated as SO_2 over the whole heat, about 40% of this occurring during melting of the charge (metal tapped analyzed 0.014% S). These effects are only reasonable. Oxygen impinging on rapidly melting surfaces of basic pig, high in carbon and containing some silicon cannot possibly raise the oxygen pressure at the melting surface to a level high enough to stabilize SO_2.

When the melting surface layer is from steel scrap (at a higher liquidus temperature, containing no silicon and a low to medium carbon steel level of carbon), some liquid wüstite is formed by reaction with the oxygen stream and the oxygen pressure can reach the optimum levels above 10^{-5} atm permitting SO_2 evolution from these surfaces.

Oxygen spray on slag surface after melt down also caused the vaporization of more or less SO_2 in every heat, which could be observed directly by the odor around the furnace. The sulfur balance and other data in Table V on a few heats with higher sulfur charges illustrates some of these results (the term "bath" here refers to the total of slag plus metal).

In the first two heats in Table V the extra sulfur charged was all in the iron and the amount lost during melting was too small to be definitely identifiable. In the last heat, sulfur was also high in the steel scrap and even though this was only 30% of the metal charge, an appreciable loss occurred during melting. The first heat was

TABLE V

Pig: scrap	S, %		Total lb, S		Input S removed during melt, %	S in metal at melt, %	Lb S in bath at tap	S at melt removed by O₂ spray on slag, %	O₂ spray period min	Slag basicity ratio	S in metal at tap, %
	In iron	In scrap	In charge	In bath at melt							
60:40	0.077	0.020	0.060	0.059	—	0.054	0.030	50	30	2.0	0.021
60:40	0.067	0.020	0.054	0.053	—	0.043	0.038	28	20	2.4	0.021
70:30	0.083	0.095	0.104	0.082	21	0.076	0.066	20	20	2.9	0.030

given two separate oxygen-spray periods on liquid slag of 15 min
each. During the first blow, 35% of the sulfur in the bath was lost
as SO_2. Before the second spray period, the sulfur in metal was
down to 0.024% and only 22% of the remaining total sulfur in slag
+ metal was lost as SO_2 during this second oxygen-spray period.

In the last heat of Table V, slag weight at 12–13% of metal weight
was well up in the normal open hearth range, yet maximum carbon
boil rate $(-dC/dt)$ during the 20 min oxygen-spray period was
above 300 points/hr, showing that slag volume is not critical as
regards oxygen transfer through slag in this boiling system. In
this heat, SO_2 elimination over all was 36% of the sulfur charged,
with 20% of the sulfur in bath at melt vaporized from slag surface
during oxygen spray. A number of these oxygen-spray heats had
low sulfur charges; the percentage loss by SO_2 evolution was lower
than the 35–65% range with higher sulfur charges, but was always
appreciable, as evidenced by the tap-sulfur range of 0.008–0.015%
in these heats with a single slag practice without run-off and with
slag basicity in the normal open hearth range. In the last four
columns of Table V, there is an indication of a decrease in SO_2 vaporization with increasing slag basicity. This is again in qualitative
agreement with theory, since either sulfide or sulfate ions in solution
should be decreased in activity by an increased mole fraction of
strongly basic ions.

In general, the observations on SO_2 interchange between slag and
gas phase are in consistent agreement with Figure 1. To attain the
high oxygen pressure level (above 10^{-5} atm) at slag surface required
to favor rapid SO_2 evolution in the face of the reducing effect of the
boil, a large oxygen pressure gradient must be obtained by very
rapid oxygen absorption at this surface.

During scrap meltdown in the open hearth, the impingement of
reducing flame zones on melting surfaces should obviously favor
sulfur absorption from fuel, but with sufficient contact of such
surfaces by preheated air or oxygen jet streams, this absorption
could even be reversed. Assuming the validity of Figure 1 and the
slow rate of oxygen absorption into slag surface in normal boil
conditions or with ore feeds, it becomes more obvious why the
amount of sulfur exchange between bath and gases after melt in the
open hearth is so very small. Not only is SO_2 a heavier molecule
with lower specific diffusivity but also its concentration is low com-

pared to the total of the oxygen-bearing gases CO_2, H_2O, and O_2; yet even oxygen transfer is only around 0.05×10^{-6} g mole/sec/cm² of slag surface.

NITROGEN CONTENT IN SMALL FURNACE HEATS

In a number of these 100-lb heats, tap metal analyses with nitrogen contents at 0.001% or below in metal at tap are of interest, mainly because a powerful electric arc was present just above the bath during all or a large portion of the time. No very systematic study was made on this aspect, but normal heats without oxygen spray gave values averaging around 0.001% N, and heats with faster scrap melting under oxygen spray and with a more violent carbon boil under oxygen spray on slag surface gave slightly lower values, averaging around 0.0008%, with 0.0005% N at tap in three of these heats.

Assuming that steel refining slags have a very low nitrogen solubility, the obvious factors favorable here are (1) rather low nitrogen contents in charge materials plus (2) a vigorous flushing action by carbon boil due to a large volume of CO formed by a large decrease in carbon from melt to tap (1.5 to 2.0% carbon eliminated). However, the values of around 0.007–0.010% N commonly occurring with steels made in direct arc furnaces appear significant by comparison. The only difference would seem to be that in this small furnace with an indirect arc placed from 3–5 in. above the slag surface, the arc never contacted the liquid metal bath, and there was no apparent current flow through the slag into the metal. This seems to offer some proof, in a negative fashion, that fixation of nitrogen compounds in an arc zone which sometimes contacts the steel, or formation of calcium cyanamide in solution in slag in local zones, is a part of the relevant mechanism leading to higher [N] values in the product of the direct arc furnace process.

NUCLEATION AND MOVEMENT OF BUBBLES

In the top-blown oxygen converter, for example, there is presumably a great deal of (1) an approach to emulsification of slag and metal phases and of (2) short circuiting of many of the reaction rate steps discussed above. This explains qualitatively why the overall rate seems limited only by oxygen supply rate, but the details are not clear and there may be some other limiting factor. In our small scale imitation of the open hearth bath system, we have not really been able to find out how fast one can push a process involving, apparently, the whole series of 11 steps postulated above. Perhaps with larger scale experiments some other limiting factor than input flow of oxygen could be discovered. In any case it is evident that transport rates and reaction rates, as well as the nucleation and growth of bubbles, all keep pace with the overall process up to more than 10 times the steady state rate of boil. This can be partially explained, at least.

Direct evidence on bubble nucleation is very meager. Larsen,[6] for example, has shown a picture of an actual hearth surface on which steel had been boiling which exhibits a very rough surface having cavities of a few millimeters diameter and downward, some of which should be incompletely wetted by the metal liquid, due to its high surface tension. Thus, on a rough hearth surface, bubbles of varying size may always be present so we do not need to nucleate new bubbles but merely to force these to grow and pop loose from this surface. This will require an excess pressure ΔP, above hydrostatic, at this surface, which is closely approximated by

$$\Delta P = 2\gamma/R \qquad (7)$$

where γ is the liquid surface tension in dynes/cm and R is some minimum value of the bubble radius in centimeters. Assuming that R is $1/2$ the cavity opening, calculations* indicate that if R is 0.1 cm, ΔP would be only about 0.04 atm; if the hole or crevice in the hearth surface was only 0.02 cm across, ΔP would be about 0.36 atm. Since bulk phase samples in boiling baths indicate potential CO pressures of from 2 up to perhaps 7–10 atm, it seems reasonable that with only moderately increased rates of oxygen flux into the metal by reaction (2) (see postulated rate steps above), bubble nuclei *would grow from more and more points* on the hearth surface. As bubble nuclei (see Fig. 1) grow at points closer together, one can picture an approach to a continuous layer of CO at the metal-hearth interface. A very smooth glazed hearth surface could completely alter this picture, but fortunately this condition is rarely approached in practice.

Visual and photographic observations* have shown clearly that the

* See Appendix, Section 6.

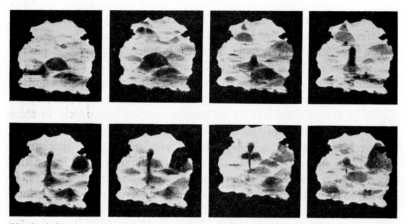

Fig. 6. A film sequence showing the stages in bubble bursting from one phase to another (in this case, a bubble entering a gas phase).

total area of slag-metal contact can increase greatly at high boil
rates.   Slag samples quickly chilled were often filled with $^1/_{32}$–$^1/_8$
in. globules of metal in amounts such as to approach equal volume
percentages of metal and slag.   Combined with the velocity effect

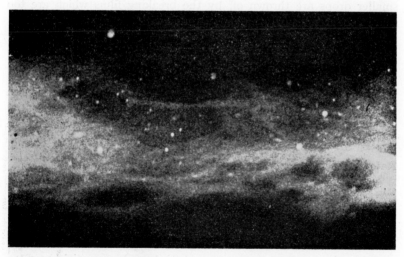

Fig. 7. One frame from a high speed film showing metal droplets from a lime boil
in an open hearth heat.

on film transport rates, this explains why the slag-to-metal oxygen transfer can "keep up" at high boil rates.

The mechanism of bubble bursting is illustrated by the picture series (from a film sequence) in Figure 6. From an initial hole in the bubble film, we progress to the dissipation of this surface energy into wave motion, part of which builds up to a focus at the bottom center of the original bubble to form a vertical jet, which, in some rather large fraction of the total number of bubble bursts, splits off one or more small droplets projected vertically. This mechanism can project slag droplets into the gases, or metal droplets into a slag layer. If the slag layer is not too thick relative to bubble size, or if a surge of metal pushes up to, or close to, the upper slag surface, metal droplets will be projected directly into the gas phase. These are shown in Figure 7 as brightly shining drops (mainly by reflection of flame radiation and surface oxidation) flying in various directions in the turbulent gases above the bath. They have been observed both in the small laboratory furnaces and in commercial open hearths. Figure 7 is from an open hearth on a foamy slag period when a violent lime boil just to the left of the view was projecting metal droplets into the gases. When slag bubble films burst, in addition to the larger droplets shown here visually, it is highly probable that much smaller drops are thrown off by the breaking films which are too small to be seen visually, and float around with the turbulent gases.

DISCUSSION

The general concept of the nature of the boil and the carbon reaction mechanism in steel refining as enunciated mainly by Darken[4] is still regarded as essentially valid by the present authors. The essential idea can be expressed in a simple way for the flux of oxygen or the related boil rate as

Rate of boil =

$$\text{(a constant)} \times \text{(an oxygen potential } [\Delta O]) \times (A/\Delta L) \quad (8)$$

The constant may include such things as a mobility or diffusion rate of some reactant such as an Fe^{3+} ion in slag or oxygen (or carbon) atoms in iron solution. The driving force or potential is obviously a concentration gradient across some phase boundary or diffusion film, such as the oxygen gradient in a liquid metal film near a CO bubble or just below the slag-metal interface [see also Eq. (A2) in Appendix, Section 3]. The term $A/\Delta L$ is the ratio of an area such as slag-metal surface per unit weight of metal to the thickness of a transport or diffusion film. Now, ΔL will naturally tend to decrease some-what with boil or stirring rate and as shown above, the interface area A tends to increase with boil rate especially due to the way the bubbles behave as they pass through a phase boundary. In effect this means that the ratio $A/\Delta L$ can increase rapidly so that the boil rate can multiply with only a moderate increase in the potential or driving force term tending to deliver oxygen into the metal solution. Since, as noted above, the number of effective bubble-growing nuclei on a porous hearth interface should increase rapidly with oxygen gradient, this explains why the *overall boil rate* may be logically dependent on either a rate of heat supply (to avoid initial freezing in a critical zone) or to a rate of oxygen supply if no critical heat supply factor is involved. It has been shown that for the steady state boil with a nitrogen-rich atmosphere above the bath, the diffusion of oxygen-bearing gas molecules in a layer above the slag appears to be the essential limiting rate factor, while in ore-feeding periods this limiting factor is the rate of heat flow through slag films to the zone just above the slag-metal interface.

By eliminating these limiting factors with oxygen spray on slag surface, we have shown that the boil rate may be multiplied some ten-to twentyfold, even though many reaction and transport rate steps are still involved in a complex boil process. Although many intimate details of mechanism are still to be explained, we seem to have a picture adequate to explain most of the factors involved in production rate in the open hearth. Finally, we have a reasonable explanation for the slow minimum boil rate that is really what makes this refining process a practical, controllable one.

CONCLUSIONS

1. The minimum boil rate, with oxygen supplied from air or combustion gases to a slag surface, involves a series of many transport and reaction rate steps but is controlled essentially by a diffusion process of O_2, CO_2, or H_2O through N_2 (mainly) in a film zone of the order of a centimeter in thickness just above the slag surface. In the open hearth, this is the critical stabilizing mechanism on which the workability of the process depends.

2. Merely displacing this diffusion film layer just over the slag surface by a stream of nearly pure oxygen can multiply the above minimum rate of oxygen flux per unit area by some 100-fold or more, and the overall boil rate by something above 10-fold, at least, with the rates of bubble nucleation, slag-metal oxygen transfer, and several other steps in the overall boil process all apparently able to speed up and "keep in step" at least over this range.

3. The increased oxygen gradient in the slag layer from such oxygen spray on its surface can cause an optimum escaping tendency of SO_2 at some slag surface areas; in small heats as much as two-thirds of the total S in the bath of slag plus metal has been removed as vaporized SO_2 by this effect. Since the optimum oxygen pressure for SO_2 vaporization is around 10^{-5} to 10^{-4} atm, the normal level of oxygen pressure at the surface of a boiling bath would appear to be at about 10^{-6} atm.

4. Under average commercial open hearth conditions, refining rates are very much dominated by the normally large heat absorption at the slag-metal interface (or still deeper in the bath). The overall process involved in carbon oxidation evolves heat, to reverse this pattern, *only* if the oxygen is supplied to the bath uncombined as pure oxygen or highly preheated air. When the oxygen supply is from *hot* CO_2 or H_2O in combustion gases, the net heat absorption is still nearly two-thirds of that involved when the source of oxygen is essentially from cold ore feeding. In the latter case, maximum boil rate is essentially limited by a rate of heat flow in some transport film in the slag layer.

The experimental work described above covered a period of many years, including many design and operating problems with small laboratory steelmaking furnaces. So many people of this laboratory were involved that it is difficult to give adequate acknowledgments. The writers are especially indebted to Quintin Henderson for urnace construction, to Glenn Momeyer for analytical work on hundreds of slag and metal samples, to John Mrvosh and James S. Morrison for assistance in furnace operating, and to K. H. Lohse for special photographic techniques.

APPENDIX

1.

Gibson[1] reports that "failure of a steam valve at the main boiler range caused a complete shut down at gas producers and power station and there was no option but to damp down the furnaces for a period which ultimately extended to two hours." The failure occurred just 15 min after the one heat had been completely melted, at 0.62% carbon; it was tapped at 0.225% C just 45 min after fuel supply was restored, with an average carbon drop rate of $14^1/_2$ points/hr. During the fuel-off period, however, metal samples every 10 min showed an almost linear rate of carbon drop of 17 points/hr (residual Mn dropped from 0.30 to 0.20% and FeO in slag increased from 10 to 14%). It appears that the operators must have been wise enough to damper at least to the point where melting chamber pressure was positive at sill level so that only a slow flow of preheated air from regenerators entered the melting chamber over the bath. Some cooling of the bath presumably occurred during the shut-down period. However, the total enthalpy changes in this bath may be calculated and the Btu loss per hour to hearth, water coolers, conduction, and radiation losses for this 75-ton furnace above floor level was reasonably approximated. Assuming all oxidation effect to be supplied from preheated air, it may be shown that at about twice this rate of carbon drop, or 35–40 points/hr, the bath should have just about held even in temperature with no fuel input.

2.

Suppose we picture an equivalent film thickness ΔL in the gas phase just above the slag where laminar flow gives a linear velocity gradient. Although the bulk of the gas is inert N_2, the oxygen gradient implies diffusion of H_2O, CO_2, and O_2 molecules downward and of CO and H_2 molecules upward. There is the difficulty of a relative absence of good transport data at this temperature range of around $1900°K$ (assuming that the gases near the slag surface are not much above its surface temperature). We can estimate that specific diffusivity values for gases will increase by some 30 times as compared to room temperature levels. But the equivalent film thickness (ΔL) tends to vary with the kinematic viscosity of the gases, which will also increase by some 25 times, so that transfer rates in the gas phase could still be comparable to low temperature systems. The mean gas velocity above the bath is so difficult to define as to perhaps preclude a direct calculation of ΔL, considering that the system is also disturbed by the bubbles from the boil.

Yet some sort of rough calculation seems desirable. Suppose we assume that the combustion gases could be replaced by an approximately equivalent mixture of 70% N_2 and 30% H_2O. If we set a linear range of oxygen pressures between limits of 10^{-2} atm in the turbulent gases outside the film, and 10^{-6} atm at the slag surface, the gas compositions (from the dissociation equilibrium $H_2O \rightleftharpoons H_2 + {}^{1}/_{2}O_2$) will be

70% N_2, 30% H_2O, $H_2 < 0.1\%$ (at ΔL above slag surface)

70% N_2, 26.5% H_2O, 3.5% H_2 (at slag surface)

We then assume that the known mean rate of oxygen transfer of $dN/dt = 4.5 \times 10^{-6}$ mole/cm^2 sec is affected by diffusion of H_2O molecules over a pressure difference $(P_G - P_s) = \Delta P = 0.035$ atm and we can treat this as a simple diffusion of one species through the inert nitrogen to a close approximation, using the relation

$$dN/dt = [K_{(H_2O - N_2)} \cdot p \cdot (\Delta p)]/R \cdot T \cdot \Delta L \cdot p_m \qquad (A1)$$

where $K_{(H_2O - N_2)}$ is the specific diffusivity of H_2O in N_2 — cm^2/sec; p and p_m are the total pressure of the furnace, and the logarithmic mean pressure of the $N_2 + H_2$, respectively; and R is 82.06 cu cm — atm/°K, gram mole.

Measurements of $K_{(H_2O - air)}$ made by Klibanov et al.[8] over a wide temperature range up to nearly 1500°K fit a curve using $T^{1.89}$ fairly well for values ranging from 0.24 at 298°K to about 4.5 at 1500°K. Assuming that $K_{(H_2O - N_2)}$ would not be appreciably different and extrapolating to 1900°K gives a value of 7.7 cm^2/sec. Solving for the film thickness as the only unknown gives

$$\Delta L = 0.27 \text{ cm}$$

The H_2 must be diffusing in the opposite direction at an equal rate, away from the slag surface. Even less data appear available on its diffusivity at high temperatures, but if one uses an estimate of $K_{(H_2 - N_2)} = 25.0$ cm^2/sec, a similar calculation gives

$$\Delta L = 0.65 \text{ cm}$$

Obviously, these values can at present be considered only rough approximations, but they do not seem unreasonable. That is, the picture given above seems a possible one, at least. For the case above reported by Gibson,[1] the diffusion was essentially O_2 molecules in N_2 instead of the H_2O in N_2 above. Using Eq. (2) with a value of $K_{(O_2-N_2)}$ estimated at 6.7 cm²/sec gives

$$\Delta L = 1.6 \text{ cm}$$

for this case which again seems roughly reasonable. With the furnace dampered and no flame gases sweeping over the bath there would still be convection in the bulk gas phase, but the equivalent diffusion film thickness should be much greater. The gases in a sweeping flame zone are very viscous, very low in density, and have a buoyancy due to being hotter than their surroundings; these factors should operate against their ability to reduce the ΔL thickness over the slag.

3.

In a small laboratory furnace[9] such as the one used here (Fig. 2), heat losses tend to be large, even with an insulated enclosure, so that a power input of some 30–35 kw is normally needed just to maintain bath temperature. With the arc and the hot graphite electrodes present, one might expect that oxygen in air entering would react with carbon to give an atmosphere relatively nonoxidizing to the slag and metal, but this is not true. With a peephole opening at the rear, the door at the front and openings around electrodes at the sides, the turbulence caused by the arc and other steep temperature gradients causes considerable air circulation over the slag. For example, in one heat made with all openings partly open, the arc raised several inches above the bath and with slag and metal both hot and fluid at 2950°F and carbon above 1.0%, the normal or steady state boil rate was 0.30% C/hr with only air oxidation. Compared to the usual steady state boil at around 0.15% C/hr in the open hearth, this is almost exactly the expected rate, in view of the relative slag-metal areas of

Open hearth—4.0 ft²/ton; lab. furnace—9.0 ft²/ton

However, if we imitated the open hearth ore-feed periods, we could feed iron oxide at any desired rate and calculate oxygen balances to give a more controllable simulation of open hearth conditions. By using a high power input such as to keep a roof temperature of around 3100°F, feeding heavy lumps of scale at rates up toward the maximum that would allow a good steady "ore boil," the carbon drop rates in a dozen or more heats were between 0.75 and 1.25% C/hr in comparison with the 0.35 to 0.60% C/hr common to heavy ore feeding in the commercial open hearth.

Assuming first that this rate is limited by a diffusion flux of oxygen through a thin transport film layer of metal just underneath the slag, we may use the equation[3]

$$-d[\text{C}]/dt = (12/16) \, K_\text{O} \, \{[\text{O}]_\text{S.E.} - [\text{O}]_\text{obs.}\}/D \cdot \Delta L \qquad (A2)$$

where K_O is the specific diffusivity of oxygen in liquid iron assumed at 6×10^{-5} cm²/sec; D the metal bath depth at rest = 18 cm; ΔL is the effective diffusion-film thickness—assumed at 0.002 cm; and $\{[\text{O}]_\text{S.E.} - [\text{O}]_\text{obs.}\}$ is the difference in wt-% between max [O] for equilibrium with an iron oxide-rich slag layer just above the metal and the observed value in the bulk metal phase, or 0.20%, assuming FeO at about activity of 1.0 due to melting scale at this interface.

We then have

$$-d[\text{C}]/dt = (12/16)(6 \times 10^{-5} \times 0.20/18 \times 0.002)$$

$$= 0.00025\% \text{ C/sec} = 0.90\% \text{ C/hr}$$

Being in the middle of the observed range, this is a reasonable approximation, but as mentioned above, merely indicates that an oxygen flux by diffusion in the metal below the slag-metal interface (step 7 in Fig. 1) is *one step in the series* of possible factors limiting the overall boil rate.

Taking the more plausible assumption that the critical limiting rate step for the *maximum* ore boil values (of 0.60% C/hr for open hearth and 1.20% C/hr for the laboratory furnace) is the *rate of heat supply* to melt and dissociate the ore or scale at the slag-metal interface, one may calculate the corresponding rates of heat absorption. [Note in Table I that due to differences in oxygen content the Q values (= $-\Delta H$) in Btu/1/2 mole of O_2 are −88,000 for pure cold hematite and −93,000 for cold scale.]

Over scale feed periods in the small furnace, oxygen balances showed an average of 80% of the oxygen from the scale and 20% from air above the slag. With a total metal weight of 112 lb and total slag-metal area of 0.5 ft², we have

$$112 \times 0.0120 \times 0.80/12 = 0.09 \text{ lb atom C or } O_2/\text{hr}$$
$$0.09 \times 93000/0.5 = 16,700 \text{ Btu/hr/ft}^2 \text{ slag-metal area}$$

Assuming the same 80% of the oxidation by ore in the open hearth from hematite feeds, then for each ton of metal containing 0.2 lb of carbon per 0.01%, we have

$$0.2 \times 60 \times 0.8/12 = 0.8 \text{ lb atom } O_2/\text{hr, ton metal}$$
$$0.8 \times 88000/4.0 = 17,600 \text{ Btu/hr ft}^2 \text{ bath area}$$

Regardless of interpretation as to mechanisms involved, the above comparisons present rather strong evidence for good simulation of commercial open hearth conditions in this very small laboratory furnace.

4.

The water-cooled oxygen lance had an ID of $1/8$ in., about a $30°$ normal angle to the slag surface and about 2 lb nozzle exit pressure. The area of slag wiped by the diverging jet will vary with distance, but in typical cases with nozzle exit distance only 4–5 in., the wiped area was localized near the center of the small bath. The ruffling of the liquid surface and in some cases, an extra brightness in the area of oxygen absorption due to the heat evolved by reaction (1) in Table I, gave a visual check on the area of rapid oxygen absorption as being around 50 cm² in certain heats. However, more specific data on limiting rates of this absorption step would require a larger scale or differently arranged setup. The average efficiency of direct oxygen absorption into the liquid slag was usually around 35–50%, but this again has little significance in such small scale tests. Heat input by the arc was usually cut off during oxygen-spray periods and the bath temperature usually dropped, without apparently affecting the boil rate, but in a few heats when oxygen feed was high at around 14–16 lb/hr, the bath temperature held up or even increased.

The initial absorption rate may be slow, especially with a very low iron oxide or a very viscous slag, but once started, tends to increase with the boil rate. In spite of increasing CO evolution, however, the slag FeO content at first increases sharply, presumably because the reaction

$$2Fe^{3+} + Fe \longrightarrow 3Fe^{2+} \tag{4}$$

PROCESS METALLURGY

TABLE VI

O₂ blown, lb/ton steel	Slag basicity ratio, b	Residual Mn, %		S distribution ratio, (S)/[S]		S content in bath at tap, %	
		observed	calc.	Obs.	Calc.	Slag	Metal
188	2.0	0.36	0.37	4.0	5 4	0 055	0 014
180	1.6	0.23	0.22	3.6	4 4	0 050	0 014

predominates over the reaction

$$2Fe^{3+} + O^{2-} \longrightarrow 2Fe^{2+} + [O] \tag{2}$$

As a violent rolling boil develops, the slag soon becomes loaded with iron droplets from bubble bursting, and in some heats, many such tiny iron droplets could be seen popping up into the gases above the slag surface.

5.

About 20 heats were made in which oxygen spray on melting scrap or slag surface showed some net loss of total sulfur from the charge during melt or from slag + metal during refining. The odor of SO_2 around the furnace was often fleeting and only a rough qualitative indicator. However, the low sulfur content in slags after oxygen blow periods was what called attention to this effect. In Table III, the drop in S content in both slag and metal occurs after both oxygen blow periods; this is a typical effect.

The conditions in two heats, at tap some 15 min after oxygen spray shown in Table VI will illustrate the reversion to steady state after oxygen blow periods.

There is an evident tendency for the slag and metal phases to approach a steady state condition closely analogous to a true equilibrium, within minutes after cessation of the heavy-boil, oxygen-spray period. Sulfur distribution is not far from an apparent equilibrium,[10] in spite of the low concentrations involved.

6.

As a bubble nucleus grows out from a hole or crevice, its radius reaches a minimum at $1/2$ the hole diameter as the bubble approaches a hemisphere. To grow further and thus detach a bubble into the bath, requires a certain equivalent CO pressure, represented by the expression

$$K = P_{(CO)}/(a_C \times a_O) \tag{A3}$$

(where K is the equilibrium constant for the carbon-oxygen reaction at the bath temperature; a_C and a_O are the activities in the liquid metal). Thus $P_{(CO)}$ must *exceed* the hydrostatic pressure at the hearth surface by an amount

$$\Delta P = 2\gamma/R \tag{7}$$

as mentioned above. The probable value of γ is in the range of about 1600–1800 dynes cm^{-1}.

Really accurate sampling for [O] in the liquid steel is difficult, but there is some indication that (1) the open hearth bath may begin to boil when [O] values in the bulk phase average as little as 0.01% above the hydrostatic equilibrium level for the values of [C] present, and (2) that the metal near the hearth may be something like 0.005% lower in [O] values than near the slag-metal interface. Considering the uncertainty in sampling, therefore, values of ΔP of around a few tenths of an atmosphere may be regarded as reasonable in magnitude.

The CO bubbles, as they rise into a turbulent metal phase must grow and circulate around in erratic flow paths before rising into slag and gas phases, but their average size as they leave the metal is not really known. If average size is assumed at 1 cm^3, some idea of magnitudes here may be given by a calculation of actual gas volumes given by the boil in a 300-ton open hearth heat. For each 0.2% of the bath boiled out as carbon in such CO bubbles, approximately 7×10^9 bubbles are evolved. As these billions of bubbles burst through the slag, in addition to metal shot formation in slag, and the metal and slag droplets seen in Figure 7, the tiny invisible droplets from shattering of bubble films have a very predominant effect on service life of roof and wall refractories. The most direct evidence here comes from analyses of fluxes absorbed in roof brick after some weeks of service, which show compositions very close to the early slags in heavy boil periods. There is a close analogy here to the formation of salt crystals from surf spray at the seashore.

References

1. Gibson, J., *J. West Scot. Iron Steel Inst.*, **63**, 65 (1955–6).

2. Larson, H., and J. Chipman, *Trans. Am. Inst. Mining Met. Engrs.*, **197**, 1089 (1953).

3. Larsen, B. M., "A New Look at the Nature of the Open Hearth Process," AIME, NOHC Special Rept. Ser., No. 1, 6–8 (1956).

4. Darken, L. S., unpublished report.

5. St. Pierre, G. R., and J. Chipman, *Trans. Am. Inst. Mining, Met. Petrol. Engrs.*, **206**, 1474 (1956).

6. See ref. 3, p. 13.

7. See ref. 3, pp. 13–18.

8. Klibanov, T. M., V. V. Pomerantsev, and D. A. Frank-Kamenetsky, *J. Tech. Phys.* (*U.S.S.R.*), **12**, 14 (1942).

9. Larsen, B. M., *J. Metals*, **206,** 1057 (1956).

10. For basis of calculation, see L. S. Darken and B. M. Larsen, *Trans. Am. Inst. Mining Met. Engrs.*, **150,** 87 (1942).

Discussion

R. D. Pehlke (*MIT*): The authors are to be commended on their approach to a problem as difficult as the kinetics of the open hearth steelmaking process. In a standard manner, they broke the process down into a series of reaction steps, each of which is potentially a rate-limiting one. Step 2, absorption of oxygen by a gas-liquid reaction at the slag surface, was supposed to be extremely rapid, and step 1, diffusion transport of oxygen atoms through a gas layer to the slag surface, was said to be the rate-limiting step on the basis of experiments with a pure oxygen jet.

Perhaps the authors were a little too hasty in their analysis and I would suggest a closer look at some of the possibilities which exist for these two steps as well as some experimental work which might better clarify which of these steps is truly the rate-determining one.

On the basis of the theory of absolute reaction rates, let us re-examine step 2 and break it into two parts, first, the formation of an activated complex, and secondly, the decomposition of that activated complex:

$$\text{(a) } {}^{1}/_{2}O_{2} \text{ (gas phase)} + 2e^{-} = O^{2-*} \text{ (activated complex)}$$

Step 2

$$\text{(b) } O^{2-*} \text{ (activated complex)} = [O^{2-}] \text{ (slag)}$$

Step (b) is extremely rapid and provided that the transmission coefficient (the fraction of complexes which decompose into oxygen ions in the slag) is fairly high, step (a) becomes the potential rate-limiting part of step 2.

Experimental evidence has shown that the reaction rate is increased from 100 to 150 times when the stagnant air phase is replaced by a wiping oxygen jet, and on this basis the authors have proposed the diffusion mechanism of step 1 as the rate-determining step 2(a) involves the combination of oxygen and nitrogen atoms in some form when nitrogen is present, a step which is not present in the pure oxygen case. It has been shown in recent experiments at MIT (R. D. Pehlke and J. F. Elliott, "Solubility of Nitrogen in Liquid Iron Alloys—A Kinetic Study," current research) that the presence of oxygen in iron greatly inhibits the rate of nitrogen absorption, indicating the possibility of formation of an oxy-nitro complex, a feasible rate-limiting step for the case under consideration.

Under the complex experimental conditions existing in a model open hearth furnace, one would find it difficult to invoke the standard experimental steps to separate a diffusion from a chemically controlled mechanism. Let us review these steps however, and see if they may, at least in part, be applied to the experimental conditions with which the authors are dealing.

1. First of all, the expected rate of the reaction should be estimated for diffusion control, such that a reaction rate much lower than the calculated one could

be attributed to chemical reaction rate control.   This step is admittedly difficult because of lack of suitable data and the authors have only been able to approximate the data necessary for such a calculation.

2.   Examine the temperature dependence of the reaction rate.   The temperature dependence is generally quite large for chemically controlled reactions whereas the diffusion-controlled rate may be expected to depend upon temperature in much the same manner as the diffusion coefficient itself.

3.   Examine the effect of convention upon the observed reaction rate.   A chemically-controlled process may be expected to be independent of convection whereas the rate of a diffusion-controlled process will be directly related to the degree of convection within the system.   The authors attempted this step but changed the gas composition which prevents one from differentiating one mechanism from the other.   One would expect that if the reaction is chemically controlled, that a jet of air wiping the slag surface would not affect the reaction rate, whereas if the reaction is diffusion controlled, the rate for an air jet would be about $1/5$ (neglecting thermal diffusion in the gas phase because of the similarity of the oxygen and nitrogen molecules) of the rate observed when using the pure oxygen jet.

B. M. Larsen and **L. O. Sordahl:**   As Mr. Pehlke probably realizes, what we are doing in such a study is to obtain a set of circumstantial evidence and then try to suggest the simplest picture of the mechanics that seems to explain all this evidence.   It is difficult enough to even reproduce an approximation to a large scale refining process of this kind in the laboratory, but to then modify this, to define and control and measure the significant kinetic variables is perhaps not impossible, but nearly so.   As we formulate such tentative pictures of mechanism as are given in this paper, it is to be hoped that these will suggest simpler experiments that are more specific in nature.

Pehlke seems to be suggesting that because there is evidence that nitrogen absorption at a liquid iron interface is affected by oxygen that (1) the *converse* would be true and that (2) this concept can be transferred to the oxygen absorption at a *liquid slag* interface.   Neither one of these two steps of analogy is necessarily valid and both seem improbable to the authors.   The bottom blown air or steam-oxygen Bessemer processes and the top-blown oxygen processes all fail to reveal any definite indication of limitation by oxygen reaction rate with either slag or metal.   The postulated reaction

$$2Fe^{2+} + 1/2O_2 \longrightarrow 2Fe^{3+} + O^{2-}$$

at a liquid slag-gas interface involves a large amount of heat evolved.   There is normally a high concentration of ferrous ions present, and a rather simple mechanism can be imagined, though it is true that we do not yet know much about the true mechanisms of heterogeneous reactions at high temperatures.   Known to the authors are only a very few that seem definitely slow, such as the reduction of Si from a liquid silicate slag and the absorption of nitrogen into solid and, probably, liquid iron.   The reaction above is not the sort one would expect to be slow.   Experiments with emulsified slag-metal systems which give indications of the order of a 1000-fold increase in rates of interphase-surface reactions point toward reaction surface area and convection as limiting-rate factors, even where concentrations are low and close to equilibrium.

As to criteria for distinguishing diffusion from chemical rate control, Pehlke's points are well taken though involving great difficulty in application. The whole carbon boil process here requires stirring by a boil involving bubble nucleation and the system has inertia, in a sense. If one could obtain a definite velocity field in the gas above the slag, a sudden change could merely transfer the limiting diffusion film from the gas to some boundary in the two-liquid system. So, in general, mass-transfer calculations become difficult. Our small heats gave no indication that the boil rate falls off appreciably with decreasing temperature, at least until the bath begins to freeze or become mushy. There is need for further experiment with the effect of temperature and of varying gas composition. Thus, in principle, we are largely in agreement with Mr. Pehlke on the kind of further study need in this field and his comments are much appreciated.

SECTION XI: DESULFURIZA-
TION IN THE STEEL PLANT

. . . .

Sulfur Control in the Blast Furnace When Using Sinter Burdens

J. G. SIBAKIN, J. C. McKAY, and P. M. AUDETTE

Metallurgical Department, The Steel Company of Canada, Ltd.,
Hamilton, Ontario, Canada

Abstract

Blast furnace operating data have been used to determine the influence of slag composition and temperature upon the desulfurizing power of blast furnace slags.

The lime-silica ratio appeared to be the best approximate method for expressing slag basicity.

From a quantitative relationship for the desulfurizing power of blast furnace slags the composition limits for slag and for self-fluxing sinter have been found.

INTRODUCTION

The sulfur content of the hot metal produced in the blast furnace is controlled by varying the basicity of the slag. The usual method of controlling the basicity of the slag is to increase the amount of flux in the charge when the sulfur content of the hot metal exceeds a specified value and to decrease the amount of flux when the slag appears to be "limy," which indicates that the sulfur content of the hot metal may be very low. This method of sulfur control introduces a time lag as a period of some 8 hr or more is required for the flux to descend through the furnace. This may result in several casts exceeding the maximum sulfur limit, particularly if the first increase of the flux to the charge was insufficient.

A better method of controlling the sulfur content of the hot metal would be to have the correct proportion of flux intimately mixed with the ores prior to their being charged into the blast furnace. The use of fluxed sinter provides such a possibility. Satisfactory sulfur control, however, will only be achieved when the basicity of the

1183

sinter used can be kept within the required limits, and when these limits are known.

The limits of sinter basicity can be determined by a means of a large-scale experimental program. An example of this is shown by the Appleby-Frodingham Steel Company where experience in using 100% sinter burdens has shown that a lime-silica ratio of 1.25 or slightly greater is desirable for producing good quality iron.[1] The operators at the steel plant in Magnitogorsk, presumably from experience, have also found that a lime-silica ratio of 1.25–1.45 is desirable.[2] The limits of basicity and the ratio used for expressing basicity may well depend upon the composition of the raw materials (different magnesia and alumina contents) employed by a particular steel company and therefore each company may have to establish the limits of basicity that are applicable to their practice.

A more desirable approach to that of a prolonged trial and error program using various sinter compositions would be to determine the quantitative influence of slag composition upon the desulfurizing power of blast furnace slags; i.e., sulfur partition ratio. From the relationship obtained, the composition limits of the sinter may be determined by means of a material balance. This is the approach that will be outlined in this study.

SELECTION OF VARIABLES

In numerous studies published on the subject of slag/metal reactions in the blast furnace, the following variables have been considered to influence the desulfurizing power of the slag: (1) Operating variables—sulfur load, slag volume, interfacial area, reaction time, and reaction temperature. (2) Metal composition—C, Si, P, and Mn. (3) Slag composition—MnO, FeO, CaO, MgO, SiO$_2$, and Al$_2$O$_3$.

Fortunately, many of these variables can be regarded as having little influence upon the desulfurization of basic blast furnace iron, either because of the small variance that occurs in practice or because of the small magnitude of their effect. All the variables listed above, with the exception of CaO, MgO, SiO$_2$, Al$_2$O$_3$, and reaction temperature may be excluded. The reasons for their exclusion are discussed below.

Sulfur Load and Slag Volume

The variables, sulfur load and slag volume, may be related to the sulfur content of the hot metal as follows:

$$S = (S)/100 \, V + [S]/100 \cdot 2000 + L$$

where S is the weight of sulfur in the charge, lb/ton hot metal, V is the weight of slag, lb/ton hot metal, (S) is the percentage of sulfur in the slag, $[S]$ is the percentage of sulfur in the hot metal, and L is the sulfur lost to the gases, lb/ton hot metal.

The amount of sulfur lost to the gases may be relatively constant and small. Thus, L can be assumed to be a constant and may be incorporated into S as $S' = S - L$, where S' is the sulfur load in the furnace in pound per ton of hot metal.

$$\therefore S' \cong (S)/100 \, V + [S]/100 \cdot 2000$$

or

$$[S] \cong 100 \, S'V/\{(S)/[S]\} + (2000/V) \tag{1}$$

From Eq. (1) it may be seen that the sulfur content of the metal is directly proportional to the sulfur load and indirectly proportional to the sulfur partition ratio and the slag volume.

As pointed out by Brower and Larsen[3] slag volume (V) and sulfur load (S') are not independent of each other in practice. An increase in slag volume necessitates an increase in coke consumption and therefore an increase in the sulfur load since about 90% of the sulfur load is attributable to the coke. Conversely, a decrease in slag volume permits a decrease in coke consumption and therefore in sulfur load. Because of this, the ratio S'/V tends to vary within rather narrow limits and the influence of the slag volume and sulfur load upon the sulfur content of the hot metal may be relatively small. If the above is true, the sulfur partition ratio should be strongly related to the sulfur content of the hot metal regardless of the normal variation in slag volume encountered in practice, and the relationship should be in the form of a hyperbola (see section entitled "Interpretation of Data").

The sulfur partition ratio is assumed to be independent of the sulfur load, an assumption that may not be strictly correct. Hatch and Chipman[4] found that for a given slag basicity the sulfur partition ratio increased with increasing sulfur content of the slag. (Their slags were believed to be at equilibrium with the molten metal.) This suggests that the partition ratio may be a function of the sulfur content of the slag. In practice, however, the sulfur content of the slag remains relatively constant as would be expected, since the ratio of sulfur load to slag volume (S'/V) is relatively constant. The dependence of the partition ratio upon the sulfur content of the slag does not, therefore, have to be considered.

Interfacial Area

Derge, Philbrook, and Goldman[5] maintain that the net rate of desulfurization of iron by slag is directly proportional to the area of slag-metal interface. This implies that in practice the area of the blast furnace hearth may be a factor in desulfurization. This, however, is doubtful as the true interfacial area is the sum of the hearth area and the surface areas of all the metal droplets passing through the slag layer, the latter area being very much greater than the former. The hearth area, then, may only be a minor variable.

Reaction Time

At the Steel Company of Canada the furnaces are tapped six times a day when using an ore burden and seven times a day when using a sinter burden. The slag formed in the hearth is flushed once at the mid-period between casts. A small portion of the slag then is in contact with the metal for a maximum period of 2 hr when using an ore burden and 1 hr and 43 min when using a sinter burden. The additional 17 min of reaction time when using an ore burden did not appear to affect the degree of desulfurization obtained.

Reaction Temperature and Carbon

Morris and Buehl[6] found that the activity of sulfur in iron increases considerably with increasing percentages of carbon in iron and slightly with increasing iron temperatures. At the saturation point for carbon in iron increases with a rise in temperature (the phosphorus content being relatively constant in basic iron), the temperature of the iron may be considered as having a strong influence upon the activity of sulfur since the carbon content of the iron is a function of temperature.

Silicon and Phosphorus

From the studies of Sherman and Chipman,[7] silicon and phosphorus are known to strongly increase the activity of sulfur in iron, but the increase is negligible for the variance and for the amounts of these elements present in basic iron; i.e., 1.5% Si max and 0.13% P max.

Manganese and Manganese Oxide

Wentrup[8] and others have found that manganese is not an efficient desulfurizer except at high manganese contents and very low metal temperature; i.e., just above the liquidus temperature of the metal. Grant et al.[9] showed that the activity coefficient of sulfur in the iron is actually decreased slightly by the presence of manganese. Because of this and because the variance in the amount of manganese in the hot metal is small, manganese may be neglected as a variable in desulfurization of iron.

The manganese oxide content of blast furnace slags is low and relatively constant owing to the fact that MnO is readily reduced in blast furnace slags. The small amount that remains unreduced in the slag probably has only a very small influence upon desulfurization, an influence so slight that Grant et al.[9] could not measure it.

Ferrous Oxide

The ferrous oxide in blast furnace slags is also low and relatively constant and may therefore be assumed to have only a minor effect upon the desulfurization of iron.

Major Variables

The only variables besides the reaction temperature that may be considered as having a major influence upon the desulfurizing power of blast furnace slags are the lime, silica, alumina, and magnesia contents of the slag. The work of Holbrook and Joseph[10] showed clearly that each slag oxide has its own effect upon desulfurization and that the degree of this effect is not constant for all ranges of composition. Their work ruled out the use of simple empirical ratios to express basicity for all ranges of composition, although for relatively narrow ranges of composition the ratios used may be sufficiently accurate for practical control purposes.

TABLE I

Variation in Composition of Slags from Consecutive Casts

		SiO$_2$, % ($\bar{x} \pm 3S$)[a]	Al$_2$O$_3$, % ($\bar{x} \pm 3S$)	CaO, % ($\bar{x} \pm 3S$)	MgO, % ($\bar{x} \pm 3S$)	S, % ($\bar{x} \pm 3S$)	S, % ($\bar{x} \pm 3S$)
		Slag					Metal
Cast No. 994	Flush slag	35.76 ± 0.66	10.16 ± 0.74	37.10 ± 0.77	11.35 ± 0.62	1.96 ± 0.12	
	Tap slag	35.53 ± 1.81	10.04 ± 1.66	37.09 ± 1.13	11.77 ± 1.06	1.96 ± 0.24	0.028 ± 0.000
Cast No. 995	Flush slag	35.19 ± 1.73	10.22 ± 0.41	37.53 ± 1.58	11.41 ± 0.80	1.96 ± 0.13	
	Tap slag	35.72 ± 0.59	10.14 ± 0.84	36.91 ± 0.50	11.75 ± 0.78	1.89 ± 0.11	0.026 ± 0.000

[a] Here, S = standard deviation.

In this study, therefore, the temperature of the slag (reaction temperature) and the lime, silica, alumina, and magnesia contents of the slag were selected as the major variables which may affect the desulfurizing power of blast furnace slags.

SAMPLING AND CHEMICAL ANALYSIS

To determine both the variation in slag composition throughout the period between casts and the accuracy of the analytical techniques employed, samples of slag, representing the first, middle, and last portions of the flush and tap slags, and samples of iron were obtained from two consecutive casts. Each sample thus obtained was split after suitable preparation into two parts and each part was analyzed. In this way, 24 chemical determinations were carried out on the flush and tap slags of the two casts.

The results of the chemical analysis showed that there was no significant difference in slag composition between the first, middle, and last portions of the flush and tap slags. In fact, as may be seen in Table I, there was no significant difference in composition either between the flush and tap slags of one cast or between those of the consecutive casts. Although it is not likely that the slags of consecutive casts would always be so similar it was assumed that the flush and tap slags for any given cast would in most cases be similar. On this assumption, a sample of slag taken any time during the flush would be representative of the slag in the hearth of the furnace during the period between casts.

It is of interest to note the maximum variance in the sulfur partition ratio that is possible through analytical error. In Table II,

TABLE II
Possible Error in Partition Ratio

		Max ratio $(S)/S$ max	Min ratio $(S)/S$ min	Range (max R — min R)
Cast No. 994	Flush slag	$2.08/0.028 \pm 74.3$	$1.84/0.028 = 65.7$	8.6
	Tap slag	$2.20/0.028 \pm 78.6$	$1.72/0.028 = 61.4$	17.2
Cast No. 995	Flush slag	$2.09/0.026 \pm 80.4$	$1.83/0.026 = 70.4$	10.0
	Tap slag	$2.00/0.026 \pm 76.9$	$1.78/0.026 = 68.5$	8.4

the maximum ratio is the maximum possible slag sulfur content ($\bar{x} +$ 3S) divided by the minimum possible metal sulfur content ($\bar{x} - 3S$) and the minimum ratio is the minimum slag sulfur content ($\bar{x} - 3S$) divided by the maximum metal sulfur content ($\bar{x} + 3S$). The range of 17.2 in the sulfur partition ratio listed in Table II indicates that any quantitative relationship for predicting the sulfur partition ratio may have a prediction deviation of ± 8.6 due to analytical errors in the analysis of the sulfur alone. This indicates the possible range of analytical accuracy that was available for this investigation.

SLAG TEMPERATURE MEASUREMENT

The temperature of the slag in the blast furnace hearth may be expected to have a strong influence upon the sulfur partition ratio,[10] and as it is difficult to measure this temperature, some reliable index must be used. The temperature of the flush slag as it issues from the furnace was believed to be a reliable index of hearth temperature.

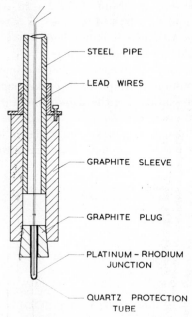

STEEL PIPE

LEAD WIRES

GRAPHITE SLEEVE

GRAPHITE PLUG

PLATINUM – RHODIUM JUNCTION

QUARTZ PROTECTION TUBE

Fig. 1. A schematic drawing of the thermocouple assembly used to measure the flush slag temperature.

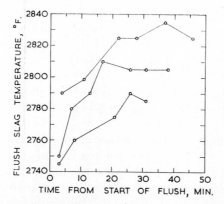

Fig. 2. The variation in flush slag temperature throughout three flush periods as measured 6 ft from the cinder notch.

The temperature of the flush slag was measured by means of an immersion thermocouple. A schematic drawing of this thermocouple is shown in Figure 1.

The variation in slag temperature during a flush was determined for a number of flush periods. The variation for three of these flush periods is illustrated in Figure 2 from which it may be seen that the temperature of the flush slag in the runner 6 ft from the cinder notch rises until a maximum is reached in about 20 min and remains relatively constant thereafter. It would appear that a period of 20 min is required before the runner has been heated to a stable temperature which will be slightly lower than that of the slag.

The temperature of the slag, when steady temperature conditions prevailed, was also measured for a number of flush periods at four locations in the slag runner: 1, 6, 13, and 25 ft from the cinder notch. In most instances, the temperatures obtained at the 1-, 6-, and 13-ft locations were not significantly different from each other, but at the 25-ft location the temperature obtained varied considerably and appeared to be dependent upon the rate of slag flow.

From the preliminary slag temperature tests it was decided to measure the temperature of the slag at least 20 min after the start of flush at a location 6 ft from the cinder notch. The 6-ft location was selected as it was convenient and safe, and as the rate of slag flow at this point did not appear to affect the temperature readings obtained. The temperature of the slag was measured twice per flush and the highest value recorded was assumed to be the correct temperature since there is less chance that the higher value would be in error. The lower value may be obtained either because the runner had not yet approached the temperature of the slag or because the tip of the thermocouple touched the bottom of the runner.

Samples of slag for chemical analysis were collected by means of a spoon ladle at the same time as the temperature measurements were made.

In using the flush slag temperature as an index of hearth temperature, the assumption that the hearth temperature remained relatively constant during the period between consecutive casts was made. It was not possible to check this assumption by comparing flush and tap slag temperatures as steady state temperature conditions for the

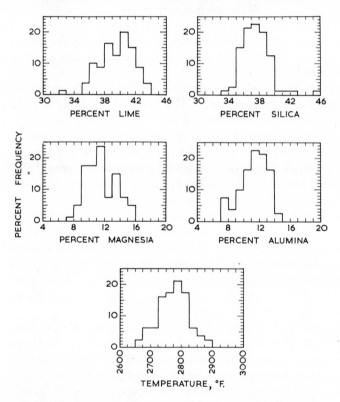

Fig. 3. The frequency histograms of the data used in this study.

tap slag were not obtained at the locations where the tap slag temperature could be measured safely.

VARIANCE OF DATA

The data collected for this study consisted of 80 values, the histograms of the data used being shown in Figure 3. The percentages of the four main oxides contained in the slags shown in Figure 3 have been corrected so that the sum of the four equals 100%. This was done in order to place all the slags on a comparable basis since the other constituents such as FeO, MnO, and S are present in small and approximately constant amounts and produce only minor changes in the desulfurizing power of the slag.

The percentages of the four oxides SiO_2, Al_2O_3, CaO, and MgO vary within a rather confined range of composition. Any quantitative relationship developed from this data would of course only be applicable to the same limited range.

The temperature of the flush slag varied over a fairly wide range; i.e., 2650–2900°F although the most frequent temperatures recorded were in the neighborhood of 2775°F.

INTERPRETATION OF DATA

As previously mentioned, if the ratio of sulfur load to slag volume is relatively constant, the sulfur partition ratio should be a hyperbolic type function of the hot metal sulfur content. The sulfur content of the hot metal was therefore plotted against the sulfur partition ratio, as shown in Figure 4. The strong hyperbolic-type relationship between the sulfur partition ratio and the sulfur in the hot metal substantiates the belief that the ratio of the sulfur load to slag volume remains relatively constant in practice.

The relationship obtained applies only to the particular practice studied. If the sulfur content of the coke was substantially greater or less than that present in the coke used; i.e., about 1.2 to 1.3%, the sulfur content of the hot metal would have been greater or less, respectively, than that indicated by the mean line in Figure 4. This is indicated by the S'/V term of Eq. (1).

From Eq. (1) it then appears that it may be possible to establish the minimum slag volume required in order to obtain the desired sul-

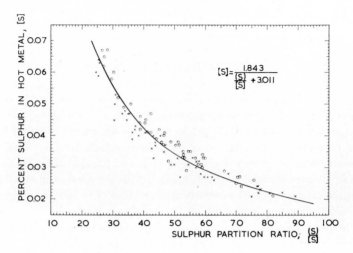

Fig. 4. The relationship between the sulfur partition ratio and the sulfur in the hot metal for B and C blast furnaces (O, C furnace; ✕, B furnace).

fur content of the hot metal when the coke analysis (sulfur load) and partition ratio (slag composition) are known.

It may be further observed in Figure 4 that the relationship for B and C furnaces are slightly different, a higher partition ratio being required in C furnace in order to maintain a similar hot metal sulfur content as that obtained in B furnace. If this difference were due to the difference in hearth diameters, the opposite condition would be expected to prevail as B furnace has a hearth diameter of 18 ft and C furnace $23^{1}/_{2}$ ft. No explanation for this difference has been established.

To arrive at a reasonable quantitative relationship from blast furnace data for predicting the influence of the major constituents in and the temperature of the slag upon the degree of desulfurization, statistical methods were used as no single variable may be maintained constant in practice.

Several attempts were made to interpret the data. The following equation derived by the method of least squares was considered to be the most reliable:

$$(S)/[S] =$$

$$(6 \times 10^{-4})[(\% \ CaO)^{3.53} \ (temp \ -2000°F)^{1.12}]/(\% \ SiO_2)^{2.55} \quad (2)$$

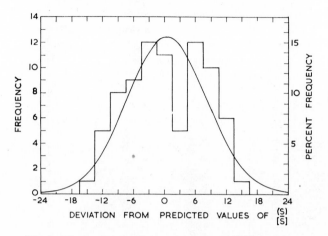

Fig. 5. The frequency histogram of the prediction errors.

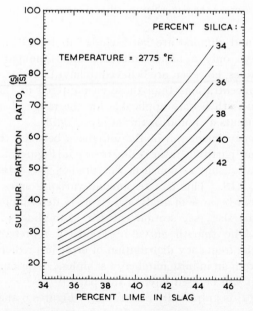

Fig. 6. The relationship between the sulfur partition ratio and the lime and silica contents of the slag when the temperature of the slag is 2775°F.

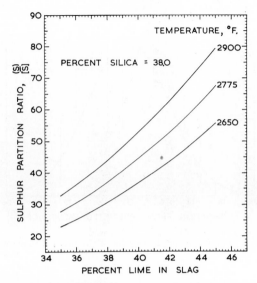

Fig. 7. The relationship between the sulfur partition ratio and the lime content and temperature of the slag when the silica content of the slag is 38.0%.

Magnesia and alumina are not included in Eq. (2) as they were found to have only a minor influence upon the partition ratio. These slag oxides, however, are believed to have an influence at higher and lower concentrations than those encountered in this study.[10,11] The equation is then only applicable for the range of alumina and magnesia contents as found in this study (Fig. 3).

The frequency histogram of the difference between the predicted and the actual partition ratio is illustrated in Figure 5. It appears that the relationship established will predict the actual partition ratio within ±18. This is a reasonable variance since an error of ±8.6 can occur because of analytical errors in determining the sulfur content of the slag (see section entitled "Sampling and Chemical Analysis"). The smooth curve in Figure 5 represents the best estimate of the frequency distribution of error in predicting the partition ratio from an infinite number of samples. This curve has been included as it will be used later in this paper.

Equation (2) is graphically illustrated in Figures 6 and 7. Figure 6 shows the change in partition ratio that occurs for given changes in the silica and lime contents of the slag when its temperature is main-

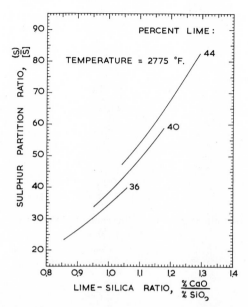

Fig. 8. The relationship between the sulfur partition ratio and the lime-silica ratio.

tained constant, and Figure 7 shows the change that occurs with changes in slag temperature for various lime contents when the silica content is maintained constant. From these figures, it is evident that a given sulfur partition ratio may be obtained in a number of ways.

The fact that magnesia and alumina did not appear to have much effect upon the desulfurizing power of the slag suggests that the lime-silica ratio preferred by the European steel industry for expressing basicity may be satisfactory for practical purposes.

For a given temperature, Eq. (2) may be rewritten as follows:

$$(S)/[S] \cong k(\% \text{ CaO}/\% \text{ SiO}_2)^{2.55} (\% \text{ CaO}) \qquad (3)$$

where $k = (6 \times 10^{-4})$ (temp $-2000°F)^{1.12}$. This equation, which has been plotted in Figure 8 for three concentrations of lime, suggests that the desulfurizing power of the slag is dependent upon the lime-silica ratio only when the lime content is constant. It appears that the lime-silica ratio may be satisfactory as a good approximation of blast furnace slag basicity. On the other hand, there seems to be

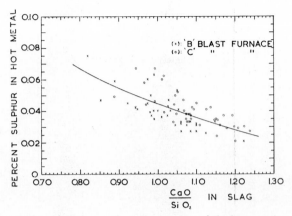

Fig. 9. The relationship between the sulfur content of the hot metal and the lime-
silica ratio of the slag.

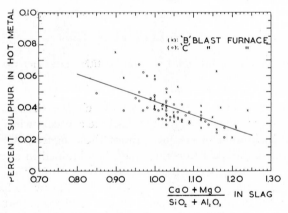

Fig. 10. The relationship between the sulfur content of the hot metal and the base
to acid ratio of the slag.

little justification for the use of the base to acid ratio in the particular
operation studied.

   The strong relationship existing between the sulfur partition ratio
and the sulfur content of metal allows a direct comparison of the slag
composition with the sulfur in the iron.   The direct comparison was
made in this case only for convenience.   In Figure 9 the sulfur in the
metal has been plotted against the lime to silica ratio and in Figure 10
against the base to acid ratio of the slag.   Both the degree of variance

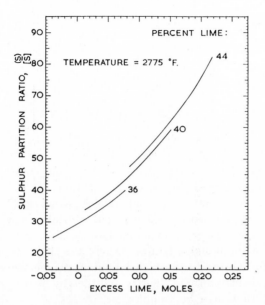

Fig. 11. The relationship between the sulfur partition ratio and the excess moles of lime in the slag.

(48.3% and 36.2%, respectively) explained by and the standard deviation ($\pm 0.008\%$ and $\pm 0.009\%$ S in the metal, respectively) obtained for the curves of best fit suggest that the lime to silica ratio seems to be a more reliable practical guide to evaluate the desulfurizing power of the slag than the base to acid ratio.   This applies, at least, for the range of MgO and Al_2O_3 that was available in our slags (Fig. 3).   The applicability of this simpler ratio for slags containing MgO and Al_2O_3 outside the range mentioned above should be checked in practice.

Assuming that the blast furnace slags encountered in practice are mainly bisilicates, it is reasonable to suggest that one mole of lime will neutralize one mole of silica.   (Magnesia and alumina within the range studied must be assumed to have neutralized each other.) The moles of lime in excess of that required to neutralize the silica is readily available in the slag to react with the sulfur in the iron and therefore on this premise the sulfur partition ratio should be a function of the excess moles of lime.   The relationship derived by means of Eq. (2) is shown in Figure 11.   Since the lines in Figure 11 do not coincide, it appears that the lime concentration may be a factor that should be considered in addition to the excess moles of lime.

Hatch and Chipman[4] in their experimental studies on blast furnace slags also found a fair correlation between the sulfur partition ratio and excess base taken as $(CaO + {}^2/_3MgO)-(SiO_2 + Al_2O_3)$.

APPLICATION OF RESULTS

In practice it is desirable to maintain the sulfur content of basic iron within the range 0.02–0.5%. Hot metal containing sulfur in excess of 0.05% will require additional refining time in the open hearth in order to meet the steel specifications for maximum sulfur content. A hot metal sulfur content of less than 0.02% is an indication that the composition region of either dicalcium silicate or periclase formation, where a small increase in lime content causes a sharp rise in the liquidus temperature of the slag,[11] is being closely approached. Owing to the higher liquidus temperatures of "limy" slags, crystals may form in the slag and thereby increase its viscosity to a point that may be troublesome.

A hot metal sulfur content of 0.02% and 0.05% is on the average equivalent to a sulfur partition ratio of 90 and 34, respectively (Fig. 4).

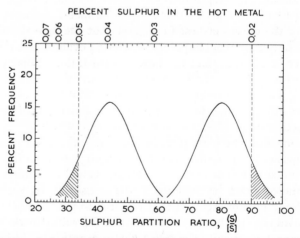

Fig. 12. The shaded bands represent 10% of the samples that will fall either above a 90 or below a 34 partition ratio when using Eq. (2) to predict sulfur partition ratios of 80 and 44, respectively.

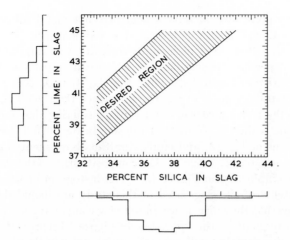

Fig. 13. A control chart for blast furnace slags containing 7–16% MgO and 7–15% Al₂O₃.

From the quantitative relationship it is possible to determine the combinations of silica, lime, and temperature that are permissible; i.e., partition ratio between 90 and 34.   The error in the relationship, however, must first be considered.   In Figure 12, curves of anticipated prediction errors (see Fig. 5) have been plotted against a scale of possible partition ratios.   The curves have been located on the scale so that only 10% of all cases will fall above a partition ratio of 90 and only 10% will fall below a partition ratio of 34.   This condition restricted the extreme values of the sulfur partition ratio to 80 and 44.   The curves could have been drawn so that at no time would the limits 90 and 34 be exceeded, but this was felt to be overly restrictive and not practical.   In using the relationship established [Eq. (2)] then, the limits to be considered are 80 and 44 rather than 90 and 34.

The temperature of the slag in the hearth is not easily controlled so a further restriction upon the composition of the slag must be imposed in order to compensate for changes in slag temperature. When the slag is "hot," a partition ratio of 90 or slightly greater is not too serious from the point of view of the formation of troublesome slags.   A temperature of 2875°F was therefore chosen to be used in predicting the slag compositions which would give a partition ratio of 80.

For any given slag basicity the highest hot metal sulfur contents will be obtained with the lowest slag temperature; i.e., 2650°F. In order to be sure that high sulfur contents will not be obtained, the lowest permissible slag basicity which can be used is that which gives a partition ratio of 44 when the slag temperature is 2650°F. A temperature of 2675°F was chosen rather than 2650°F as it was felt that the restriction was too severe considering that for only 2% of the time is the temperature of the slag below 2675°F (see Fig. 3).

By means of Eq. (2) and employing the above-mentioned restrictions, the acceptable range of slag compositions was determined and is shown graphically in Figure 13. The histogram of the silica and lime contents of the slags used in this study are included in Figure 13 to show that the range of acceptable slag compositions is sufficiently wide. Any point on the upper line in Figure 13 represents the composition of a slag that will give a partition ratio of 80 when the slag temperature is 2875°F. For the same composition but a lower slag temperature, say 2650°F, the partition ratio will be less than 80 but greater than 44. Conversely, any point on the lower limit line represents the composition of a slag that will give a partition ratio of 44 when the slag temperature is 2675°F. For the same composition but higher slag temperature, say 2900°F, the partition ratio will be greater than 44 but less than 80.

If the temperature of the slag is higher than 2650°F, all the slags of the compositions represented by the cross-hatched region in Figure 13, will be sufficiently fluid for smooth blast furnace operation since

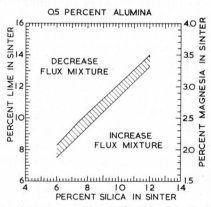

Fig. 14. The sinter composition control chart for 0.5% alumina.

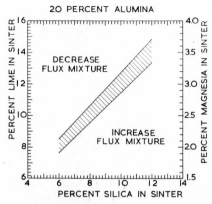

Fig. 15. The sinter composition control chart for 2.0% alumina.

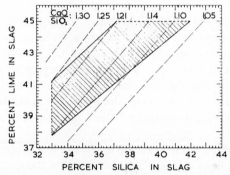

Fig. 16. The slag composition control chart showing several lines of constant lime-
silica ratios.

the desired composition region was established on the basis of slags
obtained in practice.

From Figure 13 it is possible to deduce the composition limits for
self-fluxing sinter if the burden ratio for a 100% sinter operation is
known and a coke composition is assumed. From trials carried out
on B blast furnace, it is known that the burden ratio for a 100%
sinter operation is in the range of 2.6 to 3.0.[12] By carrying out the
required raw material balance (see Appendix for method of computation) the composition limits for self-fluxing sinter were determined.

It was found that separate sinter composition control charts are
required for any given alumina content, Figures 14 and 15 being the

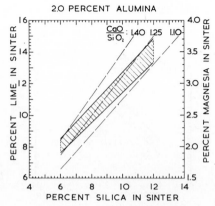

Fig. 17. The sinter composition control chart for 2.0% alumina showing several lines of constant lime-silica ratios.

control charts for 0.5 and 2.0% alumina, respectively.   The required percentage of magnesia in the sinter as shown in the control charts is related to the lime content of the sinter in the proportion: one part magnesia to four parts lime   This ratio corresponds to a 50/50 mixture of limestone and dolomite in the sinter feed and was chosen in order to duplicate the normal practice employed at the Steel Company of Canada; i.e., MgO content of the slag between 8 and 16% (see Fig. 3).

Any sinter which is used exclusively in the blast furnace along with coke and which has a composition that is within the control limits indicated in Figures 14 and 15 will yield upon smelting a slag that has a composition that falls within the limits shown in Figure 13.

Since the lime-silica ratio was found to be a reasonable ratio for expressing slag basicity, it is of interest to determine the lime-silica ratios that most nearly approximate the composition control limits established for slag and sinter shown in Figures 13 and 15.   It appears from Figure 16 that slags having a lime-silica basicity ratio of 1.14 to 1.21 will have the correct desulfurizing power.   In the case of sinter, as may be seen in Figure 17, only a lime-silica ratio of 1.25 is within the control regions for all ranges of sinter composition.

DISCUSSION

Although the results of this paper are not considered to be valid for any blast furnace operation other than that from which the data were obtained, the method used to interpret the data and derive the control limits is believed to have a general application.

From the results of this paper it appears that the control of the sulfur content of pig iron when operating on a 100% sinter burden may be entirely in the hands of the sinter plant operators, if the analysis of the sinter when produced can be determined quickly. The spectrochemical x-ray fluorescence analyzer that has been used by the cement industry may be suitable for this purpose as it will make a complete chemical analysis in 2.5 min.[13]

The raw material feed system in the sinter plant at the Steel Company of Canada consists of seven bins with feeder tables in line feeding onto a single gathering belt. The speed of all the feeder tables is controlled collectively. The feeder table for coke breeze, however, has an additional topping control which permits changes in the coke to be made without changing the proportion of the other materials in the feed. The individual feed rates are controlled by manually operating an adjustable gate on the table concerned in conjunction with tray weighings on the gathering belt. The proportion of fluxes, ores, and coke breeze in the feed may be determined by placing a tray on the gathering belt and allowing it to pass under each feeder table. The proportion of the material in the feed is thus found by dividing the weight collected in the tray from the table concerned by the weight of material obtained in a similar manner from all of the feeders. It may take $1/2$ hr or more to adjust the feeders and to determine the proportion of raw materials in the feed.

From the main collecting belt the feed passes via a cross belt to the main rising conveyor belt. The sinter fines ($-5/16$ in.) and filter cake are added to the feed on the cross belt.

A period of 45 min is required for the feed to pass through all stages of processing (i.e., mixing, sintering, cooling, and screening) and return again to the feed on the cross belt in the form of sinter fines. If the proportioning of the raw materials in the sinter feed is changed; e.g., higher percentage of fluxes, it will then take about $1^1/2$ hr for the composition of the sinter going to the blast furnaces to reflect fully that of the sinter feed because of the time required for the sinter fines to recirculate through the plant. A sample of sinter taken after a change in the sinter feed composition but before $1^1/2$ hr has elapsed is not, therefore, truly representative of the sinter being produced. After $1^1/2$ hr have passed, a sample of sinter may be obtained for analysis.   In order to have a representative sample, fractions of the sample should be collected frequently during a $1/2$-hr period since the rate of discharge of the various materials from the table feeders fluctuates.

When a representative sample has been collected it must be coned, quartered, crushed, ground, and briquetted prior to x-ray analysis. The time required for sample preparation may be about 1 hr.

It is apparent that the sinter may not be analyzed as frequently as might be desired.   A period of 4 hr would seem to be a reasonable estimate of the time required between the analyses of the sinter. Since the time between consecutive casts in the blast furnace is usually about 4 hr, a period of 4 hr between the analyses may not be too long for effective sinter composition control.

When the composition of the sinter being produced is made known to the operator, he may compare it with the correct control chart; i.e., the control chart that is applicable for the alumina content of the sinter.   If the sinter composition is only slightly out of the control region, no changes to the sinter feed need be made.   When the analysis is repeated 4 hr later and the composition of the sinter is still slightly out of control in the same direction, the required change should be made to the amount of "flux mixture" in the sinter feed. The changes made to the feed should always be small in order to avoid over-shooting the control region.

At times it may be necessary to alter the proportions of dolomite and limestone in the flux mixture since the lime and magnesia contents of either the ores or the fluxing materials may change.

The "down-time" of the x-ray analyzer can be utilized to determine the composition of the blast furnace and open hearth slags, the analysis obtained serving to control the blast furnace and open hearth operations.

In deriving the control charts, a coke composition believed to be typical of that found in practice was used; i.e., 5.15% SiO_2, 2.25% Al_2O_3, 0.6% CaO, and 0.4% MgO.   If the composition of the coke changes, then the control charts derived no longer apply.   The composition of the coke, however, would have to change by an appreciable amount before a change in the control charts would be warranted as the ash in the coke only accounts for about 8 to 14% of the slag weight.

A burden ratio of 2.8 has been used for the development of the control charts.   As will be shown in the Appendix, the burden ratio has only a very small effect upon the control charts shown in Figures 14 and 15.   This makes them applicable to the whole range of practices which use a 50–50 mix of limestone and dolomite when producing self-fluxing sinter.

CONCLUSIONS

1.   The variables selected in this study as having a major influence upon the desulfurizing power of blast furnace slags were the slag temperature and the lime, magnesia, alumina, and silica contents of the slag.

2.   Only the slag temperature and the lime and silica contents of the slag were found to affect desulfurization.

3.   The lime-silica ratio was found to be the simplest way of satisfactorily expressing the basicity of blast furnace slags.

4.   The base to acid ratio appears to be a less satisfactory index of the desulfurizing power of the slag than the lime-silica ratio.

5.   The excess moles of lime in the slag appeared to be a factor in the desulfurization of iron.

6.   Composition control limits for blast furnace slags and self-fluxing sinter have been established.   If the composition limits established can be maintained in practice, the sulfur content of the hot metal will seldom be outside of the range 0.02 to 0.05%.

7.   The lime-silica ratio for self-fluxing sinter (100% sinter burden) should be 1.25 and for blast furnace slags should be between 1.14 and 1.21.

8.   In order to use the composition control limits established in this study, a means for rapidly analyzing the sinter is required.

9.   A sample of sinter for analysis may not be obtained more frequently than once every 4 hr.

10.   The suggested method of sulfur control is only applicable to 100% self-fluxing sinter practice and then only when limestone and dolomite are used in equal quantities in the sinter mix.

APPENDIX

The purpose of the following computations is to determine the sinter composition when the desired composition of the slag (see Fig. 13) and the analysis of the coke is known.   In order to carry out the required computations it is assumed: (1) that the composition of the coke is constant and contains 5.15% SiO_2, 2.25% Al_2O_3, 0.6% CaO, and 0.4% MgO; and (2) that approximately 10.6% of the total silica in the burden is reduced and therefore 89.4% of the silica entering the furnace leaves in the slag.

The amount of silica reduced varies between 8 and 13%. The higher percentages occur when the ratio of lime to silica in the burden is low, the coke rate is high, and/or when the blast temperature is high. The lower percentages occur when the ratio of lime to silica is high, the coke rate is low, and/or when the blast temperature is low.

For brevity, the following symbols are used in the computations: c is CaO, %; s is SiO_2, %; a is Al_2O_3, %; m is MgO, %; S is the weight of slag; b is the burden ratio (wt sinter/wt coke); A (subscript) is the sinter (agglomerate); and S (subscript) is the slag.

The relationship between the gangue oxides in the sinter and those in the slag for a basis of 100 lb of coke may be found as follows:

$$\text{Wt Sinter} = 100b$$

$$\text{Wt CaO in slag} = c_S/100 \times S$$

$$= 0.6 + 100b\, c_A/100 = 0.6 + b\, c_A \quad (A1)$$

$$\text{Wt } SiO_2 \text{ in slag} = s_S/100 \times S = 0.894[5.15 + b\, s_A]$$

$$= 4.6041 + 0.894b\, s_A \quad (A2)$$

$$\text{Wt MgO in slag} = m_S/100 \times S = 0.4 + b\, m_A \quad (A3)$$

$$\text{Wt } Al_2O_3 \text{ in slag} = a_S/100 \times S = 2.25 + b\, a_A \quad (A4)$$

The sum of Eqs. (A1) to (A4) gives the weight of slag in terms of the percentages of the four oxides in the sinter.

$$S = c_S/100 \times S + s_S/100 \times S + a_S/100 \times S + m_S/100 \times S$$

$$= 7.8541 + b\, c_A + b\, a_A + n\, m_A + 0.894b\, s_A$$

(Note: $c_S + s_S + a_S + m_S = 100\%$.)

The relationship between the oxides in the slag to that in the sinter then may be found as follows:

$$c_S = (c_S \times S)/S$$

$$= [(0.6 + b\, c_A)/7.8541 + b\, c_A + b\, a_A + b\, m_A + 0.894b\, s_A] \times 100$$

Collecting terms:

$$[b - (100b/c_S)]d_A + b\,a_A + b\,m_A + 0.894s_A = (60/c_S) - 7.8541$$

Similarly for s_S:

$$b\,(c_A) + b\,a_A + b\,m_A + [0.894b - (89.4b/s_S)]s_A$$
$$= 460.41/s_S - 7.8541$$

Since the MgO content of the slag must be similar to that encountered in practice the ratio c_A to m_A has to be equal to 4. This is equivalent to using a flux mixture in the sinter feed containing equal amounts of limestone and dolomite. Therefore, since $m_A = c_A/4$ the above equations become:

$$\tfrac{5}{4}b - (100b/c_S)\,c_A + b\,a_A + 0.894b\,s_A = (60/c_S) - 7.8541$$

$$\tfrac{5}{4}b\,c_A + b\,a_A + 0.894b - (89.4b/s_S)\,s_A = (460.41/s_S) - 7.8541$$

From Figure 13 various values of c_S and s_S may be selected on the limit lines of the desired slag region. Then by assuming various values of c_A for any specific value of a_A the values of s_A and m_A may be determined to give the desired sinter compositions. The burden ratio was taken to be equal to 2.8 when carrying out the computations for Figures 14 and 15. Burden ratios of 2.6 and 3.0 change the control charts by $\pm 0.1\%$ CaO which is not enough to consider burden ratio as an addition control variable.

References

1. Ayres, H. S., "Blast Furnace Practice Using Sinter Burdens," Deuxieme Symposium International Sur L Agglomeration Des Minerais De Fer (preprint).

2. "Iron and Steelmaking in the U.S.S.R., Ural Section," British Iron and Steel Research Assocn., Feb., 1957.

3. Brower, T. E., and B. M. Larsen, Trans. Am. Inst. Mining Met. Engrs., 191, 1163 (1951).

4. Hatch, G. G., and J. Chipman, Trans. Am. Inst. Mining Met. Engrs., 185, 274 (1949).

5. Derge, G., W. O. Philbrook, and K. M. Goldman, Trans. Am. Inst. Mining Met. Engrs., 188, 1111 (1950).

6. Morris, J. P., and R. C. Buehl, Trans. Am. Inst. Mining Met. Engrs., 188, 317 (1950).

7. Sherman, C. W., and J. Chipman, Trans. Am. Inst. Mining Met. Engrs., 194, 597 (1952).

8. Wentrup, Ing. H., *The Iron and Steel Institute Carnegie Scholarship Memoirs*, vol. 24, 1935, p. 103.

9. Grant, N. J., U. Kalling, and J. Chipman, *Trans. Am. Inst. Mining Met. Engrs.*, **191,** 666 (1951).

10. Holbrook, W. F., and T. L. Joseph, *Trans. Am. Inst. Mining Met. Engrs.*, **120,** 99 (1936).

11. Osborn, E. F., R. C. Devries, K. H. Gee, and H. M. Kraner, *Trans. Am. Inst. Mining Met. Engrs.*, **200,** 33 (1954).

12. "Experience with Self-Fluxing Sinter at the Steel Company of Canada, Ltd.," 26th Blast Furnace Conf. of British Iron and Steel Research Assocn. (preprint).

13. Andermann, G., J. L. Jones, and E. Davidson, "The Evaluation of the PQX for the Analysis of Cements and Related Materials," 7th Ann. Conf. on Industrial Application of X-ray Analysis (preprint).

Discussion

J. Chipman (*MIT*): The partition of sulfur between slag and metal depends upon the properties of the slag and upon those of the metal. The authors have given a very adequate discussion and have shown a very valuable application of what is known concerning the effects of slag variables. They have also indicated the nature of some of the metal variables involved. One of these, however, has been overlooked; namely, the oxygen potential of the metal.

The actual oxygen content of metal in the blast furnace is so small that analytical controls are out of the question. There is, nevertheless, an oxygen potential to be reckoned with since the reduction reactions do not all come to equilibrium with the coke which is present. The overall transfer of sulfur from metal to slag may be thought of as a result of reaction (D1):

$$[S] + (O'') = (S'') + [O] \tag{1}$$

Sulfur in the metal reacts with oxide ion in the slag to produce sulfide ion in the slag and to increase the oxygen potential of the metal. This increase is largely offset by a subsequent reaction with carbon. For a given slag, the sulfur partition ratio is higher the lower the oxygen potential of the system.

Since the oxygen potential is not determinable directly by analysis, secondary indicators are useful. A very useful indicator is the manganese ratio as pointed out by N. J. Grant, J. W. Dowding, and R. J. Murphy [*Trans. Am. Inst. Mining Met. Engrs.*, **197,** 1451 (1953)]. They have shown that the ratio $(\% \text{ Mn})/[\% \text{ Mn}]$ is able in many instances to predict the desulfurization ratio. It will be interesting to know whether this indicator has been studied by the authors and whether it might not be used as a means for further improving the sulfur partition ratio.

J. G. Sibakin, J. C. McKay, and **P. M. Audette:** Dr. Chipman has raised a question as to why oxygen potential, described approximately by the manganese ratio, was not considered as variable for predicting the sulfur partition ratio.

In the work of N. J. Grant, U. Kalling, and J. Chipman [*Trans. Am. Inst. Mining Met. Engrs.*, **191,** 666 (1951)] and of N. J. Grant, J. W. Dowding, and R. J. Murphy [*Trans. Am. Inst. Mining Met. Engrs.*, **197,** 1451 (1953)] the presence of manganese oxide in blast furnace type slags appeared to slow down the desulfurization process. The ratio $(S)/[S]$ varied inversely with the ratio $(Mn)/[Mn]$. Since they could select and maintain any manganese ratio in their laboratory experiments, the manganese ratio could be regarded as a process control variable affecting desulfurization.

In the blast furnace system, however, the manganese ratio is not regulated easily. It is not held under control at any time during the process by the blast furnace operator. Moreover, the manganese ratio is influenced by many process variables that also affect the sulfur ratio.

The manganese ratio is believed to reflect the oxygen potential of the hot metal. It should also follow that the oxygen potential of the slag would influence the oxygen potential of the hot metal, as a result of an equilibrium in the transfer of oxygen across the slag-metal interface. The oxygen potential of the slag, expressed in terms of the oxygen attraction of basic and acid slag components (M. Rey, "Les Idées Modernes sur la Constitution des Laitiers Fondus et l'Activité Thermodynamique des Constituents des Laitiers," CESSID, 1954, pp. 14–19), may be considered a function of the main slag constituents CaO, MgO, SiO_2, and Al_2O_3.

The slag composition would determine, then, the oxygen equilibrium of the slag-metal system and, indirectly, the oxygen potential of the hot metal and the manganese ratio. The slag composition, similarly, would influence the sulfur partition ratio.

Some relationship was expected between the manganese ratio $(Mn)/[Mn]$ and the sulfur ratio $(S)/[S]$, since each ratio depended upon the slag composition. A study of our blast furnace data was revealed a strong inverse relation between the sulfur ratio and the manganese ratio.

However, the manganese ratio could not be considered as a truly independent variable in predicting desulfurization, together with % CaO, % SiO_2, or any other slag variable in the same equation. The dependence of the manganese ratio upon the ratio $(CaO)/(SiO_2)$, for example, was too significant, and would have introduced a duplication of the same variables, % CaO, % SiO_2, under separate titles. The effect upon desulfurization attributed to the manganese ratio would have been apparent and could have resulted in an erroneous interpretation.

Effects of Applied Current on Desulfurization of Iron

M. OHTANI* and N. A. GOKCEN

University of Pennsylvania, Philadelphia, Pennsylvania

Abstract

It has been found that the ultimate sulfur content of metal decreases and the rate of desulfurization increases when electric current is applied to a system consisting of liquid iron and the blast furnace type slag in a graphite crucible. The effects of (*1*) current intensity, (*2*) the composition of slag and of metal, and (*3*) bubbling of CO through the slag and metal on the rate of desulfurization have been investigated.

INTRODUCTION

Elimination of sulfur in molten iron and steel is a slow and difficult process; therefore, numerous investigations on the rate of sulfur transfer between slag and metal and the distribution of sulfur have been carried out during the past three decades. In this period, the ionic nature of molten slags has been recognized. Therefore, electrolysis of molten slags in contact with liquid iron as a method of desulfurization appeared plausible to the authors. Preliminary experiments indicated that desulfurization rate was indeed enhanced greatly by electrolysis; therefore, the effects of (*1*) current intensity, (*2*) slag and metal composition, and (*3*) bubbling of CO through the slag and metal on the rate of desulfurization were investigated.

EXPERIMENTAL PROCEDURE

The apparatus used in this investigation is shown in Figure 1. It consists of a graphite crucible $1^{1}/_{2}$ in. ID, 3 in. high with a stem, and a graphite anode $^{3}/_{8}$ in. diam, all placed in a magnesia outer crucible continuously flushed with argon. The graphite crucible

---

* Associate Professor on leave, Research Inst. of Mineral Dressing and Metallurgy, Tohoku University, Sendai, Japan.

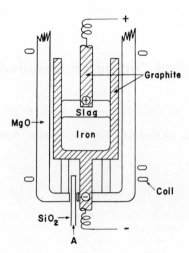

Fig. 1. Apparatus.

and its contents were heated by an induction coil connected to an Ajax converter.

The metallic charge was prepared by melting 180 g of electrolytic iron in a simple graphite crucible slightly smaller than that in Figure 1. The metal was cooled in the crucible, and the resulting ingot was removed. Commercially pure iron sulfide was used for adding sulfur into the charge remelted in the crucible shown in Figure 1. The master slags, free of iron and sulfur (listed in Table I), were also made in graphite crucibles and then crushed.

Experimental runs were made in the following manner. The graphite crucible in Figure 1 was charged with the iron ingot and a known amount of iron sulfide. The charge was heated to 1500 ± 15°C and temperature was measured with an immersed Pt-Pt + 10% Rh thermocouple. The molten metal was sampled by sucking it into a 5-mm ID silica tube. A master slag, weighing 30 g, was then charged into the crucible. A period of 2–3 min was sufficient to melt the slag. The depths of metal and slag layers were 1 and $^1/_2$ in., respectively.

After the slag was molten, the upper graphite electrode was lowered to the desired position and a current of 5–15 amp was applied. With the acid slags, S-I and S-III, however, the applied current was of the order of 0.5 amp. The applied potential was 10 v except 15

TABLE I
Composition of Master Slags

	SiO_2, %	CaO, %	Al_2O_3, %	$V =$ CaO/SiO_2
S-I	59.7	38.2	—	0.64
S-II	45.3	52.8	—	1.17
S-III	57.7	31.5	10.7	0.56
S-IV	39.5	48.4	10.3	1.22
S-V	—	50.0	50.0	—

v for heat H-9, 14 v for H-13, and 6.6 v for H-15 and H-27.   For comparison, the normal rates of desulfurization without current and with or without bubbling CO through the metal were also obtained. At suitable intervals the metal was sampled by sucking it into a silica tube.   At the end of each run the slag was also sampled similarly with a copper tube.   The slag and the metal samples were analyzed by the usual methods for their constituents.

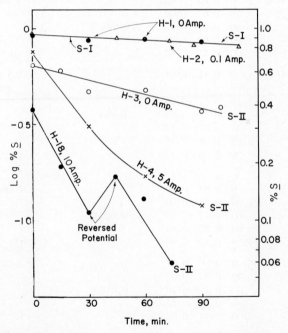

Fig. 2. Desulfurization of iron at 1500°C with acid and basic slags.

TABLE II
Experimental Results at 1500°C

Heat No.	Time, min	Metal, wt-% S, %	Metal, wt-% Si, %	$-d \log S, \%$ / d (time)	FeO, %	Remarks
Acid slag						
S-I: H-1	0	0.75	0.007			0 amp
	30	0.71	0.075			
	60	0.71	0.105	0.0005		
	90	0.68	0.154			
	120	0.64	0.22			
H-2	0	0.16	0.005			0.1 ~ 0.15 amp[a]
	45	0.71	0.084			
	73	0.69	0.159	0.0005		
	86	0.65	0.194			
	116	0.64	0.27			
Acid slag						
S-III: H-9	0	0.62	0.03			1 amp
	15	0.67	0.09			
	30	0.62	0.15	0.0005		
	60	0.62	0.25			
	90	0.57	0.37			$(S, \%) = 0.69$[b]
H-13	0	0.11	0.01			0.5 amp at 30 min
	15	0.11	0.03			
	30	0.11	0.34	0.001		
	45	0.07	0.13			
	60	0.08	0.16			
	90	0.09	0.20			$(S, \%) = 0.24$
Basic slag						
S-II: H-3	0	0.64	0.00			0 amp
	30	0.46	0.00			
	60	0.47	0.02	0.0024		
	90	0.37	0.05			
	100	0.39	0.06			$(S, \%) = 2.34$
H-4	0	0.76	0.01			5 amp
	30	0.31	0.07			
	60	0.17	0.10	0.013		
	90	0.12	0.15			
	100	0.13	0.38			$(S, \%) = 3.78$

(*continued*)

TABLE II (*continued*)

Heat No.	Time, min	Metal, wt-% S, %	Metal, wt-% Si, %	$-d \log S$, % d (time)	FeO, %	Remarks
Basic slag						
S-II:						
H-11	0	0.09	0.01	0.0025		0 amp
	20	0.09	0.08			10 amp at 21 min
	35	0.07	0.24			
	50	0.05	0.16	0.015		
	65	0.03	0.26			
	90	0.01	0.45			(S, %) = 0.58
H-18	0	0.38	0.03			10 amp
	15	0.19	0.21			
	30	0.11	0.40	0.018		S-II slag
	44	0.17	0.47			
	59	0.13	0.70			
	74	0.06	0.78			(S, %) = 2.04
H-19	0	0.18	0.04			9 amp
	15	0.09	0.09			CO = 50 cu cm/min
	30	0.05	0.18	0.018		
	45	0.03	0.34			
	60	0.02	0.49			
H-20	0	0.16	0.02			0 amp
	15	0.11	0.32			CO = 50 cu
	30	0.09	0.07	0.007		cm/min
	45	0.07	0.09			
	60	0.06	0.11			(S, %) = 0.63
H-21	0	0.14	0.01			0 amp
	15	0.10	0.05			CO = 250 cu
	30	0.09	0.03	0.005		cm/min
	45	0.08	0.10			
	60	0.07	0.12			(S, %) = 0.55
H-22	0	0.15	0.01			9 amp
	15	0.08	0.13			
	30	0.05	0.23	0.018		CO = 250 cu
	45	0.03	0.40			cm/min
	60	0.03	0.37			(S, %) = 0.65

(*continued*)

TABLE II (*continued*)

Heat No.	Time, min	Metal, wt-%		$-d \log S, \%$	FeO, %	Remarks
		S, %	Si, %	d (time)		
Basic slag						
S-II:　H-25	0	1.13	0.015			0 amp
	5	0.94	0.016		0.77	
	10	0.89	0.024		1.02	
	15	0.83	0.008	0.004	0.99	
	30	0.73	0.024		1.26	
	60	0.58	0.032		0.99	
H-26	0	0.96	0.030			5 amp
	5	0.76	0.028		0.55	
	10	0.66	0.033	0.014	0.55	
	15	0.51	0.132		0.73	
	30	0.28	0.099		0.60	
	52	0.11	0.132		1.74	
H-27	5	0.85			0.174	14.5 amp
	10	0.69	0.035		0.365	
	15	0.50		0.024	0.425	
	30	0.23	0.18		0.78	
	60	0.05	0.23		0.58	
H-28	0	0.25				14 amp
	20[c]	0.04[c]		0.036[c]		MgO crucible[c]
	30	0.02				
	40	0.06				
Basic slag						
S-IV:　H-8	0	0.57	0.02			0 amp
	15	0.44	0.09			
	30	0.43	0.04	0.0037		
	60	0.34	0.05			
	90	0.27	0.07			
H-10	0	0.57	0.01			10 amp
	15	0.48	0.02	0.013		
	33	0.24	0.06			
	50	0.19	0.09			
H-14	0	0.09	0.01			5 amp
	15	0.05	0.07	0.015		
	30	0.01	0.10			
	45	0.01	0.14			

(*continued*)

TABLE II (*continued*)

Heat No.	Time, min	Metal, wt-% S, %	Si, %	$-d \log S, \%$ d (time)	FeO, %	Remarks
Basic slag						
S-IV: H-15	0	0.09	0.03			14.5 amp
	15	0.03	0.07	0.030		
	30	0.01	0.12			
H-17	0	0.18	1.36			10 amp
	15	0.04	1.69			
	30	0.03	1.97	0.036		Initial
	60	0.01	1.89			$\underline{Si} = 1.4\%$
	90	0.01	2.10			$\overline{(S, \%)} = 0.59$
Basic slag						
S-V: H-23	0	0.36				0 amp
	15	0.18				
	30	0.06	0.04	0.017		
	60	0.00				Final $\underline{Al}$ =
	90	0.01	0.02			0.04%
H-24	0	0.37				8 amp
	7	0.21				
	15	0.12	0.03	0.034		
	45	0.01				
	75	0.00	0.02			Final Al 0.2%

[a] Potential drop across electrodes 10 v except as follows: H-9, 15 v; H-13, 14 v; H-15 and H-27, 6.6 v.

[b] (S, %) represents sulfur in final slag.

[c] In MgO crucible; all others in graphite crucibles.

Experimental results are presented in Table II, and the data for sulfur are represented in Figures 2 to 5, except those for H-18-22 and H-28 for the sake of clarity and brevity.

DISCUSSION OF RESULTS

Possible mechanisms for the transport of sulfur from iron to slag have been presented by Wagner[1] and King and Ramachandran.[2] It seems quite likely that desulfurization is diffusion controlled and therefore should follow the principles outlined elsewhere in adequate detail.[1,3] Accordingly a plot of logarithm of sulfur content versus time should give a straight line provided that the equilibrium sulfur

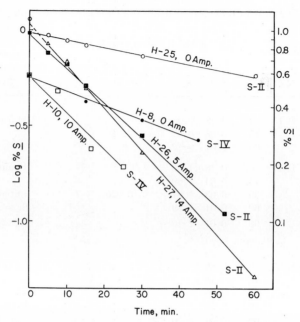

Fig. 3. Desulfurization of iron at 1500°C with basic slags.

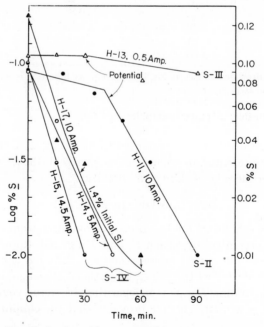

Fig. 4. Desulfurization of iron at 1500°C with acid and basic slags.

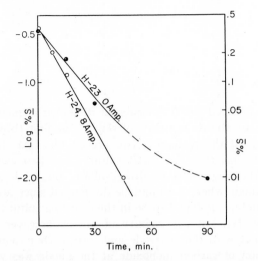

Fig. 5. Desulfurization of iron at 1500°C with slag S-V containing 50% CaO and 50% Al₂O₃.

is much smaller than the actual sulfur content. The results without applied potential represented in Figures 2 to 5 thus follows a straight line within experimental errors, though the change in sulfur contents is not large enough to show other possible trends. For run H-23 the change in sulfur is large, but the last point is subject to large analytical errors since the amount of sulfur is rather small. For the acid slags S-I and S-III, the upper lines in Figures 2 and 4, the rate of desulfurization is much slower than the basic slags, particularly as compared with slag S-V, upper line in Figure 5. The intensity of current through the acid slags was too small (i.e., 0.1 and 0.5 amp even when the voltage was raised to 14 v as in run H-13); hence, the effect of current on desulfurization is very small. No further comments concerning the acid slags are therefore necessary.

The results with applied potential are also represented on the same coordinates in Figures 2 to 5, without necessarily implying that the mechanism of desulfurization with applied potential is the same.

Electrode Processes

The electrode processes in these experiments may be summarized as follows:

$$S + 2e = S^{2-} \tag{1}$$

$$Si^{4+} + 4e = \underline{Si} \tag{2}*$$

$$Al^{3+} + 3e = \underline{Al} \tag{3}$$

$$C(or\ \underline{C}) + O^{2-} = CO(g) + 2e \tag{4}$$

$$Fe = Fe^{2+} + 2e \tag{5}$$

where the underlined symbols represent dissolved elements in iron, and the ions are the constituents of slag. The first three processes are cathodic and the remaining two are anodic. At the cathode; i.e., metal-slag interface dissolved sulfur gains two electrons and passes into the slag. The resulting sulfide ion tends to migrate toward the anode where it cannot be discharged since all the sulfur leaving the metal was found to be in the slag (see sulfur analysis for slag in Table II). In the vicinity of anode, however, the oxide ions, O^{2-}, react with the electrode and form carbon monoxide (Eq. (4). Evolution of carbon monoxide at the anode was visually observed as soon as the current was passed through the system. The resulting bubbles cause a slight but observable fluctuation in current because of polarization. Figures 2 to 5 show clearly that the applied current drastically increases the rate of desulfurization. Examination of the results for run H-18 in Figure 2 shows that when the direction of current was reversed the desulfurization process was also reversed.

The Si^{4+} (or the silicate ions) are reduced according to Eq. (2). Typical results are illustrated in Figure 6. The amounts of $\underline{Al}$ in iron with slag S-V (see H-23 and H-24) are too small to show that the reduction of Al^{3+} is enhanced by the applied current according to Eq. (3). A certain amount of iron also goes into slag in accordance with Eq. (5) (see Fig. 7) but later returns to metal by the reverse reaction.

Effect of Current Intensity

Examination of data shows that increasing amperage, i.e., increasing current density in these experiments, increases the rate of desulfurization irrespective of the initial sulfur content; i.e., for the same slag the slope is nearly the same with varying initial sulfur but increases in absolute value with increasing current as shown in Figure

---

* Other ionic species; e.g., SiO_3^{2-}, AlO_2^-, etc., may also be used in writing Eqs. (2) and (3); e.g., $SiO_3^{2-} + 4e = Si + 3O^{2-}$.

8.   For example, with 5 and 15 amp of currents for 30 min, sulfur contents decrease to 0.021 and 0.01%, respectively, from approximately 0.1% initial sulfur according to H-14 and H-15 in Figure 4. Increasing current also increases the rate of reduction of silicon (or silicate) ion much more rapidly than other ions as shown in Figure 6; e.g., at 30 min, for 5 amp, $\underline{Si},\%$ = 0.07; and for 10 amp, Si,%

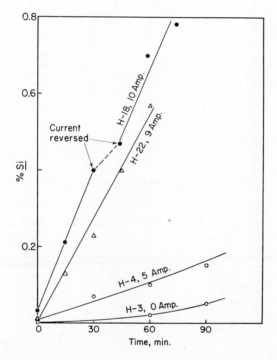

Fig. 6. Rate of reduction of silica from slag S-II at 1500°C.

= 0.4, or more than fivefold increase.   Increase in aluminum content is not sufficiently large to draw a similar conclusion (see heats H-23 and H-24).   Figure 7 shows the effect of increasing current on the iron ion concentration of slag, arbitrarily represented as (FeO)%. It is evident that the results without current, H-25, is in qualitative agreement with King et al.[2,4]   Increasing current obviously decreases Fe^{2+} ions for any given period by providing electrons which tend to reverse Eq. (5).   However, iron has a tendency of going into slag

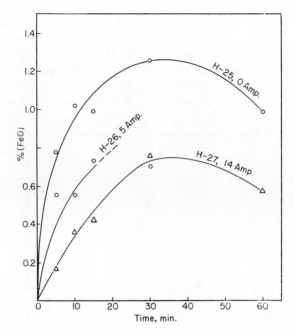

Fig. 7. Variation of iron oxide content of slag S-II with time and current.

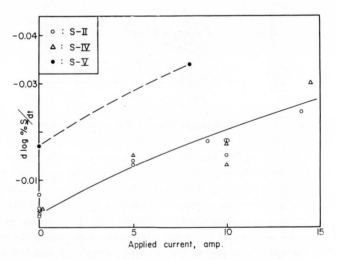

Fig. 8. Variation of $d \log \%S/dt$ with applied current.

faster with sulfur at the beginning than later for some unknown reason.

Iron in slag was determined as described by Ramachandran et al.[4] after the removal of suspended iron.   Complete removal of suspended iron particles in slag is open to question; hence, the results may be somewhat higher than the true iron content.   In view of the fact that the magnitude of analytical errors may be the same for all the runs, it seems reasonable that the relative positions of the curves in Figure 7 are at least of the correct order of magnitude.

Figure 8 shows that the rate of desulfurization expressed as the derivative of log $S,\%$ with time: i.e., $d \log \%S/dt$, increases in absolute value with current intensity.   Further, the rate is much higher for slag S-V than for slags S-II and S-IV.

Effect of Slag Composition

Slag S-IV contains 10.3% Al_2O_3 and S-II contains none, but the V ratio is nearly the same for both.   Effect of this alumina content on desulfurization rate is not noticeable as shown in Figure 4.   Slag S-V containing equal amounts of CaO and Al_2O_3 has a very large desulfurization power as shown in Figure 5.   Comparison of the results for all slags indicate that decreasing the SiO_2 content of slags or eliminating it as in S-V, increases the rate of desulfurization.

Decreasing the SiO_2 content from 45.3 to 39.5% as in slags S-II and S-IV decreases the activity of SiO_2 to a much larger extent and thus decreases the rate of reduction of SiO_2 (cf. runs with S-II and S-IV).

Effect of Bubbling Carbon Monoxide

The effect of bubbling carbon monoxide through the metal was investigated by runs H-19 to H-22.   The results show that a fivefold change in the rate of bubbling CO has very little effect on desulfurization with or without applied potential.   On the other hand, bubbling *without* current does accelerate the rate of desulfurization somewhat as can be seen by comparing H-20 and H-21 with H-3.   Comparison of H-19 and H-22 with H-18 shows that, at approximately the same amperage, bubbling, or the lack of it, has no effect on the rate of desulfurization.

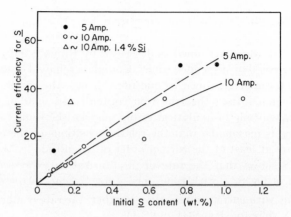

Fig. 9. Variation of the current efficiency for sulfur with initial sulfur during the first 10 min.

Effect of Metal Composition

It is evident from Figures 2 to 4 that for the same slag with the same current the rate of desulfurization, $d \log \underline{S},\%/dt$, is approximately independent of the initial sulfur content (see also Fig. 8). When the initial sulfur content is high as in H-4 (Fig. 2), the rate of desulfurization toward the end decreases with time because the sulfur content of slag increases considerably.

Initial addition of 1.4% silicon in H-17 doubles the rate of desulfurization as can be readily seen by comparison with H-18, H-19, and H-22 at the same amperage.*

Current Efficiency for Sulfur

The initial current efficiency for the transfer of sulfur from metal to slag increases with increasing initial sulfur as shown in Figure 9. When silicon is initially added into the melt, as in H-17, the current efficiency increases; this signifies that a portion of current carried by Si^{4+} in the absence of initial $\underline{Si}$, is made available for $\underline{S}$ by the added $\underline{Si}$. It would be interesting to investigate the effect of initial $\underline{Al}$, which is expected to yield results similar to $\underline{Si}$.

An uncertain part of the current is carried through the anode-slag-

---

* Addition of Si and Al also increases the rate without current. See for example, Grant et al. and Goldman et al.[5]

graphite crucible where the slag is in contact with the crucible.   It is, however, unlikely that this current is significantly large for three reasons: (1) changing the position of anode from the center to near the periphery does not alter the voltage drop for the same amperage, (2) the distance between the anode and the melt is smaller than the anode and the crucible, and (3) the result obtained with a magnesia crucible (i.e., heat H-28) does not differ much from the results with graphite crucibles though a substantial amount of magnesia is dissolved in slag during the experiment.   Further investigations are necessary to evaluate this source of current dissipation.

CONCLUDING REMARKS

The results presented in this paper represent the preliminary phase of an investigation on desulfurization by means of applied current. Additional results are necessary to ascertain the effects of slag and metal composition, voltage gradient, and current density.   Quantitative determination of carbon monoxide evolved during electrolysis may be valuable for the interpretation of results and possibly detecting any other reactions.   The same electrode processes are expected to occur with liquid steel, but making appropriate electrode contact with small melts is difficult.   A similar process may be feasible for dephosphorization.

This research has been sponsored by the Bureau of Aeronautics, U. S. Navy and by the American Iron and Steel Institute.

References

1. Wagner, C., in J. F. Elliott, ed., *Physical Chemistry of Steelmaking*, Wiley, New York, 1958, p. 237.

2. King, T. B., and S. Ramachandran, in J. F. Elliott, ed., *Physical Chemistry of Steelmaking*, Wiley, New York, 1958, p. 125.

3. See, for example, S. Glasstone, K. J. Laidler, and H. Eyring, *The Theory of Rate Processes*, McGraw-Hill, New York, 1941, p. 578.

4. Ramachandran, S., T. B. King, and N. J. Grant, *Trans. Am. Inst. Mining, Met. Petrol. Engrs.*, **206**, 1549 (1956).

5. Grant, N. J., O. Troili, and J. Chipman, *Trans. Am. Inst. Mining Met. Engrs.*, **191**, 672 (1951); K. M. Goldman, G. Derge, and W. O. Philbrook, *ibid.*, **200**, 534 (1954).

Factors Affecting Dephosphorization and Desulfurization in Basic-Electric Steel Production

JOHN ZOTOS

General Thomas J. Rodman Laboratory, Watertown Arsenal,
Watertown, Massachusetts

Abstract

Statistical analyses of equilibrium steelmaking data indicated that good correlation was obtained when: (1) the dephosphorizing power $(P)/[P]$ = (phosphorus in the slag, %)/[phosphorus in the metal, %] was a logarithmic function of a slag parameter equal to the product of the slag's basicity $(CaO, \%)/(SiO_2, \%)$, times its oxidizing power $(FeO, \%)$, and (2) the desulfurizing power $(S)/[S]$ = (sulfur in the slag, %)/[sulfur in the metal, %] was a logarithmic function of a slag parameter equal to the quotient of the slag's basicity divided by its oxidizing power. Slag and metal compositions existing during the production of 4140, high nickel 4325, 4330, and 1040 AISI basic-electric steels were statistically analyzed using the same relationships. The results indicate that the dynamic (or nonequilibrium) dephosphorizing and desulfurizing powers of basic-electric slags are lower than their corresponding equilibrium values and can be estimated at any stage of a heat using the following equations:

$$(P)/[P] = 0.776 \ [(CaO, \%) \ (FeO, \%)/(SiO_2, \%)]^{0.69}$$

and $\quad (S)/[S] = 10.38 \ [(CaO, \%)/(SiO_2, \%) \ (FeO, \%)]^{0.48}$

These equations reveal that maximum dephosphorization and desulfurization conditions cannot exist simultaneously during basic-electric steel production due to the opposite effect of the slag's oxidizing power in the two slag parameters.

INTRODUCTION

A full study of the chemistry of the basic-electric steelmaking process must take into consideration the reactions between the liquid metal and the various slags. The composition and chemical behavior of these slags are quite complex and their refining action on steel depends primarily upon their basicity and oxidizing power. Several

1229

investigators have evaluated the effect of slag basicity and oxidizing power on the dephosphorization and desulfurization of pure iron in contact with basic slags under controlled laboratory condition, and have revealed a great deal of information about slag-metal inter-reactions.[1-9]

Winkler and Chipman[2] used a basic-lined induction furnace to study the equilibrium distribution of phosphorus between liquid iron (with 0.1% carbon) and various basic slags. Their results showed that dephosphorization improved with an increase in the slag's basicity and FeO content and a decrease in temperature.

Other investigators concerned with the removal of phosphorus from liquid steel studied the effect of metallic elements in the liquid metal and the oxidizing power of basic slags on the dephosphorizing power.[3,4]

Fetters and Chipman[5] studied the equilibrium distribution of sulfur between liquid iron and basic slags. Their investigation was conducted under controlled laboratory conditions using a basic induction furnace and slag compositions which varied in oxidizing power and basicity. Their results indicated that desulfurization improved with an increase in the slag basicity and a decrease in the FeO content of the slag.

Other investigators who studied the factors affecting the desulfurizing power of basic slags in contact with liquid iron include Grant and Chipman,[6] Taylor and Chipman,[7] Darken and Larsen,[8] Rocca, Grant, and Chipman,[9] and many others.

A review of the published data revealed that little information was available on the dynamic (or nonequilibrium) phosphorus and sulfur distribution between slag and metal during the production of basic-electric steels. This report presents the results of an investigation conducted to determine a method of predicting the dynamic distribution of phosphorus and sulfur between slag and metal (dephosphorizing and desulfurizing powers) during basic-electric steel production as a function of the slag's basicity and oxidizing power.

INTERPRETATION OF PROCESS VARIABLES

Dephosphorization

Chipman, Elliott, Winkler, etc.,[1-3] report in the literature that phosphorus removal from molten iron and steel is aided by high slag basicity and increased oxidizing power. Recently, Grandpierre and

Elliott[4] found that temperature had no significant effect on the dephosphorization of steel within the temperature range encountered during the steelmaking process. Expressed mathematically, the dephosphorizing power $(P)/[P]$ = (P, % in the slag)/[P, % in the metal] is a function of the slag's basicity (CaO, %)/(SiO$_2$, %) and its oxidizing power (FeO, %), i.e.,

$$(P)/[P] = \phi \, [(\text{CaO, \%})/(\text{SiO}_2, \%), (\text{FeO, \%})] \tag{1}$$

Using Eq. (1) as a guide, what variable parameter composed of both the slag's basicity and oxidizing power can be correlated to a change in the dephosphorizing power? To answer this question, a general expression equating the dephosphorizing power as a function of a parameter equal to the slag's basicity times its oxidizing power was established as the mathematical model, i.e.,

$$(P)/[P] = \phi \, [(\text{CaO, \%}) (\text{FeO, \%})/(\text{SiO}_2, \%)] \tag{2}$$

Equilibrium data from Winkler and Chipman's investigation (Table I) were used to test three mathematical relationships between the two variables of Eq. (2), i.e.,

$$(P)/[P] = N[(\text{CaO, \%})(\text{FeO, \%})/(\text{SiO}_2, \%)] + C \tag{3}$$

$$(P)/[P] = N' \log \, [(\text{CaO, \%})(\text{FeO, \%})/(\text{SiO}_2, \%)] + C' \tag{4}$$

$$\log (P)/[P] = N'' \log \, [(\text{CaO, \%})(\text{FeO, \%})/(\text{SiO}_2, \%)] + \log C''$$

$$\text{or} \; (P)/[P] = C''[(\text{CaO, \%})(\text{FeO, \%})/(\text{SiO}_2, \%)]N'' \tag{5}$$

where N, N', N'', C, C', and C'' are constants.

The statistical analyses of these data in Eqs. (3), (4), and (5) indicated that the best correlation between the dephosphorizing power and the slag parameter is obtained using the log-log relationship expressed by Eq. (5).

A linear regression analysis of the eleven slag and metal compositions given in Table I (see Appendix A), in accordance with Eq. (5), produced a correlation coefficient of 0.925. The resultant expression for the dash line illustrated in Figure 1 was

$$(P)/[P] = 4.28[(\text{CaO, \%}) (\text{FeO, \%})/(\text{SiO}_2, \%)]^{0.69} \tag{6}$$

and the standard error of estimate for these data was equal to 0.144 log cycle.

TABLE I

Data Obtained from Winkler and Chipman's Equilibrium Study of the Distribution of Phosphorus between Liquid Iron and Basic Slags[a]

Heat No.	Temp., °C	Temp., °K	Slag analysis in per cent					P in metal, % [P, %]	Dephosphorizing power $(P, \%)/[P, \%]$	$\dfrac{(CaO, \%)(FeO, \%)}{(SiO_2, \%)}$
			(CaO)	(SiO₂)	(FeO)	(P₂O₅)	(P)			
E-40	1595	1868	37.15	2.20	25.68	7.66	3.35	0.0084	399	434
E-40	1583	1856	30.24	2.14	39.04	6.57	2.87	0.0066	435	552
E-40	1623	1896	29.37	2.54	39.54	6.34	2.77	0.0092	301	457
E-37	1622	1895	37.93	24.70	25.61	1.14	0.497	0.007	71.0	39.3
E-37	1611	1884	41.01	29.98	14.21	0.85	0.371	0.009	41.2	19.42
E-37	1590	1863	37.97	28.78	22.04	0.68	0.297	0.0054	55.0	29.0
E-37	1591	1864	37.19	31.70	18.11	0.61	0.267	0.008	33.3	21.3
E-29	1617	1890	23.01	10.86	58.06	1.90	0.829	0.011	75.4	112.5
E-29	1621	1894	22.84	10.84	58.28	1.80	0.785	0.015	52.3	122.6
E-29	1594	1867	24.21	9.90	55.86	4.02	1.76	0.016	110.0	136.7
E-29	1590	1863	26.99	9.10	51.21	6.91	3.02	0.020	151	152.0

[a] See ref. 2.

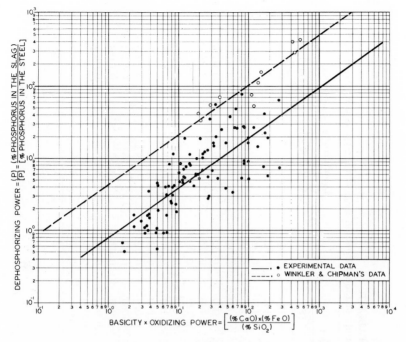

Fig. 1. Effect of slag basicity and oxidizing power on the dephosphorizing power during the production of basic-electric steels.

As a result of this good correlation it was decided to subject similar data obtained during the production of basic-electric steels to the same analysis and the results are discussed later in this report.

Desulfurization

Chipman, Fetters, Grant, and others report in the literature that sulfur removal from steel is aided by high slag basicity and low oxidizing power.[5-9] In addition, they found that temperature had no significant effect on the desulfurization of steel within the temperature range encountered during the steelmaking process.[1] Mathematically speaking, the desulfurizing power $(S)/[S] = (S, \%$ in slag$)/[S, \%$ in metal$]$ is a function of the slag's basicity and the inverse of its oxidizing power, i.e.,

$$(S)/[S] = \phi\ [(CaO, \%)/(SiO_2, \%),\ 1/(FeO, \%)] \tag{7}$$

TABLE II

Data Obtained from Fetters and Chipman's Equilibrium Study of Liquid Iron and Slags of the System CaO–MgO–FeO–SiO$_2$[a]

Heat No.	Temp., °C	Temp., °K	Slag analysis in per cent			(S)	S in metal, % [S, %]	Desulfurizing power (S, %)/[S, %]	(CaO, %)/(SiO$_2$, %) / (FeO, %)
			(CaO)	(SiO$_2$)	(FeO)				
E-22	1602	1875	15.69	2.02	77.94	0.120	0.023	5.22	0.1283
E-22	1615	1888	21.90	1.36	71.78	0.130	0.022	5.91	0.224
E-22	1596	1869	26.01	1.44	67.41	0.140	0.020	7.00	0.268
E-22	1638	1911	35.24	6.94	51.38	0.130	0.021	6.18	0.0986
E-15	1625	1898	29.98	13.58	48.70	0.090	0.025	3.60	0.0453
E-15	1624	1897	29.76	13.84	48.35	0.090	0.026	3.46	0.0443
E-15	1619	1892	35.82	9.94	47.05	0.140	0.021	6.67	0.0766
E-15	1601	1874	34.90	7.38	51.36	0.140	0.018	7.78	0.0920
E-15	1632	1905	39.81	6.84	47.18	0.150	0.017	8.82	0.1260
E-15	1640	1913	39.53	5.72	48.83	0.160	0.014	11.43	0.1415
E-15	1637	1910	39.25	5.46	48.83	0.250	0.024	10.42	0.1472
E-16	1636	1909	18.63	11.22	62.55	0.070	0.022	3.18	0.0265
E-16	1648	1921	19.11	14.26	57.63	0.060	0.022	2.73	0.0233
E-16	1660	1963	16.69	22.22	49.26	0.040	0.022	1.82	0.0153
E-16	1597	1870	14.34	26.02	44.10	0.020	0.024	1.25	0.0125
E-16	1616	1889	13.15	27.52	41.29	0.030	0.023	1.304	0.01158
E-16	1608	1881	11.75	29.22	39.41	0.030	0.024	1.25	0.01022

[a] See ref. 5.

Using Eq. (7) as a guide, a general expression equating the desulfurizing power as a function of a parameter equal to the slag's basicity divided by its oxidizing power was established as the mathematical model, i.e.,

$$(S)/[S] = \phi \ [(CaO, \%)/(SiO_2, \%) \ (FeO, \%)] \qquad (8)$$

Equilibrium data from Fetters and Chipman's investigation (Table II) were used to test three mathematical relationships between the two variables of Eq. (8) [similar to Eqs. (3), (4), and (5)], and the statistical analyses indicated that the best correlation between the desulfurizing power and the slag parameter is obtained using the log-log relationship expressed by Eq. (9):

$$\log (S)/[S] = N \log [(CaO, \%)/(SiO_2, \%)(FeO, \%)] + \log C$$

or $\qquad (S)/[S] = C \ [(CaO, \%)/(SiO_2, \%)(FeO, \%)]^N \qquad (9)$

where C and N are constants.

A linear regression analysis of the seventeen slag and metal compositions given in Table II (see Appendix B), in accordance with Eq. (9) produced a correlation coefficient of 0.927. The resultant expression for the dash line illustrated in Figure 2 was

$$(S)/[S] = 26.0 \ [(CaO, \%)/(SiO_2, \%) \ (FeO, \%)]^{1.63} \qquad (10)$$

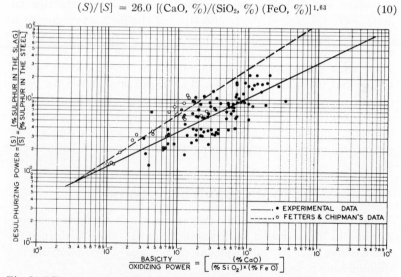

Fig. 2. Effect of slag basicity and oxidizing power on the desulfurizing power during the production of basic-electric steels.

and the standard error of estimate for these data was equal to 0.118 log cycles.

This good correlation was the basis for analyzing steel production data in the same manner and the results are discussed later in this report.

PROCEDURE

The factors affecting dephosphorization and desulfurization in the production of basic-electric steels were studied during the development of an operating procedure for producing high quality, low phosphorus, and low sulfur steel in a 9-ft diam, basic-electric arc melting furnace. This melting practice, which has previously been reported in detail,[10] initially produced 4140 steel castings and was later used to evaluate its effectiveness in producing 4330, high nickel 4325, and 1040 AISI steel castings. The procedure consisted of a two slag process and (at the conclusion of the initial investigation) produced five types of steel castings containing 0.010% maximum sulfur and phosphorus.[11]

At periodic time intervals during each of the nine steel heats of the operating procedure development, test samples of the slag and metal were taken, and the temperature of the bath was recorded by means of either a platinum, platinum-10% rhodium immersion thermocouple, or by an optical pyrometer. The steel was analyzed for carbon, manganese, silicon, chromium, molybdenum, nickel, sulfur, and phosphorus content. The slag was analyzed for silicon dioxide, iron oxide, calcium oxide, sulfur, and phosphorus content. These data coupled with the results of the literature survey were used to study some of the factors affecting the dephosphorizing and desulfurizing powers of slags during the production of basic-electric steels.

RESULTS AND DISCUSSION

The chemical analyses of the slag and steel test specimens obtained during this investigation are listed in Table III, along with their calculated slag basicity and oxidizing power, and dephosphorizing and desulfurizing powers.

As mentioned previously, the data obtained during the production of 4140, high nickel 4325, 4330, and 1040 AISI cast steels were graphically analyzed to evaluate the dynamic effect of slag basicity and oxidizing power on the dephosphorizing power. The statistical analysis of the 97 data units (see Appendix C) resulted in a correlation coefficient of 0.765. A linear regression analysis of the logarithmic relationship between the two major variables was conducted and the resultant line (solid line) illustrated in Figure 1 had the following equation:

$$(P)/[P] = 0.776 \ [(CaO, \%) \ (FeO, \%)/(SiO_2, \%)]^{0.69} \qquad (11)$$

The standard error of estimate for these data was equal to 0.321 log cycle.

Comparison of the two regression lines illustrated in Figure 1 and the other statistical results is interesting. Examination of Winkler and Chipman's and the production data by the variance ratio test or F-test (see Appendix E-1) proved statistically that the difference between the variance of both populations is significant at the 0.05 confidence level.[12,13] The student's t-test (see Appendix F-1) could then be applied to these results and showed statistically (again at the 0.05 confidence level) that the two sets of data analyzed do belong to two distinct populations.[12,13]

Comparison of Eqs. (6) and (11) for the lines best fitting the results verifies the conclusions of the statistical analyses because their constant terms vary considerably ($C_1 = 4.28$ and $C_3 = 0.776$) while their slopes are the same ($N_1 = N_3 = 0.69$). This indicates that while exposed to similar slag compositions, Winkler and Chipman attained dephosphorizing powers during their controlled laboratory investigations that were consistently five and one-half times greater than those observed during the production investigation, and both dephosphorizing powers increase at the same rate with an increase in slag basicity and FeO content.

It is evident that Winkler and Chipman obtained equilibrium dephosphorizing conditions by: (1) melting pure iron in a basic crucible, (2) allowing adequate contact time between the slag and metal, and (3) increasing the surface area of contact between the slag and metal by induction melting. Dephosphorization during the production investigation was considerably reduced because equilibrium was not attained.

In the same manner, the data obtained during the production investigation were graphically analyzed to evaluate the dynamic ef-

TABLE

Slag and Metal Analyses, and Other Data Obtained During tbe Production

Dephosphorizing and

Heat information		Temp, °F	Time after melt-down, min	Steel analysis, %							
Type of steel	Operation[a]			[C]	[Mn]	[Si]	[S]	[P]	[Cr]	[Mo]	[Ni]
AISI 4140	MD	2850[b]	0	0.45	0.29	0.02	0.024	0.022	0.05	—	—
	CSO	2800	20	0.39	0.26	0.01	0.026	0.008	0.08	—	—
	OSO	2850[b]	80	0.05	0.07	0.06	0.028	0.004	0.04	—	—
	WSO	3000	150	0.03	—	0.05	0.025	0.001	—	—	—
		2950[b]	171	0.04	0.04	0.03	0.024	0.002	—	—	—
	SU	2950[b]	180	0.055	0.03	0.09	0.029	0.003	—	—	—
		2950[b]	190	0.055	0.03	0.03	0.024	0.003	—	—	—
		2950[b]	200	0.06	—	0.03	0.020	0.007	0.90	0.19	—
		2950	230	0.305	—	0.03	0.018	0.008	0.67	0.18	—
	TAP	3050	246	0.43	0.99	0.55	0.017	0.008	1.01	0.23	—
AISI 4140	MD	2870	0	0.495	0.36	0.06	0.024	0.008	0.24	0.04	—
	CSO	2880	25	0.465	0.37	0.04	0.023	0.011	0.28	0.04	—
	OSO	2930	95	0.04	0.14	0.09	0.024	0.007	0.17	0.04	—
	WSO	2870	167	0.045	0.03	0.05	0.025	0.007	0.10	0.04	—
	SU	2950[b]	190	0.06	0.13	0.05	0.028	0.005	0.11	0.04	—
		3050	205	0.08	0.02	0.04	0.025	0.007	0.97	0.20	—
		2950[b]	215	0.06	0.02	0.04	0.026	0.006	0.95	0.22	—
		2950	225	0.11	—	0.04	0.028	0.007	0.94	0.22	—
		2980	240	0.36	0.02	0.02	0.028	0.008	0.91	0.23	—
	TAP	3120	260	0.385	1.03	0.40	0.021	0.010	1.15	0.23	—
AISI 4140	MD	2850	0	0.475	0.28	0.03	0.020	0.012	0.04	—	—
	OSI	3040	30	0.415	0.38	0.05	0.024	0.008	0.08	—	—
	OSO	2850[b]	95	0.02	0.11	0.01	0.027	0.005	0.02	—	—
	WSO	2850[b]	145	0.03	—	—	0.032	0.007	—	—	—
	SU	2950[b]	184	0.11	0.10	0.03	0.033	0.002	0.02	—	—
		2950	200	0.12	—	0.03	0.024	0.005	—	—	—
		3000	215	0.10	0.02	—	0.028	0.005	0.86	0.21	—
		2900	230	0.12	—	—	0.026	0.005	0.94	0.21	—
		2950[b]	250	0.33	—	—	0.022	0.006	0.95	0.21	—
	TAP	3100	263	0.345	1.08	0.55	0.019	0.006	1.11	0.21	—
AISI 4140	MD	2850[b]	0	0.38	0.46	0.06	0.025	0.007	0.28	0.04	—
	OSI	3000	20	0.35	0.42	0.02	0.024	0.011	0.30	—	—
	OSO	2900	95	0.04	0.05	0.02	0.025	0.007	0.09	0.06	—
	WSO	3080	155	0.07	0.09	0.06	0.028	0.004	0.08	0.05	—
	SU	2950[b]	190	0.105	0.04	0.02	0.030	0.002	0.05	0.07	—
		2950[b]	205	0.105	0.09	0.03	0.029	0.002	0.09	0.05	—
		2950[b]	220	0.10	0.06	0.05	0.029	0.003	0.10	0.05	—
		2950[b]	235	0.06	0.09	0.04	0.028	0.002	0.08	0.05	—
		2950[b]	250	0.34	0.02	0.03	0.030	0.002	0.47	0.14	—
	TAP	3130	274	0.395	0.89	0.35	0.024	0.008	0.96	0.22	—

III
of Nine Basic-Electric Steel Heats, to Evaluate the Factors Affecting the
Desulfurizing Powers

(CaO)	(SiO₂)	(S)	(P)	(Fe)	(FeO)	Dephos-phorizing power, (P)/P	$\frac{(CaO, \%)}{(FeO, \%)}$ (SiO₂, %)	Desul-furizing power, (S)/S	$\frac{(CaO, \%)}{(SiO_2, \%)}$ (FeO, %)
33.92	17.62	0.076	0.062	10.68	13.80	2.82	26.6	3.17	0.1395
36.52	18.04	0.083	0.093	8.58	11.00	11.62	22.4	3.19	0.1850
32.36	17.55	0.060	0.150	23.07	29.7	37.50	54.8	2.14	0.0622
26.00	7.35	0.095	0.041	37.50	48.3	41.00	171.0	3.80	0.0733
52.76	3.76	0.285	0.015	15.41	19.80	7.50	278.0	11.88	0.709
58.60	5.14	0.315	0.017	12.92	16.60	5.67	189.5	10.86	0.688
67.75	4.16	0.315	0.023	7.92	10.20	7.66	164.5	13.12	1.598
51.20	10.08	0.172	0.027	7.31	9.40	3.86	47.7	8.59	0.540
39.00	14.12	0.102	0.024	7.76	10.00	3.00	27.6	5.66	0.276
—	—	—	—	—	—	—	—	—	—
42.05	19.14	0.129	0.043	4.34	5.60	5.38	12.32	5.37	0.507
40.45	20.88	0.088	0.020	3.84	4.90	1.82	9.48	3.83	0.395
32.55	17.29	0.058	0.114	19.68	25.30	16.30	47.60	2.42	0.0744
23.16	7.23	0.081	0.100	33.26	42.80	14.30	137.0	3.24	0.0747
51.68	9.34	0.225	0.048	14.00	18.00	9.10	99.7	8.03	0.307
53.00	14.06	0.426	0.037	4.14	5.30	5.29	20.0	17.05	0.712
51.20	14.37	0.267	0.036	3.92	5.00	6.00	17.8	10.26	0.712
47.72	15.71	0.249	0.048	5.71	7.30	6.85	22.2	8.90	0.416
40.76	14.93	0.103	0.044	40.76	9.70	5.50	26.5	3.67	0.281
35.38	22.28	0.116	0.016	35.38	2.30	1.60	3.65	5.52	0.690
44.74	17.92	0.143	0.081	9.52	12.30	6.74	30.7	7.15	0.203
40.92	19.84	0.063	0.081	8.40	10.80	10.12	22.3	2.67	0.1906
26.74	20.72	0.033	0.124	24.20	32.40	24.80	41.8	1.222	0.0398
20.48	11.96	0.092	0.065	39.43	50.7	9.25	87.0	2.87	0.0338
64.20	5.38	0.303	0.045	11.26	14.50	22.50	173.5	9.18	0.823
54.16	10.50	0.220	0.042	13.33	17.20	8.40	87.2	9.17	0.295
49.20	9.24	0.203	0.026	11.76	15.10	5.20	80.5	7.24	0.353
43.20	8.92	0.153	0.026	16.35	21.0	5.20	102.0	5.88	0.231
47.88	10.72	0.287	0.020	10.42	13.40	3.33	60.0	13.04	0.333
51.16	22.80	0.320	0.007	1.21	1.60	1.167	3.58	16.85	1.400
42.12	22.20	0.098	0.131	8.62	11.10	18.70	21.0	3.92	0.1706
39.36	26.12	0.091	0.051	6.05	7.80	4.63	11.76	3.79	0.1935
23.36	20.62	0.044	0.104	23.30	30.0	14.86	32.5	1.760	0.0361
23.68	8.88	0.085	0.066	29.34	37.8	16.50	99.3	3.03	0.0703
54.56	9.52	0.314	0.053	11.92	15.4	26.50	88.3	10.46	0.372
48.00	10.06	0.320	0.055	14.56	18.7	27.50	84.8	11.03	0.243
41.60	9.74	0.310	0.058	18.14	23.3	19.34	99.5	10.70	0.1835
40.56	9.06	0.176	0.054	20.61	26.5	27.0	118.7	6.28	0.168
36.32	10.30	0.172	0.054	14.11	18.20	27.0	64.1	5.73	0.1935
40.48	20.56	0.192	0.013	2.69	3.50	1.625	6.90	8.00	0.563

(continued)

TABLE

Type of steel	Operation[a]	Temp, °F	Time after meltdown, min	[C]	[Mn]	[Si]	[S]	[P]	[Cr]	[Mo]	[Ni]
AISI 4140	MD	2900	0	0.60	0.54	0.04	0.025	0.009	1.28	0.29	—
	OSI	2850[b]	20	0.54	0.51	—	0.021	0.008	1.33	0.29	—
	OSO	2930	80	0.10	0.27	0.03	0.022	0.012	0.86	0.26	—
	WSO	2850[b]	115	0.06	0.19	—	0.016	0.006	0.89	0.31	—
(Si, Mn+)	SU	2950	140	0.20	0.72	0.20	0.017	0.012	0.94	0.26	—
		2950	155	0.20	0.77	0.18	0.017	0.013	0.93	0.30	—
		2900	170	0.25	0.70	0.15	0.018	0.013	0.95	0.31	—
		2900	185	0.405	0.73	0.10	0.016	0.013	0.97	0.29	—
		2950[b]	200	0.44	0.71	0.10	0.015	0.014	1.08	0.30	—
		2950[b]	215	0.435	0.72	0.32	0.014	0.013	1.07	0.29	—
	TAP	3050	231	0.43	0.80	0.19	0.013	0.014	1.07	0.25	—
AISI 4330	MD	2850[b]	0	0.25	0.51	0.08	0.029	0.008	0.95	0.36	2.03
	OSI	2850[b]	20	0.445	0.46	0.05	0.026	0.007	0.37	0.42	2.01
	OSO	2850	80	0.13	0.08	0.03	0.024	0.004	0.07	0.38	2.18
	WSO	2850[b]	120	0.065	0.07	0.04	0.025	0.002	0.19	0.37	2.12
(Si, Mn+)	SU	2950[b]	165	0.265	0.63	0.26	0.014	0.008	0.12	0.36	2.07
		2950[b]	180	0.245	0.60	0.17	0.011	0.006	0.18	0.36	2.11
		2950[b]	190	0.24	0.56	0.16	0.012	0.006	0.17	0.35	2.09
		2900	205	0.24	0.55	0.16	0.009	0.008	0.17	0.36	2.04
		2950[b]	220	0.24	0.53	0.12	0.008	0.008	0.17	0.36	2.08
		2950[b]	235	0.265	0.54	0.08	0.007	0.008	0.95	0.35	2.01
	TAP	3100	269	0.29	0.96	0.23	0.005	0.007	0.96	0.37	2.04
AISI 4330	MD	2900	0	0.42	0.57	0.09	0.024	0.011	0.60	0.33	1.72
	OSI	2850[b]	20	0.42	0.52	0.02	0.023	0.010	0.58	0.35	1.77
	OSO	2900	80	0.07	0.11	0.01	0.029	0.008	0.09	0.35	1.78
	WSO	2900	110	0.02	0.09	0.04	0.024	0.002	0.14	0.32	1.72
(Si, Mn+)	SU	2950[b]	150	0.19	0.42	0.19	0.016	0.007	0.20	0.34	1.74
		2950[b]	170	0.21	0.51	0.13	0.018	0.005	0.23	0.31	1.67
		2950[b]	185	0.20	0.48	0.12	0.015	0.006	0.52	0.36	2.06
		2950[b]	200	0.20	0.47	0.11	0.017	0.006	0.86	0.37	2.02
		2950[b]	215	0.31	0.44	0.08	0.014	0.006	0.86	0.38	2.07
		3000	230	0.305	0.42	0.06	0.014	0.006	0.85	0.37	2.08
		2950[b]	245	0.31	0.39	0.08	0.014	0.005	0.85	0.37	2.07
	TAP	3100	260	0.31	0.94	0.20	0.012	0.011	0.88	0.36	2.02
AISI 4325	MD	2900	0	0.405	0.60	0.14	0.023	0.009	0.60	0.45	2.28
	OSI	2900	20	0.41	0.59	0.01	0.023	0.008	0.54	0.41	2.36
	OSO	2920	80	0.06	0.13	0.04	0.023	0.006	0.25	0.44	2.44
	WSO	2900	115	0.05	0.06	0.05	0.020	0.005	0.14	0.41	2.38
(Si, Mn+)	SU	2900	159	0.20	0.50	0.16	0.017	0.006	0.20	0.39	2.37
		2950[b]	170	0.19	0.52	0.19	0.014	0.006	0.23	0.38	2.28
		2960	185	0.19	0.46	0.17	0.012	0.007	0.25	0.38	2.28
		2950[b]	200	0.19	0.45	0.07	0.011	0.007	0.26	0.40	2.31
		2950[b]	215	0.25	0.45	0.08	0.011	0.005	0.79	0.46	2.42
		2970	230	0.24	0.41	0.07	0.011	0.007	0.77	0.45	2.41
		2950[b]	245	0.235	0.40	0.12	0.011	0.008	0.77	0.46	2.43
	TAP	3120	260	0.260	1.46	0.45	0.010	0.012	0.90	0.45	2.45

III (*continued*)

	Slag analysis, %					Dephos-phorizing power, (P)/P	$\dfrac{(CaO, \%)\ (FeO, \%)}{(SiO_2, \%)}$ %	Desul-furizing power, (S)/S	$\dfrac{(CaO, \%)\ (SiO_2, \%)}{(FeO, \%)}$ %
(CaO)	(SiO₂)	(S)	(P)	(Fe)	(FeO)				
33.5	19.7	0.062	0.052	8.2	10.55	5.78	17.90	2.48	0.161
39.5	20.8	0.118	0.067	6.0	7.72	8.37	14.66	5.62	0.246
30.8	20.8	0.037	0.049	8.7	11.20	4.08	16.60	1.68	0.1312
38.4	11.3	0.153	0.157	15.7	20.2	26.20	68.70	9.55	0.1684
60.6	19.0	0.283	0.011	1.5	1.93	0.916	6.16	16.64	1.654
55.3	21.7	0.288	0.014	1.0	1.29	1.076	3.29	16.95	1.975
47.9	21.0	0.160	0.007	1.7	2.19	0.54	5.00	8.88	1.040
37.8	17.0	0.148	0.012	2.4	3.09	0.923	6.90	9.25	0.722
46.3	21.6	0.138	0.015	1.8	2.32	1.07	4.97	9.19	0.922
46.6	22.3	0.131	0.012	1.8	2.32	0.923	4.85	9.35	0.901
45.6	22.8	0.105	0.013	1.3	1.67	0.928	3.34	8.07	1.196
37.1	18.0	0.131	0.130	12.16	15.67	16.25	32.20	4.52	0.1315
38.9	15.2	0.150	0.140	10.60	13.64	20.0	34.90	5.77	0.1875
25.2	19.0	0.048	0.139	16.80	21.60	34.7	28.60	2.00	0.0633
39.4	13.8	0.140	0.097	17.95	23.10	48.5	66.0	5.60	0.1234
50.1	21.0	0.310	0.015	1.68	2.16	1.875	5.16	22.10	1.106
56.4	22.7	0.240	0.008	0.92	1.18	1.333	2.94	21.80	2.11
56.6	24.0	0.117	0.004	0.52	0.67	0.667	1.58	9.74	3.53
56.2	25.5	0.140	0.004	0.60	0.77	0.500	1.685	15.56	2.85
53.9	26.6	0.065	0.012	1.48	1.90	1.500	3.86	5.42	1.07
53.4	25.6	0.067	0.009	0.87	1.12	1.125	2.33	8.37	1.856
44.5	29.3	0.044	0.007	1.90	2.44	1.00	3.71	8.80	0.623
33.48	21.73	0.093	0.093	5.44	7.0	8.45	10.80	3.87	0.221
32.52	23.33	0.071	0.116	4.76	6.1	11.60	8.50	3.09	0.229
23.88	22.27	0.069	0.150	9.08	11.7	18.75	12.54	2.38	0.0916
30.96	10.20	0.17	0.153	20.6	26.7	76.5	80.8	7.08	0.1136
49.28	15.59	0.35	0.029	1.78	2.3	4.14	7.27	21.90	1.375
48.16	19.15	0.29	0.021	1.52	2.0	4.20	5.04	16.10	1.260
42.48	21.25	0.23	0.021	1.44	1.9	3.50	3.82	15.35	1.058
39.24	21.67	0.12	0.027	2.20	2.8	4.50	5.01	7.06	0.639
39.24	20.74	0.12	0.024	2.72	3.5	4.00	6.63	8.57	0.541
46.75	20.10	0.054	0.038	3.32	4.3	6.33	10.02	3.85	0.542
35.40	20.85	0.048	0.042	3.40	4.4	8.40	7.48	3.43	0.386
34.00	26.23	0 069	0.018	1.36	1.8	1.635	2.34	5.75	0.720
40.80	20.42	0.071	0.069	7.17	9.2	9.88	18.40	3.09	0.217
39.44	21.06	0.083	0.090	6.05	7.8	11.25	14.60	3.61	0.240
26.40	20.54	0.048	0.074	14.56	18.7	12.34	24.1	2.09	0.0687
35.44	6.16	0.186	0.096	25.87	33.3	19.20	191.5	9.30	0.1726
56.92	18.56	0.240	0.017	2.04	2.6	2.83	7.98	14.10	1.180
55.12	20.24	0.240	0.015	2.22	2.9	2.50	7.92	17.15	0.940
48.84	21.38	0.122	0.022	2.35	3.0	3.14	6.84	10.30	0.760
49.20	21.02	0.086	0.022	2.60	3.6	3.14	8.42	7.82	0.650
46.44	20.74	0.088	0.020	2.91	3.7	4.00	8.29	8.00	0.606
47.74	20.84	0.068	0.029	3.02	3.9	4.14	8.93	6.18	0.587
38.26	21.44	0.026	0.038	4.76	6.1	4.75	10.40	2.36	0.279
40.08	25.38	0.040	0.020	1.85	2.4	1.665	3.85	4.00	0.668

(*continued*)

| Heat information | | Temp, °F | Time after melt-down, min | Steel analysis, % | | | | | | | |
Type of steel	Opera-tion[a]			[C]	[Mn]	[Si]	[S]	[P]	[Cr]	[Mo]	[Ni]
AISI 1040	MD	2800	0	0.44	0.29	0.09	0.024	0.011	—	—	—
	OSI	2900	20	0.39	0.28	0.06	0.022	0.009	—	—	—
	OSO	2950	80	0.35	0.02	—	0.033	0.003	—	—	—
	WSO	2850[b]	135	0.35	—	0.01	0.029	0.001	—	—	—
(Si, Mn+)	SU	2900	175	0.33	0.41	0.12	0.017	0.009	—	—	—
		2950[b]	185	0.36	0.40	0.12	0.020	0.004	—	—	—
		2950[b]	200	0.375	0.40	0.10	0.020	0.005	—	—	—
		2950[b]	215	0.365	0.33	0.04	0.020	0.005	—	—	—
		2950[b]	230	0.38	0.30	0.11	0.020	0.005	—	—	—
		2950[b]	245	0.455	0.28	0.03	0.021	0.005	—	—	—
		2950[b]	260	0.44	0.31	0.03	0.021	0.008	—	—	—
	TAP	3160	277	0.40	0.92	0.21	0.014	0.013	—	—	—

[a] MD = melt down; CSO = charge slag on; OSI = ore slag in; OSO = ore slag on; WSO = wash slag on; SU = shape up of the reducing slag.
[b] Optical pyrometer temperature readings.

fect of slag basicity and oxidizing power on the desulfurizing power. The statistical analysis of the 97 data units (see Appendix D) resulted in a correlation coefficient of 0.746. A linear regression analysis of the logarithmic relationship between the two major variables was conducted and the resultant line (solid line) illustrated in Figure 2 had the following equation:

$$(S)/[S] = 10.38 \ [(CaO, \%)/(SiO_2, \%) \ (FeO, \%)]^{0.48} \qquad (12)$$

The standard error of estimate for these data was equal to 0.190 log cycle.

Comparison of the two regression lines illustrated in Figure 2 and the other statistical results was accomplished by subjecting Fetters and Chipman's, and the production data to the F-test (see Appendix E-2) and again showed statistically that the difference between the variance of both populations is significant at the 0.05 confidence level.[12,13] The student's t-test (see Appendix F-2a) could then be applied to these results and proved statistically (again at the 0.05 confidence level) that the two sets of data analyzed do belong to two distinct populations at desulfurizing powers greater than 1.1.[12,13] However, for desulfurizing powers less than 1.1, the student's t-test (see Appendix F-2b) failed to show statistically (also at the 0.05 confidence level) that the two sets of results belong to separate families.

III (*continued*)

Slag analysis, %						Dephos-phorizing power, (P)/P	(CaO, %)(FeO, %)(SiO₂), %	Desul-furizing power, (S)/S	(CaO, %)(SiO₂, %)(FeO, %)
(CaO)	(SiO₂)	(S)	(P)	(Fe)	(FeO)				
53.68	16.70	0.152	0.058	8.96	11.5	5.27	36.9	6.33	0.279
42.48	17.70	0.192	0.115	8.51	11.0	12.78	26.4	8.72	0.218
26.16	19.82	0.220	0.163	24.86	32.0	55.3	34.5	6.66	0.043
29.60	5.04	0.176	0.065	35.62	45.9	65.0	269.0	6.07	0.128
61.52	16.60	0.278	0.024	4.03	5.2	6.00	19.30	16.35	0.713
54.48	19.28	0.246	0.019	2.46	3.2	4.75	14.72	12.30	0.884
51.20	20.60	0.136	0.027	3.81	4.9	5.40	12.20	6.78	0.508
41.84	20.70	0.132	0.035	4.70	6.0	7.00	12.12	7.60	0.337
47.92	20.92	0.064	0.040	5.15	6.6	8.00	15.12	3.20	0.347
47.76	21.12	0.074	0.038	4.70	6.0	7.60	12.90	3.53	0.358
40.80	21.04	0.070	0.040	4.70	6.0	5.00	11.62	3.33	0.322
35.36	20.96	0.053	0.030	4.26	5.5	2.31	9.28	3.85	0.307

Comparison of Eqs. (10) and (12) for the lines best fitting the data verifies the conclusions of the statistical analysis because both their constant terms ($C_2 = 26.0$ and $C_4 = 10.38$) and slopes ($N_2 = 0.63$ and $N_1 = 0.48$) vary. This indicates that while exposed to similar slag compositions, the desulfurizing powers obtained by Fetters and Chipman in their controlled laboratory experiments are greater (at $[(CaO, \%)/(SiO_2, \%)(FeO, \%)] > 4 \times 10^{-3}$—see Fig. 2) than those achieved during the production investigation. In addition, as the slag's basicity increases and its oxidizing power decreases, both desulfurizing powers increase but at different rates ($N_2 > N_4$).

These results show that Fetters and Chipman obtained maximum desulfurization under equilibrium laboratory conditions while during the production investigation the desulfurization was reduced because equilibrium was not attained.

By comparing Eqs. (11) and (12), it is evident that while maintaining a constant basicity during the production of basic-electric steels, maximum dephosphorizing and desulfurizing conditions cannot exist at the same moment, due to the opposite effect of the slag's oxidizing power in the two slag parameters. Therefore, in order to remove both detrimental elements from steel, the melting process must be split into two portions, i.e., one part using a highly oxidizing slag (high FeO, %) for maximum dephosphorization and the second part using a minimum oxidizing level in the slag (low FeO, %) for maximum desulfurization. Such results are realized using a well-controlled, two-slag, basic-electric practice.[10]

CONCLUSIONS

Statistical analyses of equilibrium steelmaking data showed good correlation was obtained when (1) the dephosphorizing power was a logarithmic function of the product of the slag's basicity times its oxidizing power, and (2) the desulfurizing power was a logarithmic function of the quotient of the slag's basicity divided by its oxidizing power. A statistical analysis of slag and metal compositions obtained during the production of nine basic-electric steel heats revealed that the dynamic or nonequilibrium dephosphorizing and desulfurizing power of basic-electric slags are lower than their corresponding equilibrium values and can be estimated at any stage of a heat using the following equations:

$$(P)/[P] = 0.776 \ [(CaO, \%)(FeO, \%)/(SiO_2, \%)]^{0.69} \text{ and } (S)/[S] =$$

$$10.38 \ [(CaO, \%)/(SiO_2, \%)(FeO, \%)]^{0.48}$$

The author is deeply appreciative to the members of the Rodman Laboratory who assisted in the statistical analyses of the data.

APPENDIX A

Linear Regression Analysis of Some of the Data from Winkler and Chipman's Equilibrium Study of the Distribution of Phosphorus between Liquid Iron and Basic Slags

$Y' = (P)/[P]$ (see Table I)
$Y = \log Y'$
$\bar{Y} = (\Sigma Y/N) = (22.261/11) = +2.024$
$X' = [(CaO, \%) \times (FeO, \%)/(SiO_2, \%)]$ (see Table I)
$X = \log X'$
$\bar{X} = (\Sigma X/N) = (22.172/11) = +2.016$

Summation results:

1. $N = 11$
2. $\Sigma(X - \bar{X}) = -0.003$
3. $\Sigma(Y - \bar{Y}) = -0.003$
4. $\Sigma(X - \bar{X})^2 = +2.862209$
5. $\Sigma(X - \bar{X})(Y - \bar{Y}) = +1.97283$
6. $\Sigma(Y - \bar{Y})^2 = +1.589451$

Correlation coefficient r:

$$r = \frac{\dfrac{\Sigma(X - \bar{X})(Y - \bar{Y})}{N} - \dfrac{\Sigma(X - \bar{X})}{N} \times \dfrac{\Sigma(Y - \bar{Y})}{N}}{\sigma_X \times \sigma_Y} = +0.925$$

where

$$\sigma_X = \left[\frac{\Sigma(X - \bar{X})^2}{N} - \left(\frac{\Sigma(X - \bar{X})}{N} \right)^2 \right]^{1/2} = +0.510$$

$$\sigma_Y = \left[\frac{\Sigma(Y - \bar{Y})^2}{N} - \left(\frac{\Sigma(Y - \bar{Y})}{N} \right)^2 \right]^{1/2} = +0.380$$

Equation for best fitting straight line:

$$(Y - \bar{Y}) = (r\sigma_Y/\sigma_X)(X - \bar{X}) - \text{Negligible}$$

$$(Y - 2.024) = 0.69(X - 2.016)$$

$$Y = 0.69X + 0.632$$

$$\log Y' = 0.69 \log X' + \log 4.28$$

$$(Y') = 4.28 (X')^{0.69}$$

$$\therefore (P)/[P] = 4.28[(CaO, \%) \times (FeO, \%)/(SiO_2, \%)]^{0.69}$$

Standard error of estimate:

$$S_Y = \sigma_Y(1 - r^2)^{1/2} = 0.144 \text{ log cycle}$$

APPENDIX B

Linear Regression Analysis of Some of the Data from Fetters and Chipman's Equilibrium Study of the Distribution of Sulfur between Liquid Iron and Basic Slags

$$Y' = (S)/[S] \text{ (see Table II)}$$

$$Y = \log Y'$$

$$\bar{Y} = (\Sigma Y/N) = (10.468/17) = 0.616$$

$$X' = [(CaO, \%)/(SiO_2, \%)(FeO, \%)] \text{ (see Table II)}$$

$$X = \log X'$$

$$\bar{X} = (\Sigma X/N) = -(21.417/17) = 1.260$$

Summation results:

1. $N = 17$
2. $\Sigma(X - \bar{X}) = +0.003$
3. $\Sigma(Y - \bar{Y}) = -0.004$
4. $\Sigma(X - \bar{X})^2 = +3.583909$
5. $\Sigma(X - \bar{X})(Y - \bar{Y}) = +2.270755$
6. $\Sigma(Y - \bar{Y})^2 = +1.675022$

Correlation coefficient r:

$$r = \frac{\dfrac{\Sigma(X - \bar{X})(Y - \bar{Y})}{N}}{\sigma_X \times \sigma_Y} = +0.927 \text{ (see Appendix A)}$$

where

$$\sigma_X = +0.459 \text{ (see Appendix A)}$$

$$\sigma_Y = +0.314 \text{ (see Appendix A)}$$

Equation for best fitting straight line:

$$(Y - \bar{Y}) = (r\sigma_Y/\sigma_X)(X - \bar{X}) \text{ (see Appendix A)}$$

$$(Y - 0.616) = 0.63\,(X + 1.260)$$

$$Y = 0.63\,X + 1.415$$

$$\log Y' = 0.63 \log X' + \log 26.0$$

$$(Y') = 26.0\,(X')^{0.63}$$

$$\therefore (S)/[S] = 26.0[(CaO, \%)/(SiO_2, \%)(FeO, \%)]^{0.63}$$

Standard error of estimate:

$$S_Y = \sigma_Y\,(1 - r^2)^{1/2} = 0.118 \text{ log cycle}$$

APPENDIX C

Linear Regression Analysis of the Data Obtained While Studying the Effect of Slag Basicity and Oxidizing Power on the Dephosphorizing Power during the Production of Basic-Electric Steels

$Y' = (P)/[P]$ (see Table III)
$Y = \log Y'$
$\bar{Y} = [\Sigma Y/N] = (+74.995/97) = +0.773$
$X' = [(CaO, \%) \times (FeO, \%)/(SiO_2, \%)]$ (see Table III)
$X = \log X'$
$\bar{X} = [\Sigma X/N] = (+123.471/97) = +1.272$

Summation results:

1. $N = 97$ ·
4. $\Sigma(X - \bar{X})^2 = +29.245327$
2. $\Sigma(X - \bar{X}) = -0.085$
5. $\Sigma(X - \bar{X})(Y - \bar{Y}) = +20.284574$
3. $\Sigma(Y - \bar{Y}) = -0.031$
6. $\Sigma(Y - \bar{Y})^2 = +24.014751$

Correlation coefficient r:

$$r = \frac{\dfrac{\Sigma(X - \bar{X})(Y - \bar{Y})}{N}}{\sigma_X \times \sigma_Y} = +0.765 \text{ (see Appendix A)}$$

where

$$\sigma_X = +0\ 549 \text{ (see Appendix A)}$$
$$\sigma_Y = +0.498 \text{ (see Appendix A)}$$

Equation for best fitting straight line:

$$(Y - \bar{Y}) = (r\sigma_Y/\sigma_X)(X - \bar{X}) \text{ (see Appendix A)}$$
$$(Y - 0.773) = 0.69\ (X - 1.272)$$
$$Y = 0.69\ X - 0.110$$
$$\log Y' = 0.69 \log X' + \log 0.776$$
$$(Y') = 0.776\ (X')^{0.69}$$
$$\therefore (P)/[P] = 0.776\ [(CaO, \%) \times (FeO, \%)/(SiO_2, \%)]^{0.69}$$

Standard error of estimate:

$$S_Y = \sigma_Y\ (1 - r^2)^{1/2} = 0.321 \log \text{cycle}$$

APPENDIX D

Linear Regression Analysis of the Data Obtained While Studying the Effect of Slag Basicity and Oxidizing Power on the Desulfurizing Power during the Production of Basic-Electric Steels

$$Y' = (S)/[S] \text{ (see Table III)}$$
$$Y = \log Y'$$
$$\bar{Y} = (\Sigma Y/N) = (77.615/97) = +0.800$$
$$X' = [(CaO, \%)/(SiO_2, \%)(FeO, \%)] \text{ (see Table III)}$$
$$X = \log X'$$
$$\bar{X} = (\Sigma X/N) = (-43.822/97) = -0.452$$

Summation results:

1. $N = 97$ 4. $\Sigma(X - \bar{X})^2 = +19.247010$
2. $\Sigma(X - \bar{X}) = -0.022$ 5. $\Sigma(X - \bar{X})(Y - \bar{Y}) = +9.182292$
3. $\Sigma(Y - \bar{Y}) = +0.115$ 6. $\Sigma(Y - \bar{Y})^2 = +7.889883$

Correlation coefficient r:

$$r = \frac{\dfrac{\Sigma(X - \bar{X})(Y - \bar{Y})}{N}}{\sigma_X \times \sigma_Y} = +0.746 \text{ (see Appendix A)}$$

where

$$\sigma_X = +0.445 \text{ (see Appendix A)}$$

$$\sigma_Y = +0.285 \text{ (see Appendix A)}$$

Equation for best fitting straight line:

$$(Y - \bar{Y}) = (r\sigma_Y/\sigma_X)(X - \bar{X}) \text{ (see Appendix A)}$$

$$(Y - 0.800) = 0.48 - (X + 0.452)$$

$$Y = 0.48X + 1.016$$

$$\log Y' = 0.48 \log X' + \log 10.38$$

$$(Y') = 10.38(X')^{0.48}$$

$$\therefore (S)/[S] = 10.38[(CaO, \%)/(SiO_2, \%)(FeO, \%)]^{0.48}$$

Standard error of estimate:

$$S_Y = \sigma_Y (1 - r^2)^{1/2} = 0.190 \text{ log cycle}$$

APPENDIX E

Variance Ratio Test or F-Test Calculations

1.   Dephosphorizing data:

$$F = \frac{\text{Greater variance estimate}}{\text{Lesser variance estimate}} = \frac{(\acute{\sigma}_G)^2}{(\acute{\sigma}_L)^2} = \frac{\left(\dfrac{n_G}{n_{G-1}}\right) S_G^{\,2}}{\left(\dfrac{n_L}{(n_L - 1)}\right) S_L^{\,2}}$$

(ref. 12, p. 213)

where

Greater variance estimate (see Appendix A) — $S_1 = 0.321$; $n_1 = 97$
Lesser variance estimate (see Appendix B) — $S_2 = 0.144$; $n_2 = 11$

$$F_A = \frac{\left(\dfrac{97}{97-1}\right)(0.321)^2}{\left(\dfrac{11}{11-1}\right)(0.144)^2} = 4.56$$

$F_T[96,10]_{0.05} = 2.6$ (ref. 12, p. 487, Table E)

Since $F_A > F_T$, the difference between variances is significant at the 0.05 confidence level.

2.   Desulfurizing data:

Greater variance estimate (see Appendix C) — $S_1 = 0.190$; $n_1 = 97$

Lesser variance estimate (see Appendix D) — $S_2 = 0.118$; $n_2 = 17$

$$F_A = \frac{\left(\dfrac{97}{97-1}\right)(0.190)^2}{\left(\dfrac{17}{17-1}\right)(0.118)^2} = 2.38$$

$F_T[96,16]_{0.05} = 2.20$ (ref. 12, p. 487, Table E)

Since $F_A > F_T$, the difference between variances is significant at the 0.05 confidence level.

APPENDIX F

Student's t'-Distribution

1.   Dephosphorizing data:

$$t = \frac{\text{Error in mean}}{\text{Standard error of mean}} = \frac{|\bar{X}_1 - \bar{X}_2|}{(S_{\bar{X}_1}^2 + S_{\bar{X}_2}^2)^{1/2}} = \frac{0.723}{(0.003147)^{1/2}}$$

$$= 12.90$$

where

$$S_{\bar{X}_1}^2 = (S_1)^2/(n_1 - 1) = (0.321)^2/(97 - 1)$$
$$= 0.001073 \text{ (see Appendix E)}$$

$$S_{\bar{X}_2}^2 = (S_2)^2/(n_2 - 1) = (0.144)^2/(11 - 1)$$

$$= 0.002074 \text{ (see Appendix } \mathbf{E)}$$

$$|\bar{X}_1 - \bar{X}_2| = |0.723 - 0| = 0.723 \text{ (see Fig. 2)}$$

$$t[\text{crit.}]_{0.05} = \frac{S_{\bar{X}_1}^2(t_1) + S_{\bar{X}_2}^2(t_2)}{S_{\bar{X}_1}^2 + S_{\bar{X}_2}^2} = \frac{0.006756}{0.003147} = 2.15$$

where

$$t_1]_{0.05} = 1.990 \text{ (ref. 11, p. 484, Table C)}$$

$$t_2]_{0.05} = 2.228 \text{ (ref. 11, p. 484, Table C)}$$

Since $t > t_{\text{crit.}}$, the two sets of results belong to two distinct populations at the 0.05 confidence level.

2. Desulfurizing data:

$$\text{a.} \quad t[\text{crit.}]_{0.05} = \frac{S_{\bar{X}_1}^2(t_1) + S_{\bar{X}_2}^2(t_2)}{S_{\bar{X}_1}^2 + S_{\bar{X}_2}^2} = \frac{0.002687}{0.001246} - 2.15$$

where

$$S_{\bar{X}_1}^2 = (0.190)^2/(97 - 1) = 0.000376 \text{ (see Appendix C)}$$

$$S_{\bar{X}_2}^2 = (0.118)^2/(17 - 1) = 0.000870 \text{ (see Appendix D)}$$

$$t_1]_{0.05} = 1.990; \quad t_2]_{0.05} = 2.228 \text{ (ref. 11, p. 484, Table C)}$$

$\therefore$ at $t > 2.15$, the difference in the levels of the two sets of results at the 0.05 confidence level is significant because $t > t_{\text{crit.}}$. This condition occurs at a desulfurizing power where the mean difference $|\bar{X}_2 - \bar{X}_1|_{\text{min.}} = 2.15 \ (0.001246)^{1/2} = 0.075$. This occurs (Fig. 2) at a desulfurizing power = 1.1.

b. At $t < 2.06$, the difference in the levels of the two sets of results is not significant at the 0.05 confidence level because $t < t_{\text{crit.}}$. Thus, at desulfurizing power <1.1, the two sets of data could belong to the same population.

References

1. Bever, M. B., H. B. Emerick, B. M. Larsen, and W. O. Philbrook, *Basic Open Hearth Steelmaking*, Am. Inst. Mining Metallurgical Engrs., New York, 1951, 2nd ed., pp. 632–3, 728–44.

2. Winkler, T. B., and J. Chipman, *Trans. Am. Inst. Mining Met. Engrs.*, **167**, 111 (1946).

3. Elliott, J. F., and F. W. Luerssen, *Trans. Am. Inst. Mining, Met. Petrol Engrs.*, **203**, 1129 (1955).

4. Grandpierre, F., and J. F. Elliott, paper presented at International Symposium on the Physical Chemistry of Process Metallurgy but not received for inclusion in this volume.

5. Fetters, K. L., and J. Chipman, *Trans. Am. Inst. Mining Met. Engrs.*, **145**, 95 (1941).

6. Grant, N. J., and J. Chipman, *Trans. Am. Inst. Mining Met. Engrs.*, **167**, 134 (1946).

7. Taylor, C. R., and J. Chipman, *Trans. Am. Inst. Mining Met. Engrs.*, **154**, 228 (1943).

8. Darken, L. S., and B. M. Larsen, *Trans. Am. Inst. Mining Met. Engrs.*, **150**, 87 (1942).

9. Rocca, R., N. J. Grant, and J. Chipman, *Trans. Am. Inst. Mining Met. Engrs.*, **191**, 319 (1951).

10. Zotos, J., "Development of a Standard Operating Procedure for a Six and One-Half Ton Basic Electric Steel Furnace Using Optimum Conditions of Desulphurization and Dephosphorization," Production Preparedness Measure Rept. No. 10/7, Rodman Process Laboratory, Watertown Arsenal, Oct., 1956.

11. Zotos, J., *Electric Furnace Steel Proc.*, **1958**, 16.

12. Bowman, E. H., and R. B. Fetter, *Analysis for Production Management*, Richard D. Irwin, Inc., Homewood, Ill., 1957, pp. 208–19, 484, 487.

13. Monroney, M. J., *Facts from Figures*, Penguin Books, Baltimore, Md., 1951, pp. 226–236, 271–302.

Discussion

F. C. Langenberg (*Crucible Steel Co. of America, Pittsburgh, Pa.*): The author has neglected the effect of temperature on desulfurization and dephosphorization with the statement that this is justified when the temperature range is not excessive. However, the sizes of commercial electric furnaces vary from 1 ton capacity to over 200 ton capacity. Generally, the smaller the furnace, the higher the topping temperature; this is necessary to prevent "skulls" in the ladle and to permit an adequate teeming temperature. Thus, it is my opinion that the range of temperatures found in commercial electric furnaces is great enough that the effect of temperature on desulfurization or dephosphorization cannot be ignored.

The author claims he can predict the dephosphorizing and desulfurizing power of basic-electric slags by the equations describing the two regression lines. This infers foresight, whereas the time required for a slag analysis relegates such a prediction to hindsight. We can analyze for P and S in the metal before we can obtain an accurate slag analysis. Even assuming we can get rapid estimations of slag basicity and oxidizing power, the scatter in the predicted distribution ratios is still too great for practical application.

J. Zotos: In our investigation at Watertown Arsenal the temperature range encountered was 2800 to 3160°F. Statistical testing of the temperature variable in both slag parameters showed that within the operating temperature range, temperature was an insignificant variable throughout the basic-electric melting process. These results conformed to the information published in the literature and referenced in this report.

The evolution of these two slag parameters was initiated to compare the level of equilibrium obtained during the production of basic-electric steels, in order to correlate the degree of efficiency which the operating metallurgist can hope to attain. I realize that this information without a rapid slag test will not be effective but wish to point out to Dr. Langenberg that an attempt to develop these tests will be initiated in the near future.

E. T. Turkdogan (*B.I.S.R.A., London*): I should like to sound a word of caution on the application of laboratory data to the works practice. Although in steelmaking furnaces an equilibrium may be maintained at the slag-metal interface, the samples taken from the bath represent the bulk compositions which may differ considerably from the equilibrium values. To keep the reactions occurring in the favorable direction in steelmaking furnaces there must remain a chemical potential gradient between the bulk of the slag and that of the metal. For example, it is well known that the oxygen potential of the slag is much higher than that of the metal, and at the interface the effective oxygen potential has an intermediate value. The estimation of this oxygen potential is very difficult and an empirical method suitable for one type of practice may not hold for another refining practice. The author has used ferrous oxide concentration as a measure of the state of oxidation in the bath. This may be quite suitable for slags having similar compositions, but for the reasons mentioned above the value of the product "basicity X oxidizing power" derived from the bulk composition of the slag will be higher than that expected from the equilibrium data.

J. Zotos: I realize the difficulty in attempting to extrapolate laboratory data to an industrial size melting practice. However, I feel that producing steel in a $6^1/_2$-ton basic-electric furnace creates a pseudo-industrial level of basic electric steelmaking.

C. E. A. Shanahan (*Richard Thomas & Baldwins, England*): Mr. Zotos has made several statistical comparisons of experimental data obtained under different degrees of control, e.g., small scale laboratory experiments on the one hand and larger plant trials on the other. He referred to the use of the F- and t-tests for comparing the similarity of the two types of data. While the t-test is eminently suitable for this purpose it is difficult to visualize any support from the F-test. The latter is designed to compare the variances of two sets of data regardless of their means and it is to be expected therefore that significant F-test differences will generally be obtained when comparing laboratory tests with larger plant trials due to the much lower degree of control on the plant. This does not signify, however, that the two sets of data represent fundamentally different refining reactions.

J. Zotos: The F-test was used to statistically determine whether the difference between the variance of both populations was significant. If the variance between both of these populations, namely, the theoretical data vs the production data, was significant, then the student's t-test was applied to statistically determine whether or not the two sets of data analyzed in this investigation belonged to two distinct populations.

SECTION XII: HYDRO- AND ELECTRO-METALLURGY

. . . .

A Process for Direct Leaching Zinc Sulfide Concentrates with Sulfuric Acid and Oxygen under Pressure

F. A. FORWARD

Department of Mining and Metallurgy, University of British Columbia, Vancouver, B. C.

and

H. VELTMAN

Research and Development Division, Sherritt Gordon Mines, Ltd., Fort Saskatchewan, Alberta, Canada

Abstract

A process is described, based on the reaction

$$ZnS + H_2SO_4 + {}^1\!/_2O_2 \longrightarrow ZnSO_4 + S^\circ + H_2O$$

by which commercial zinc sulfide concentrate can be oxidized in an autoclave at 110–115°C in 2–4 hr to produce a substantially quantitative amount of elemental sulfur and extract 95 to 99% of the Zn in a single stage leach, giving a leach solution high in Zn^{2+} which is amenable to conventional purification and electrolysis-producing cathode zinc and H_2SO_4 for recycling. The process, in which roasting is eliminated, obviates the need for recovering sulfur dioxide and permits recovery of most of the sulfur in ZnS as elemental sulfur. As the zinc loss in residues caused by ferrite formation in conventional roasting and leaching processes is eliminated, the ratio of iron to zinc in the concentrate has substantially no effect on zinc recovery.

INTRODUCTION

The recovery of zinc by roasting and leaching methods combined with electrolysis has been described fully in the literature[1-4] since its commercial introduction in 1916. Particularly in locations where low cost electrical energy is available the process has been used to treat a variety of zinc sulfide concentrates in which zinc is the principal constituent but which also contain appreciable amounts of lead or copper and iron sulfides. Among the factors that affect the economic outcome in respect to capital or operating costs and metal recoveries are: (a) a high iron/zinc ratio in the concentrate causes excessive formation of insoluble zinc ferrite during roasting with consequent low zinc recoveries, (b) efficient recovery of zinc necessitates using a more or less complex two stage countercurrent leach, and (c) the sulfur dioxide produced in roasting, which must be disposed of in some manner, is usually converted to sulfuric acid, the location of the roasting plant being dictated by economic necessity rather than by optimum operating conditions and cost in the zinc leaching and electrolytic plant.

It is reasonable to expect that some advantage may be gained if a process were employed in which extraction of zinc is very high regardless of the iron or zinc content of the concentrate, in which a single stage leach is used and where no sulfur dioxide is produced, the sulfur content of the zinc sulfide being recovered instead as elemental sulfur. It is the purpose of this paper to delineate such a process.

PREVIOUS WORK

The general aspects of oxidative leaching under pressure have been discussed in an earlier publication[5] and reference has been made by several investigators to the formation of elemental sulfur during aqueous oxidation of sulfides. Tronev and Baudin[6] make mention of oxidation of artificial ZnS at high pressures in alkaline solutions. Downes[7] was concerned principally with the oxidation of pyrrhotite (Fe_nS_{n+1}) to form iron oxide and elemental sulfur. Cornelius and Woodcock,[8] in studying the oxidation of pyrite to $FeSO_4$ and H_2SO_4, considered the oxidation to $S°$ to be unimportant (ref. 8, p. 85) and suggested in accordance with Stokes[9] that it may be produced by interaction between $Fe_2(SO_4)_3$ and FeS_2 once $Fe_2(SO_4)_3$ had been formed by oxidation of $FeSO_4$. McKay and Halpern[10] show that pyrite (FeS_2), because of the considerable excess of sulfur present, can be oxidized in aqueous solutions at 100 to 130°C to form Fe^{2+}, Fe^{3+}, SO_4^{2-}, and $S°$, the amount of product SO_4^{2-} relative to $S°$ increasing with temperature and with pH. Their work indicates that higher acid concentration tends to promote the formation of elemental sulfur. Warren[11] reports the formation of elemental sulfur when leaching chalcocite in sulfuric acid solutions with pH below 1.4 at 160°C under 40 psi O_2 pressure. Jackson and Strickland[12] describe the formation of elemental sulfur by oxidation of PbS (galena) at room temperature in an acid solution containing free chlorine. Seraphim and Samis[13] note the formation of S° in the oxidation of galena by O_2 under pressure in an acidic ammonium acetate solution. Current work[14] shows that galena is oxidized by oxygen under pressure in a sulfuric acid solution at elevated temperatures as follows:

$$PbS + H_2SO_4 + {}^1/_2O_2 \longrightarrow PbSO_4 + S° + H_2O \qquad (1)$$

Pawlek and Pietsch[15] determined the extent of dissolution of ZnS in H_2SO_4 under $N_2 + H_2S$ pressure at 100–135°C where the equilibrium is a function of the H_2S pressure in the system. It has been established[16] that zinc sulfide (sphalerite) leaches readily in the presence of dissolved oxygen in an aqueous ammoniacal solution to produce zinc ammines $[(Zn(NH_3)_x]^{2+}$ and ammonium sulfate.

Björling[17] mentions the reaction

$$ZnS + H_2SO_4 + {}^1/_2O_2 \longrightarrow ZnSO_4 + S° + H_2O \qquad (2)$$

as having been carried out using oxygen under pressure, but he points out that it proceeds so slowly that it is impractical for Zn extraction from ZnS unless nitric acid is also present as a promoter. The nitric acid, he states, presents obvious difficulties in subsequent electrolysis. He concludes that because of these difficulties and the added problem of recovering sulfur from the leach residue "acid decomposition of zinc blend is unfavourable."

Unexpectedly, in the face of Björling's results, the present work shows that ZnS can be readily oxidized quantitatively to Zn^{2+} and S° in a solution containing H_2SO_4 in sufficient amount to combine stoichiometrically with the Zn in ZnS without nitric acid being present. The necessary conditions for carrying the reaction out efficiently have been developed in a series of laboratory tests and the principal elements of a cyclic process established.

Materials

The materials used in the series of tests described were commercial products having the composition given in Table I.

TABLE I

Product, %	Zinc-lead concentrate	Zinc-copper concentrate	Lead concentrate	Pyrrhotite concentrate
Zn	41.5	53.0	3.5	0.4
Pb	7.8	tr	65.5	0.4
Cu	tr	1.1	tr	n.d.
Fe	10.0	8.8	11.2	50.5
S	24.5	32.6	20.7	32.1
Insol.	5.1	tr	n.d.	12.6

To provide maximum reaction rates the concentrates were ground in a laboratory ball mill to substantially 100% minus 325 mesh before leaching.

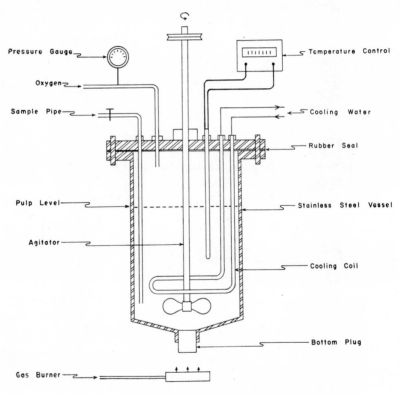

Fig. 1. Low pressure autoclave.

Equipment

The leaching tests were carried out in a 10 by $7^1/_2$ in. stainless steel autoclave (Fig. 1) with external gas flame heating, internal cooling coil and agitator, and equipped with automatic controls which could maintain the temperature of the reacting pulp within a range of $\pm 3°C$. Commercial oxygen was supplied through a suitable pressure reducing and control valve. Samples could be withdrawn at required intervals through a sampling valve.

Procedure

In conducting a leaching test the zinc concentrate, usually 500 g, was charged to the open autoclave as a water slurry. The required amount of H_2SO_4 was then added together with more water to give a pulp density of about 14%. The autoclave was closed, the agitator started, and oxygen admitted to prevent H_2S formation during the heating up period; the temperature was raised to the required level and residual nitrogen from the air initially present purged by releasing the pressure momentarily. The release valve was closed, the vapor pressure read, and oxygen admitted to give the required partial pressure.

The autoclave was then operated continuously for the desired period—from $^1/_2$ to 4 hr—the temperature, pressure, and agitation being maintained throughout.

In the tests run above the melting point of sulfur, the molten sulfur formed globules which "wetted" and occluded unoxidized sulfides and solidified on cooling to form small pellets.

In the tests run below the melting point of sulfur (119°C) the elemental sulfur formed was finely divided. Two methods were used for separating the sulfur from the oxidized solids and leach solution, (*1*) pelletizing or (*2*) flotation.

1. Pelletizing

At the end of the leaching period the pulp temperature was raised to 140°C for 15–30 min to form molten sulfur globules. The pellets, formed on cooling below 100°C, were separated from the oxidized products and leach solution by screening on a 150-mesh screen. The oxidized solids ($Fe(OH)_3 \cdot x H_2O$, $PbSO_4$, SiO_2, etc.) were separated from the leach solution by filtration and the filter cake washed with water.

2. Flotation

The pulp at the end of the leaching period was cooled to room temperature, filtered, and the filter cake washed with water. The filter cake was then repulped with water to 15% solids and floated with a small amount of xanthate and pine oil in a laboratory cell to produce concentrate, middling, and tail, the latter comprising the oxidized solids and insolubles.

In some tests the pellets or flotation concentrates were heated to 400°C to distill sulfur and the residual sulfides returned to a subsequent leach. Separation of sulfur from sulfides by filtering at 130°C was examined qualitatively on both types of product.

A few tests were carried out to examine the removal of Fe^{3+} from leach solutions by pH adjustment with $CaCO_3$. The Fe-free solution was considered to be ready for conventional Cu-Cd removal. No experiments were carried out to test cementation or electrolysis.

Leaching Variables

Once it had been established that ZnS (sphalerite) reacted quantitatively with H_2SO_4 and O_2 under pressure at 110°C in an aqueous solution to produce $ZnSO_4$ and S°, tests were carried out to ascertain the conditions necessary for conducting the operation most effectively. The variable examined included: grind, temperature, O_2 partial pressure, H_2SO_4 concentration, time, and zinc ion concentration.

None of these was studied exhaustively, the approach being substantially empirical with the object of establishing limits and conditions that could conceivably be translated into practical terms, leaving the more detailed kinetic studies for investigation at a later date.

In a subsequent paper[14] the reaction between PbS, H_2SO_4, and O_2 to produce $PbSO_4$ and S° is discussed. Although molten elemental sulfur wets unreacted sphalerite, chalcopyrite, and pyrite, the coherent layer of $PbSO_4$ which forms on the surface of galena effectively prevents wetting by the molten sulfur and the pellets of sulfur, when formed, occlude only inconsequential amounts of Pb as PbS or $PbSO_4$. Similarly, in flotation, only the clean sulfides and sulfur will float while the $PbSO_4$-coated galena particles remain with the oxidized products in the flotation tailing.

Grind

The zinc-lead flotation concentrate used in most of the experiments described was dry as received but contained numerous lumps up to $1/4$ in. in diameter. The concentrate was prepared in four different ways as follows: (1) 2-hr grind in laboratory pebble mill, (2) 10-min grind in laboratory pebble mill, (3) lumps broken by hand in mortar, and (4) as-received, including small lumps.

TABLE II
Effect of Grind

Conditions:
Charge   = Zinc-lead concentrate
Pulp density   = 14%
H_2SO_4 addition = 1 stoichiometric[a] amount for Pb + Zn
Temperature   = 110°C
Time   = $1^1/_2$ hr
O_2 pressure   = 20 psi

Grind	100%–325	98%–325	92%–325	As-received
Analysis of Products				
Solution, g/liter				
Zn	64.0	61.0	42.0	46.0
Fe	2.3	3.0	11.5	9.1
pH (final)	1.1	0.9	0.6	0.6
Pellets, %				
Zn	15.2	15.0	33.0	33.0
S°	69.2	69.8	35.0	35.8
Residue, %				
Zn	1.0	1.2	0.1	0.2
Pb	23.0	18.5	54.2	38.0
Fe	33.7	27.5	5.7	15.5
S	7.0	10.7	10.4	11.0
Zn Distribution, % (based on concentrate)				
Solution	88	88	62	62
Pellets	11	11	37	37
Residue	1	1	<1	<1

[a] In this and succeeding tables this refers to Eqs. (1) and (2).

Screen analyses were: (*1*) 100% minus 325-mesh, (*2*) 98% minus 325-mesh, (*3*) 92% minus 325-mesh, and (*4*) not determined.

The four products were oxidized under standard conditions in the autoclave. The operating conditions and results are shown in Table II.

It is evident that for this particular concentrate a light grind is required but no advantage is gained by excessive grinding.

Temperature

In preliminary tests carried out at 140°C it was found that the conversion to $ZnSO_4$ and $S°$, though very rapid initially, ceased com-

TABLE III
Effect of Temperature

Conditions:
Charge	= Zinc-lead concentrate
Grind	= 100% minus 325 mesh
Pulp density	= 14%
H_2SO_4 addition	= 1 stoichiometric amount for Zn + Pb
Pressure	= 20 psi O_2 overpressure
Time	= $1^1/_2$ hr

Temperature	90°C	110°C	115°C	120°C	140°C
Analysis of Products					
Solution, g/liter					
Zn	47.0	64.0	75.0	53.0	57.0
Fe	7.8	2.3	2.0	0.9	0.9
pH	0.5	1.1	1.1	0.8	0.8
Pellets, %					
Zn	33.0	15.2	12.5	27.7	25.0
S°	38.4	69.2	75.4	49.2	52.1
Residue, %					
Zn	1.2	1.0	2.0	2.0	1.7
Pb	24.7	23.0	18.9	13.6	10.2
Fe	22.3	27.5	28.1	27.0	30.2
S	12.0	10.7	11.7	11.5	10.0
Zn Distribution, % (based on concentrate)					
Solution	62	88	90	70	73
Pellets	37	11	8	28	25
Residue	1	1	2	2	2

pletely in about 10 min giving 65 to 72% dissolution of Zn, the higher figure resulting when O_2 partial pressure was increased from 20 to 60 psi. In every case the oxidized residue contained less than 2% of the original zinc; the balance of the ZnS remaining undissolved was occluded in the pellets. Continuation of the leach for up to 6 hr at 140°C effected only minor (1–2%) additional dissolution of Zn.

From this it soon became apparent that if maximum dissolution of Zn were to be achieved the reaction would have to be carried out below the melting point of sulfur even at the expense of a somewhat lower reaction rate.

The results of a series of tests in which all conditions except temperature remained constant are shown in Table III.

TABLE IV
Effect of Oxygen Pressure

Conditions:

Charge	= Zinc-lead concentrate
Grind	= 100% minus 325 mesh
Pulp density	= 14%
H_2SO_4 addition	= 1 stoichiometric amount for Zn + Pb
Temperature	= 110°C
Time	= $1^1/_2$ hr

O_2 overpressure	10 psi	20 psi	60 psi
Analysis of Products			
Solution, g/liter			
Zn	48.0	64.0	67.0
Fe	4.0	2.3	1.0
pH	1.0	1.1	1.0
Pellets, %			
Zn	29.0	15.2	5.5
S°	46.1	69.2	86.0
Residue, %			
Zn	1.0	1.0	0.9
Pb	18.0	23.0	21.4
Fe	27.0	27.5	32.9
S	10.2	10.7	10.0
Zn Distribution, % (based on concentrate)			
Solution	70	88	96
Pellets	29	11	3
Residue	1	1	1

The advantage of conducting the oxidation in the 110–115°C range is clearly evident.

Oxygen Pressure

In the series of tests carried out to evaluate the effect of oxygen pressure at 110°C, the results of which are shown in Table IV, it is ap-

TABLE V
Effect of Sulfuric Acid Ratio

Conditions:

Charge	= Zinc-lead concentrate
Grind	= 100% minus 325 mesh
Pulp density	= 14%
H₂SO₄ addition for Pb	= 1 stoichiometric amount [Eq. (1)]
Temperature	= 110°C
Pressure	= 20 psi O₂ overpressure
Time	= 4 hr

H₂SO₄ (% of stoichiometric[a] amount for Zn)	45%	70%	90%	100%
Solution, g/liter	Analysis of Products			
Zn	38.0	50.0	65.0	72.0
Fe	0.5	0.4	0.4	1.0
pH	2.1	1.7	1.4	1.2
Pellets, %				
Zn	40.0	27.2	11.5	3.8
S°	13.9	24.0	73.2	90.4
Residue, %				
Zn	1.0	0.7	1.0	1.0
Pb	23.7	22.8	20.3	16.9
Fe	33.8	32.3	31.8	28.7
S	5.5	5.6	12.5	22.8[b]
Zn Distribution, % (based on concentrate)				
Solution	51	75	91	97
Pellets	48	24	8	2
Residue	1	1	1	1

[a] See Eq. (2).
[b] Contains some S° due to pellets passing through screen.

parent that, under the conditions used, increasing the O_2 partial pressure from 10 to 60 psi has a marked effect on the products obtained in $1^1/_2$ hr. Reference to Table VI shows, however, that in 4 hr at 20 psi O_2 the results are almost identical with those obtained in $1^1/_2$ hr at 60 psi O_2.

Higher O_2 pressure accelerates ZnS oxidation and conversion of Fe^{2+} to Fe^{3+}—a not unexpected result.

The final pH is the same in all three examples because in none of the three was all the added H_2SO_4 consumed.

TABLE VI
Effect of Time

Conditions:

Charge	= Zinc-lead concentrate
Grind	= 100% minus 325 mesh
Pulp density	= 14%
H_2SO_4 addition	= 1 stoichiometric amount for Zn + Pb
Pressure	= 20 psi O_2 overpressure
Temperature	= 110°C

Leaching time, hr	$^1/_2$	1	$1^1/_2$	2	3	4
Solution, g/liter		Analysis of Products				
Zn	41.0	62.0	64.0	65.0	70.0	72.0
Fe	5.6	3.0	2.3	0.4	0.6	1.0
pH	0.6	0.9	1.1	1.3	1.3	1.2
Pellets, %						
Zn	35.0	17.5	15.2	10.0	6.3	3.8
S°	35.0	55.0	69.2	77.4	85.8	90.4
Residue, %						
Zn	0.8	1.2	0.7	0.5	1.0	1.0
Pb	17.3	21.1	23.0	19.9	20.3	16.9
Fe	25.6	34.2	33.7	35.0	32.7	28.7
S	11.3	7.4	7.0	7.4	10.7	28.8[a]
Zn Distribution, % (based on concentrate)						
Solution	62	86	88	92	96	97
Pellets	37	13	11	7	3	2
Residue	1	1	1	1	1	1

[a] Contains some S° due to pellets passing through screen.

Sulfuric Acid Requirement

One object of the investigation was to confirm that the extent of dissolution of ZnS was directly proportional to the amount of free H_2SO_4 added.   Because the PbS reacts more rapidly than ZnS it was necessary to add H_2SO_4 equivalent to the PbS present and then to add more H_2SO_4 to give the desired ratio for the ZnS.   The tests were run for 4 hr to ensure that the oxidation and dissolution of ZnS had reached a maximum (note effect of time in Table VI).

The data provided in Table V show a reasonably parallel relationship between the per cent stoichiometric amount of H_2SO_4 added and the per cent Zn dissolved.

Time

Although it might have been possible to obtain some of the data in Table VI by making a single run under the stated conditions and withdrawing samples at suitable intervals, it seemed preferable to run separate tests for the times shown and to establish a material balance for each test.

The interesting aspect of this series is that, after 2 hr of leaching, Zn dissolution is over 90%, the Fe in solution is reduced to less than 1.0 g/liter and the pH has reached a maximum of 1.3.   It should be noted that the oxidized residue at no time contains more than 1% of the Zn.

Zinc Ion Concentration

A test was made to determine the effect of zinc ion concentration and to approximate the conditions that might exist in a practical operation.

The procedure which followed the flow diagram shown in Figure 2 was as follows.

A charge of zinc concentrate was oxidized under the conditions given in Table VII, the sulfur pellets were removed by screening, and the residue filtered off.   To the zinc sulfate solution $CaCO_3$ was added to raise the pH to 4.5 and precipitate Fe^{3+} which was separated by filtration.   To the Fe-free solution, concentrated H_2SO_4 was added to give a solution containing Zn-55 g/liter, H_2SO_4-110 g/liter, resembling return electrolyte.

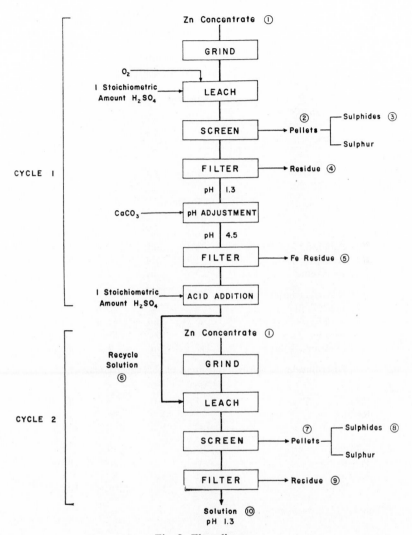

Fig. 2. Flow diagram.

A second charge of zinc concentrate was oxidized under conditions similar to the first, but using the above recycle solution instead of water. The second product was screened and filtered to give a Zn-SO$_4$ solution containing Zn-120 g/liter, Fe-1.8 g/liter, having a pH of 1.3, which would be ready for purification and electrolysis.

TABLE VII
Effect of Zinc Ion Concentration

Conditions:

Charge	= Zinc-lead concentrate
Grind	= 98% minus 325 mesh
Pulp density	= 14%
H_2SO_4 addition	= 1 stoichiometric amount for Zn + Pb
Temperature	= 110°C
O_2 pressure	= 20 psi
Time	= 4 hr

Cycle No.	Item	Zn	Pb	Fe	S_{total}	$S°$
		Analysis of Products				
1	(1) Zn concentrate, %	41.5	7.8	10.0	24.5	—
	(2) Pellets, %	10.5	nil	3.7	80.7	76.6
	(3) Sulfides, %	45.0	nil	16.0	16.0	—
	(4) Residue, %	1.0	15.4	26.3	11.6	0.2
	(5) Fe residue, %	3.5	nil	2.9	12.7	nil
2	(6) Recycle solution, g/liter	55.0	nil	tr	68.8	—
	(7) Pellets, %	9.2	nil	3.5	81.3	77.0
	(8) Sulfides, %	41.0	nil	17.0	17.0	—
	(9) Residue, %	0.7	19.4	29.5	11.2	4.4
	(10) Solution,[a] g/liter	117.0	nil	1.7	61.0	—
	Distribution, % (based on content of concentrate added)					
1	Solution	92	0	5	0	
	Pellets	7	0	8	82	
	Residue	1	100	87	18	
	Total	100	100	100	100	
2	Solution	94	0	10	0	
	Pellets	5	0	10	85	
	Residue	1	100	80	15	
	Total	100	100	100	100	

[a] Includes 10% wash water.

Within the range examined the zinc ion concentration has no adverse effect on leaching.

Zinc-Copper Concentrate

The results of a series of tests run under conditions similar to those given in Table VII but using a zinc-copper concentrate ground to

100% minus 325 mesh are shown in Table VIII, the flowsheet being similar to that in Figure 2.

The zinc dissolution and distribution are substantially the same as for the zinc-lead concentrate.

TABLE VIII
Effect of Zinc Ion Concentration on Zinc-Copper Concentrate Leaching

Cycle No.	Item	Zn	Cu	Fe	S_{total}	$S°$
	Analysis of Products					
1	(1) Zn-Cu concentrate, %	53.0	1.1	8.8	3.26	—
	(2) Pellets, %	11.0	1.0	4.2	80.0	74.6
	(3) Sulfides, %	51.0	4.6	18.0	26.0	—
	(4) Residue, %	3.4	0.8	33.7[a]	5.1	0.4
	(5) Fe residue, %	10.0	1.6	3.4	12.0	nil
2	(6) Recycle solution, g/liter	63.0	0.3	nil	80.4	—
	(7) Pellets, %	6.5	1.3	3.9	87.0	82.8
	(8) Sulfides, %	39.0	8.0	22.0	22.0	—
	(9) Residue, %	2.8	1.4	30.8[a]	18.7	13.1
	(10) Solution, g/liter	140.0	0.8	0.5	79.0	—
	Distribution, % (based on content of concentrate added)					
1	Solution	91	47	7	0	
	Pellets	8	38	18	96	
	Residue	1	15	75	4	
	Total	100	100	100	100	
2	Solution	95	34	4	0	
	Pellets	4	36	13	86	
	Residue	1	30	83	14	
	Total	100	100	100	100	

[a] Residues contain some Fe from laboratory grinding operation.

Sulfur Conversion

An interesting aspect of the results obtained in the cyclic tests described above is presented in Table IX. The amount of $S°$ produced parallels the decomposition of ZnS as measured by zinc extraction, thus substantiating within experimental limits the stoichiometry of the reaction

$$ZnS + H_2SO_4 + \tfrac{1}{2}O_2 \longrightarrow ZnSO_4 + S° + H_2O$$

TABLE IX
Sulfur Conversion

Material	Condition	Zinc extraction, %	Sulfur converted to S°, %
Zn-Pb concentrate	4 hr (1) cycle	92	84
	4 hr (2) cycle	94	87
Zn-Cu concentrate	4 hr (1) cycle	91	90
	4 hr (2) cycle	95	92

Lead Concentrate

A single test was run (see Table X) using a Pb concentrate having the composition: Pb-65.5%, Zn-3.5%, Fe-11.2%, S-20.7%, which was ground to 100% minus 325 mesh. The H_2SO_4 was added in sufficient amount to provide for conversion of PbS to $PbSO_4$ and S°, and of ZnS to $ZnSO_4$ and S°.

In 1 hr at 110°C under 20 psi partial pressure of O_2 the zinc extraction was 89%. This is substantially the same as the extraction obtained under similar conditions with the zinc-lead concentrate, as shown in Table VI.

High Fe-Zn Ratio

To test the effect of high iron content in the concentrate a charge was prepared by mixing equal parts of zinc and pyrrhotite concentrates. Although not exactly comparable to a natural product, the iron/zinc ratio, which is very high, resembles that in a lead-zinc middling product.

The zinc loss in oxidized residue is less than 5%, a result that could not be approached by conventional roasting and leaching methods for a material of this composition.

DISCUSSION

The reaction $ZnS + H_2SO_4 + \frac{1}{2}O_2 \rightarrow ZnSO_4 + S° + H_2O$ appears to proceed readily at 110–115°C when the pH of the leaching solution is below 2.0, the extent of reaction being primarily dependent on the amount of H_2SO_4 present in the reaction mixture. The rate, as may be expected, depends on the surface area of the ZnS, the temperature

TABLE X

Effect of High Fe/Zn Ratio in Concentrate

Conditions:

Charge	=	Zinc concentrate + pyrrhotite (1:1 ratio)
Grind	=	100% minus 325 mesh
Pulp density	=	14%
H_2SO_4 addition	=	1 stoichiometric amount for Zn + Pb
O_2 pressure	=	20 psi
Time	=	4 hr

	Zn	Pb	Fe	S_{total}	$S°$	Insol.
Concentrate (head), %	21.0	4.4	32.0	26.5	—	7.0

Analyses

Products						
Solution, g/liter	72.0	—	1.8	38.2	—	pH-1.3
Pellets, %	8.0	—	5.8	86.0	76.8	
Oxidized residue, %	1.0	4.9	39.4	5.9	3.5	

Distribution, % (based on head analysis)

Solution	85	0	4	0
Pellets	11	0	5	83
Oxidized residue	4	100	91	17

(below the melting point of $S°$), and oxygen pressure, but does not appear to be notably affected by the concentration of Zn^{2+} and SO_4^{2-} ions in the leach solution. Agitation, which also affects the rate, was not studied independently in the present investigation.

As the zinc concentrate used in the majority of the experiments contained marmatite (Zn, Fe)S, it is apparent that the substitution of some Fe in the ZnS lattice does not affect adversely the progress of the reaction. The galena (PbS) present, amounting to about 10%, reacts with H_2SO_4 at 110° to produce $PbSO_4$ and $S°$ according to Eq. (1).

This reaction, as shown in a subsequent paper,[14] is much more rapid than the corresponding reaction with ZnS and is substantially complete by the time 5% of the ZnS has reacted. Therefore in most of the experiments described a stoichiometric amount of H_2SO_4 for the Pb present in the Zn concentrate was also added.

In the early stages of leaching a small amount of iron is dissolved as $FeSO_4$ but, as the reaction proceeds and the amount of ZnS present decreases, the Fe^{2+} present is oxidized to Fe^{3+} in which form it hydrolyzes and precipitates. The rate of oxidation of Fe^{2+} to Fe^{3+} was not studied in detail but it was observed that the final total Fe content of the leach solution could be reduced to less than 1.0 g/liter.

As the leach solutions produced were substantially similar to those produced in conventional zinc leaching operations and as it was considered that they could be purified in the conventional manner (for electrolysis), no purification tests were carried out with the exception of the examples in which $CaCO_3$ was added to increase the pH to about 4–4.5 to precipitate most of the dissolved Fe. The behavior of As and Sb, present in small amounts, was not examined, nor were Cu and Cd removal attempted. The distribution of Ag was not examined but it is assumed that any dissolved Ag would be precipitated in the course of Cu-Cd removal, the remainder reporting in the oxidized residue.

In a number of tests the pellets and flotation concentrates were heated to 400°C to remove S° by distillation, or were heated to 130°C to separate sulfur from sulfides by filtration, and the residual sulfides reground and returned to a subsequent leach. This sulfide product, which consisted largely of the unreacted cores of original ZnS particles or ZnS that had been coated with elemental S, leached as readily as the original concentrate.

The present study does not pretend to provide data relating to the details of the reactions involved or to offer an unequivocal explanation of any of them, or even to define all the limits. One could justifiably postulate that the S° produced in the reaction is derived from the ZnS but this remains to be proved, possibly by the use of radioactive tracers. The role of Fe^{2+} and Fe^{3+} has not been defined.

It has been shown, however, that it is possible to treat a finely ground zinc concentrate with a solution containing about 60 g/liter Zn and 10% to 12% free H_2SO_4 by agitation in an autoclave at 110°C using an O_2 pressure of 20 psi to extract 99% of the Zn from a 40% Zn concentrate in 2–4 hr. · The Pb present is converted to $PbSO_4$ and is present together with iron hydroxide and other insoluble oxides in a residue which is separated by filtration. The S present in ZnS can be quantitatively converted to S° and can be either converted to pellets or separated as a high sulfur concentrate by flotation, thus obviating the necessity of producing sulfur dioxide or sulfuric acid in an electrolytic zinc operation. Sulfur can be separated from the pellets or concentrate by hot filtration and the undissolved ZnS returned to the leach. The resulting solution, having a pH of 1.0–1.5, and a Zn^{2+} content of 120 g/liter or higher, should be amenable to purification by

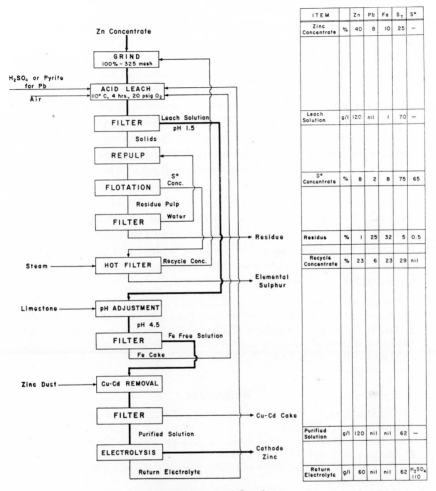

AVERAGE ANALYSIS

ITEM		Zn	Pb	Fe	S_T	S°
Zinc Concentrate	%	40	8	10	25	—
Leach Solution	g/l	120	nil	1	70	—
S° Concentrate	%	8	2	8	75	65
Residue	%	1	25	32	5	0.5
Recycle Concentrate	%	23	6	23	29	nil
Purified Solution	g/l	120	nil	nil	62	—
Return Electrolyte	g/l	60	nil	nil	62	H_2SO_4 110

Fig. 3. Proposed flowsheet.

conventional methods prior to electrolysis, which would produce cathode zinc and regenerate H_2SO_4 for recycling to a subsequent autoclave leaching operation. The residue containing Pb, etc., could be treated by smelting or by the hydrometallurgical procedures described in a subsequent paper.[14]

Although the H_2SO_4 required for reaction with ZnS is regenerated quantitatively by electrolysis it is obviously necessary to supply from outside sources the H_2SO_4 to react with PbS. This comparatively small amount can be added as manufactured acid or it can be produced *in situ* by addition of a small amount of pyrite to the leaching charge.

The flowsheet in Figure 3 depicts in outline a suggested procedure for treating a zinc concentrate to recover elemental sulfur and to extract 99% of the Zn in a single leaching stage. The data show that zinc extraction of more than 95% can be obtained in this way regardless of the ratio of Zn to Fe in the sulfide mixture, and that Zn extraction is independent of the Pb content of the starting material providing sufficient H_2SO_4 is added to react with PbS present.

Autoclave design and techniques are well established for treating sulfide materials at 100 psig and 110°C using solutions at pH 1–2.[18] The amount of heat generated by the reaction should be sufficient to maintain the autoclave at reaction temperature (110–115°C). The amount of air required is only that necessary to oxidize S^{2-} to $S°$ and to oxidize the Fe present. The design of a plant and the selection of optimum operating techniques and conditions would necessarily require careful study in a suitable pilot plant.

The grateful thanks of the authors is extended to Mr. V. N. Mackiw for collaboration and constructive assistance throughout the course of this study, and to Mr. E. L. Brown and Sherritt Gordon Mines Ltd. for encouragement and consistent support of the work and for permission to publish the results. The assistance and advice given by Dr. W. C. Lin and Mr. A. Vizsolyi are gratefully acknowledged.

References

1. Ralston, O. C., *Electrolytic Deposition and Hydrometallurgy of Zinc*, McGraw-Hill, New York, 1921.

2. Liddell, *Handbook of Non-ferrous Metallurgy, Recovery of the Metals*, Vol. II, McGraw-Hill, New York, 1945, pp. 379–443.

3. Mantell, *Industrial Electrochemistry*, 3rd ed., McGraw-Hill, New York, 1950, pp. 347–364.

4. Cominco Zinc Department, *Can. Mining J.*, **75**, 262 (1954).

5. Forward, F. A., and J. Halpern, *Trans. Inst. Mining Met.*, **66**, No. 5, 191 (1956–57).

6. Tronev, V. G., and S. M. Baudin, *Compt. rend. acad. Sci. U.R.S.S.*, **23**, No. 6, 541 (1939).

7. Downes, K. W., and R. W. Bruce, *Can. Mining Met. Bull.*, **48**, 127 (1955).

8. Cornelius, R. J., and J. T. Woodcock, *Proc. Australasian Inst. Mining Met.*, **185**, 65 (1958).

9. Stokes, H. M., *U. S. Geol. Surv. Bull.*, No. **186**, 1901.

10. McKay, D. R., and J. Halpern, *Trans Met. Soc. AIME*, **212**, 301 (1958).

11. Warren, I. H., *Australian J. Appl. Sci.*, **9**, No. 1, 36 (1958).

12. Jackson, K. J., and J. D. H. Strickland, *Trans. Met. Soc. AIME*, **212**, (1958).

13. Seraphim, D. S., and C. S. Samis, *AIME J. Met.*, 1096 (1956).

14. Forward, F. A., and A. Vizsolyi, "A Process for Producing Lead from Galena by Aqueous Acid Oxidation and Ammine Leaching," to be published.

15. Pawlek, F., and H. Pietsch, *Erzmetall.*, **10**, 373 (1957).

16. Canadian Pat. 526,348 (June 12, 1956).

17. Björling, G., *Erzmetall.*, **8**, 781 (1954).

18. Pearce, R. F., J. P. Warner, and V. N. Mackiw, "Refining of Nickel-Copper-Cobalt Mattes by Pressure Leaching and Hydrogen Reduction," AIME San Francisco Meeting, Feb., 1959.

Discussion

J. Dasher (*Crucible Steel Research, Pittsburgh, Pa.*): How much of the S in ZnS goes to sulfate (to supply make-up acid for Pb)? That is, how much lower yield of $S°$ than extraction of Zn? Results at 60 psi show better iron rejection and faster reaction. High pressure operation would require much less heat (due to lower steam content of tail gas) and lead to a cheaper process. The thicker vessel would be smaller and cost no more. Power for agitation would be less.

F. A. Forward and **H. Veltman:** In the experiments described, sufficient H_2SO_4 was added to react with ZnS plus PbS, as indicated on page 1266. Table V shows a relationship between Zn dissolved and H_2SO_4 added which indicates that with decreasing H_2SO_4 concentration, the amount of sulfur oxidized to sulfate increased. Yet it was also observed that under optimum leaching conditions at 100% H_2SO_4 addition the amount of $S°$ produced was usually approximately 5% less than the amount expected, which could mostly be detected in the iron residue, probably in the form of basic iron sulfate.

Generally speaking, higher oxygen pressure increases the reaction rate and hence cuts down the retention time. However, a medium pressure, like 20 psi, turns out to be the optimum for a number of reasons; 100 lb compressed air (20 psi O_2) is much cheaper to produce than 300 lb air (60 psi O_2). Vessels operating at higher pressures may not be higher in initial cost due to smaller size, but operating cost is definitely higher with higher pressures due to the operating problems involved in valves, glands, corrosion, etc. Since the oxidation of the sulfide concentrate is exothermic, more heat lost through the exhaust vapor at lower operating pressure is an advantage because less cooling is required.

R. E. Lund (*St. Joseph Lead Co., Monaca, Pa.*): Has information been gathered on response of various minerals which permits setting forth the sequence in which minerals will be sulfated?

F. A. Forward and **H. Veltman:** The information on response of various minerals is not by any means precise, but there is some indication that the order of difficulty is about as follows, the first named responding most readily:

FeS, PbS, CuS, ZnS, (NiFe)S, $CuFeS_2$, FeS_2

G. Björling (*Dept. of Nonferrous Metallurgy, K. T. H., Sweden*): First, I want to thank Professor Forward and Mr. Veltman for their interesting paper. Some years ago I made a study on the same subject. The rate of reaction for the type of sphalerite I used was, however, very slow, but I found it could be promoted by special agents such as nitric acid, copper salts, and iron salts. As you have used zinc concentrates relatively high in either copper or iron content, I should be glad to get your opinion, Professor Forward, if you think your high rates of oxidation could be caused by these substances acting as catalysts.

F. A. Forward and **H. Veltman**: Professor Björling's interesting paper on this subject published in 1954 and his continuing interest in it have provided valuable contributions to the field. We agree that it is most difficult to effect sulfation with H_2SO_4 producing $S°$ if pure minerals are used. The introduction of an oxygen carrier or catalyst accelerates the conversion to $S°$ (instead of H_2S). We have not used HNO_3 and have no definite proof of the value of Cu salts although there is a possibility that they may contribute in some measure; the presence of Fe salts is particularly effective, but as noted in the paper their role has not been fully defined.

Observations on the Kinetics of the Reduction of NiSO₄ in Aqueous Solutions

W. G. COURTNEY*

Experiment, Inc., Richmond, Virginia

and

F. A. SCHAUFELBERGER

CIBA Ltd., Basle, Switzerland

Abstract

The preparation of metal by chemical reduction of metal salt from aqueous solution has been developed into a commercial process by Chemical Construction Corp. and other companies and is now being practiced in several refineries. This paper deals with reaction kinetics in the chemical reduction at 150–200°C of NiSO₄ from aqueous H_2SO_4 and NH_3–$(NH_4)_2SO_4$ solution by various reducing agents to form nickel metal particles. The results of exploratory studies of kinetics of nucleation of nickel metal with various reducing agents and of growth kinetics in the Ni(II)–H_2 reaction are given.

INTRODUCTION

The preparation of metals by reduction of the metal ion from salt solution by reducing gases such as hydrogen has been known for almost a hundred years[1] and has recently been developed into commercial processes by Chemical Construction Corp. and other companies (Sherritt-Gordon Mines, Howe Sound Mining Co., National Lead Co., Freeport Sulphur Co., Whitaker Metals Corp.). However, there is only limited fundamental information on the thermodynamics[2,3] and particularly the kinetic aspects of the reduction processes.[4] Recent investigations of the kinetics of the reduction of Co(II) by H_2 from ammoniacal aqueous solution by Kaneko and

* Formerly with Chemical Construction Corporation, New York.

Wadsworth[5] and Courtney[6] gave conflicting results. Mackiw, Lin, and Kunda[7] have reported on the reduction of Ni(II) by H_2 from ammoniacal aqueous solution. This paper presents the results of an exploratory study of reduction kinetics in the Ni(II)-H_2 reaction. General observations about nucleation, growth, and agglomeration in the Ni(II)-H_2 reduction are given, and reduction kinetics are separated into nucleation and growth kinetics when possible.

GENERAL EXPERIMENTAL APPROACH

From a fundamental viewpoint, metal reduction from solution can be divided into nucleation, growth, and agglomeration. Nucleation is usually defined as the formation of the smallest thermodynamically stable particle (nucleus) of new phase from the parent phase. Nucleation can be either homonucleation, where the metal nucleus is formed directly from metal atoms produced by chemical reduction in the bulk solution, or heteronucleation, where the initial deposition of metal takes place on the surface of a foreign catalytic particle (e.g., dust or insoluble salt particle). Growth is the subsequent atom-by-atom deposition of metal onto the metal nucleus or a large metal particle. Agglomeration is the formation of a stable "biparticle" or "multiparticle" from two separate metal particles or smaller agglomerates.

Therefore, our experimental approach was specifically oriented (a) to investigating nucleation, growth, and agglomeration phenomena individually insofar as possible and (b) to interpret a commercial reduction rate in terms of these individual phenomena. It should be noted that an observed rate of reduction usually involves both nucleation and growth kinetics, and conclusions about the separate kinetics are warranted only if the experimental conditions are carefully selected.

Nickel, cobalt, or copper metal was readily formed (the metal particles readily nucleated and grew) by H_2 reduction of the metal ion from acidic solution at 150–200°C (equilibria were discussed in refs. 2 and 3). In basic NH_3-$(NH_4)_2SO_4$ solution, however, these metals did not homonucleate by H_2 although they readily grew by H_2. Thus, homonucleation by H_2 is a bottleneck in H_2 reduction of these ions from basic solution.

However, unless a selective copper or nickel reduction as a separation from nickel or cobalt[2,3] is to be carried out, most commercial processes prefer to reduce from basic solution because of greater ease of operation. This paper discusses the use of small amounts of foreign materials to nucleate the $NiSO_4$-H_2 reaction and also growth and agglomeration in basic solution.

Most experimental work was done in a 3-liter stirred autoclave. The stuffing box was Teflon-packed without lubrication because other work indicated that reduction could be initiated with oil particles or autoclave "dirt." Temperature was controlled to within 0.5°C by an electric heater located directly inside the autoclave together with an electrically heated Dowtherm jacket around the body of the autoclave. All metal parts in contact with the charge solution were titanium. Bomb samples were cooled, filtered on the bench, and analyzed for nickel by electrodeposition or spectrophotometric techniques. Other work indicated negligible dissolution of metal or any basic salt in the sample by this technique. Reagent grade chemicals were used. The H_2 was obtained from the Air Reduction Co. and used from the cylinder without purification. The H_2 partial pressure during a run could be maintained constant within 10 psig.

Preliminary bench tests were made examining the effect of agitation parameters (rpm, baffles, etc.) and permitted selecting different types of agitation which gave a wide variation in the dispersion of powder particles and gas bubbles through the liquid.

Some work was also done using a windowed autoclave (a sight glass) which permitted visual observation of the reacting solution. The windowed autoclave was heated in an oven and stirred by rotation.

RESULTS AND DISCUSSION

Reduction kinetics depended drastically upon whether or not a basic nickel sulfate precipitated in the solution. Attention is drawn to the fact that the solubility of most compounds decreases rapidly above about 120°C.[3] Nucleation, growth, and agglomeration in solutions giving no salt precipitate are described first. Results where a salt precipitates, which occurs with most commercial solutions, are then described briefly.

Nucleation

The difficult Ni(II)-H$_2$ homonucleation from NiSO$_4$-NH$_3$-(NH$_4$)$_2$-SO$_4$ solution can be bypassed either by using chemical reducing agents which homonucleate Ni metal particles by chemical reduction

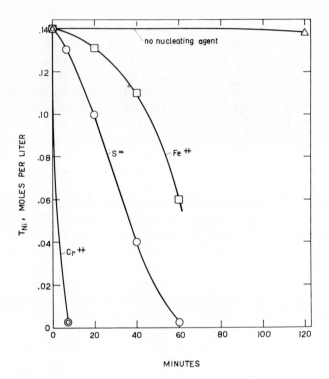

Fig. 1. Nucleation of Ni(II) solution. Conditions: 0.138 mole NiSO$_4$, 0.95 mole (NH$_4$)$_2$SO$_4$, 0.36 mole NH$_3$, 175°C, 600 psig H$_2$ pp, 0.018 mole Fe(II) as FeSO$_4$, 0.030 mole S^{2-} as Na$_2$S, 0.020 mole Cr(II) as CrSO$_4$. Catalyst solution rapidly injected into cold solution.

of Ni(II) ion (these particles then act as seed particles for the Ni-(II)-H$_2$ reduction) or by using catalysts which heteronucleate the Ni(II)-H$_2$ reduction. Although the subsequent Ni(II)-H$_2$ reduction will of course take place with either type of nucleation, the rate of reduction will depend upon the number of Ni metal particles initially formed, i.e., nucleation kinetics.

The effect of various chemical reducing agents and catalysts on the nucleation of the Ni(II)-H_2 reduction was explored at 150–200°C and 600 psig H_2 using a dilute solution containing (g/liter) 22 $NiSO_4$, 110 $(NH_4)_2SO_4$, and 6.1 NH_3 (initial mole ratio of NH_3/ Ni(II) = 2.6). This solution was chosen because it did not precipitate a visible salt at the temperature of reduction (being heavily buffered) and because it did not nucleate nickel metal by H_2 reduction but would grow additional metal by H_2 reduction onto any particles formed by the nucleating agents. The efficiency of the nucleation agent was analyzed by measuring the rate of the subsequent Ni(II)-H_2 reduction.

Figure 1 gives typical results with no nucleating agent and with Cr(II), S^{2-}, and Fe(II) added and shows that Cr(II) is a very efficient nulceation agent, S^{2-} is less efficient, and Fe(II) is still less efficient. Reproducibility was limited to 50%.

Nucleation was drastically affected by the degree of agitation and particularly by the method whereby the nucleating agent was mixed with the Ni(II) solution. Efficient nucleation required a very high level of agitation in the liquid; for example, Cr(II) nucleation was negligible with merely "medium" agitation.

Ferrous ion gave nucleation in 15 min (Fig. 1) when an aqueous solution of ferrous ammonium sulfate was rapidly injected into the Ni(II) solution at 25°C, the solution heated to 175°C, and H_2 added, but injection of the ferrous solution into the Ni(II) solution at 175°C and immediately followed by H_2 addition usually gave nucleation only after about 45 min. The Fe(III)/Fe(II) ratio seemed to be unimportant. However, addition of $Fe(OH)_2$ never nucleated the Ni(II)-H_2 reaction. These results suggest that a mixed Fe(II)-Ni(II) hydroxide or basic sulfate is involved in nucleating the Ni-(II)-H_2 reaction even though the nickel solution without catalyst does not precipitate a salt. It would appear that the exact nucleation mechanism will be difficult to determine. Of further interest is that chemical and x-ray analyses after injection of Fe(II) solution but before H_2 addition indicated the formation of solid Fe_3O_4 and nickel metal. Evans and Wanklyn[8] found that $NiSO_4$ catalyzed the disproportionation of $Fe(OH)_2$ to form Fe_3O_4, H_2O, and H_2.

Chromous sulfate solution* rapidly nucleated the Ni(II)-H_2

* Prepared by the reduction of acidified $Cr_2(SO_4)_3$ solution with Zn-Hg or with chromium metal.

reaction (Fig. 1). Rapid mixing at 25°C was best, and excellent agitation was required. The Cr(II)/Cr(III) ratio was unimportant, and addition of Cr(OH)$_2$ was not effective. Therefore, we again conclude that a mixed Cr(II)-Ni(II) salt seems to be important in nucleation.*

Cyanide and sulfide ions (added as aqueous solution of NaCN or Na$_2$S) were between Fe(II) and Cr(II) in nucleation effectiveness. However, addition of solid Ni(CN)$_2$.4H$_2$O, NiS, or Ni$_3$S$_2$ was not effective. Again, formation of a mixed salt seems to be important. It is curious to note that x-ray analysis indicated the formation of a small amount of Ni$_3$C in cyanide nucleation of the Ni(II)-H$_2$ reduction.†

Sodium hypophosphite and hydrazine nucleated the Ni(II)-H$_2$ reaction, but the chemistry of the nucleation reactions is uncertain. Hypophosphite ion probably formed some nickel phosphide. Also, we occasionally (and inadvertently) nucleated by unknown auto-clave dirt; that is, for no apparent reason.

No nucleation was observed with Fe$_3$O$_4$, NiO, copper metal, titanium metal, stainless steel, TiC, quartz, colloidal graphite (Aquadag, Acheson Colloid Company), or by NiSO$_4$.(NH$_4$)$_2$-SO$_4$.6H$_2$O.

In summary, nucleation of the Ni(II)-H$_2$ reaction usually seems to involve a mixed salt of Ni(II) and the reducing agent with only transient nucleation effectiveness, and elucidation of the nucleation mechanisms will be difficult.

Growth

Once nucleation is finished and nickel metal particles are formed, the gross reduction rate of the Ni(II)-H$_2$ reaction will depend upon the surface area of the particles which are present and also the growth

* It should be pointed out here that the lowest H$_2$ reduction temperatures known to us were made possible using Cr(II) nucleation. One molar nickel solutions were completely reduced at temperatures as low as 70–90°C at H$_2$ partial pressures of 300 psig in as little as 3 min! The decanted metal product was a very active seed for the next few densification reactions at similarly mild conditions. Cr(II) was not effective in nucleating slightly acidic NiSO$_4$ solutions at similar temperatures.

† Cyanide nucleation of the Co(II)-H$_2$ reduction in aqueous ammoniacal solution resulted in the formation of an unidentified organic compound, possibly CH$_3$NH$_2$.

kinetics, which involve diffusion of nickel ion and H_2 to the surface of the growing metal particles and chemical reaction at the surface.

We investigated growth kinetics at the surface by using (a) Ni solutions which did not nucleate or precipitate a salt at the reduction temperature (which would obscure growth kinetics), (b) a high level of agitation to avoid slow H_2 transfer from the gas to the solution or slow diffusion of species in the bulk solution, and (c) nickel metal seed particles whose surface area did not change appreciably during reduction and which did not agglomerate or fracture during reduction.

The rate of disappearance of Ni(II) from an aqueous $NiSO_4$-NH_3-$(NH_4)_2SO_4$ solution containing nickel metal seed powder was investigated at 150–175°C and 50–600 psig H_2 partial pressure. The

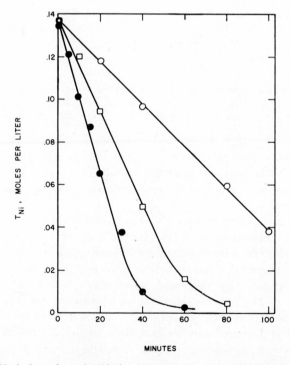

Fig. 2. Variation of total Ni(II) with time at various H_2 partial pressures (psig): 0, 50; □, 200; ●, 600. Conditions: 0.138 mole $NiSO_4$, 0.41 mole NH_3, 0.95 mole $(NH_4)_2SO_4$, 100 g/liter metal powder, 150°.

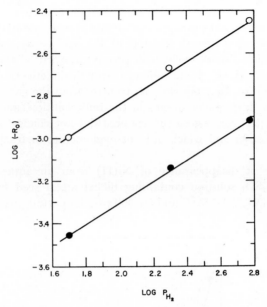

Fig. 3. Effect of H_2 partial pressure on reduction rate. Conditions: O, 0.138 mole $NiSO_4$, 0.41 mole NH_3, 0.95 mole $(NH_4)_2SO_4$, 100 g/liter metal powder, 150°; ●, 0.138 mole $NiSO_4$, 0.41 mole NH_3, 1.7 mole $(NH_4)_2SO_4$, 50 g/liter metal powder, 150°.

seed powder was previously prepared by H_2 reduction of $NiSO_4$ solution. The particles had diameters between 50 and 100 μ and a BET surface area of 0.5 m²/g, indicating considerable internal surface area.

Figure 2 shows typical plots of T_{Ni} vs time, where T_{Ni} is the total molar concentration of Ni(II) in the solution. Reduction rates $R(= -dT_{Ni}/dt)$ were constant for 80% of the run under all conditions investigated. The reduction rates tended to decrease as the Ni(II) concentration decreased below about 0.03 mole because of approach to the Ni(II)-NH_3-H_2-H^+ equilibrium.[2] Results were reproducible within 10% except that reduction rates tended to decrease after the seed powder had been used for more than about ten reductions, indicating a decrease in specific surface area of the metal seed particles.

The values of R were independent of agitation parameters, indicating that the rate-controlling reaction in reduction was at the sur-

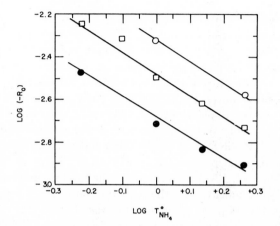

Fig. 4. Effect of $(NH_4)_2SO_4$ on reduction rate. Conditions: O, 0.138 mole NiSO₄, 0.41 mole NH₃, 50 g/liter metal powder, 600 P_{H_2}, 175°; □, 0.138 mole NiSO₄, 1.24 mole NH₃, 50 g/liter metal powder, 600 P_{H_2}, 175°; ●, 0.138 mole NiSO₄, 0.41 mole NH₃, 50 g/liter metal powder, 600 P_{H_2}, 150°.

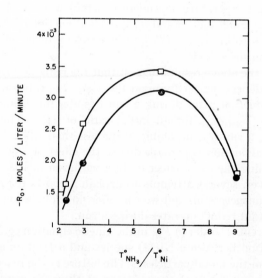

Fig. 5. Effect of mole ratio of NH₃ to Ni (II) on reduction rate. Conditions: □, 0.138 mole NiSO₄, 1.7 mole $(NH_4)_2SO_4$, 50 g/liter metal powder, 600 P_{H_2}, 175°; ●, 0.138 mole NiSO₄, 0.95 mole $(NH_4)_2SO_4$, 50 g/liter metal powder, 600 P_{H_2}, 150°.

face of the growing nickel metal particles. No reduction could be observed in identical runs without seed, indicating negligible nucleation.

The reduction rates at zero time R_0 do not involve the variation in Ni(II), NH_3, and NH_4^+ concentrations during the run and were analyzed first. Two series of runs were made at various H_2 partial pressures with other initial conditions held constant during each series. Figure 3 shows that plots of log $(-R_0)$ vs log P_{H_2} were linear with slopes of $1/2$. Runs were then made at various initial total concentrations of $(NH_4)_2SO_4$, T_{NH_4}, with other initial conditions constant. Figure 4 shows that plots of log $(-R_0)$ vs log T_{NH_4} were again linear with slopes of -1. Runs varying only the total initial concentration of NH_3, $T_{NH_3}°$, indicate that the reduction rate went through a maximum when the $T_{NH_3}°/T_{Ni}°$ mole ratio was about 6 (Fig. 5). These results indicate a preliminary rate expression of

$$R^0 = A \cdot f(T_{NH_3}) \cdot \frac{P_{H_2}^{1/2}}{T_{NH_4}°}$$

where A is a temperature-dependent constant which includes kinetic and thermodynamic factors and $f(T_{NH_3}°)$ is a function of $T_{NH_3}°$. Several attempts to interpret $f(T_{NH_3}°)$ in terms of the Ni(II)-NH_3 complexes were unsuccessful.

Although the above results suggest that the reduction rate during a run should depend markedly upon the T_{NH_3}/T_{Ni} ratio, we observed constant reduction rates during a run despite, for example, a 50% variation in T_{NH_3}/T_{Ni} for an initial ratio of 2.2. The change in T_{NH_4} during a run was negligible, being less than 10%. A constant rate during reduction is perhaps due to the effect of T_{Ni} on R essentially canceling the T_{NH_3} effect or to a variation in the solubility of H_2. However, several attempts to explain a constant rate on these bases were unsuccessful, and we can offer no explanation for the observed constant reduction rates during a run.

The apparent $1/2$ order in P_{H_2} in the kinetic equation could be due to a slow reaction between a Ni(II) species and a H atom adsorbed on the surface of the metal particles. The nature of the reactive Ni species is uncertain. Visual observations of these Ni solutions in the windowed autoclave showed that the blue solution turned green at about 150°C, indicating that little Ni(II) was present as the tetrammine or higher ammine complexes at the reduction conditions used here.* The decrease in R_0 with a high value of $T_{NH_3}°$ suggests that ammoniated Ni(II) species are not reducible and are present in appreciable concentrations at the high $T_{NH_3}°/T_{Ni}°$ ratios. The inverse order in $T_{NH_4}°$ suggests that the reactive nickel species may be the NiOH$^+$ ion.

Agglomeration

Agglomeration between the growing metal particles during a reduction is important because it will affect the surface area available for growth; that is, the gross reduction rate of the Ni(II)-H$_2$ reaction would decrease abruptly if individual metal particles suddenly agglomerated to form a single dense cluster.

In actual practice, the end-product powder from a Fe(II)-, Cr(II)-, or S^2-nucleated Ni(II)-H$_2$ reduction consists of loose, irregularly shaped agglomerates with overall dimensions ranging from 10 to 100 μ (Fig. 6) and which in turn are composed of 1–3 μ primary metal particles. For comparison, the CN$^-$-nucleated powder consists of rather dense, spherical, 10–100 μ agglomerates (Fig. 7) which in turn are occasionally composed of 0.05 μ primary metal particles according to x-ray line broadening. The hypophosphite-nucleated powder consists of linear agglomerates about 20 μ long and 2 to 5 μ wide, and this linear agglomeration is accentuated by a reduction in a magnetic field.[9]

The internal area (BET adsorption) of the Fe(II)-nucleated agglomerates is ten to a thousand times the silhouette area, but this internal area usually can be utilized in the reduction. In commercial operation, the agglomerates from a nucleation run are repeatedly used as seed powder for the reduction of another batch of solution. In commercial operation this is done up to 25 times or more.[7] However, it occasionally happens that the seed suddenly loses its "activity" for another reduction, indicating that the agglomerate was filled in and now only the silhouette area is available for growth.

Agglomeration theory[10] predicts that the primary nickel metal particles will grow to a certain critical size before they agglomerate, and

* There appears to be no information in the literature on the thermodynamic stabilities of the Ni(II)-NH$_3$ complexes at the present elevated temperatures, and data at room temperature cannot be extrapolated with confidence. It may be noted that the blue Co(II)-NH$_3$ complexes also tend to break up at about 150°C, but the blue Cu (II)-NH$_3$ complexes appear to be stable to at least 200°C.

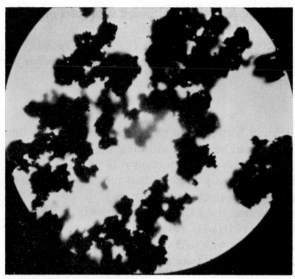

Fig. 6. Typical agglomeration of Ni metal powder prepared by Fe(II) catalysis of Ni(II)-H_2 reduction. Conditions: 0.138 mole $NiSO_4$, 0.95 mole $(NH_4)_2SO_4$, 0.36 g/liter NH_3, 0.018 mole Fe(II) as $FeSO_4$, 175°C, 700 psig H_2 pp. Sample taken after 60 min of reduction. One scale division = 3.6 μ.

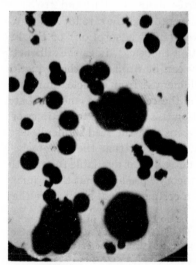

Fig. 7. Typical agglomeration of Ni metal powder prepared by CN^- catalysis of Ni(II)-H_2 reduction. Conditions: identical to Fig. 6 except 0.04 mole CN^- as NaCN, no Fe(II). One scale division = 3.6 μ.

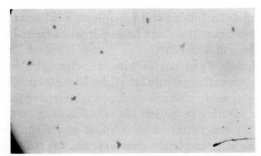

Fig. 8. Early stage of agglomeration in Fe(II) catalysis of Ni(II)-H$_2$ reduction. Conditions: identical to Fig. 6 except sample taken after 15 min of reduction. Magnification: 1 mm = 3.6 μ. Monoparticles are at the upper left, biparticles at upper right, and triparticles at lower left.

our results indicate that Ni metal particles do not agglomerate until they reach a diameter of 2 to 5 μ in basic solution and 5 to 10 μ in acid solution. Figure 8 shows single nickel metal particles about 3 μ in diameter and also shows biparticle, triparticle, and tetraparticle agglomerates of these primary particles. Nickel particles with diameters to 800 A have been photographed by the electron microscope. However, agglomeration theory is of limited usefulness in predicting the size or shape of the multiparticle agglomerates noted above.

It may be noted that the primary particles or the agglomerates will also tend to agglomerate to the walls of the autoclave, particularly at the poorly agitated surfaces. Recognizing and overcoming this "plating" effect in the early stages of commercial development of these H$_2$ reductions was difficult. Wall agglomeration ranges from a foil (composed of the primary particles) to a thick sponge (composed of the large agglomerates). We have never seen a true wall plate such as would be formed from atom-by-atom growth on the autoclave wall.

In the above-mentioned window autoclave, agglomeration can be followed directly. Very often (Cu reduction, for instance) it appears to be a matter of seconds that out of a solution turbid to the eye large metal agglomerates (up to 1–3 mm dimension) will form.

Commercial Reduction

The commercial operation of H$_2$ reduction from ammoniacal or acidic solution is economical only if concentrated metal solutions are processed. Even when quite heavily buffered, however, concentrated ammoniacal nickel solutions still precipitate a substantial fraction of their Ni(II) ion as an ill-defined basic salt when heated to the reduction temperature of 150–175°C.

This salt drastically interferes with reduction phenomena because microscopic observations showed that the Ni metal particles nucleate, grow, and agglomerate inside the salt particles during the early stages of reduction. During reduction the salt dissolves, tending to maintain the Ni(II) concentration in solution at its equilibrium value. Eventually the salt completely dissolves, and the reduction now continues on the pre-formed metal agglomerates. Therefore, an analysis of commercial reduction in terms of conventional nucleation, growth, and agglomeration is almost impossible.

In extreme cases this salt precipitate can prevent reduction. For example, if a Ni(II) solution (for instance, g/liter): 110 $NiSO_4$, 27 $NH_3(NH_3/Ni(II) = 2.1)$ containing Fe(II) ion and only 100 g/liter $(NH_4)_2SO_4$ is heated to 175°C for 2 hr, it becomes very viscous due to precipitation of the basic salt. Addition of H_2 at this point gives little or no reduction, perhaps because the mass transfer of H_2 into the gelatinous mixture is very poor or because some basic salts during the prolonged heating may become refractory to reduction. Also, in the Co(II)-H_2 reduction from acidic solution, $CoSO_4 \cdot (NH_4)_2SO_4 \cdot 6H_2O$ occasionally precipitates. This salt can coat any cobalt metal seed particles present and completely prevent reduction, even though solution composition, temperature, and H_2 partial pressure permit reduction.

The authors are pleased to acknowledge the advice of Messrs. Dasher, Hulburt, McGauley, Roberts, and Roy and numerous other people. Particular thanks are due to Messrs. Shaw, Sullivan, and others, who conducted the experimental work.

References

1. Literature reviews are given in refs. 2 and 3.
2. Schaufelberger, F. A., and T. K. Roy, *Bull. Inst. Mining Met.*, **581**, 375 (1955).
3. Schaufelberger, F. A., *J. Metals*, **8**, 695 (1956).
4. Halpern, J., and collaborators, for references see E. R. MacGregor and J. Halpern, *Trans. Met. Soc. AIME*, **212**, 244 (1958).
5. Kaneko, T. M., and M. E. Wadsworth, *J. Phys. Chem.*, **60**, 457 (1956).
6. Courtney, W. G., *J. Phys. Chem.*, **61**, 693(1957).
7. Mackiw, V. N., W. C. Lin, and W. Kunda, *J. Metals*, **9**, 786(1957).
8. Evans, U. R., and J. N. Wanklyn, *Nature*, **162**, 27 (1948).
9. Courtney, W. G., *J. Chem. Phys.*, **23**, 1174 (1955).
10. Kruyt, H. R., *Colloid Science*, Vol. I, Elsevier, New York, 1952.

Theoretical Aspects of the Pickle Lag Phenomenon

W. G. HINES

The Steel Company of Canada, Ltd., Hamilton, Ontario, Canada

Abstract

The concepts of "pickle lag" and "lag layer" are re-examined in the light of experimental results with annealed black plate. The "pickle lag" reflects indirectly the more fundamental characteristics of the surface and is of limited value in assessing these properties.

The shape of the reaction rate curve, on which the pickel lag depends, can be deduced on the basis of a non-uniform layer theory.

Experimental evidence is inconsistent with this view, and suggests that the controlling factor in the production of pickle lag is varying cathodic polarization. This leads to the same mathematical consequences as above, so that the lag layer hypothesis is unnecessary.

INTRODUCTION

Steel, immersed in hot concentrated hydrochloric acid, reacts rapidly with a consequent loss in weight. The rate of the reaction may be, and has been, studied by periodic determinations of the weight loss, either on a single specimen or on a group of specimens removed one at a time at intervals. Both weight loss techniques possess inherent inaccuracies, especially when reaction periods of the order of 5–30 sec are involved. In addition, the need for repeated weighings makes the methods tedious and unsuitable for routine production testing.

The autographic test procedure developed by the American Can Company avoids the time-consuming drawbacks of the weight loss method and is extensively used to evaluate the pickle lag of black plate. In this method, the hydrogen evolved during the reaction is collected and the rate of the reaction is followed by means of the rise in pressure as gas is evolved. The apparatus is represented diagrammatically in Figure 1. This pressure rise is recorded as a function of

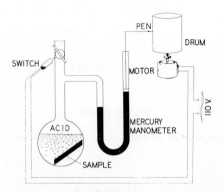

Fig. 1. Apparatus for autographic test procedure.

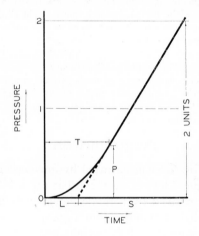

Fig. 2. Idealized pickle lag.

time by a pen which traces a graph on a steadily rotating drum.   In general, curves similar to the idealized one of Figure 2 are obtained.

During an initial period T, the rate of change of pressure (proportional to the reaction rate) is gradually increasing from its initially low value to a higher final rate (ideally taken as constant).   This final rate can be characterized by the slope of the pressure-time line which in turn can be measured by the time interval S required for the pressure to change by 2 units (the normal range used in the test).   The final rate of pressure change is then $\Delta p/\Delta t = 2/S$.

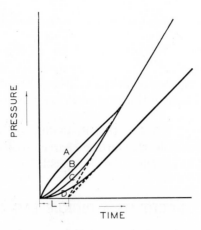

Fig. 3. Typical experimental curves.

When the period T has elapsed, the acid has reacted with sufficient iron to yield the hydrogen which produces a pressure P. It is this amount of iron which has frequently been considered as constituting the "lag layer" on the surface.

Interest in pickle lag stems from observations reported by Willey, Krickl, and Hartwell[1] indicting a significant inverse correlation between the pickle lag of black plate and the shelf life of tin cans made from it, i.e., lower pickle lags corresponded to longer shelf life.

The pickle lag value L has been defined by the originators of the test as the time interval cut off on the time axis by the backward extrapolation of the straight portion of the pressure-time curve.

From the similarity of the triangles it follows that

$$(T - L)/S = P/2$$

or the pickle lag

$$L = T - (P \cdot S)/2 \qquad (1)$$

This clearly shows the dependence of the pickle lag on three other quantities which can be simply interpreted in terms of a layer picture.

The pickle lag value is not, however, a primary concept. It can perhaps be regarded formally as a period during which no hydrogen is evolved, following which reaction at the final rate would produce the observed amount of hydrogen for any period greater than T. Such an approach emphasizes what may well be a rather serious deficiency in the pickle lag as an indication of surface properties—the fact that it ignores almost entirely the behavior of the steel surface during the period of initial attack. This weakness shows up clearly in Figure 3. This represents a number of different curves, all of shapes which have been encountered in experimental work on the annealing of black plate.

It is hard to avoid a feeling that these differences in shape reflect substantial differences in the surface characteristics which are only too easily masked by assigning the same pickle lag value to each of the specimens.

THE CONCEPT OF A PICKLE LAG LAYER

The shape of the pressure-time curve does not by itself indicate the mechanism of the corrosion reaction occurring at the metal surface. It does, however, provide a basis for evaluating the plausibility of any suggested hypothesis. This can be inferred from the degree to which the curve deduced mathematically from the hypothesis agrees in its characteristics with the curves obtained experimentally.

Perhaps the simplest interpretation which can be proposed to account for the phenomenon of pickle lag involves the concept of a "pickle lag layer." This is considered as a layer of material somehow less reactive than the underlying steel. Accordingly, until it is removed (presumably in the time period T), reaction proceeds less rapidly than is ultimately possible; the pressure-time curve bends upward as this layer is gradually removed.

A second interpretation, proposed by Koehler,[2] is that the lag effect is the result of the presence of oxides in the grain boundaries, the lag continuing until the inhibiting effect of the oxides has been eliminated, presumably by their dissolution.

MATHEMATICAL ASPECTS OF THE PICKLE LAG CURVE

1. Uniform Layer

The assumed existence of a homogeneous layer of uniform thickness implies immediately that the reactivity of the layer increases as it is penetrated; only such a changing susceptibility to corrosion could account for the gradual increase in slope of the curve as reaction proceeds.

The variation of the reaction rate with time would appear to be entirely fortuitous, consequently, little can be predicted about the shape of the curve, or about the interrelations of the various characteristics, L, T, P, and S. However, since the amount of material to be removed before a constant rate of attack is attained is definite, it would be expected that the value of P should remain the same, regardless of the conditions of the test.

2. Nonuniform Layer

(a) Constant Rate of Attack

An alternative approach is to assume that certain areas of the steel surface react initially at a slower rate than does the normal steel surface. It is possible (but not essential) to regard these areas as being covered with a lag layer which evolves hydrogen more slowly (if at all) than does the "clean" steel which, at all times, reacts at a rate characteristic of the steel itself and unchanged as attack proceeds.

The apparent increase in the rate of attack results, in such a view, from the gradual reduction in area of the more slowly reacting (or at least hydrogen-producing) material until it disappears, after a time T, and the rate is then everywhere the same.

Such a picture lends itself readily to mathematical treatment.

If the rate of pickling is measured by the rate of pressure change it can be expressed by

$$(dp)/(dt)_t = [A_t \cdot 2/S] + [(1 - A_t) \cdot (2/S) \cdot F] \qquad (2)$$

where $(dp/(dt)_t$ is the rate of change of pressure at the instant t; A_t is the fraction of the test area corroding at the normal or final rate, at the instant t; F is the ratio of the rates of hydrogen evolution from the areas of low rate compared with those corroding at the final rate; and $2/S$ is the final (constant) rate of hydrogen evolution (from "normal" steel).

Integrating this equation, the pressure at any instant is given by the expression

$$p = [(2Ft)/S] + 2(1 - F)/S \int_0^t A_t dt \qquad (3)$$

When the area of slow attach has just disappeared (i.e., $t = T$)

$$p = P = 2/S [FT + (1 - F) \int_0^T A_t dt] \qquad (4)$$

Various assumptions as to the way in which A_t varies with time may then be made, and the shape of the calculated pressure-time curve compared with the shape observed to decide on the validity of the assumed relationship.

The simplest assumption, consistent with the observed behavior, is that the area of steel corroding at the normal or final rate increases linearly with time; i.e.,

$$A_t = A_0 + (1 - A_0)t/T \tag{5}$$

where A_0 is the fraction of the surface initially reacting at the rate $(2/S)$ $(1 > A_0 > 0)$.

Substituting this relationship in Eq. (4) and carrying out the necessary integration and simplification, the resulting expression is

$$\begin{aligned} P &= T/S \left[1 + F + A_0 (1 - F)\right] \\ &= T/S (1 + R) \text{ where } R = [F + A_0 (1 - F)] \end{aligned} \tag{6}$$

When this value of P is substituted in Eq. (1), viz., $L = T - (PS/2)$, the expression for the pickle lag value becomes

$$L = T/2 (1 - R) \tag{7}$$

The values of F and A cannot readily be evaluated. The combination, as R, is easily determined since it represents the ratio of the initial rate of hydrogen evolution to the final rate. Thus,

$$\begin{aligned} (dn)/(dt)_0 &= [A_0(2/S)] + (1 - A_0) 2F/S \\ &= 2/S [F + A_0 (1 - F)] = R(2/S) \end{aligned} \tag{8}$$

or the initial rate $= R \times$ (the final rate). Equation (7) can be of course rewritten as

$$L/T = (1 - R)/2 \tag{9}$$

and Eq. (6) as

$$PS/T = (1 + R) \tag{10}$$

Multiplication together of these two equations yields equation

$$L\,PS/T^2 = (1 + R) (1 - R)/2 = (1 - R^2)/2 \tag{11}$$

In the case of many steels, R turns out to be a small fraction, often less than 0.1 and rarely above 0.25. When R is negligibly small, then to a close approximation, Eqs. (9), (10), and (11) above reduce to

$$L/T = 0.5; \ P \cdot S/T = 1.0; \ L \cdot P \cdot S/T^2 = 0.5$$

The last relation should be quite generally true since even when R is not negligible (e.g., 0.25), the value of R^2 is very small (e.g., 0.06).

To investigate the applicability of the theory, data from a study of the effect of temperature on pickle lag values were analyzed. The results are shown in Table I.

TABLE I

Temp, °C	Pickle lag L, sec	Value of the ratio		
		L/T	$P \cdot S/T$	$L \cdot P \cdot S/T^2$
25	720	0.58	0.86	0.50
35	280	0.51	1.01	0.51
45	138	0.55	1.01	0.55
55	78	0.48	1.04	0.50
65	45	0.50	1.03	0.52
75	25	0.48	1.06	0.51
85	15	0.50	1.06	0.53
90	11	0.50	0.99	0.50

The constancy of the three ratios is rather striking, particularly in view of the range of values for the pickle lag (and correspondingly for T and S).

In general, the ratio of T to L will be somewhat in excess of $2:1$, in fact, if $R = 0.1$, the ratio would be $2.2:1$. In Koehler's work,[2] he determined the time required for a test specimen to attain a constant potential as his lag characteristic. In discussing Koehler's work, Vaurio of the U. S. Steel Co. pointed out that these values were almost twice the pickle lag value as conventionally determined and submitted a graph showing an approximate ratio of $2.3:1$. No reason for this was adduced at the time. If, however, it is assumed that the attainment of constant potential occurs at the same time as the attainment of the maximum pickling rate, a quite reasonable supposition, then this ratio of $2.3:1$ is seen to be quite in line with the above derivation.

These indications, while not an irrefutable proof of the hypothesis, at least render plausible the picture of the phenomenon as resulting from a combination of a normal rate of attack on certain areas and of a slower attack on others, the area of the latter decreasing more or less linearly with time.

The mathematical consequences of this picture are the same whether this area of slower attack is the result of a lag layer or of some other (e.g., electrochemical) inhibiting factor.

(b) Varying Rate of Attack

The above discussion has assumed that the rate of attack was constant, though different, on each of the two kinds of surface (i.e., on lagged and nonlagged areas).   It is conceivable that the rates vary and this is, in certain respects, the view of Koehler.[2] He suggests that the rate of attack on the steel is somehow inhibited locally by the presence of "grain boundary oxides."   These dissolve at a rate which will be different from that of the steel, and in any event, as they do not result in the formation of hydrogen, the rate of hydrogen evolution will "differ" from that from the steel.

As the oxides are removed, the inhibiting effect on the surrounding steel decreases so that the steel, although itself unmodified, now corrodes at a more rapid rate.

This view can be thought of as divising the surface into an area of grain boundary oxides evolving hydrogen at one constant rate (probably zero) and an area of steel corroding at a steadily increasing rate. However, the behavior of this model of the surface appears to be almost identical to that already described if we redivide the surface on a different basis.

If it be assumed that the inhibiting effect of any grain boundary oxide is restricted to a small surrounding area, perhaps only to immediately adjacent ferrite grains, the slowly corroding area can be taken as the area of (oxide + inhibited ferrite grains) and the area of normal attack as made up of ferrite grains not so inhibited.   By considering the surface in this way, the mathematical treatment becomes parallel to that already outlined and the same relationships between L, T, P, and S may be derived.

A similar approach may be used with any electrochemical theory based on inhibition (such as that to be proposed later) to convert it into the form considered under "constant rate of attack on nonuniform layers."   Accordingly, these theories cannot be differentiated on the basis of the mathematical consequences as already derived. Additional data are required.

WEAKNESS IN THE LAYER CONCEPT

The mathematical consequences of the layer concept have already been discussed and may be summarized briefly here.

The concept of a uniformly affected surface layer inplies that P is constant under varying test conditions, but it affords no predictable relations between L, T, P, and S.

The concept of a nonuniform lag layer either with constant or varying rates of attack does suggest the existence of certain interrelations between L, T, P, and S; experimental support of these relationships has been found. However, similar results can be obtained from alternative pictures involving localized electrochemical inhibition over a gradually decreasing area.

The experimental results which tend to refute any layer hypothesis will now be presented.

1. Inconstancy of the Final Rate of Attack

The basic assumption underlying the use of the pickle lag apparatus is that the pickling rate of the steel becomes constant. In fact, in using the test equipment, it is assumed that this occurs before the volume of hydrogen produced exceeds the capacity of the apparatus. (Test specimens 65 × 8.5 mm. Gas volume 30 ml. Maximum pressure 3 units or 12 in. of mercury.) Hence, in practice, the layer must be less than 150 millionths of an inch thick (0.15 thousandths).

That this assumption is frequently in error has been demonstrated in two ways. The error was in fact first encountered when attempts were made to work with fractional test specimens. In theory, the pickle lag value should be independent of the sample area, changes in area merely resulting in changes in the pressure scale. It was soon found, however, that the smaller the sample, the higher the pickle lag value.

The reason for this unexpected result was quickly traced to the fact that with smaller samples, longer total test times were involved. As the test continued, the final "constant" rate of attack increased rather slowly, resulting in a "rolling" of the extrapolated line around the curve and in an increase in the value of the pickle lag intercept.

This slow increase in final rate was confirmed by continuing a standard test past the normal endpoint by releasing the pressure periodically and continuing to determine the pickling rate on the same test specimen.

The results of one such test are shown in Table II.

From the volume of hydrogen produced during the test reported in Table II, it is easy to calculate that a layer of iron at least 0.5 thousandths of an inch thick must have been removed before the final rate was attained (and even then its constancy was not evident). This

TABLE II
Time Required for 2 in. Chart Reading at Constant Rate of Attack

Test period	Value of S, sec
Initial	42
2nd	34
3rd	30
4th	26
5th	24
6th	23

is not the sort of thickness normally envisioned for the lag layer and suggests that there is no sharply defined boundary between the layer and the inner steel.

2. Pickle Lag with Other Acids

If a uniformly thick layer of "lag material" existed in the surface of the steel, it would seem reasonable that the same decreased activity should be noted in other acids as in hydrochloric. While different numerical values of the pickle lag could be expected, the value of P would be expected to be the same on any uniform layer theory.

This inference does not conform with the experimental evidence. The use of phosphoric or lactic acid in the pickle lag test results in little, if any, sign of a pickle lag. With $12N$ sulfuric acid, a gradually curving pressure-time curve was obtained, so that a pickle lag could be determined. However, the value of P at which the reaction rate became almost constant was about three times that found with hydrochloric acid, and the change in pickling rate was by no means so pronounced.

3. Changes in Test Conditions on P

By a similar argument, P should be unchanged with changes in acid concentration and/or temperature in the pickle lag test, if a uniform lag layer existed. In point of fact, changes in acid concentration or in temperature resulted in the values of P shown in Tables III and IV.

TABLE III		TABLE IV	
Influence of Acid Concentration on P		Influence of Temperature on P	
Acid concn., N	P units	Temp. °C	P units
4.5	6.0	75	5.8
5.0	4.4	80	5.0
5.5	4.4	85	5.3
6.0	3.5	90	4.3

The results of both 2 and 3 seem to refute the idea of a uniform lag layer. The result of 2 probably would require some additional theorizing to justify the idea of a nonuniform layer, although 3 can be explained merely by assuming that either F or T/S or both varied with temperature or acid concentration.

4. Abrasion of the Surface

Metallographic polishing apparently removes the pickle lag completely, as has been reported by Koehler and other workers. This observation is consistent with a lag layer concept.

However, mild abrasion of the surface of annealed black plate prior to temper rolling has been found to result in very substantial *increases* in the apparent pickle lag. The magnitude of the effect seems to depend to some extent on the pickle lag already possessed by the specimen. Typical results are recorded in Table V.

Several points are of interest. First, is the fact that abrasion somehow increases the apparent pickle lag. It is difficult to interpret this as an increase in thickness of a lag layer. Secondly, the increases in lag value differ for the two steels, the low value increasing least. Thirdly, and this is perhaps significant, the increase in pickle lag is accompanied by a decrease in the final rate of attack. This point especially is difficult to interpret on any layer basis. Whatever happens to the surface layers during abrasion, it is hard to see how these changes can alter the rate of attack once those surface layers have been removed.   In fact, it seems possible that perhaps the inhibiting factor is *not* removed and continues to exert an influence on the entire corrosion process.

TABLE V
Effect of Handling on Pickle Lag Values

	Steel A[a]		Steel B[b] Value of $S+$	
Treatment	Lag	S	Lag	S
Freshly annealed	11–12	31–34	1–2	20–28
Wiped with tissue paper	16	33	3	21
Rubbed gently with 4-0 emery	34	45	$7^1/_2$	39
Fluting test	23	40	6	33
Fingerprinted	52	38	11	29

[a] The B fluting test was the same material as A, but had had the pickle lag substantially removed by reheating in a dry atmosphere.

[b] Here, S is an inverse measure of the pickling rate.   The higher is S, the lower is the rate of pickling ($= 2/S$).

Finally, a metallographically polished specimen with no residual pickle lag was abraded lightly with emery paper after the pickle lag test.   It then possessed a pickle lag of 4–5 sec.   Abrading the specimen after this test produced a still further lag of about the same amount.

5. Mechanical Working of the Steel

Probably related to the above phenomenon are the changes in pickle lag value resulting from mechanical working of the annealed black plate.   The passage of specimens through the test machine used in the fluting test results in bending the strip into an arc.   The pickle lag value is then found to have increased (see Table V).

In none of these cases is it evident how the lag layer thickness can have been increased by the treatment, yet the amount of lag as measured increases.   Further, the changes affect the final rate of attack; i.e., the surface changes appear to have affected the interior of the steel.

6. Chemical Treatment of the Surface

The presence of traces of copper in the test acid or on the steel surface has been found to result in quite remarkable increases in the apparent pickle lag.

Further, test specimens which have reached a relatively steady rate of attack in the hydrochloric test acid, and hence have no pickle lag, develop quite appreciable lags again on brief (10–15 sec) dipping in 10% nitric acid solution.

Fingerprints have also been found to result in large increases in apparent pickle lag values, far in excess of what could be expected in terms of the area contaminated. Thus an 11-sec lag became 50–53 sec while a 1–2-sec lag increased to 11 sec, when the test specimens were covered with fingerprints. If the lag value alone increased, it might be ascribed to an "oil-film blanket" taking longer to remove than the lag layer alone. However, the final rate of attack was also affected, the S values rising from 33 to 38 and from 21–24 to 29 sec. Apparently, the effect somehow manages to reach the inner layers of steel.

7. Removal of the Lag

It has been reported that a pickle lag developed by annealing the steel under improper atmospheres (e.g., with moisture, oxygen, or carbon dioxide present) may be removed from the steel by reheating under an atmosphere of the proper composition.

When this is done, it is frequently found that the pressure-time curve is no longer of the conventional form shown in Figure 2. Very frequently, after a brief period (0–2 sec) of slow reaction, a very rapid rate is obtained, which is faster than the final "steady" rate. An example of the type of data obtained is given in Table VI.

TABLE VI

	Pickle lag, sec	Value of S,[a] sec
Original material	8	40
After lag removal	3	30
Above specimen continued	—	30
		36 (final)

[a] Inversely related to the rate.

In fact, cases have been found in which extrapolating back the final steady rate results in an intersection with the time axis to the left of the starting point, i.e., to nominally negative pickle lags.

If the pickle lag is due to a layer of less reactive material, such "negative" lags must be interpreted as due to a layer of more reactive material. Furthermore, this layer appears to be thicker than was the original lag layer. These results are curious and require a more elaborate theory than is provided by a simple layer concept.

In connection with this reverse curvature of the pressure time, a word of caution is perhaps in order. As designed, the test equipment will automatically produce a slight curvature of the pressure-time graph, to the right, when the rate of pickling is constant. This effect, while frequently noticeable, results in an error only of the order of 1 sec in the value of S for normal steels. The degree of curvature noted with reannealed material is considerably in excess of this and represents a real decrease in pickling rate as the test specimen dissolves.

ELECTROCHEMICAL APPROACH TO THE PICKLE LAG PHENOMENON

The lag layer interpretation of the pickle lag phenomenon has the advantage of simplicity, and the nonuniform layer theory does lead to some interesting and apparently correct relations between certain characteristics (L, T, P, and S) of the pressure-time curve. Its various points of conflict with other data, however, seem to argue against the validity of the concept and suggest that the misleading analogy has been pressed too far.

The only direct conclusion that can be drawn from the normal pressure-time curve is that annealed black plate corrodes in hot hydrochloric acid less rapidly initially than it does subsequently.

Since the corrosion is an electrochemical phenomenon, it seems reasonable to look for an explanation along electrochemical lines. Koehler[2] has already suggested such an approach, postulating a mechanism connected with the presence of grain boundary oxides. Certain of the results described above, in which surface alterations result in rather deep-seated changes in the corrosion pattern suggest that such an explanation cannot account for all the observations.

A review of certain theoretical considerations may be useful, however, in extending the electrochemical interpretation along more general lines.

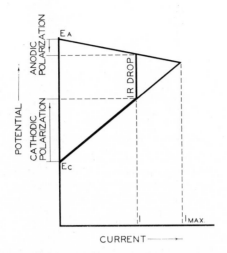

Fig. 4. Polarization diagram.

A metal surface such as that of black plate is not uniform but con-sists of a number of grains and the boundaries between them.   The grains are not necessarily or even likely to be identical.   Inclusions, segregation, or other random factors ensure that the properties of the surface vary from point to point.   Accordingly, when such a sur-face is immersed in an acid, reaction is not equally likely to occur everywhere.   Rather, from some areas (referred to as anodic) metal ions enter the solution, the reaction being represented as

$$M \longrightarrow M^+ + e \tag{A}$$

This would leave the metal negatively charged, were it not for the fact that simultaneously, at cathodic areas, a second reaction occurs

$$H^+ + e \longrightarrow H \tag{B}$$

If the anode and cathode were electrically insulated from each other, so that the electrons could not flow from one to the other through the basis metal, the reaction would quickly cease, with each area at-taining an electrical potential due to a gain or loss of electric charges. The situation can be illustrated graphically as in Figure 4, with the anode potential as shown at E_A and the cathode potential at E_C, when the current flowing between them is zero.   If the electrodes are now joined through a resistance R, current of an amount I will flow between the anode and the cathode.   This flow produces changes in the two electrodes which cause their potentials to change along the

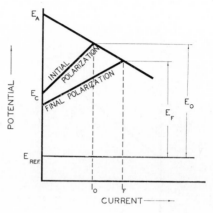

Figure 5.

sloping lines as shown. The open-circuit potential difference (E_A — E_C) is now made up of three parts, the anodic polarization, the IR drop through the resistance (including the resistance through the solution), and the cathodic polarization.

As the resistance between anode and cathode decreases, the increased current flow results in increasing polarization, until, if R could be made zero, a current $I_{\max}$ would flow between the electrodes which would now both appear to have the potential E mixed, often referred to as the "Mischpotential."

This is the potential which the metal strip (consisting of both anodes and cathodes) will appear to have if compared with the potential of some reference electrode. At the same time, the current $I_{\max}$ flowing between the local anodes and cathodes will be producing the reactions of metal dissolving and hydrogen evolving in amounts determined according to Faraday's law.

Koehler's experimental work on the potential changes in black plate immersed in hot hydrochloric acid can best be understood by reference to the concept of Mischpotential. He measured this potential with reference to a calomel half-cell whose reference potential is shown in Figure 5 as E_{ref}. The potential difference he found initially is that designated as E_0. As the reaction proceeded, he found the value of E_0 to *decrease*, i.e., E_{mixed} moved in a downward direction to E_F.

At the same time, the pickle lag test indicates clearly that reaction at the steel surface was occurring more rapidly than before; that is.

I_{max} had increased from I_0 to I_F. Thus the point of intersection of the two polarization curves had moved *downward* and *to the right*. It is clear that this can only occur if the cathode polarization curve has changed its position, either by E_C decreasing, by the slope decreasing, or by a combination of the two (as illustrated).

Changes in anodic polarization may occur, but cannot in themselves effect the necessary changes. It thus appears that the behavior of the cathodic areas is the essential characteristic determining pickle lag.

Conway[3] has recently reviewed the mechanism of electrode reactions of the type involved here, and his findings accord with, and extend, the above interpretation. The essential reactions are of course at the anode

$$\text{Fe} \longrightarrow \text{Fe}^{2+} + 2e \qquad\qquad\qquad (C)$$

and at the cathode

$$2\text{H}^+ + 2e \longrightarrow \text{H}_2 \qquad\qquad\qquad (D)$$

This latter reaction is, however, not simple, but is considered to occur in one of several possible ways, depending on the circumstances of metal and electrolyte. For iron in acid solution, Conway[3] presents considerable evidence that the steps are

$$\text{H}^+ + e + \text{M} \longrightarrow \text{MH}_{ads} \qquad\qquad\qquad (E)$$

followed by

$$\text{H}^+ + e + \text{MH}_{ads} \longrightarrow \text{M} + \text{H}_2 \qquad\qquad\qquad (F)$$

(Here, MH_{ads} represents adsorption of atomic hydrogen on the surface of the cathode.)

The rate-determining reaction of all these is step (F). Conway goes on to show that the rate of this step appears to be closely related to the tenacity with which atomic hydrogen is adsorbed by the metal. This is related to the heat of adsorption which is high when the hydrogen is strongly adsorbed, low when the bonding is weaker.

On the basis of the importance of the cathodic reaction as established by Koehler's work and of the interpretation of the polarizability of the cathode as presented by Conway, it would appear then that reduced to its simplest form, the pickle lag phenomenon reflects rather indirectly the manner in which the affinity of the cathodic areas for atomic hydrogen varies as the corrosion of the surface proceeds.

APPLICATION OF THE ELECTROCHEMICAL
INTERPRETATION OF EXPERIMENTAL RESULTS

The interpretation of the pickle lag phenomenon in terms of the properties of cathodic areas (in particular their affinity for atomic hydrogen) does not make easier the quantitative prediction of pickle lag values on the basis of other experimental quantities. The affinity could perhaps be evaluated in terms of heats of adsorption but the experimental determination of such a quantity is difficult at best, and in the present case, it is the adsorption on only a small fraction of the surface, not readily distinguishable or isolatable from the rest, that is required.

Qualitatively, however, it is in accord with experiment, and does appear capable of reconciling all the apparently conflicting experimental results.

That anodic and cathodic areas do occur is quite evident. There is no need to assume, nor is it likely, that all cathodes are identical, either chemically or physically. In the interior of the steel, however, the distribution of cathodic areas of various kinds is more or less uniform, and, unless changes occur on the surface, will be similar to the distribution over the surface. Any changes on the surface, however, will affect either the pattern or the hydrogen-adsorption properties of the cathodic surfaces.

It is immediately understandable, if not predictable, that mild abrasion, chemical treatment (as with nitric acid or a moist annealing atmosphere), or fingerprinting can change either the number, nature, or heat of hydrogen adsorption of the cathodic areas. (The adsorption properties of surfaces are notoriously sensitive to very minor traces of contaminants or variations in surface preparation.)

Since these changes result in altered rates of corrosion, differences between the corrosion rate controlled by surface cathodes and those controlled by "internal" cathodes (not initially exposed) lead to the pickle lag phenomenon.

However, these surface cathodes are not necessarily a layer—they may well be true "surface." They are not removed by electrochemical dissolution—this occurs only at the anodes. Only as cathodic areas are undermined by the removal of the surrounding anodic grains do they cease to influence the rate of corrosion; at the same time new, unaltered, "internal" cathodes are becoming exposed.

The more successful the external cathodes are in suppressing the reaction of local anodes, the more slowly does this undermining occur; hence, the longer the period before a constant rate of attack (controlled by the polarization characteristics of "internal" cathodes, now become "external") is finally attained. It is also understandable that if the external cathodes can be "activated" (by reducing their affinity for hydrogen), a rate of attack higher than that ultimately achieved may occur; hence, the appearance of "negative" pickle lags.

The electrochemical approach, involving the concept of the rate of corrosion as cathodically controlled thus makes understandable all the observed aspects of pickle lag, in terms of the surface characteristics of cathodic areas which unfortunately are not readily susceptible of experimental study.

It is true that it involves the idea that constancy of rate of attack only occurs after the removal of the (altered) surface cathodes. It differs with the layer concept, however, in that it emphasizes that what is removed with accompanying hydrogen evolution is *not* primarily the cathodes but the anodes. And since the anodes do not constitute a discrete layer, it is pointless to look for one. The cathodes themselves may, but need not, form a layer. They may be inclusions or oxides, and as such, have physical dimensions; they may, on the other hand, be purely surface modifications of a material basically similar to the anodes. Both types may occur simultaneously.

Since, however, the "special" cathodes normally control the reaction rate at a lower level than the "normal" cathodes, we can divide the surface into areas specially controlled and areas normally controlled. The mathematical treatment of such a picture is again identical with that outlined above, and all the relationships deduced there are just as logically derived from the electrochemical view as from a nonuniform layer concept.

CONCLUSIONS

1. The phenomenon of pickle lag is essentially an electrochemical phenomenon, the rate of corrosion of black plate in hydrochloric acid being controlled by cathodic polarization. This, in turn, is related to the surface characteristics of the cathodes presumably as they affect the affinity for atomic hydrogen.

2.   The adsorption characteristics of the cathodic areas can be affected very markedly by variations in physical or chemical treatment, such as environment.   Hence the corrosion characteristics and the pickle lag may be affected by such treatments.

3.   The cathodic areas tend to be perpetuated during the corrosion, unless directly attacked by the acid (as, for example, if oxides are involved).   Consequently, the effect of changes in such cathodes tends to affect the behavior (rate of corrosion) of iron well below the surface. This accounts for the influence of surface changes not only on the initial rate of attack but also on the "final" rate (final, at least, so far as the limited time involved in the pickle lag test is concerned).

4.   The polarizability of the cathodes initially on the surface is normally greater than that of the internal cathodes eventually exposed.   Therefore, in general, the rate of attack increases as these fresh cathodes are exposed, leading to the normal shape of the pickle lag test curve.

5.   The shape of the curve is in general agreement with that proposed on the assumption that the area controlled by the surface cathodes decreases more or less linearly with time.

6.   The pickle lag value is a derived value, based on other quantities which seem more immediately connected with the characteristic of the surface.   As a resultant quantity, its use tends to obscure the differences between surfaces of different corrosion characteristics. There is a definite pickle lag value for each surface, but for a given pickle lag value, a variety of surface conditions may exist.   The surface conditions are closely connected with the shape of the pressure-time curve, which is not uniquely reflected by the pickle lag value.

References

1. Willey, A. R., J. L. Krickl, and R. R. Hartwell, *Corrosion*, **12**, 433 (1956).
2. Koehler, E. L., *Trans. Am. Soc. Metals*, **44**, 1076 (1952).
3. Conway, B. E., *Chemistry in Canada*, **9**, No. 4, 39 (1957).

Discussion

C. E. A. Shanahan (*Richard Thomas & Baldwins, England*): The author is to be congratulated on his theoretical approach to the very empirical pickle lag test. The mathematical treatment based on the layer concept is useful but, as the author pointed out, depends on an assumed rate of appearance of "normal rate" metal through the layer.   Moreover, the same analysis may be used for many different proposed dissolution mechanisms and does not help therefore in selecting the most likely process occurring in the pickle lag test.

The most realistic approach to understanding the mode of sample dissolution is that involving polarization curves as shown in Figures 4 and 5. Koehler has shown that the variable steel dissolution rates are mainly associated with cathodic control. Now the slopes of the polarization curves are functions of current density and it would seem therefore that if the cathodic area of a specimen were increased (with negligible effect on the anodic area) the dissolution rate would increase. On this basis, the deposition of cathodic materials; for example, copper, on the specimen would be expected to flatten the cathodic polarization curves in Figure 5 and lead to increased attack and in all probability lower pickle lag values. This conclusion is apparently at variance with the author's practical findings.

SECTION XIII: PROCESS CONTROL AND STATISTICAL METHODS

. . . .

Statistical Design of Experiments in Process Metallurgy

DANIEL CUTHBERT

New York, New York

Abstracts

Four fairly common defects in plant historical data are: (*1*) heterogeneity produced by the sudden change of some unrecorded but influential factor; (*2*) correlation between two or more independent variables; (*3*) lack of real duplicates; (*4*) occasional wild values.

The value of "factorial experiments" in preventing, spotting, and minimizing these defects is emphasized. A factorial experiment on four factors influencing the desulfurization of ladle iron is given as an example. The advantage of balance, of blocking, and of randomization are pointed out.

INTRODUCTION

Like all other fields, statistics is developing unevenly. Some parts of statistics, for example, least squares, have remained unchanged since the eighteenth century. Some parts of the field, dubbed "modern statistics" by men in their fifties, have developed most rapidly in this century. Some parts such as stochastic processes, time series, spectral analysis, renewal theory, and mathematical programing have shown their main development only in the past decade.

The accompanying paper of G. F. Lilly takes its methods from Gauss's work, done 150 years ago. It should be pointed out that Gauss's methods are developed further in Lilly's paper and that modern computing machinery is required to take advantage of the older methods.

Among the most recent developments may be put the various parts of "mathematical programing." The allocation of resources, especially under complicated sets of restrictions, is an important problem with many immediate applications. Linear programing and its modifications are recent developments in this area; D. C. Hilty's paper deals with some applications of mathematical programing.

The beginnings of modern statistics may all be put within the last ninety years. Mendel, Galton, Karl Pearson, and W. S. Grossett made major contributions between 1870 and 1910. The landmark paper entitled "Student"[1] is now 51 years old. Grossett was a chemist. Even though statisticians have wandered widely through other fields, principally biological, in the past half-century, we now see once more major application and major development in the chemical and metallurgical areas and especially in process chemistry and process metallurgy. There are major current developments but this paper will be concerned mainly with some of the older ones, which must be well understood before the newer types of statistical designs can be profitably exploited. The type of factorial experiment to be described was proposed by Yates in 1937.[2]

The familiar description of scientific advance, whether given by Dewey, Eisenstein, or Box, always contains the same elements, though not always the same emphasis. All agree on a cycle that progresses through the steps: a feeling of puzzlement; the production of a conjecture (or a hypothesis, or more rarely a theory); a search for relevant and decisive data; a study of the new plus the old data; and then the confirmation, modification, or generalization of the earlier conjecture. In this way a new round is started, not circularly, but on an advancing spiral, it is hoped.

Many young scientists start their research somewhere near the middle of the cycle just outlined; that is, as laboratory assistants collecting data in a pattern decided upon by senior scientists to answer questions often asked by still other scientists. Their feeling of puzzlement is sometimes limited to the question: Why should just these data be required?

Similarly, most statisticians are likely to find their early experiences with data confined to "data processing," to the condensation and summary of large masses of data, or to the analysis by standard curve-fitting methods of data already taken, perhaps for other purposes, perhaps by other scientists. It must be admitted that the use of classical "least-squares curve fitting" on other people's data is occasionally rewarded with success. Except for lucky cases this can

only be expected when the statistical knowledge required is connected with a serious theory of the process under study, through a
definite and manageable set of model equations. Finally the data
must be *good* data, as defined in the following. These conditions
appear to be met in the accompanying paper by Lilly.

DEFECTS IN DATA

A clear theory, or more modestly, a testable set of conjectures,
is not all that is required. The *data* must meet certain requirements
if they are to test a theory. If they do not meet these requirements
they may still be compatible with the theory, but compatibility is
only necessary and not sufficient.

The commonest defects in "as is," or "historical," data appear to
be these four: heterogeneity of conditions, correlations between
independent variables, unknown magnitude of random error, and
wild values.

Data are called heterogeneous when, because of some systematic
unrecorded change in some influential independent variable, the
different *sections* of the data are inconsistent. They represent different parts of the response surface. Even in data with very small
random error, this defect will usually make it impossible to check a
conjecture. Again, even if the effect of the unknown variable is of
the simplest kind—a shift of all readings in one part of the data by
the same amount—the testing of alternative conjectures is likely to
be impracticable.

It may be felt that heterogeneity is simply a polysyllabic way of
saying that the model equation (or conjecture, or theory) is not
correct. But the model rarely is correct in any very final sense.
Our hope always is to get some inkling of the effect of the variables we
now think are important, even if some other variables, not now
known to us, are also influential. There actually are ways to do
this, but the required conditions, to be discussed later, will only
rarely be met accidentally.

If two factors (i.e., independent variables) vary closely together
in the several pieces of data available, it may be difficult or impossible to disentangle their effects. Indeed the results may appear to
be due to one factor when in fact they are due to the other. The
inadvertent, or even deliberate, variation of two factors together is a
common attribute of historical data.

The third common defect in historical data is its failure to provide a good estimate of *error*, that is, of the average effect of the uncontrolled and unrecorded factors in the system under study. When many factors are varying independently, there is only a small chance that even one pair of exact duplicates will have been run. In analyses of accumulated data, we would like to have perhaps between 100 and 300 points. It would be desirable to have from 20 to 50 estimates of random error, well spread over the range of all variables, but it is still true that 10 "degrees of freedom" for error are better than none. Without any objective estimate of the average random variation, we cannot be entirely objective in our judgments about the quality of the fit we have obtained, nor can we judge how well we have estimated the coefficients in the equation used.

The fourth ill that afflicts data—whether historical or not—is the presence of a small proportion of "wild" values. It is the moderately wild values that cause the most trouble. If a few *very* wild ones appear, they can almost always be spotted, and removed, by experienced workers in the field, needing no aid from statistical methods at all. If a few values are only a little wild, then they usually will not make much difference in estimates made or in the conclusions drawn. Moderately wild values are, however, difficult to spot in *un*balanced data. Depending on their location in the data, they may influence the estimated coefficients heavily (if they are near the "edges" of the data) or hardly at all (if they are near the center of gravity of the mass of data). Indeed in the former case, it sometimes happens that the fit of the equation to the bad points is so good that they are not detected at all.

Now it must be remembered that, in spite of the preceding jeremiad, some sets of data are subject to *none* of these defects. The methods invented over 150 years ago by Gauss are now relatively easy to apply thanks to modern computing machinery. If the equations to be fitted are *linear in the coefficients to be estimated* (not necessarily linear in the independent variables) then reliable "least-squares" estimates can often be obtained. When the equations are nonlinear in the coefficients, iterative methods are available and are being further developed (by G. E. P. Box at Princeton, among others). They have already shown their usefulness.

As a last warning it should be remembered that a fifth defect of historical data, usually not mentioned in polite society, has been known to appear. This is *worthlessness*. Sometimes plant data sheets are filled in at the beginning of each shift to save time; sometimes data are garbled in the complexities of clerical operations; and sometimes data are, possibly, even transposed into the wrong columns in analytical laboratories.

There is often, however, no alternative to taking the data as given. One has, then, to develop equations that describe a realistic model of events, to criticize and even to omit some data values if plausible reasons can be given for the deletions, and then to estimate coefficients and error as well as possible from the revised data.

THE PLACE OF PLANNING IN THE TAKING OF DATA

Is is sometimes possible to plan and to enforce the plan for the taking of data under desired conditions. There is of course much more to planning experiments than the simple suggestions to be made. It will be best if we can remember that these suggestions concern the *statistical* part of planning experiments.

To avoid heterogeneity, we must avoid having large clusters of data points taken together, so that they might all be influenced by the same level of some unknown or unrecorded factor. Put another way, heterogeneous data usually come from the accidental correlation of the independent variables we *are* varying, with some others that are not known to us.

There is a reliable way to minimize this hazard. It is called "randomization of treatments." It was invented by R. A. Fisher and is sometimes said to be his major contribution to the theory and practice of experimentation. Randomization is often opposed by the experimenter because it seems to slow down the accumulation of information by requiring that conditions be changed just when, as the experimenter feels, he is well set up to get a lot of information over a wide range of conditions.

When a large piece of equipment is more or less stabilized at, say, some distribution of temperatures, it may then be easy to whisk through a lot of variations in some minor conditions and thus gather a lot of information in the effects of varying those conditions. But the effects of temperature can only be found by varying the temperature. If temperature is varied in a systematic way (say, in a steadily increasing sequence of levels), then it should be recognized that the data secured may be the result of the sequence of temperatures and not just the result of the temperature at which observations are recorded. Experiments in which some variables are so to speak nested inside others are called "split-plot" experiments. Such experiments may correspond closely with what the experimenter would like to *do*, but it must be emphasized again that this may not correspond with what he would like to *find out*.

In order to randomize a set of multifactor observations it is necessary to use a table of random numbers or some other objective device to specify the order in which the several "runs" are to be made. Such a scheme minimizes the likelihood that the values of *any* of the independent variables will match those of some unknown variable closely enough to confuse the experimenter as to what is cause, what effect, and what mere chance.

When the conditions under which the data are to be taken can be specified beforehand, it will always pay to vary the factors (independent variables) *independently*, that is, without mutual correlation. Independence of variation does *not* mean varying one factor at a time. It does mean that factors must not always vary together in the same way. Thus if the chosen values of two factors, call them x_1 and x_2, lie on a straight line in the x_1-x_2 plane, they have been varied together and their effects cannot be separated. If the chosen values lie in a pattern with two-way symmetry, for example, if they cover a rectangle or a circle uniformly, then the effects of the factors can be disentangled.

FACTORIAL EXPERIMENTS

We might get some clue to the first-order effects of varying two factors, over some range of interest, by doing *four* runs. If the factors are called A and B, the experimental conditions for the four runs can be indicated by the four symbols A_0B_0, A_0B_1, A_1B_0, A_1B_1. A still shorter nomenclature for the four runs is (1) b, a, ab, respectively. Thus, the factors that are at their high levels are indicated by lower case letters. The absence of a letter means that the corresponding factor is in that run at its lower level. Thus b means "factor A is at its lower level; factor B, at its higher level."

If factor B has a consistent effect, this fact will be disclosed by the results of the four runs. The difference between the response at b and that at (1) measures the effect of varying B *at low A*. The difference between the responses at ab and at a measures the effect of varying B *at high A*. If these two differences (or effects) are about the same we will want to average them.

In this way we could get more *precision* in estimating the effect of varying B, at the same time that we gain in comprehensiveness, since we have varied B over a range of settings of A. If you are not familiar with this type of "factorial plan," you will be interested to work out for yourself how the same four runs can be used to get a precise and general estimate of the effect of varying the factor A.

Now if this precision, or this generality, or both, were not sufficient, we could duplicate the whole set of four runs, perhaps at two levels of a new factor C. The eight runs can now be used to estimate the overall effects of factors A, B, and C, each as precisely as if only one factor had been varied. But still more can be done.

Going back for a moment to the original four runs, we can use them to see if varying B does about the same thing at low and at high A. This is done by comparing the difference $b - (1)$ with the difference $ab - a$. It is admitted that the same symbols are used here to indicate the *responses* to the factor levels that were used before to indicate the factor levels themselves. The context invariably makes clear which reference is applicable. If these two differences or effects are about the same, we say that factors A and B operate approximately *additively*. If the two differences are not at all the same, we speak of the factors as "interacting." In either case the magnitude of the quantity $(ab - a) - [b - (1)]$ or more simply, $ab - a - b + (1)$, measures the AB interaction.

Since there is a set like the one just mentioned at low C and another set at high C in the eight-run sequence, the AB interaction in the eight runs can be estimated with double precision. Similarly, the AC and the BC interactions can be judged by using the same data. The whole sequence is called a 2^3 factorial experiment, for obvious reasons.

A 2^4 FACTORIAL EXPERIMENT ON THE DESULFURIZATION OF MOLTEN IRON

It is wished now to show the results of a *four* factor experiment done in the field of process metallurgy. It was carried out to study the effects of injecting powdered calcium carbide, CaC_2, into ladle iron as a desulfurizing agent. The four factors varied were, the initial per cent sulfur in the iron (A), the amount of CaC_2 added (B), the depth of the injection lance (C), and the ladle temperature of the iron (D). Each factor was used at two levels, in all combinations. Thus *16* runs were made, in a random order specified beforehand. In each run the *final* per cent sulfur was measured.

The first factor, initial per cent sulfur, was not a factor that was deliberately varied. Instead the experimenters had to wait until a ladle turned up with about the desired per cent sulfur. It was suspected that this waiting might make the experiment a long one, and it was feared that other conditions might drift about in such a long period of time. This drift would increase the apparent random variability and thus decrease the efficiency of the experiment.

One way of diminishing this sort of disturbance is by "blocking." Blocking is simply a grouping of smaller sets of conditions in such a way that the desired comparisons (here the *effects* of the four factors) can be made inside each block and therefore, hopefully, with more precision.

The eight runs listed in the upper half of Table I are a balanced

TABLE I
Data and Conclusions from a 2^4 Factorial Experiment

Run no.	Exptl. con- ditions	Final S, %	Effects (8 runs)		Effects (16 runs)	
			Magnitude	Name	Magnitude	Name
3	d	0.026	0.0295	$M + ACD$		
2	a	0.042	0.0190	$A + CD^*$	0.0132	A^*
6	bd	0.023	−0.0095	$B + ABCD^*$	−0.0097	B^*
7	ab	0.044	−0.0025	$AB + BCD$	−0.0045	AB
8	c	0.021	−0.0085	$C + AD^*$	−0.0077	C^*
5	acd	0.048	0.0005	$AC + D$	−0.0030	AC
4	bc	0.010	−0.0090	$BC + ABD^*$	−0.0070	BC^*
1	abcd	0.022	−0.0050	$ABC + BD$	−0.0032	ABC
16	(1)	0.016	0.0195	$M − ACD$	0.0035	D
9	ad	0.035	0.0075	$A − CD^*$	−0.0008	AD
11	b	0.016	−0.0100	$B − ABCD^*$	−0.0018	BD
14	abd	0.025	−0.0065	$AB − BCD$	−0.0020	ABD
15	cd	0.019	−0.0070	$C − AD^*$	0.0057	CD
13	ac	0.028	−0.0065	$AC − D$	0.0100	ACD^*
12	bcd	0.012	−0.0050	$BC − ABD$	0.0020	BCD
10	abc	0.005	−0.0015	$ABC − BD$	0.0002	$ABCD$

half of the full set of 16 runs, so chosen that the effect of factor B, the amount of CaC_2 injected, and its interactions are measured without confusion. The average effects of factors A, C, and D are each measured along with a complementary interaction. Thus if any one of the interactions AC, AD, or CD is large, we will probably be deceived into thinking we have observed the complementary main effect (B, C, or A, respectively).

The third column of Table I shows the actual per cent sulfur reached in each run. In the fourth column are shown the average effects of each factor as computed from these eight runs. The average A effect is computed in Table II as an example.

TABLE II

	Low A			High A	
d	0.026		a	0.042	
bd	0.023		ab	0.044	
c	0.021		acd	0.048	
bc	0.010		$abcd$	0.022	
Sum	0.080			0.156	
Avg	0.020			0.039	
	Avg difference $0.039 - 0.020 = 0.019$				

Put in words, this computation tells us that the average effect of raising the initial per cent sulfur from its low value (it happened to be 0.03%) to its high value (set in these experiments at 0.06%) was to increase the final per cent sulfur by about 0.019%.

Having only the roughest idea of the size of the random errors in our data, we might guess that factors A, B, and C, marked with asterisks in Table I, had some effects and that possibly there was a BC interaction. Each effect is followed by its name. These names each appear as the sum of two effects. Since only half of the 16 runs required for full separation of all the effects and interactions have been done at this point, there is a necessary ambiguity in the meaning of each of the averages. Sometimes one can tell which of the two names of an average is the correct one, but sometimes this cannot be done and occasionally both the effects are real and only their sum or difference is measurable. Here, M stands for the true mean of the 16 runs.

Let us look at what our conclusions might have been if we had first done the *other* eight runs, which are equally well-balanced, and had then tried to draw similar conclusions. The lower half of Table I gives the data and the average effects. Here again A, B, and C have produced the largest average effects but there is no clear break between these effects and the next smaller ones.

Putting all 16 runs together permits us to estimate the average effects of all factors and all measures of the consistency of these effects. These are shown in Table I with their names in the last two columns.

Since there appears to be a BC interaction, the "$B \times C$ table" of averages should be made up and studied. It is most simply computed by averaging the four values at each of the four conditions (1), b, c, and bc. The results are as follows:

	Low B	High B
Low C	0.030	0.027
High C	0.029	0.012

We see now that increasing either the amount of CaC_2 (at shallow lance immersion) or the lance depth (at lower rate of CaC_2 feed) has little effect on final sulfur. It is only when both are done together that the reduction is considerable. This suggests that even greater reductions may be expected if *both* factors can be increased still more.

The large and consistent effect of factor A (initial per cent sulfur), together with the combined B and C effect just discussed, were the main findings of this set of runs. Other findings included an estimate of the error of duplicate runs (roughly 0.004), the discovery that blocking the runs into two balanced sets gave about 45% better precision, and the fact that varying the iron temperature at which the CaC_2 was added over the range 2400–2600°F had little if any effect on the final per cent sulfur.

To take one last parting look at one-factor-at-a-time variation, let us consider the parts of the above experiment that would correspond to such a method of work. The relevant runs are those labeled (1), a, b, c, d. We should revise the values actually observed in runs a and c by -0.010 since these two were done in the block for which the level was high by just 0.010. The five values we might have obtained, then, would be: (1), 0.016; a, 0.032; b, 0.016; c, 0.011; and d, 0.016.

From these five runs we might have concluded (*1*) correctly, that factor *A* makes a big difference in final per cent sulfur; and (*2*) incorrectly, that *B* is without effect although *C* perhaps has an effect. No faint hint of the especially favorable combination *bc* could have come from these five runs.

This so-called "2^4 singly replicated factorial experiment" was part of a larger program, planned to study several desulfurizing agents, carried out at one of the plants of the U.S. Steel Corporation. Mr. Saul Gilbert of the Applied Research Laboratory of the same corporation carried out the original analysis of these data. The more general metallurgical conclusions are discussed in a paper by Hornak and Whittenberger.[3]

CONCLUSIONS

The present discussion has been arranged to show how some of the common defects of historical data can be eliminated by planning the conditions under which data are to be taken. The three principles that control this planning might be summarized as follows:

1. *Balance* the experimental conditions, to avoid correlation among the independent variables.

2. *Block* the runs in sets balanced as well as possible to take advantage of the smaller random variation in smaller periods of time.

3. *Randomize* the order of runs inside the blocks to avoid heterogeneity resulting from drifts and trends caused by unknown factors.

All three of these principles were easily applied to the experiment just described. Several further advantages of using these principles should be pointed out. First, the numerical analysis of balanced factorial experiments is easy. Secondly, high precision is gained *without* duplication of work. Thirdly, although it has not been discussed in this paper, *two* somewhat defective runs (*abc* and *bcd*) were spotted and revised.

In summary, three devices of statistical experimental design appear to be applicable with profit to some process metallurgical problems. These are balancing, blocking, and randomizing. An example has been given of the use of all three and some indication has been made of the ease of interpretation of the resulting data.

References

1. Grossett, W. S., *Biometrika*, **6,** 1 (1908).
2. Yates, F., "The Design and Analysis of Factorial Experiments," Tech. Commun. No. 35, Imperial Bur. of Soil Science, Harpenden, England, 1937.
3. Hornak, J. N., and E. J. Whittenberger, *AIME Natl. Open Hearth Committee Proc.*, **39,** 189–201 (1956).

Mathematical Model for Sulfur Distribution in the Open Hearth

GORDON F. LILLY

United States Steel Corporation, Monroeville, Pennsylvania

Abstract

A mathematical model is derived which relates the sulfur content of low-carbon open hearth steels at tap to the relevant operating variables, such as slag volume, slag composition, metal weight, and sulfur in the charge. The model appears valid for the carbon range 0.05 to 0.20% and for tap-slag basicities greater than 2.0. The model may be used to evaluate changes in open hearth practice.

The extremely large number of open hearth process variables and the difficulty of measurement at high temperatures have delayed the development of a complete technology of steelmaking. However, the study of steelmaking is proceeding in two largely separate fields, heat transfer and process chemistry. Sulfur removal is a most important part of the chemistry of basic open hearth steelmaking. Although the primary objectives of refining are the removal of carbon and the attainment of the correct temperature, the experienced operator does not accelerate the rate of carbon removal to its maximum until he is reasonably sure that the sulfur content can be reduced to the specified range prior to achieving the desired top carbon. The sulfur problem, which sometimes limits the rate of normal refining with ore additions, may also limit the faster refining rates possible when roof oxygen lances are used. Recently, Kesterton[1] in writing about the oxygen-lance practice at the Steel Company of Wales, described a slag-control system in which the rate of oxygen flow was reduced in the early stages of refining for a period that depended directly on the sulfur content of the steel at melt.

The object of the work described in the present paper was the derivation of a mathematical model, or set of equations, showing the effect of important operating variables on the sulfur content of basic open hearth steel at tap. Such a model could be used to select a practice that would minimize the sulfur problem during the refining period.

The mathematical model of the process must be consistent both with the observed chemistry of the process and with the restrictions that are implied by material balances. The first requirement for the derivation of the model is an equation for predicting the sulfur partition ratio between slag and metal at tap.

This prediction equation must be reasonably accurate and must be sufficiently simple in structure to permit its incorporation into the more complex equations for predicting the sulfur content of the steel at tap.

After an examination of previously published work, it was decided that the sulfur partition ratio should be related to individual slag constituents rather than to an arbitrarily chosen basicity expression. Two papers were examined carefully in the hope that they might provide a prediction equation for sulfur partition which was immediately suitable for inclusion in the model.

The first paper, by Darken and Larsen,[2] provided an equation that was successful in predicting sulfur partition ratios in open hearth heats. However, Darken and Larsen's equation was too complex for use in the general set of equations that constitute the sulfur model.

The second paper, by Grant and Chipman,[3] was based on laboratory work. The equation they derived was as follows:

$$(S)/[S] = 1.3 + 16 \, (nCaO + nMnO + nMgO - 2nSiO_2 \pm 4nP_2O_5 \\ - 2nAl_2O_3 - nFe_2O_3)$$

in which $nCaO$ — moles CaO per 100 g of slag, etc.

The quantity within the brackets is known as the excess base and is the quantity of basic oxides remaining after the assumed formation of the compounds $2CaO \cdot SiO_2$, $4CaO \cdot P_2O_5$, $2CaO \cdot Al_2O_3$, $CaO \cdot Fe_2O_3$, and similar compounds of MgO and MnO. Chipman and Grant claimed that the variation of FeO content over the range 5–70% did not affect the sulfur partition ratio. The equation was readily reduced to a more practical form by dividing each coefficient by the appropriate molecular weight, which yielded the equation:

$$(S)/[S] = 1.3 + 0.20CaO\% + 0.40MgO\% + 0.23MnO\% - 0.53SiO_2\% \\ - 0.45P_2O_5\% - 0.31Al_2O_3\% - 0.10Fe_2O_3\%$$

It is reasonable to question the validity of the coefficients in Chipman's equation on theoretical grounds. First, compounds may be formed in the slag other than those postulated by Chipman. Secondly, the activities of the free bases present may not be equal to their concentrations. Finally, chemical interaction undoubtedly exists between the sulfur in the slag and some of the other slag components. For example, Chipman himself stated in a later paper[4] that "magnesia additions to slags increase the activity coefficient of the sulfide ion, which favors low concentration of sulfur in the slag."

In addition, although Chipman and Grant's equation satisfactorily explained the variation of sulfur partition ratio for laboratory melts, it did not appear to be directly applicable to open hearth data. With these objections in mind, it was decided to use the form of Chipman's equation but to estimate the coefficients empirically.

The relationship between sulfur partition and slag composition was required for tapping conditions only. Further, the slag is most likely to be homogeneous at tap, and the slag metal system is probably closer to equilibrium at tap than during an earlier stage of refining. Therefore, only samples taken at tap or just before block were considered. Published literature[5-10] and unpublished data obtained in the U. S. Steel Corporation provided much information in the carbon range 0.05 to 0.20%. These data are listed in Table I. The alumina content is not listed in this table because the value was not always quoted in the literature. Also, FeO and Fe_2O_3 are combined into one total FeO (Σ FeO, %) figure following the practice of one of the papers used as a source of data.[9] Limited data were also available for higher carbon heats but did not cover a sufficiently wide range of slag compositions to permit reliable conclusions.

The form of Chipman's equation was considered sufficient justification for presuming that the effects of the slag components were linear and additive. Consequently, a multiple regression technique was used to analyze the data.

Statistical analysis of the data from 114 heats showed that only four of the slag components, CaO, MnO, SiO_2, and P_2O_5, affected the sulfur partition ratio ((S)/[S]). Two components appeared to have no influence on the sulfur partition ratio. These were MgO and FeO. The best equation to fit the data was

$$(S)/[S] = 3.3 + 0.25CaO\% + 0.41MnO\% - 0.55SiO_2\% - 0.97P_2O_5\%$$

TABLE I

Analyses of Slag and Metal Samples Taken at Tap from Low Carbon Heats

Heat No.	Sulfur partition ratio	Slag composition, %							Metal composition, %				Ref.
		CaO	MnO	MgO	ΣFeO	SiO_2	P_2O_5	ΣS	C	Mn	P	S	
Plant A													
129	5.1	40.9	6.4	8.0	22.0	11.5	2.6	0.203	0.08	0.15	—	0.040	USS
133	3.4	42.6	7.1	9.9	15.4	15.0	3.8	0.088	0.17	0.19	—	0.026	USS
106	6.7	45.6	7.8	5.1	17.4	14.9	3.8	0.141	0.15	0.20	—	0.021	USS
233	5.7	38.9	5.5	8.1	27.6	9.8	1.6	0.130	0.07	0.11	—	0.023	USS
213	6.5	39.0	7.1	6.6	25.2	11.2	2.9	0.182	0.10	0.36	—	0.028	USS
045	5.7	40.2	10.8	7.5	17.4	14.3	3.1	0.295	0.15	0.22	—	0.052	USS
060	3.1	37.3	13.5	8.0	13.8	18.6	2.5	0.112	0.13	0.23	—	0.036	USS
121	3.6	44.4	8.5	7.0	16.4	16.8	3.1	0.123	0.18	0.21	—	0.034	USS
179	3.6	40.5	8.5	10.6	19.4	16.1	2.5	0.130	0.18	0.23	—	0.036	USS
103	3.1	37.9	12.0	9.9	12.4	18.9	3.1	0.122	0.12	0.28	—	0.039	USS
192	4.0	41.5	7.6	7.4	19.1	14.8	5.8	0.127	0.15	0.18	—	0.031	USS
292	9.5	43.6	5.4	8.4	22.8	11.0	3.4	0.238	0.11	0.11	—	0.025	USS
297	8.7	41.6	8.2	8.8	24.1	9.3	4.4	0.213	0.16	0.15	—	0.025	USS
308	8.6	45.3	7.4	7.4	25.3	7.7	2.5	0.232	0.18	0.13	—	0.027	USS
Plant B													
506	6.1	44.9	4.6	10.7	23.1	10.5	1.9	0.230	0.10	0.10	—	0.038	USS
524	6.3	47.4	3.7	8.6	22.8	11.0	1.9	0.240	0.19	0.08	—	0.038	USS
Plant C													
501	3.6	42.2	4.1	6.8	24.9	14.0	0.9	0.115	0.06[a]	—	—	0.032	USS
013	6.4	45.1	2.4	2.5	23.1	15.5	0.9	0.180	0.06[a]	—	—	0.028	USS
017	4.5	40.4	2.5	4.8	28.1	11.6	0.6	0.104	0.06[a]	—	—	0.023	USS
911	6.4	42.9	1.7	6.4	26.7	11.6	0.7	0.245	0.07[a]	—	—	0.038	USS

Plant D

Heat													
091	6.3	40.5	4.1	6.2	34.3	9.1	1.5	0.17	0.08[a]	—	—	0.027	USS
097	6.3	37.6	6.0	5.7	31.7	11.6	2.5	0.20	0.05[a]	—	—	0.032	USS
119	4.5	35.4	6.6	6.2	29.5	12.6	2.4	0.113	0.05[a]	—	—	0.025	USS
121	6.5	42.7	4.1	7.2	30.0	10.3	1.5	0.267	0.08[a]	—	—	0.041	USS
132	3.7	37.3	7.0	7.7	25.8	14.5	2.3	0.116	0.07[a]	—	—	0.031	USS
134	4.1	38.2	6.9	6.1	26.0	18.3	2.6	0.157	0.07[a]	—	—	0.038	USS
065	5.7	48.3	2.0	10.2	16.9	16.0	1.6	0.16	0.09	0.05	0.012	0.028	USS
096	2.2	44.8	2.3	10.5	14.6	23.0	1.6	0.08	0.20	0.05	0.011	0.037	USS
241	3.2	40.5	3.4	8.8	14.9	25.8	1.4	0.08	0.08	0.05	0.008	0.025	USS
330	6.4	44.2	3.7	7.1	25.2	15.5	1.0	0.21	0.06	0.06	0.006	0.033	USS
292	11.0	46.9	3.1	6.9	22.6	10.2	1.2	0.45	0.06	0.04	0.004	0.041	USS
267	4.9	47.2	3.7	6.6	21.3	16.1	1.5	0.17	0.07	0.08	0.005	0.035	USS
256	2.6	43.8	5.5	6.6	12.5	24.3	1.6	0.10	0.08	0.14	0.011	0.039	USS
254	7.0	45.9	5.3	8.0	21.5	14.8	1.5	0.23	0.09	0.11	0.004	0.033	USS
256	5.8	45.5	5.1	6.2	20.8	17.6	1.9	0.18	0.06	0.10	0.007	0.031	USS
251	4.1	47.5	4.0	6.7	14.7	18.9	1.8	0.17	0.05	0.12	0.008	0.041	USS
261	9.4	48.7	3.9	5.6	25.3	11.8	1.4	0.32	0.07	0.08	0.005	0.034	USS
243	5.0	43.2	7.9	4.2	22.4	16.2	1.6	0.15	0.07	0.11	0.008	0.030	USS
259	5.9	44.6	4.7	5.6	23.1	15.8	1.8	0.27	0.06	0.07	0.004	0.046	USS
279	10.6	48.8	6.2	4.7	24.9	10.9	2.1	0.36	0.07	0.11	0.010	0.034	USS
225	10.3	47.5	5.0	4.9	27.5	11.9	1.5	0.35	0.05	0.08	0.006	0.034	USS
168	3.6	40.4	7.5	7.8	16.7	19.8	1.3	0.12	0.07	0.11	0.009	0.033	USS
172	2.2	41.4	7.2	7.1	13.0	25.1	1.6	0.08	0.10	0.16	0.016	0.036	USS
175	3.7	44.0	6.1	6.0	16.7	18.2	1.6	0.11	0.09	0.14	0.011	0.030	USS

(continued)

TABLE I (*continued*)

Heat No.	Sulfur partition ratio	Slag composition, %							Metal composition, %				Ref.
		CaO	MnO	MgO	ΣFeO	SiO_2	P_2O_5	ΣS	C	Mn	P	S	
J	2.1	35.4	6.3	9.3	19.0	17.9	2.5	0.107	0.15	0.085	0.016	0.050	2
L	1.5	39.2	5.9	11.8	15.4	20.3	2.0	0.074	0.095	0.107	0.016	0.051	2
N	2.4	38.4	5.8	11.6	20.7	19.2	2.9	0.114	0.12	0.083	0.010	0.048	2
P	2.9	39.1	6.1	11.3	16.1	21.6	2.1	0.130	0.14	0.078	0.017	0.045	2
R	1.1	38.5	7.3	10.2	15.1	21.0	2.0	0.040	0.15	0.102	0.017	0.037	2
T	4.9	43.0	10.2	6.0	16.7	14.2	4.4	0.113	0.07	0.190	0.010	0.023	2
U	5.4	37.5	6.2	9.0	27.9	14.1	3.5	0.250	0.11	0.109	0.017	0.046	2
V	3.8	45.3	4.5	8.3	18.3	17.8	2.0	0.168	0.14	0.077	0.009	0.044	2
I	4.5	43.0	12.6	5.4	14.2	19.7	2.6	0.288	0.18	0.24	—	0.064	2
II	4.7	44.5	8.8	6.9	18.0	16.8	2.4	0.302	0.09	0.20	—	0.064	2
III	6.4	46.5	8.3	2.7	18.0	15.9	2.6	0.356	0.13	0.16	—	0.056	2
IV	6.2	44.0	10.2	2.7	21.2	15.4	3.2	0.274	—	0.16	—	0.044	2
V	3.8	42.5	13.4	2.9	14.2	20.0	2.7	0.210	0.19	0.29	—	0.055	2
VI	3.7	45.0	10.5	2.5	16.1	19.0	2.8	0.192	0.16	0.19	—	0.051	2
VII	8.0	45.0	10.8	3.6	18.1	16.5	2.8	0.343	0.13	0.20	—	0.043	2
VIII	7.7	42.0	3.1	7.8	34.2	10.3	1.5	0.343	0.08	0.08	—	0.045	2
IX	4.4	47.0	5.2	5.8	19.3	16.5	2.7	0.274	0.09	0.18	—	0.062	2
X	9.6	45.8	4.1	4.9	26.8	11.8	2.3	0.383	0.11	0.12	—	0.040	2
XI	6.4	43.5	5.3	5.3	28.3	12.4	2.1	0.288	0.07	0.12	—	0.045	2
XII	6.5	49.0	6.5	5.3	14.2	18.8	2.3	0.398	0.10	0.22	—	0.061	2
XIII	10.2	51.5	5.7	3.4	19.3	14.0	2.2	0.549	0.10	0.16	—	0.054	2
XIV	7.2	44.0	10.3	4.2	26.7	12.1	1.9	0.274	0.08	0.18	—	0.038	2
XV	9.9	49.0	6.7	3.8	21.3	12.6	2.8	0.377	0.13	0.12	—	0.038	2
XVI	9.2	41.5	11.9	4.2	20.0	15.4	3.1	0.425	0.09	0.20	—	0.046	2

6200	9	0.030	—	0.12	0.07	0.37	1.1	6.3	32.0	6.4	5.8	46.0	12.3
6201	9	0.028	—	0.08	0.07	0.40	1.1	6.0	33.7	6.5	5.2	46.2	14.3
6203	9	0.036	—	0.11	0.06	0.42	1.1	7.0	29.3	6.1	5.4	48.4	11.7
6204	9	0.039	—	0.11	0.05	0.48	1.5	7.6	28.8	6.8	3.7	47.8	12.3
6205	9	0.025	—	0.11	0.06	0.29	1.4	9.3	28.3	7.2	5.2	46.1	11.6
6207	9	0.049	—	0.09	0.06	0.55	1.9	10.9	26.5	6.4	5.3	45.6	11.2
6208	9	0.054	—	0.13	0.07	0.69	1.5	8.9	24.5	6.4	5.6	49.8	12.8
6210	9	0.030	—	0.07	0.05	0.22	1.5	10.6	31.4	7.4	4.8	41.1	7.3
6211	9	0.028	—	0.09	0.07	0.34	1.0	7.4	29.0	6.5	4.7	48.1	12.1
6212	9	0.025	—	0.10	0.08	0.31	1.3	9.1	25.8	6.7	4.4	49.7	12.4
6214	9	0.046	—	0.10	0.06	0.61	1.1	6.4	33.8	8.7	4.8	42.2	13.3
6215	9	0.046	—	0.08	0.08	0.57	1.2	7.6	31.3	7.3	4.7	45.6	12.4
6320	9	0.035	—	0.09	(<0.07)	0.41	1.5	7.1	31.8	8.4	5.0	43.8	11.7
6321	9	0.036	—	0.11	0.07	0.42	1.5	8.5	30.8	8.1	5.9	42.5	11.7
6322	9	0.038	—	0.13	0.09	0.46	1.3	8.3	29.8	6.6	5.5	44.3	12.1
6323	9	0.038	—	0.09	0.06	0.43	1.2	7.8	29.8	6.7	4.7	46.0	11.3
6324	9	0.045	—	0.10	0.07	0.54	1.6	7.6	35.0	7.2	5.2	41.8	12.0
6325	9	0.042	—	0.14	0.08	0.54	1.6	6.8	33.3	8.4	6.3	41.2	12.9
6326	9	0.044	—	0.12	0.08	0.56	1.5	8.1	28.4	7.1	5.5	43.8	12.7
6327	9	0.048	—	(>0.10)	0.10	0.56	1.6	9.4	27.0	6.8	5.3	46.8	11.7
6427	9	0.033	—	0.08	0.07	0.28	1.5	8.3	34.5	9.1	6.7	37.5	8.5
6433	9	0.024	—	0.08	0.06	0.27	1.1	5.6	37.4	6.1	5.3	40.2	11.2
6437	9	0.027	—	0.12	0.06	0.34	1.3	8.2	33.6	5.6	7.1	40.5	12.6
215	9	0.024	—	0.14	0.06	0.26	0.9	7.2	35.0	8.9	7.5	38.2	10.8
216	9	0.038	—	0.12	0.05	0.40	0.8	7.0	35.7	7.3	5.9	38.6	10.4
217	9	0.030	—	0.12	0.05	0.30	0.8	8.3	30.5	8.2	6.3	40.2	10.0
1465	7	0.077	0.030	0.25	0.05	0.316	5.2	13.1	17.2	6.1	7.7	46.2	4.1
5311	7	0.078	0.030	0.23	0.06	0.320	8.6	12.0	17.3	5.0	8.7	43.7	4.1
5315	7	0.062	0.020	0.28	0.05	0.509	6.8	8.4	21.8	5.3	7.7	49.8	8.2
3033	7	0.030	0.029	0.19	0.09	0.068	3.2	21.9	13.4	7.4	6.3	43.0	2.3

(continued)

TABLE I (continued)

Heat No.	Sulfur partition ratio	Slag composition, %							Metal composition, %				Ref.
		CaO	MnO	MgO	ΣFeO	SiO₂	P₂O₅	ΣS	C	Mn	P	S	
I	6.5	42.8	9.5	10.4	15.9	16.3	1.1	0.20	0.06	0.51	0.010	0.031	10
II	11.4	38.4	10.4	8.3	23.3	7.8	1.6	0.33	0.11	0.52	0.010	0.029	10
III	8.5	36.8	15.6	4.9	17.1	13.3	1.2	0.36	0.08	0.48	0.017	0.042	10
IV	14.6	36.6	17.3	7.7	13.8	17.3	0.8	0.54	0.11	0.57	0.014	0.037	10
V	12.3	33.5	10.9	10.4	15.5	10.6	0.6	0.27	0.09	0.42	0.021	0.022	10
3 C 5141	5.6	41.8	13.0	7.5	14.5	17.9	1.7	0.22	0.07	0.47	0.015	0.039	8
3 A 4864	10.0	43.4	16.4	6.3	12.7	15.7	1.9	0.28	0.20	0.50	0.018	0.028	8
3 B 5200	10.8	40.4	15.4	4.7	20.6	16.8	1.3	0.28	0.15	0.34	0.020	0.026	8
3 A 4862	5.7	41.0	14.8	4.0	14.3	18.6	1.9	0.21	0.17	0.29	0.012	0.037	8
I	4.0	38.4	13.6	7.8	11.6	23.2	2.5	0.12	0.09	0.34	0.03	0.03	8
II	9.3	41.6	10.0	10.8	16.6	17.0	1.7	0.28	0.12	0.27	0.01	0.03	8
III	10.7	40.2	11.4	12.7	17.1	14.4	2.2	0.32	0.08	0.29	0.01	0.03	8
IV	6.3	42.3	10.1	10.5	12.5	19.7	1.9	0.19	0.07	0.38	0.02	0.03	8
V	5.3	41.6	9.4	11.2	17.1	16.6	1.7	0.21	0.10	0.23	0.01	0.04	8
VI	4.0	41.2	11.9	10.8	15.4	15.7	2.5	0.12	0.16	0.29	0.01	0.03	8
VII	7.3	43.1	11.2	12.3	15.3	13.2	2.0	0.22	0.14	0.36	0.01	0.03	8

ᵃ Estimated from ladle analysis.

This equation explained 74% of the variation in partition ratio. Additional information from the statistical examination is shown in Table II.

TABLE II

Important Coefficients in Sulfur-Partition-Ratio Regression Analysis
(Carbon content 0.05 to 0.20%)

	Independent variable			
	CaO%	MnO%	SiO$_2$%	P$_2$O$_5$%
Simple correlation coefficients	0.365	0.016	-0.595	-0.287
Partial correlation coefficients	0.660	0.568	-0.811	-0.524
Regression coefficients	0.25 $\pm$ 0.05	0.41 $\pm$ 0.11	-0.55 $\pm$ 0.08	-0.97 $+$ 0.30
Standard error of estimate	1.86			

Figure 1 is a plot of the partition-ratio values obtained by chemical analysis versus the partition-ratio values predicted from the equation. The scatter about the identity line is perhaps a little greater than the scatter about Darken and Larsen's equation, which represents the best alternative method of relating sulfur partition ratio to slag composition. The present work does not apply over as wide a variation of steel carbon content as the work of Darken and Larsen. However, the present equation has the virtue of a much greater simplicity, which is needed for deriving the model. The equation is valid under the following range of conditions: Carbon content of the steel, 0.05–0.20%; CaO content of the slag, 34–51%; SiO$_2$ content of the slag, 6–25%; MnO content of the slag, 2–17%; P$_2$O$_5$ content of the slag, 1–5%; and lime-silica ratio of the slag, 2.0 minimum.

Before the derivation of the model is shown, it is appropriate to discuss the system underlying the choice of symbols used. Almost all the symbols referred to are either weights of materials expressed in pounds per net ingot ton, or concentrations in weight per cent. The weights are denoted by the letter W and the concentrations by the appropriate chemical symbols. The subscripts are used to further identify the material considered and the source of the material. A few examples will clarify the system of symbols used: S_{st} is the percentage of sulfur in the *steel* (only considered at tap), S_{ts} is the percentage of sulfur in the *tap slag*, $(CaO)_{fs}$ is the percentage of lime in the *flush slag*, W_{ts} is the weight of *tap slag*, and W_{hm} is the weight of *hot metal*.

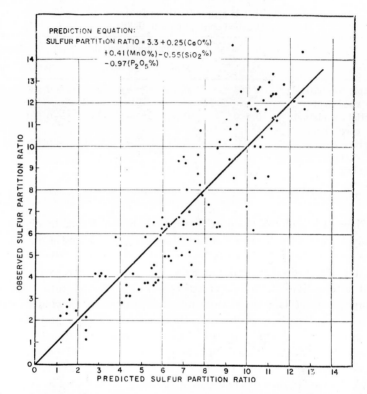

Fig. 1. Sulfur partition ratio (low carbon heats) calculated vs predicted values.

Double subscripts are used when both the material and the source of the material must be defined: $W_{S \cdot ts}$ is the weight of *sulfur* in the *tap slag;* $W_{S \cdot B}$ is the weight of *sulfur* in the slag and metal *bath* at tap, also called the sulfur burden; and $W_{CaO \cdot rf}$ is the weight of CaO from the *refractories.*

The symbols used in the final model are defined in Table III. Symbols not shown in Table III will be defined as they are used in the derivation of the model, which follows.

TABLE III. Definition of Symbols and Selected Base Practice

Symbol	Definition	Selected value
S_{st}	Sulfur content of steel at tap, %	0.0275% (calc)
$W_{S \cdot B}$[a]	Weight of sulfur in steel and slag bath at tap	—
$W_{CaO \cdot B}$	Weight of CaO in steel and slag bath at tap	—
$S_{SiO2 \cdot B}$	Weight of silica in steel and slag bath at tap	—
$W_{Mn \cdot B}$	Weight of manganese in steel and slag bath at tap	—
$W_{P \cdot B}$	Weight of phosphorus in steel and slag bath at tap	—
W_{hm}	Weight of hot metal charged	—
M	Hot metal as percentage of total metallic charge	60%
a	Ore charged (pounds per pound of hot metal)	0.21
Fe_{or}	Iron content of the ore (natural basis), %	60%
W_{ls}	Weight of limestone charged	110
W_{lm}	Weight of lime fed	0
$W_{S \cdot ga}$	Weight of sulfur from furnace gases	0.1
$W_{S \cdot rf}$	Weight of sulfur from refractories	0.0123
$W_{CaO \cdot rf}$	Weight of CaO from refractories	36
$W_{SiO_2 \cdot rf}$	Weight of silica from refractories	5
W_{fs}	Weight of flush slag	150
S_{hm}	Sulfur content of hot metal	0.036%
S_{or}	Sulfur content of ore	0.020%
S_{sc}	Sulfur content of scrap	0.036%
S_{ls}	Sulfur content of limestone	0.059%
S_{lm}	Sulfur content of lime	0.100%
$(CaO)_{ls}$	CaO content of limestone	53%
$(CaO)_{lm}$	CaO content of lime	90%
$(CaO)_{fs}$	CaO content of flush slag	15%
Si_{hm}	Silicon content of hot metal	1.2%
$(SiO_2)_{or}$	Silica content of ore	3.0%
$(SiO_2)_{sc}$	Silica content of scrap	0.5%
$(SiO_2)_{ls}$	Silica content of limestone	0.5%
$(SiO_2)_{lm}$	Silica content of lime	0.9%
$(SiO_2)_{fs}$	Silica content of flush slag	20%
Mn_{hm}	Manganese content hot metal	1.8%
Mn_{or}	Manganese content ore	0.2%
Mn_{sc}	Manganese content scrap	0.35%
Mn_{fs}	Manganese content flush slag	11.0%
P_{hm}	Phosphorus content hot metal	0.3%
P_{or}	Phosphorus content ore	0.05%
P_{sc}	Phosphorus content scrap	0.02%
P_{fs}	Phosphorus content flush slag	1.31%

[a] All weights expressed in lb/net ingot ton.

The equation for predicting the sulfur partition ratio L from the slag composition for low carbon heats with tapping slags of normal basicity was reported earlier[2] as

$$L = S_{ts}/S_{st} = 3.3 + 0.25(CaO)_{ts} - 0.55(SiO_2)_{ts} + 0.41$$
$$(MnO)_{ts} - 0.97(P_2O_5)_{ts} \quad (A)$$

wherein the subscript indicates the tap slag.

The material balance for sulfur for an individual heat may be stated

$$\text{Sulfur input} = \text{sulfur output}$$

$$\Sigma W_S = W_{S \cdot fs} + W_{S \cdot ts} + W_{S \cdot st}$$

the weight of sulfur in the flush slag, the tap slag, and the steel being listed separately. This provides two definitions of the sulfur burden, or the weight of sulfur in the slag and the steel bath at tap as follows:

$$W_{S \cdot B} = W_{S \cdot ts} + W_{S \cdot st} \quad (B)$$

$$W_{S \cdot B} = \Sigma W_S - W_{S \cdot fs} \quad (C)$$

If pit scrap is $1\frac{1}{2}\%$ of the steel, 2030 lb of liquid steel must be made for each net ton of ingots. Thus, the weight of sulfur in the steel and in the tap slag can be expressed

$$W_{S \cdot st} = 2030 \times S_{st}/100$$

$$W_{S \cdot ts} = W_{ts} \times S_{ts}/100$$

Substituting for $W_{S \cdot st}$ and $W_{S \cdot ts}$ in Eq. (B) gives

$$100\ W_{S \cdot B} = 2030 \times S_{st} + W_{ts} \times S_{ts}$$

But $S_{ts} = L \times S_{st}$, therefore $100\ W_{S \cdot B} = S_{st} (2030 + L \times W_{ts})$, and $S_{st} = 100\ W_{S \cdot B}/(2030 + L \times W_{ts})$.

Since L is known in terms of the tap-slag composition by Eq. (A), the expression can be substituted for L to give

$$S_{st} = 100 W_{S \cdot B}/\{2030 + W_{ts}[3.3 + 0.25(CaO)_{ts} - 0.55(SiO)_{ts}$$
$$+ 0.41(MnO)_{ts} - 0.97(P_2O_5)_{ts}]\} \quad (D)$$

By stoichiometry, $(MnO)_{ts} = 1.29\ (Mn)_{ts}$ and $(P_2O_5)_{ts} = 2.29\ (P_{ts})$; therefore, substituting in Eq. (D) gives

$$S_{st} = 100 W_{S \cdot B}/\{2030 + W_{ts}[3.3 + 0.25(CaO)_{ts} - 0.55(SiO_2)_{ts}$$
$$+ 0.53(Mn)_{ts} - 2.22(P)_{ts}]\} \quad (E)$$

To convert the slag-composition terms to burden terms, we may use the following equations:

$$W_{ts} \times (CaO)_{ts} = 100_{CaO \cdot B} \tag{F}$$

$$W_{ts} \times (SiO_2)_{ts} = 100 \ W_{SiO_2 \cdot B} \tag{G}$$

$$W_{ts} \times (Mn)_{ts} = 79 \ W_{Mn \cdot B} \tag{H}$$

$$W_{ts} \times (P)_{ts} = 89 \ W_{P \cdot B} \tag{J}$$

The coefficients in Eqs. (H) and (J) arise from the fact that some manganese and phosphorus remain in the metal. Material balances for low carbon heats reported by Philbrook[11] in Tables 6–6 and 6–8 show that an average of 79% of the manganese burden and 89% of the phosphorus burden goes to the slag. Data from U. S. Steel Corporation plants confirm that for individual low carbon heats, there is not much variation from these proportions.

Substituting in Eq. (E) the burden terms from Eqs. (F) to (J) gives

$$S_{st} = 100W_{S \cdot B}/(2030 + 3.3W_{ts} + 25W_{CaO \cdot B} - 55W_{SiO_2 \cdot B}$$
$$+ 42W_{Mn \cdot B} - 198W_{P \cdot B}) \tag{L}$$

An approximation permits $3 \cdot 3W_{ts}$, the tap-slag-weight term, to be included with $25W_{CaO \cdot B}$, the lime-burden term, since additions of lime influence the sulfur at tap by increasing the basicity and the tap-slag weight. Assume that the tap slag contains 40% CaO, then

$$W_{ts} = W_{CaO \cdot B} + 100/40$$

$$3.3W_{ts} = 8.25 \ W_{CaO \cdot B}, \text{ say, } 8W_{CaO \cdot B}$$

If the extreme variation of $(CaO)_{ts}$ is taken as 33 to 50%, the coefficient 8.25 might actually be as low as 6.6 or as high as 9.9. This variation is considered negligible when $8W_{CaO \cdot B}$ is added to $25W_{CaO \cdot B}$ in Eq. (L), to give the final equation

$$S_{st} = 100W_{S \cdot B}/(2030 + 33 \ W_{CaO \cdot B} - 55W_{SiO_2 \cdot B}$$
$$+ 42W_{Mn \cdot B} - 198 \ W_{P \cdot B}) \tag{1}$$

Up to this point, the burdens have been defined by equations similar to Eq. (B) for sulfur. For the final model, equations similar to Eq. (C) are used. Equation (C) is expanded here for the sulfur

TABLE IV

Variation of the Sulfur Content of the Flush Slag with Sulfur Input

Heat No.	S_{fs}	W_S	Heat No.	S_{fs}	W_S
Plant A			Plant B	—	—
18P106	0.054	0.71	13A366	0.085	1.32
15P133	0.066	0.82	13A506	0.130	1.48
15P129	0.082	1.47	13A382	0.076	1.30
31P233	0.076	1.09	13A524	0.095	1.24
32P213	0.088	1.45			
55P060	0.084	1.15	Plant C		
55P121	0.067	1.00	12C013	0.081	1.06
55P179	0.087	1.19	12C017	0.080	0.93
57P103	0.120	1.14	14C911	0.141	1.67
57P192	0.082	0.99	29C485	0.077	1.03
55P045	0.103	1.94	29C501	0.095	1.07
71P290	0.062	0.97	127336	0.070	0.93
71P297	0.103	1.01	127338	0.080	1.06
70P292	0.118	1.17	125113	0.090	0.84
75P308	0.108	1.04	121695	0.080	0.85
33392	0.081	0.91	123136	0.090	0.88
33399	0.072	0.66			
32387	0.078	0.77	Plant D		
32390	0.075	0.76	08E091	0.104	1.17
33415	0.068	0.78	08E119	0.074	0.95
33423	0.078	0.67	08E132	0.082	0.93
33426	0.081	0.71	08E097	0.106	1.34
33420	0.078	0.71	08E121	0.161	1.86
33422	0.067	0.73	08E134	0.088	1.31
42224	0.105	1.10	06E368	0.070	0.92
42225	0.093	1.04	10E310	0.070	0.08
42232	0.090	0.92	11E395	0.073	0.88
42233	0.119	1.27			
40226	0.093	0.92			

burden to show the method employed, and a similar treatment was used for the lime, silica, manganese, and phosphorus burdens.

$$W_{S \cdot B} = \sum W_S - W_{S \cdot fs}$$

$$100 \ W_{S \cdot B} = W_{hm} \times S_{hm} + W_{or} \times S_{or} + W_{sc} \times S_{sc} + W_{ls}$$
$$\times S_{ls} + W_{lm} \times S_{lm} + 100 \ W_{S \cdot rf}$$
$$+ 100 \ W_{S \cdot ga} \ W_{fs} \times S_{fs} \quad (M)$$

Although this equation is valid, it cannot be used as it stands because it contains variables on the right-hand side of the equation that

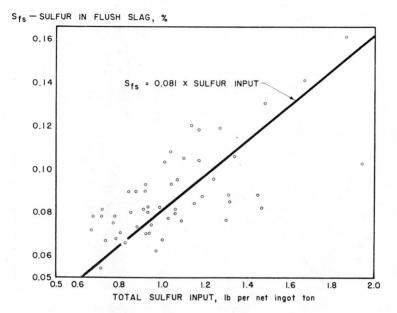

Fig. 2. Total sulfur input versus sulfur in flush slag.

cannot be varied independently.   For example, the hot-metal charge expressed in pounds per net ingot ton cannot be changed unless the scrap charge is adjusted.

With reasonable values of 89.8% liquid-steel yield and 88.5% ingot yield, the total metallic charge is 2260 lb for 2030 lb of liquid steel and 2000 lb of ingots.   Then,

$$W_{hm} = 2260 \times M/100$$

$$W_{or} = 2260 \times M/100 \times a$$

$$W_{sc} = 2260 \left(1 - (M/100) - (M/100) \times a \times \mathrm{Fe}_{or}\right)$$

A further relationship of value is the effect of the total sulfur input on the sulfur content of the flush slag.   If no sulfur enters the system, no sulfur can be present in the flush.   This fact together with the plant data shown in Table IV and plotted in Figure 2 yield a best straight line

$$S_{fs} = 0.081 \times \textstyle\sum W_{\mathrm{S}} = 0.00081 \times \left(100 \textstyle\sum W_s\right)$$

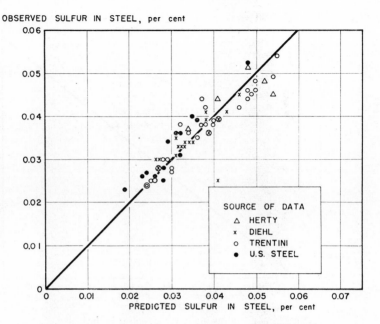

Fig. 3. Check of partly developed sulfur prediction equation.

When substitution is made for W_{hm}, W_{or}, W_{sc}, and S_{fs} in Eq. (M),

$$100W_{\text{S-}B} = [2260 \times M/100 \times S_{hm} + 2260 \times a \times M/100$$
$$\times S_{or} + 2260 [1 - (M/100) - a \times \text{Fe}_{or} \times$$
$$(M/100)] \times S_{sc} + W_{ls} \times S_{ls} + W_{lm} \times S_{lm} + 100W_{\text{S-}rf}$$
$$+ 100 \ W_{\text{S-}ga}] (1 - 0.00081W_{fs}) \quad (2)$$

The equations for the lime, silica, manganese, and phosphorus burdens [Eqs. (3), (4), (5), and (6)] were derived by a similar procedure. Equations (1) through (6) constitute the sulfur model, which is stated as follows:

$$S_{st} = 100W_{\text{S-}B}/(2030 + 33W_{\text{CaO-}B} - 55W_{\text{SiO}_2\text{-}B}$$
$$+ 42W_{\text{Mo-}B} - 198W_{\text{P-}B}) \quad (1)$$

$$100W_{\text{S-}B} = [2260 \times M/100 \times S_{hm} + 2260 \times a \times M/100$$
$$\times S_{or} + 2260 [1 - (M/100) - a \times \text{Fe}_{or} \times M/100]$$
$$\times S_{sc} + W_{ls} \times S_{ls} + W_{lm} \times S_{lm} + 100W_{\text{S-}rf}$$
$$+ 100W_{\text{S-}ga}] (1 - 0.00081W_{fs}) \quad (2)$$

$$100W_{\text{CaO}\cdot B} = W_{ls} \times (\text{CaO})_{ls} + W_{lm} \times (\text{CaO})_{lm} + 100W_{\text{CaO}\cdot rf}$$
$$- W_{fs} \times (\text{CaO})_{fs} \quad (3)$$

$$100W_{\text{SiO}_2\cdot B} = 2260 \times M/100 \times 2.14 \times \text{Si}_{hm} + 2260 \times a$$
$$\times M/100 \times (\text{SiO}_2)_{or} + 2260[1 - (M/100) - a$$
$$\times \text{Fe}_{or} \times M/100] \times (\text{SiO}_2)_{sc} + W_{ls} \times (\text{SiO}_2)_{ls} + W_{lm} \times (\text{SiO}_2)_{lm}$$
$$+ 100W_{\text{SiO}_2\cdot rf} - W_{fs} \times (\text{SiO}_2)_{fs} \quad (4)$$

$$100W_{\text{Mn}\cdot B} = 2260 \times M/100 \times \text{Mn}_{hm} + 2260 \times a \times M/100$$
$$\times \text{Mn}_{or} + 2260 \, (1 - M/100 - a \times \text{Fe}_{or} \times M/100)$$
$$\times \text{Mn}_{sc} - W_{fs} \times \text{Mn}_{fs} \quad (5)$$

$$100W_{\text{P}\cdot B} = 2260 \times M/100 \times \text{P}_{hm} + 2260 \times a \times M/100$$
$$\times \text{P}_{or} + 2260 \, [1 - (M/100) - a \times \text{Fe}_{or} \times M/100]$$
$$\times \text{P}_{sc} - W_{fs} \times P_{fs} \quad (6)$$

No data sufficiently complete to be of use for verifying the complete model have been recorded. However, data are available[5-9] for estimating the sulfur, lime, silica, manganese, and phosphorus burdens for more than 60 heats from the weights and compositions of the steel and the slag at tap. The calculated values for sulfur at tap for these heats are plotted against the analytical results in Figure 3. The scatter about the equality line is very small, inasmuch as it includes analytical error for eight components analyzed at many different laboratories over a period of 35 years. The one point that shows a serious discrepancy is for a heat that had a lime-silica

TABLE V
Variations of Sulfur Pickup in Trial Heats

No of exptl heats	Fuel used	Avg $W_{\text{S}.ga}$ (by difference), lb/net ingot ton
3	Natural gas	−0.14
2	Coke-oven gas[a] Natural gas	0.06
4	Oil	0.06
15	Tar Natural gas	0.11
1	Tar	0.19
4	Coke-oven gas[a] Tar	0.28
4	Coke-oven gas[a]	0.52

[a] Coke-oven gas not desulfurized at the time of these trials.

ratio of only 1.57 at tap. The model is considered valid only for heats with a lime-silica ratio greater than about 2.0 at tap.

This model is incomplete in two respects. First, it does not relate the sulfur pickup from the furnace atmosphere to variables within the operators' control. Second, it does not show how the operator might vary the flush-slag composition to remove more sulfur in the flush.

Although the absorption of sulfur from the furnace atmosphere is not quantitatively understood, some of the factors that might be expected to influence the magnitude of sulfur absorption from the furnace atmosphere are as follows.

1. The sulfur content of the fuel. Trentini[9] has shown that for an oil-fired furnace, the sulfur absorption is linearly related to the sulfur content of the oil.

2. The time of exposure of solid scrap. Robertson et al.[12] have reported that most of the sulfur absorption from the furnace gas occurs during charging and during the early part of the melting period before the charge is covered with slag. However, no quantitative relationship is available to show the effect of exposure time.

3. Oxygen content of the furnace gas. A theoretical paper by Richardson and Withers[13] suggests that an oxidizing atmosphere should minimize sulfur pickup.

Experimental data quoted in Table V show the variation of sulfur pickup when different fuels are used. This information is obviously inadequate for prediction, and the problem of sulfur pickup would seem to warrant a systematic experimental study.

The mechanism that determines the flush-slag composition in the open hearth has not been adequately studied experimentally; therefore, it cannot be properly treated in the sulfur model at present.

Although the sulfur model is not yet complete in these respects, it still shows the importance of sulfur pickup from the atmosphere and of flush-slag analysis to the general problem of sulfur removal. In addition, reasonable and constant values for these variables can be postulated so that the effect of changing other variables in the process can be studied.

To study the effects of individual variables, a base practice must be selected. Table III, which defines the symbols used to express the operating variables considered in the model, also lists the values of those variables selected to represent the particular base practice considered. From these arbitrary standard values, the sulfur content of the steel at tap was calculated by using the model. The value obtained was 0.0275% sulfur. In the figures illustrating the effect of changes in practice on the sulfur in the steel at tap, the base-practice conditions are represented by a dot on each curve. It must be noted that if a different base practice is chosen, the form of the calculated curves will differ from those shown.

Figure 4 shows the effect of the amount of limestone charged on the sulfur content of the steel at tap. Since the curve is concave upward, the more limestone added, the less effect from any given incremental addition. Because the weight of the tap slag increases with the amount of limestone charged, a slag with a high limestone charge is not as greatly affected in composition by an additional quantity of limestone than a slag with a lower limestone charge.

Figure 5 shows that the effect of the amount of burnt lime fed is similar to the effect of the amount of limestone charged. However, burnt lime has more effect than limestone, weight for weight, because of its higher CaO content.

When the percentage of hot metal charged to the open hearth is increased, the ore charge must be increased more than proportionately. Therefore, the ore-charge practice recommended by Philbrook[11] was used to calculate the ore charge and the total metallic charge. Figure 6 shows this ore-charge practice. The effect of the percentage of hot metal charged is shown in Figure 7. The sulfur problem is greater for high hot metal heats than for low hot metal heats because of the greater silica input from the increased hot metal and ore.

The effect of sulfur in the hot metal charged is linear, as shown in Figure 8. The relationship may be used to evaluate desulfurization techniques if it is assumed that the desulfurized hot metal is efficiently slagged off so that the reduction in sulfur content of the hot metal really corresponds to a reduction in sulfur input.

Figures 9 and 10 show the effects of sulfur in the scrap and the limestone, respectively. The effects are naturally smaller than the effect of sulfur in the hot metal.

Figure 11 strikingly shows the importance of using low sulfur fuels, or of desulfurizing coke-oven gas, if economics dictate its use.

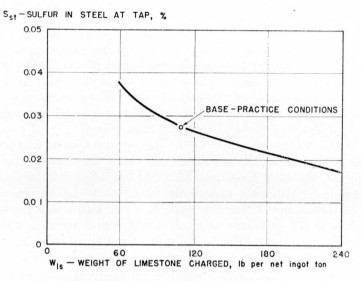

Fig. 4. Effect of limestone charged on sulfur in steel at tap.

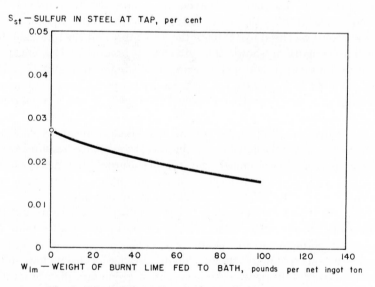

Fig. 5. Effect of burnt-lime feed on sulfur in steel at tap.

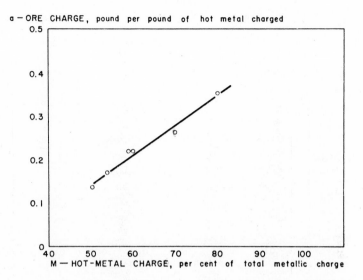

Fig. 6. Adjustment of ore charge with varying hot metal charge.

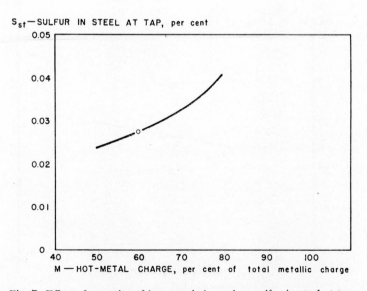

Fig. 7. Effect of quantity of hot metal charged on sulfur in steel at tap

S_{st}—SULFUR IN STEEL AT TAP, per cent

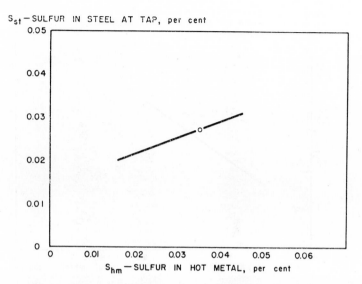

Fig. 8. Effect of sulfur in hot metal on sulfur in steel at tap.

S_{st}—SULFUR IN STEEL AT TAP, per cent

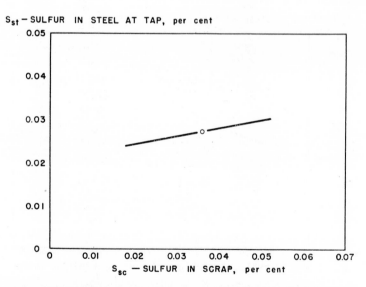

Fig. 9. Effect of sulfur in scrap on sulfur in steel at tap.

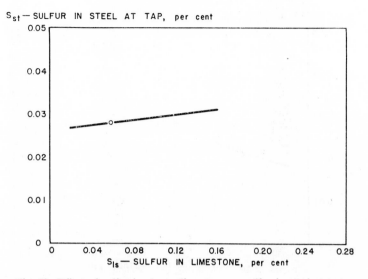

Fig. 10. Effect of sulfur in charge limestone on sulfur in steel at tap.

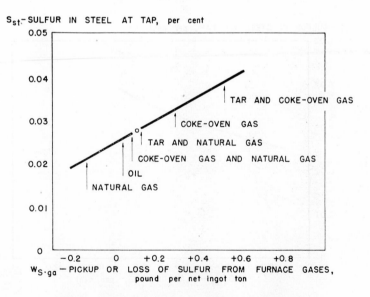

Fig. 11. Effect of fuel used on sulfur in steel at tap.

S_{st} — SULFUR IN STEEL AT TAP, per cent

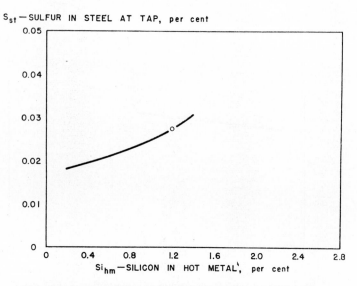

Fig. 12. Effect of silicon in hot metal on sulfur in steel at tap.

S_{st} — SULFUR IN STEEL AT TAP, per cent

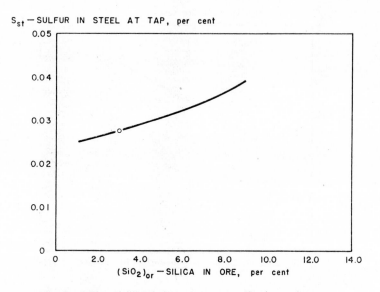

Fig. 13. Effect of silica in charge ore on sulfur in steel at tap.

S_{st}—SULFUR IN STEEL AT TAP, per cent

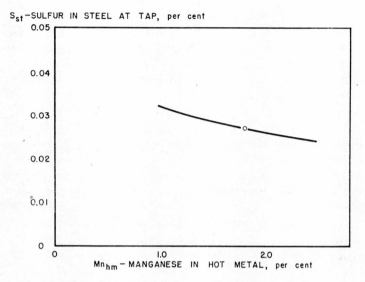

Fig. 14. Effect of manganese in hot metal on sulfur in steel at tap.

S_{st}—SULFUR IN STEEL AT TAP, per cent

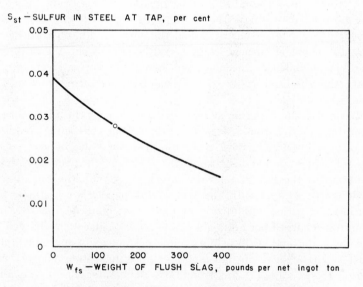

Fig. 15. Effect of weight of flush slag on sulfur in steel at tap.

The arrows show the estimated sulfur pickup from several fuel combinations previously shown in Table V.

In showing the effect of silicon in the hot metal, Figure 12 shows that desiliconization of the hot metal may be as effective as desulfurization. Only the effect of a changing silicon burden is considered. Additional effects may result from the influence of hot desiliconized iron on the flush practice. Again, it is assumed that the treated hot metal is completely slagged off.

Figure 13 shows the effect of the silica content of the ore and confirms the long-recognized importance of low silica charge ores.

Although the effect of higher manganese is beneficial, Figure 14 indicates that the benefit of using a high-manganese iron is rather less marked than is generally supposed. Figure 14 shows only the effect of varying the manganese content of the hot metal. If increased manganese is achieved by greater recirculation of open hearth slag, the effect of increased phosphorus in the hot metal will partly offset the effect of the manganese on the sulfur content of the steel at tap.

The importance of the weight of the flush slag was emphasized by Mayo.[14] Figure 15 verifies Mayo's conclusions.

At this point, an example may be given to illustrate how the model can be used to evaluate the results of a change in practice. In a recent paper,[15] Speer has described the effect of adding open hearth slag to the blast furnace charge. Although all the relevant data were not included in Speer's paper, enough data were given to illustrate the potential value of the model in evaluating a change of practice.

Basically, the experiment consisted of altering the blast furnace charging practice from a slag-free charge to one containing about 400 lb of mixed open hearth slag per ton of hot metal produced. Over the subsequent period of eight months, the manganese and phosphorus contents of the hot metal were observed, as was the open-hearth ladle sulfur content. In the text of his paper, Speer stated that during this period, the fluxing practice was changed from 100 lb of limestone charged per net ingot ton to 55 lb of limestone charged per net ingot ton and 40 lb of burnt lime per net ingot ton added after flush. The change in hot-metal composition observed over the period (Speer's Fig. 1) was from 1.3% manganese and 0.15% phosphorus to 3.0% manganese and 0.40% phosphorus. The average ladle sulfur decreased during the experimental period (Speer's Fig. 4) from about 0.0285% to about 0.023%.

To apply the sulfur model to this problem in the absence of complete data, the same standard base practice was assumed as elsewhere in this report, except for the particular variables Mn_h, P_h, W_{ls}, and W_{lm}. Table VI shows the calculated values.

TABLE VI

Calculation	Mn_{hm}	P_{hm}	W_{ls}	W_{lm}	Calc. S_{st}, %
1	1.3	0.14	100	0	0.0278
2	3.0	0.40	100	0	0.0254
3	3.0	0.40	55	40	0.0231

Calculations 1 and 3 in Table VI show a remarkable and perhaps fortuitous agreement with observed results. The interesting fact that emerges is from calculation 2. This calculation indicates that only about 50% of the total improvement in sulfur content was caused by the change in hot-metal analysis and that the balance of the improvement resulted from changes in the fluxing practice in the open hearth.

Finally, the model can be used to aid in a comparison of the costs of different practices. Any comparison of practices must be made in the light of existing conditions in a particular plant. If, in the present discussion, the plant is assumed to have a set of operating conditions that can be described by the base practice quoted in Table III, what changes in practice could be made to reduce the average tap sulfur from 0.0275% to 0.020%?

1. An average lime feed of 46 lb/ton. This practice would involve increased slag weight of about 80 lb/ton with a lower yield, a lower fuel efficiency, and a longer heat time. The magnitude of these disadvantages would need to be determined experimentally.

2. An average limestone charge of 190 lb/ton. The heat required for calcination would be an additional disadvantage to those described for feeding lime.

3. Desulfurization of hot metal to 0.016% sulfur. If the calcium carbide injection technique were used to reduce the sulfur from 0.036 to 0.016%, 8 lb of carbide would be required for each ton of hot

metal treated.[16]   A current cost estimate for this treatment might be $0.78 per ton of hot metal or about $0.53 per ingot ton.

4.   Desiliconization of hot metal from 1.20 to 0.48% silicon. Oxygen requirements would be about 500 cu ft/ton of hot metal. With oxygen costing $6 per ton, assuming that a tonnage oxygen plant has been constructed, desiliconization would cost about $0.25 per ton of hot metal, or about $0.17 per ingot ton.   This figure does not include the cost of operating the fume-control equipment that might be necessary.

5.   Increase of flush slag to 300 lb/ton.   The major item of cost would be a decreased yield.

6.   Change-over to 100% natural gas firing.   Data on sulfur pickup from the fuel are limited, but changing the fuel fired from tar and natural gas (base practice) to 100% natural gas might reduce the tap sulfur from 0.0275 to 0.021%.   Fuel costs and the effect of production rate would determine the feasibility of the change.

The author wishes to thank the U. S. Steel Corporation for permission to publish this paper, and he is indebted to Messrs. J. H. Richards, W. L. Kerlie, F. A. Sorensen, and B. M. Larsen for their valuable advice and criticisms.

References

1. Kesterton, A. J., *J. Metals*, **9**, 274 (1957).

2. Darken, L. S., and B. M. Larsen, *Trans. Am. Inst. Mining Met. Engrs.*, **150**, 87 (1942).

3. Grant, N. J., and J. Chipman, *Trans. Am. Inst. Mining Met. Engrs.*, **167**, 134 (1946).

4. St. Pierre, G. R., and J. Chipman, *J. Metals*, **8**, 1475 (1956).

5. Diehl, A. N., *AISI Yearbook*, **1926**, 54.

6. Herty, C. H., C. F. Christopher, and R. W. Stewart, *Mining Met. Investigations Cooperative Bull.* 38.

7. Petersen, O., *Stahl u. Eisen*, **30**, 1 (1910).

8. Schenck, H., *Arch. Eisenhüttenw.*, **3**, 505 (1929–30).

9. Trentini, B., A. Peters, and G. Husson, *Rev. mét.*, **53**, 529 (1956).

10. Bardenheuer, P., and G. Thanheiser, *Mitt. Kaiser-Wilhelm Inst. Eisenorsch.*, **17**, 133 (1935).

11. Philbrook, W. O., *Basic Open Hearth Steelmaking*, AIME Seely Mudd Series, 1951.

12. Robertson, F. L., C. H. Bacon, and J. W. Till, *Trans. Am. Inst. Mining Met. Engrs.*, **191**, 1031 (1951).

13. Richardson, F. D., and G. Withers, *J. Iron Steel Inst. (London)*, **165**, 66 (1950).

14. Mayo, W. H., "Training Personnel in Control of Sulfur in the Open Hearth," Proceedings of the AISI Regional Technical Meetings, 1952, p. 457.

15. Speer, E. B., "Use of Open Hearth Slag in the Blast Furnace and Effect on Open Hearth Practices," Proceedings of the AIME Blast Furnace, Coke Oven and Raw Materials Conference, 1955, p. 181.

16. Hornak, J. N., and E. J. Whittenberger, "The Desulfurization of Molten Iron," Proceedings of the AIME Blast Furnace, Coke Oven, and Raw Materials Conference, 1956, p. 125.

Discussion

C. F. Taylor, C. L. McCabe, and F. D. Richardson were concerned about the extent to which laboratory investigations are used in statistical analyses of plant operations. It was suggested by Dr. Taylor that the physical-chemical model of the system might give closer agreement than the simple model used by Mr Lilly.

General Discussion

At the conclusion of the meeting John Elliott and Law McCabe led a discussion on the direction for future research in the field of process metallurgy. A number of people were in favor of having the next conference within five years. The following written comments were presented.

John Chipman: This meeting has demonstrated one thing quite clearly; namely, that insofar as metallurgy is concerned ferrous and nonferrous topics are miscible in all proportions. With respect to The Metallurgical Society it has also demonstrated that three active committees from the three separate divisions can cooperate to produce a symposium of great benefit to all and with a strengthening and unifying influence on the Society.

Thermodynamics has necessarily held a position of pre-eminence in our discussions of process metallurgy during recent years. It is gratifying to note how an increasing role which kinetic studies are playing in the understanding of metallurgical processes. These two equally essential themes must continue to guide our research thought during the coming years.

Professor Eyring's lecture gave an impressive account of the tremendous power of statistical mechanics as applied both to thermodynamics and to kinetic studies. Herein lies a key to understanding the structures of the phases with which we are dealing and the mechanisms by which processes are brought about. And while it is quite true as Eyring stated that the subject is duller with the algebra, it is nonetheless essential that metallurgists acquire greater facility with mathematical techniques.

Many of the problems of process metallurgy are the same as those which chemical engineers have faced and which are often very familiar in their lower temperature counterparts. The same kind of thinking which has gone into the development of chemical engineering needs to be brought into metallurgy on a larger scale than in the past.

Since the objective of process metallurgy is generally to produce a metal, it is essential that the properties and qualities of the metal itself be understood by the operating metallurgist. The chemical metallurgist, therefore, can never afford to overlook the teachings of physical metallurgy.

It is unlikely that we shall develop many process metallurgists who can excel in all of the branches of the science which I have mentioned as essential to the development of the whole field.   Inevitably we shall have some members of our group whose major interest is theoretical; others will favor the practical.   Some will be mathematically inclined; others not.   And so it goes.   In the training of metallurgists we must not seek to suppress this diversity but rather to encourage it. We can do this not only by flexible curricula but more particularly by bringing into the field people whose primary training has been in the diverse fields of physics, chemistry, chemical engineering, mathematics, etc.   The schools of metallurgy cannot begin to fill the demand.   Recruits from these other fields are essential.

How fast is new information being put to practical use?   Those of us who work in laboratories somewhat separated from production sometimes wonder how long it will take for new ideas to percolate into operations.   The reason for existence of such a field as process metallurgy is production.   Unless we are all aware of this, it would be better for the more theoretically inclined to revert to pure chemistry or pure physics.   It is the tie-in between research and operations, the contacts between laboratory and plant which can lead to growth of the field and advancement of the profession.

The tying-in of scientific research with plant operations is not an easy matter.   It is not a one-man job in any plant or industry.   It requires collective action of a group.   A lone chemical metallurgist in a producing company cannot but be frustrated if he attempts to carry on research and to apply his findings to production.   Such efforts require the combined activities of groups of people, and the group must be above a certain critical size in order to function effectively.   One thing which has been demonstrated quite clearly during the course of this meeting is that in at least a few cases industrial groups of researchers have been successful in attaining that critical size.

W. O. Philbrook: I should like to direct the discussion toward industrial applications.   Some years ago a certain gentleman in England voiced the heretical opinion that thermodynamics (or perhaps it was physical chemistry) had not made a single real contribution to the art of steelmaking, and there was much consternation and soul searching to find convincing rebuttal. In the past few days we have had a number of fine examples of the application of physical chemistry, together with other scientific or engineering principles, to practical steelmaking problems.

It seems to me that this trend is bound to continue at an accelerating rate, and this points up one of the important functions of applied research and development groups and plant metallurgists. These are the men who are primarily charged with the responsibility of keeping up with the activities of the fundamental research people in academic institutions and other laboratories, interpreting their results in terms of potential applications and finally adapting them to practical use. They are the middle-man between the producer of new knowledge and the ultimate consumer—the plant operator. The flow is not all in one direction by any means, however, because information or ideas from operations or development activities often contribute to new research. Conferences such as this, which improve communication and understanding in both directions, should have an important catalytic effect in accelerating the rate of progress in both the art and science of steelmaking.

F. D. Richardson: In summing this conference one inevitably compares it with others, and especially with the Faraday Society Symposium devoted to this same subject and held in Britain in 1948. I have only one criticism, so let me come to it right away. This is certainly the largest and most hard-working conference I have ever attended, and the crowded program, with its frequent simultaneous sessions, has given us too little opportunity for personal discussion. I would entreat whoever here may plan the next conference to leave an hour free each morning and afternoon for such important matters.

Compared with the Faraday meeting, this conference has been notable for the diversity of the topics discussed, this in itself reflects the breadth of our subject at the present time—is there any kind of reaction that does not come within its purview?—and the vast effort now being devoted to it by chemists and metallurgists. Many new results have been presented here, and our knowledge of liquid structure and reaction rates has been usefully extended. New thermodynamic data for the solutions of concern to the metallurgist have been reported, but our theory of such solutions is still woefully weak, though admittedly stronger than in 1948.

The contributions made toward the end of the conference particularly distinguish this conference from that held in 1948. I refer, of course, to the use of fundamental physical chemistry in the control and "optimising" of metallurgical processes. The paper by Hilty (not recieved for publication in this volume) is not an extension of anything we heard in 1948: it is a new departure—a new and valuable way of using the fundamental knowledge that is coming year by year from the laboratory and combining it with empirical works knowledge so as to guide the process engineer in his day-to-day decisions on how to produce the best product at the lowest cost. This is far removed from the best we have had hitherto— analyses of industrial processes in terms of thermodynamic, chemical kinetic, and sometimes process engineering principles. I can only hope that much more of our basic knowledge will find such fruitful application in production during the next decade. In addition to this we have interesting examples (vide Delve, Meyer, and Lander on titanium in the blast furnace, P. 1111) of concurrent works trials and fundamental laboratory experiments, undertaken by companies in order to solve their own particular process problems.

The planning and running of such an exciting and successful conference as this places a great burden on the organizers. On behalf of the foreign visitors, therefore, I would like to thank Professors Law McCabe and John Elliott for all they have done over the past few months. Let me add a word of thanks, also, to Professor George St. Pierre who is editing the published proceedings.

H. U. Ross: Dr. Elliott suggested that another conference might be held in another ten years. I should like to ask why wait for ten years; why not have another symposium of this kind in five years? This conference has been received with great enthusiasm, and I am sure that another in the not-too-distant future would be highly welcome. The subject of physical chemistry of process metallurgy is growing and is of sufficient interest to attract enough important papers to draw up an acceptable program for 1964.

It has been intimated that this symposium has been a little too long to digest fully all papers presented. Therefore, it would probably be better in the future if these conferences were a little shorter but held more often.

The papers by Brant and Marshall (p. 647) and by Henderson (p. 671) dealing with the rate of reduction of iron oxide materials are of great importance because of the growing interest in the so-called "direct reduction processes" which are attracting much attention at present. Further research in the kinetics of reduction is essential if these processes are to grow in importance. Closely associated with this field of endeavour is that dealing with ore preparation, particularly those processes involving the agglomeration of fine materials. I believe that studies into the ways and means of suitably preparing ores in order to increase their rate of reduction should be a particularly fruitful direction for research.

J. S. Kirkaldy: The second law of thermodynamics tells us that the entropy of an isolated dissipative system is always increasing toward that state of maximum entropy which defines equilibrium. The law does not, however, tell us the path between initial and final states. That is the role of irreversible thermodynamics.

It has been known for a long time that individual details of the path can be described approximately by linear phenomenological relations. These are familiarly known as Fick's law for diffusion, Fourier's law for heat conduction, and Ohm's law for electrical conduction. There are corresponding relations for viscous flow and chemical reaction. The first, rather modest, success of the general theory was to provide a rational way of describing systems which involve one or more dissipative processes and two or more components, and to introduce in a very natural way the description of the interactions between the various processes. This simply involved the assumption that every "flux" J_i is linearly related to every thermodynamic "force" X_k in the system, i.e.,

$$J_i = \sum_k L_{ik} X_k \qquad (1)$$

Statistical mechanics assures us that this is a good approximation for near-equilibrium processes and that for suitable choices of fluxes and conjugate forces, the matrix of the coefficients $[L_{ik}]$ is symmetric (Onsager's principle of microscopic reversibility). Furthermore, certain of the off-diagonal coefficients vanish since Curie's theorem (P. Curie, *Oeuvves*, Soc. French de Physique, Paris, 1908) denies the possibility of thermodynamic forces giving rise to fluxes of different tensorial character. For example, there is no possibility of a diffusive flow (fector character) arising from either a viscous force (tensor character) or chemical affinity (scalar character). On the other hand, the interactions between the fluxes of the same vector character-diffusion, thermal conduction, and electrical conduction exist, and these have been extensively studied. Thermoelectric effects and thermal diffusion effects are in this category. They have been used, among other phenomena, to confirm Onsager's reciprocity relations.

It appears unlikely that the aforementioned interactions will have an important bearing on current problems of process metallurgy. There is, however, one of the same type which may be important, and that is the interaction between independent diffusion flows in mixtures of ternary and higher order constitution. Since Darken demonstrated in 1949 that carbon could diffuse against its own gradient in the presence of a steep silicon gradient [L. S. Darken, *Trans. AIME*, **180,** 430 (1949)], it has been recognized that the interaction terms in the diffusion matrix are often large and accordingly cannot generally be ignored in the calculation of diffusion flows in multi-component systems. For example, it is not *a priori* valid to discuss the diffusion of one component across a metal-slag interfacial film without taking account of the gradients of other components in the film. Chemical engineers are currently taking cognizance of this fact and are examining the possibility of refining liquid and gaseous mixtures by judicious arrangement of these multicomponent interactions (H. L. Toor, Carnegie Inst. Technology, private communication).

Process metallurgists could well look to the evaluation of these effects as rate-determining features in many of their processes. Fortunately, the mathematical formalism for the description of multicomponent diffusion is well advanced and we can now handle with facility all those systems which have been studied analytically for binary chemical diffusion [J. S. Kirkaldy, *Can. J. Phys.*, **37,** 30 (1959)]. The current researches of the writer, under the auspices of the American Iron and Steel Institute, are in this direction. We are looking for multicomponent diffusion effects as a factor in the process of carburization, as a factor in banding and segregation, as a cause of hardenability effects, and as an explanation of high temperature stability of certain alloy steels. The main difficulty in all this work is in the determination of the experimental values for the diffusion coefficients—data which are at present almost nonexistent.

Another broad application of the linear scheme has been developed by Machlin [E. S. Machlin, *Trans. AIME*, **197,** 437 (1953)] for the description of constant temperature and pressure processes occurring by motion of an interface. He has specified the appropriate fluxes and forces and applied the equations to such diverse phenomena as recrystallization and solidification.   Needless to say, the formalism is directly applicable to many of the interfacial reactions in process metallurgy.   This field of application is as yet completely unexplored.

One of the most important steps in this type of thermodynamic analysis involves the specification of the appropriate fluxes and forces. The thermodynamic requirement is that the rate of irreversible entropy production per unit volume be expressible as a bilinear function of the fluxes and forces (S. R. deGroot, *Thermodynamics of Irreversible Processes*, North-Holland Publishing Co., Amsterdam, p. 6) viz.,

$$\sigma = \sum_i J_i X_i \qquad (2)$$

One will recognize that this has the structure of a sum of Joule heats (e.g., current x electromotive force), a form which meets the requirement that the rate of dissipation of available energy be proportional to the rate of irreversible entropy production.

The function σ holds a further very important place in the general theory for it has been demonstrated that for a steady state dissipative system the configuration can be described as a state of minimum rate of entropy production.   Paraphrasing Prigogine (I. Prigogine, *Introduction to Thermodynamics of Irreversible Processes*, Charles C. Thomas, Springfield, Ill., p. 104), nature chooses a path of "maximum dynamical efficiency."   This generalization is often quoted as the "principle of minimum entropy production" or the "principle of minimum dissipation" and can be expressed as the variation principle

$$\delta \int \frac{\sigma \, dV}{\text{volume}} = 0, \text{ minimum} \qquad (3)$$

The above expression has almost the stature, if not the precision, of a law of thermodynamics, for it is possible to derive from it the field equations for all the common dissipative processes, including their interactions [W. Byers Brown, *Trans. Faraday Soc.*, **54,** 772 (1958)].

This statement has more than just academic value because it gives us a device for qualitatively understanding a process whose progress is too complex for description by the usual field equations.   In the writer's Symposium paper (p. 865), for example, it was noted that dendritic growth of an alloy is a clear exemplification of the principle of minimum dissipation, since this morphology (as compared to a flat interface) leads to the maximum rate of conservation of available energy in the form of solute segregation, surface energy, and defect structures.   One could undoubtedly find a similar rationalization of the complex morphological development in growth of crystals from the vapor, in dendrites formed in electrolytic cells, and in beds of solids undergoing forced transformation.

There is at least one other aspect of the principle of minimum dissipation that bears examination in connection with process metallurgy, and this is its relationship to Ostwald's rule (L. S. Darken and R. W. Gurry, *Physical Chemistry of Metals*, McGraw-Hill, New York, 1953, p. 311).   The rules notes that in chemical reactions there is a strong tendency to pass through metastable states on the way toward equilibrium.   This behavior is usually interpreted on the basis of relative energies of activation.   It appears to us that it may also be interpreted in terms of the general thermodynamic principle, for nature prefers that her systems maintain states of high available energy and succeeds in this intent to an extent determined by the overall driving force.   The greater the force, the greater the possibility of attaining high metastable energy states since the promoting forces will also be greater.   There is a good prospect that Ostwald's rule can be expressed in a mathematical form for systems of metallurgical interest.   If so, we may be able, for one thing, to explain in a unified way the partition along the complex reaction chain that occurs in the blast furnace.

It is perhaps appropriate to conclude this prognostication with some advice for the novice.   One should first appreciate that this new thermodynamic approach is not the wherewithal for solution of all outstanding problems of process metallurgy.   It merely takes its place along with statistical mechanics, chemical kinetics, and classical thermodynamics as a signpost for directing the difficult task of extracting a little more useful information from nature. Furthermore, since it is simply an extension of classical thermodynamics, it is a phenomenological theory and therefore depends on the availability of accurate experimental data in its most powerful applications.

In the second place, one should not be dismayed by the apparent abstruseness of the theory.   The thorough mastery of the concepts of entropy and entropy balance is the only prerequisite, and these are already required for successful classical thermodynamic studies. The apparent complexity of some of the relations does not arise because of a complex theory but simply because we are trying to treat complex systems. As metallurgists, we have already chosen to live with the latter.

Finally, as a good scientist, the process metallurgist must direct his initial efforts toward understanding selected sub-systems. Particularly amenable from the experimental and mathematical points of view are those which can be arranged into a steady state. He must also look to general physical chemistry and physical metallurgy for related advances and appreciate the essential unity of thermodynamic theories as applied to diverse fields. Then, with time, he will surely be able to synthesize the available knowledge toward a better understanding of any complex process of interest.

Registration List

Conference on International Symposium on the Physical Chemistry of Process Metallurgy

Pittsburgh, April 27–May 1, 1959

Aas, H. H., Union Carbide Metals Co., Niagara Falls, N. Y.
Abendroth, R. P., Union Carbide Metals Co., Niagara Falls, N. Y.
Aborn, R. H., U. S. Steel Corp., Monroeville, Pa.
Aksoy, A. M., Crucible Steel Co., Syracuse, N. Y.
Albert, R. E., E. I. du Pont de Nemours & Co., Wilmington, Del.
Alcock, C. B., Imperial College, London, England
Angus, J. C., University of Michigan, Ann Arbor, Mich.
Anthony, B. F., Ferro Engineering Co., Cleveland, Ohio
Arant, N. R., Roll Manufacturers Institute, Pittsburgh, Pa.
Argyriades, Dimitri, E. I. du Pont de Nemours & Co., Wilmington, Del.
Baak, Tryggve, University of Toledo, Toledo, Ohio
Babcock, D. E., Republic Steel Corp., Cleveland, Ohio
Balzhiser, R. E., University of Michigan, Ann Arbor, Mich.
Bayers, W. E., Jr., Pittsburgh, Pa.
Beaver, H. O., Jr., The Carpenter Steel Co., Reading, Pa.
Beeghly, H. F., Jones & Laughlin Steel Corp., Pittsburgh, Pa.
Beer, Sylvan, Mellon Institute, Pittsburgh, Pa.
Behrman, J. R., Alan Wood Steel Co., Conshohocken, Pa.
Beinlich, J. J., U. S. Steel Corp., Pittsburgh, Pa.
Benz, M. G., Massachusetts Institute of Technology, Cambridge, Mass
Bianchi, L. M., Westinghouse Electric Corp., Blairsville, Pa.
Bicknese, Eugene, Union Carbide Metals Co., Niagara Falls, N. Y.
Billinghurst, R. G., Assumption University, Windsor, Ontario, Canada
Bishop, H. L., Jr., Allegheny Ludlum Steel Co., Brackenridge, Pa.
Bjorling, Gotthard, Royal Institute of Technology, Stockholm, Sweden
Bloom, R. A., Timken Roller Bearing Co., Canton, Ohio
Bodsworth, C., University of Liverpool, Liverpool, England
Bogeatzes, Andy, St. Joseph Lead Co., Monaca, Pa.
Bolling, G. F., Westinghouse Electric Corp., Pittsburgh, Pa.
Boni, R. E., Armco Steel Corp., Middletown, Ohio
Borland, Paul, Latrobe Steel Co., Latrobe, Pa.
Boucek, V. C., American Steel and Wire Div., U. S. Steel Corp., Donora, Pa.
Braaten, Orvar, Elektrokemisk A. S., New York, N. Y.
Brant, H. H., Armco Steel Corp., Middletown, Ohio
Brantley, F. E., U. S. Bureau of Mines, Salt Lake City, Utah

Brockmiller, Charles, St. Joseph Lead Co., Monaca, Pa.
Bryan, E. A., Jones & Laughlin Steel Corp., Pittsburgh, Pa.
Bryan, R. J., Allegheny Ludlum Steel Corp., Brackenridge, Pa.
Buchovecky, W. A., Crucible Steel Co., Pittsburgh, Pa.
Buehl, R. C., Crucible Steel Co., Midland, Pa.
Burr, W. H., Duquesne Works, U. S. Steel Corp., Duquesne, Pa.
Buskie, J. W., Tennessee Products & Chemical Corp., Lookout Mountain, Tenn.
Carlson, R. F., Allegheny Ludlum Steel Corp., Brackenridge, Pa.
Carter, Ralph, General Electric Co., Schenectady, N. Y.
Cavett, A. D., National Lead Company of Ohio, Cincinnati, Ohio
Cech, R. E., General Electric Co., Schenectady, N. Y.
Ceckler, W. H., Jones & Laughlin Steel Corp., Pittsburgh, Pa.
Chang, M. C., Crucible Steel Co., Pittsburgh, Pa.
Chipman, John, Massachusetts Institute of Technology, Cambridge, Mass.
Cooper, C. F., Carnegie Institute of Technology, Pittsburgh, Pa.
Cosgarea, Andrew, Jr., University of Michigan, Ann Arbor, Mich.
Courtney, W. G., Experiment, Inc., Richmond, Va.
Crago, R. A., Union Carbide Metals Co., Niagara Falls, N. Y.
Crosta, T. W., Algoma Steel Corp., Sault Ste. Marie, Ontario, Canada
Custer, C. C., Bethlehem Steel Co., Steelton, Pa.
Cuthbert, Daniel, New York, N. Y.
Dancy, E. A., Carnegie Institute of Technology, Pittsburgh, Pa.
Dancy, T. E., Jones & Laughlin Steel Corp., Pittsburgh, Pa.
Danver, W. M., Crucible Steel Co., Pittsburgh, Pa.
Darken, L. S., U. S. Steel Corp., Monroeville, Pa.
Dasher, John, Crucible Steel Co., Pittsburgh, Pa.
Dastur, P., Crucible Steel Co., Syracuse, N. Y.
Davis, W. L., Jr., U. S. Steel Corp., Monroeville, Pa.
Davison, M. H., General Electric Co., Schenectady, N. Y.
Dawson, W. R., Republic Steel Corp., Cleveland, Ohio
Decker, A. M., Centre National de Recherches Metallurgiques, Liège, Belgium
Delve, F. D., Jones & Laughlin Steel Corp., Pittsburgh, Pa.
Derge, Gerhard, Carnegie Institute of Technology, Pittsburgh, Pa.
DeRolf, H. J., Pittsburgh Coke & Chemical Co., Pittsburgh, Pa.
Dietz, J. R., National Steel Corp., Weirton, W. Va.
Dismukes, E. B., Southern Research Institute, Birmingham, Ala.
Douglass, D. L., General Electric Co., Schenectady, N. Y.
Dowd, J. D., Aluminum Company of America, New Kensington, Pa.
Dukelow, D. A., Jones & Laughlin Steel Corp., Pittsburgh, Pa.
Durham, F. N., Algoma Steel Corp., Ltd., Sault Ste. Marie, Ontario, Canada
Dvorak, Robert, St. Joseph Lead Co., Monaca, Pa.
Edlund, D. L., Vanadium Corp. of America, New Concord, Ohio
Edstrom, J. O., The Sandvik Steel Works Co., Ltd., Sandviken, Sweden
Emerick, H. B., Jones & Laughlin Steel Corp., Pittsburgh, Pa.
Ennor, W. T., Aluminum Co. of America, Pittsburgh, Pa.
Farley, R. W., Republic Steel Corp., Chicago, Ill.
Farnsworth, W. B., Linde Co., Tonawanda, N. Y.

Fazzalari, F. A., International Business Machines Corp., Yorktown Heights, N. Y.

Fenn, E. M., E. I. du Pont de Nemours & Co., Wilmington, Del.

Fetters, K. L., Youngstown Sheet & Tube Co., Youngstown, Ohio

Few, W. E., Tennessee Products & Chemical Corp., Nashville, Tenn.

Fidock, M. P., Republic Steel Corp., Independence, Ohio

Fincham, C. J. B., National Research Corp., Cambridge, Mass.

Fink, W. L., Aluminum Co. of America, New Kensington, Pa.

Fisher, Henry, General Electric Co., Schenectady, N. Y.

Fitterer, G. R., University of Pittsburgh, Pittsburgh, Pa.

Floridis, T. P., U. S. Steel Corp., Monroeville, Pa.

Forward, F. A., University of British Columbia, Vancouver, B. C., Canada

Foster, L. M., Aluminum Co. of America, New Kensington, Pa.

Frank, W. B., Aluminum Co. of America, New Kensington, Pa.

Franklin, F. F., Vanadium Corp. of America, Cleveland, Ohio

Franklin, R. L., U. S. Steel Corp., Pittsburgh, Pa.

Freeman, H., Universal-Cyclops Steel Corp., Bridgeville, Pa.

Fullman, R. L., General Electric Co., Schenectady, N. Y.

Fulton, J. C., Allegheny Ludlum Steel Corp., Brackenridge, Pa.

Furmidge, J. E., Jones & Laughlin Steel Corp., Pittsburgh, Pa.

Garrett, L. W., Jr., M. W. Kellogg Co., New York, N. Y.

Gautschi, R. H., Crucible Steel Co., Pittsburgh, Pa.

Gee, K. H., Bethlehem Steel Co., Bethlehem, Pa.

Gill, D. H., Union Carbide Metals Co., Niagara Falls, N. Y.

Gleiser, Molly, Massachusetts Institute of Technology, Cambridge, Mass.

Godleski, S. D., United Engineering & Foundry Co., Vandergrift, Pa.

Gokcen, N. A., University of Pennsylvania, Philadelphia, Pa.

Goldstein, David, Crucible Steel Co., Pittsburgh, Pa.

Goldstein, E. M., New Brunswick, N. J.

Gorsuch, P. D., General Electric Co., Schenectady, N. Y.

Grace, L. F., U. S. Steel Corp., Monroeville, Pa.

Grace, R. E., Purdue University, Lafayette, Ind.

Green, J. J., Vanadium Corp. of America, Pittsburgh, Pa.

Greetham, Homer, Cleveland Electro Metals Co., Cleveland, Ohio

Griffith, C. B., Republic Steel Corp., Cleveland, Ohio

Gross, Philipp, Fulmer Research Institute, Ltd., Stokes Poges, Bucks, England

Gummer, W. K., Aluminum Laboratories, Ltd., Arvida, Quebec, Canada

Gupta, Y. P., Massachusetts Institute of Technology, Cambridge, Mass.

Hall, C. F., National Lead Co. of Ohio, Cincinnati, Ohio

Healy, G. W., Union Carbide Metals Co., Niagara Falls, N. Y.

Heaton, LeRoy, Argonne National Laboratory, Lemont, Ill.

Henderson, J. B., The Broken Hill Proprietary Co., Ltd., Shortland, N. S. W., Australia

Henrie, T. A., U. S. Bureau of Mines, Boulder, Colo.

Hepworth, M. T., Colorado School of Mines, Golden, Colo.

Hibbard, W. R., Jr., General Electric Co., Schenectady, N. Y.

Hilty, D. C., Union Carbide Metals Co., Niagara Falls, N. Y.

Hiltz, R. H., Thompson Ramo Wooldridge, Cleveland, Ohio
Hindson, R. D., Steel Co. of Canada, Ltd., Hamilton, Ontario, Canada
Hines, W. G., Steel Co. of Canada, Ltd., Hamilton, Ontario, Canada
Hockings, W. A., Michigan College of Mining & Technology, Houghton, Mich.
Hohman, E. J., Jones & Laughlin Steel Corp., Pittsburgh, Pa.
Holmquist, Stig, U. S. Steel Corp., Pittsburgh, Pa.
Hopkins, R. J., The Broken Hill Associated Smelters Pty. Ltd., Melbourne,
    Victoria, Australia
Hucke, E. E., University of Michigan, Ann Arbor, Mich.
Hudson, R. G., Carnegie Institute of Technology, Pittsburgh, Pa.
Hunter, W. Z., U. S. Bureau of Mines, Albany, Ore.
Ingvoldstad, Donald, The Bunker Hill Co., Kellogg, Idaho
Jackson, J. H., Battelle Memorial Institute, Columbus, Ohio
Jarrett, Noel, Aluminum Co. of America, New Kensington, Pa.
Jazwinski, S. T., Phoenix Steel Corp., Harrisburg, Pa.
Johnson, A. F., Boulder, Colo.
Johnston, D. C., The Metallurgical Society of AIME, New York, N. Y.
Jordan, Walter, E. I. du Pont de Nemours & Co., Wilmington, Del.
Justusson, W. M., Ford Motor Co., Dearborn, Mich.
Kameda, Mitsuo, Tôhoku University, Sendai, Japan
Karasev, Robert, Soviet Academy of Science, Moscow, USSR
Kato, Eiichi, University of Michigan, Ann Arbor, Mich.
Kellogg, H. Y., Columbia University, New York, N. Y.
Kerlie, W. L., U. S. Steel Corp., Monroeville, Pa.
Kerschbaum, H. P., Armco Steel Corp., Middletown, Ohio
King, R. J., United States Steel Corp., Monroeville, Pa.
King, T. B., Massachusetts Institute of Technology, Cambridge, Mass.
Kirkaldy, J. S., McMaster University, Hamilton, Ontario, Canada
Kirkbride, L. D., General Electric Co., Schenectady, N. Y.
Kirkwood, D. H., Massachusetts Institute of Technology, Cambridge, Mass.
Kleppa, O. J., University of Chicago, Chicago, Ill.
Knapp, L. L., Aluminum Co. of America, New Kensington, Pa.
Komarek, K. L., New York University, New York, N. Y.
Kommel, United Engineering and Foundry Co., Vandergrift, Pa.
Koros, P. J., Jones & Laughlin Steel Corp., Pittsburgh, Pa.
Koump, V., U. S. Steel Corp., Monroeville, Pa.
Kruh, R. F., University of Arkansas, Fayetteville, Ark.
Kundrata, F. L., Ford Motor Co., Dearborn, Mich.
Kurfman, V. B., The Dow Chemical Co., Midland, Mich.
Kuzell, C. R., Phelps Dodge Corp., Phoenix, Ariz.
Lambert, R. H., Carnegie Institute of Technology, Pittsburgh, Pa.
Lander, H. N., Jones & Laughlin Steel Corp., Pittsburgh, Pa.
Landis, A. L., Atomics International, Division of North American Aviation Corp.,
    Canoga Park, Calif.
Langenberg, F. C., Crucible Steel Co., Pittsburgh, Pa.
Larsen, B. M., U. S. Steel Corp., Monroeville, Pa.
Latimer, I. A., Ira S. Latimer Co., Warren, Mich.

Leontis, T. E., The Dow Chemical Co., Midland, Mich.
Leslie, W. C., U. S. Steel Corp., Monroeville, Pa.
* Li, Kun, Jones & Laughlin Steel Corp., Pittsburgh, Pa.
Lichy, E., Jones & Laughlin Steel Corp., Aliquippa, Pa.
Lightner, M. W., U. S. Steel Corp., Pittsburgh, Pa.
Lilly, G. F., U. S. Steel Corp., Monroeville, Pa.
Long, Carleton, St. Joseph Lead Co., Monaca, Pa.
Long, George, Aluminum Co. of America, New Kensington, Pa.
Loria, E. A., Climax Molybdenum Co., Pittsburgh, Pa.
Luerssen, F. W., Inland Steel Co., East Chicago, Ind.
Lumsden, John, Imperial Smelting Corp., Avonmouth, Bristol, England
Lund, A. W., University of Toronto, Toronto, Ontario, Canada
Lund, Robert, St. Joseph Lead Co., Monaca, Pa.
McBride, D. L., U. S. Steel Corp., Pittsburgh, Pa.
McCabe, C. L., Carnegie Institute of Technology, Pittsburgh, Pa.
McCauley, J. K., Crucible Steel Co., Pittsburgh, Pa.
McCoy, C. W., Crucible Steel Co., Pittsburgh, Pa.
McCoy, R. C., University of Pittsburgh, Pittsburgh, Pa.
McIntosh, T. J., Tennessee Products & Chemical Corp., Chattanooga, Tenn.
McKewan, W. M., U. S. Steel Corp., Monroeville, Pa.
McNutt, C. R., Olin Mathieson Chemical Corp., New Haven, Conn.
Mackiw, V. N., Sherrill-Gordon Mines, Fort Saskatchewan, Alberta, Canada
Maeda, Genzo, Fuji Iron & Steel Co., Ltd., New York, N. Y.
Mahan, W. M., U. S. Bureau of Mines, Pittsburgh, Pa.
Mangelsdorf, P. C., Jr., University of Chicago, Chicago, Ill.
Mao, G. W., Foote Mineral Co., Berwyn, Pa.
Marble, E. R., Jr., American Smelting & Refining Co., South Plainfield, N. J.
March, E. A., Crucible Steel Co., Midland, Pa.
Marzke, O. T., U. S. Steel Corp., Pittsburgh, Pa.
Mayer, W. C., Jr., Tennessee Coal & Iron Division, U. S. Steel Corp., Fairfield, Ala.
Meerbaum, Sam, M. W. Kellogg Co., Jersey City, N. J.
Meeter, Gordon, Cameron Iron Works, Houston, Texas
Melcher, Norwood, U. S. Bureau of Mines, Pittsburgh, Pa.
Mellgren, Svante, Amco Research Inc., Carteret, N. J.
Meyer, H. W., Jones & Laughlin Steel Corp., Pittsburgh, Pa.
Michal, E. J., National Lead Co., South Amboy, N. J.
Miller, K. Dexter, Jr., M. W. Kellogg Co., New York, N. Y.
Momich, Peter, Crucible Steel Co., Pittsburgh, Pa.
Morgan, A. T., Inland Steel Co., East Chicago, Ind.
Morgan, E. R., Jones & Laughlin Steel Corp., Pittsburgh, Pa.
Morgan, Joseph, St. Joseph Lead Co., Monaca, Pa.
Morkel, Andre, Massachusetts Institute of Technology, Cambridge, Mass.
Morris, J. P., U. S. Bureau of Mines, Pittsburgh, Pa.
Muan, Arnulf, The Pennsylvania State University, University Park, Pa.
Murphy, D. W., Bethlehem Steel Co., Bethlehem, Pa.

Nees, J. M., National Lead Co., Brooklyn, N. Y.
Nelson, E. C., Linde Co., Tonawanda, N. Y.
Nelson, F. D., Inland Steel Co., East Chicago, Ind.
Nieberlein, Vernon, U. S. Bureau of Mines, Rolla, Mo.
Notini, Ulf, Jernkontoret, Stockholm, Sweden
Noy, J. M., Quebec Iron & Titanium Corp., Sorel, Quebec, Canada
Ohtani, M., University of Pennsylvania, Philadelphia, Pa.
Olette, M., IRSID, St. Germain en Laye, France
Oliver, B. F., The Pennsylvania State University, University Park, Pa.
Oriani, R. A., General Electric Co., Schenectady, N. Y.
Pakkala, M. H., U. S. Steel Corp., Pittsburgh, Pa.
Paliwoda, E. J., Jones & Laughlin Steel Corp., Pittsburgh, Pa.
Pehlke, R. D., Massachusetts Institute of Technology, Cambridge, Mass.
Pfeifer, W. A., Allegheny Ludlum Steel Corp., Brackenridge, Pa.
Perbix, Gottfried, Technische Hochschule Aachen, Aachen, West Germany
Peters, A. T., Inland Steel Co., East Chicago, Ind.
Petrilli, Frank, Jones & Laughlin Steel Corp., Cleveland, Ohio
Petrovich, Anton, Lukens Steel Co., Coatesville, Pa.
Philbrook, W. O., Carnegie Institute of Technology, Pittsburgh, Pa.
Pidgeon, L. M., University of Toronto, Toronto, Ontario, Canada
Pillay, T. C. M., Massachusetts Institute of Technology, Cambridge, Mass.
Poliskin, J., Crucible Steel Co., Pittsburgh, Pa.
Powers, R. E., Koppers Co., Inc., Pittsburgh, Pa.
Preusch, C. D., Crucible Steel Co., Pittsburgh, Pa.
Queneau, B. R., Tennessee Coal & Iron Division, U. S. Steel Corp., Fairfield, Ala.
Ragone, D. V., University of Michigan, Ann Arbor, Mich.
Raleigh, D. O., Atomics International, Div. of North American Aviation, Canoga
    Park, Calif.
Ramachandran, S., Allegheny Ludlum Steel Corp., Brackenridge, Pa.
Ramstad, H. F., Jones & Laughlin Steel Corp., Pittsburgh, Pa.
Ratz, G. A., United States Steel Corp., Duquesne, Pa.
Rawling, J. R., Massachusetts Institute of Technology, Cambridge, Mass.
Reese, G. W., Jr., Allegheny Ludlum Steel Corp., Watervliet, N. Y.
Reichmayr, Josef, Pennsylvania Engineering Corp., New Castle, Pa.
Rein, R. H., Youngstown Sheet & Tube Co., Youngstown, Ohio
Rengstorff, G. W. P., Battelle Memorial Institute, Columbus, Ohio
Ribbe, P. H., Corning Glass Works, Corning, N. Y.
Richards, J. H., U. S. Steel Corp., Monroeville, Pa.
Richardson, F. D., Imperial College, London, England
Rist, Andre, IRSID, St. Germain en Laye, France
Robbins, H. D., Linde Co., Tonawanda, N. Y.
Roorda, H. J., International Nickel Co., Copper Cliff, Ontario, Canada
Ross, H. U., University of Toronto, Toronto, Ontario, Canada
Roy, A. S., Columbia University, New York, N. Y.
Russell, A. S., Aluminum Co. of America, New Kensington, Pa.
Russell, John, Republic Steel Corp., Chicago, Ill.
St. Clair, H. W., U. S. Bureau of Mines, Bethesda, Md.

St. Pierre, G. R., Ohio State University, Columbus, Ohio
Samways, N. L., Jones & Laughlin Steel Corp., Pittsburgh, Pa.
Scherrer, E. D., Armco Steel Corp., Middletown, Ohio
Schlaim, David, U. S. Bureau of Mines, College Park, Md.
Schnaible, H. W., U. S. Steel Corp., Monroeville, Pa.
Schuhmann, R., Jr., Purdue University, Lafayette, Ind.
Shanahan, C. E. A., Richard Thomas & Baldwins, Ltd., Aylesbury, England
Shaw, R. B., Allegheny Ludlum Steel Corp., Brackenridge, Pa.
Shearman, R. W., The Metallurgical Society of AIME, New York, N. Y.
Shupe, K. M., Latrobe Steel Co., Latrobe, Pa.
Sibakin, J. G., Steel Co. of Canada, Ltd., Hamilton, Ontario, Canada
Simcic, N. F., Jr., Jones & Laughlin Steel Corp., Pittsburgh, Pa.
Simpkinson, T. V., Republic Steel Corp., Warren, Ohio
Skolnick, Leonard, Massachusetts Institute of Technology, Cambridge, Mass.
Smith, Joan, St. Joseph Lead Co., Monaca, Pa.
Smith, L. W., Symington Wayne Corp., Depew, N. Y.
Smith, Tennyson, Atomics International, Div. North American Aviation, Canoga
    Park, Calif.
Smura, B. B., Solvay Process Co., Div. of Allied Chemical Corp., Syracuse, N. Y.
Snow, R. B., U. S. Steel Corp., Monroeville, Pa.
Sommer, A. W., Atomics International, Div. of North American Aviation, Canoga
    Park, Calif.
Speight, G. E., Richard Thomas & Baldwins, Ltd., Aylesbury, England
Speiser, Rudloph, Ohio State University, Columbus, Ohio
Spretnak, J. W., Ohio State University, Columbus, Ohio
Squires, A. M., Hydrocarbon Research, Inc., New York, N. Y.
Starner, B. M., Aluminum Co. of America, New Kensington, Pa.
Steeves, A. F., General Electric Co., Schenectady, N. Y.
Sterling, Edwin, M. W. Kellogg Co., Jersey City, N. J.
Stone, A. J., Battelle Memorial Institute, Columbus, Ohio
Strang, V. C., Kelsey Hayes Co., Utica, N. Y.
Strauss, S. W., U. S. Naval Research Laboratory, Washington, D. C.
Stroup, P. T., Aluminum Co. of America, New Kensington, Pa.
Stubbles, J. R., Princeton University, Princeton, N. J.
Stukel, J. F., Cleveland Cliffs Iron Co., Cleveland, Ohio
Su, E. C., Jones & Laughlin Steel Corp., Pittsburgh, Pa.
Tanczyn, Harry, Armco Steel Corp., Baltimore, Md.
Tarassoff, Peter, Massachusetts Institute of Technology, Cambridge, Mass.
Taylor, C. R., Armco Steel Corp., Middletown, Ohio
Thurner, C. R., Bethlehem Steel Co., Bethlehem, Pa.
Tiller, W. A., Westinghouse Electric Co., Pittsburgh, Pa.
Truesdale, E. C., New Jersey Zinc Co., Palmerton, Pa.
Trzeciak, M. J., Battelle Memorial Institute, Columbus, Ohio
Turillon, P. P., Kelsey-Hayes Co., New Hartford, N. Y.
Turkdogan, E. T., British Iron and Steel Research Assn., London, England
Upthegrove, W. R., University of Oklahoma, Norman, Okla.
Urbain, Georges, IRSID, St. Germain en Laye, France

Uys, J. M., Massachusetts Institute of Technology, Cambridge, Mass.
Van Der Heem, P., Netherlands Embassy, Washington, D. C.
Veltman, Herbert, Sherritt Gordon Mines, Ltd., Vancouver, B. C., Canada
Verhoeven, J. D., University of Michigan, Ann Arbor, Mich.
Volin, M. E., Michigan College of Mining and Technology, Houghton, Mich.
Wagstaff, J. M., U. S. Steel Corp., Monroeville, Pa.
Wakeley, Duane, St. Joseph Lead Co., Monaca, Pa.
Walker, J. L., General Electric Co., Schenectady, N. Y.
Walsh, J. H., Department of Mines and Technical Surveys, Ottawa, Ontario, Canada
Walsh, R. H., Columbia-Southern Chemical Corp., Barberton, Ohio
Walther, W. D., The Dayton Steel Foundry Co., Dayton, Ohio
Walz, Heinrich, Timken Roller Bearing Co., Canton, Ohio
Warner, J. P., Sherritt Gordon Mines, Ltd., Fort Saskatchewan, Alberta, Canada
Warnes, Don, St. Joseph Lead Co., Monaca, Pa.
Weart, H. W., Westinghouse Electric Corp., Pittsburgh, Pa.
Webster, A. H., Dept. of Mines and Technical Surveys, Ottawa, Ontario, Canada
Weeks, J. R., Brookhaven National Laboratory, Upton, N. Y.
Weinstein, Martin, Massachusetts Institute of Technology, Cambridge, Mass.
Whiteway, Stirling G., National Research Council, Halifax, Nova Scotia, Canada
Wiberg, Orjan, Svenska Metallverken, Vasteras, Sweden
Wilder, A. B., National Tube Div., U. S. Steel Corp., Pittsburgh, Pa.
Willey, L. A., Aluminum Co. of America, New Kensington, Pa.
Willis, G. M., University of Melbourne, Melbourne, Australia
Wojcik, W. M., Jones & Laughlin Steel Corp., Pittsburgh, Pa.
Woolf, P. L., U. S. Bureau of Mines, Pittsburgh, Pa.
Worner, H. K., Broken Hill Proprietary Co., Ltd., Newcastle, N. W. S., Australia
Wriedt, H. A., U. S. Steel Corp., Monroeville, Pa.
Yang, Ling, Carnegie Institute of Technology, Pittsburgh, Pa.
Young, H. E., Cameron Iron Works, Inc., Houston, Texas
Yue, A. S., The Dow Chemical Co., Midland, Mich.
Zellars, G. R., U. S. Bureau of Mines, Pittsburgh, Pa.
Zotos, John, Rodman Lab., Watertown Arsenal, Watertown, Mas.